The Algae of Illinois

The Algae of Illinois

By

Lewis Hanford Tiffany

and

Max Edwin Britton

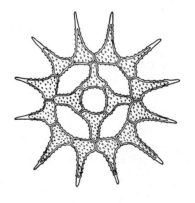

(Facsimile of the 1952 edition)

HAFNER PUBLISHING COMPANY
New York
1971

12/17/73

Published by
HAFNER PUBLISHING COMPANY, INC.
866 Third Avenue
New York, N. Y. 10022

Library of Congress Catalog Card Number: 76-164675

Printed in U.S.A. by
NOBLE OFFSET PRINTERS, INC.
NEW YORK 3, N. Y.

TO

Edgar Nelson Transeau

PREFACE

THIS volume is the second in a series planned a decade ago by the department of botany at Northwestern University to put on record our knowledge of the algae of Illinois. The first publication was Britton's *A Catalog of Illinois Algae*, appearing in 1944 as No. 2 of the "Northwestern University Studies in the Biological Sciences and Medicine." Although the algae of Illinois have been studied with varying degrees of assiduity for over a century, Britton was the first to assemble a comprehensive list of the known species of the state. The *Catalog* summarized the information, published and unpublished, available at the time. It was largely bibliographic, dealing with the taxonomy, classification, and distribution of all the algal species known from the state. The present volume represents an attempt to supplement the *Catalog* by furnishing descriptions, keys and figures to these species.

The authors believe that such a comprehensive analysis of the algal flora of Illinois will be useful at considerable distances from the confines of the state. It is hoped that the report will stimulate interest in phycology both locally and generally, and that it will contribute to our knowledge of the distribution and taxonomy of the group.

In assembling the data necessary for this volume, all possible sources of information have been tapped. The authors have seen many of the species recorded here in their own collections or in those of other phycologists. Some species are known only from the literature. It is not humanly possible, even when supported by diagrams and descriptions, always to be certain that some species are accurately recorded. Even herbarium specimens, though usually of great value, are not always dependable, particularly in dealing with those algae difficult to recognize when desiccated or long-preserved, and in those samples containing more than a single species or variety. Published records have been discarded whenever there was a reasonable doubt of their validity. This separation of "the sheep from the goats" is in the last analysis a personal one, and the authors make no claim to infallibility.

The systematic arrangement of the algae follows recent and modern views regarding the taxonomy and interrelationships of the several groups. The phyla are briefly delimited in the Introduction. The classes are indicated by a short synoptic key and by descriptions in the text. Orders and families are adequately separated by concise descriptions. Genera and species receive rather detailed analyses, and keys are furnished to all the genera in each class. Keys to species follow the generic description. The reader is referred to texts, monographs and recent literature for special and more detailed descriptions of any of the epithets. The species are illustrated by nearly 1,200 figures.

How best to use the volume depends upon the training and experience of the reader. A complete single key to all genera of the algae found in the state has not been attempted because its value in determining an unknown alga is dubious, to say the least. Too many decisions are required of the uninitiated, and the phycologist rarely takes time to "run through" a key of such length. It is generally fairly easy to recognize the class to which an alga belongs: brief microscopic inspection will usually suffice to spot, for example, a diatom, a green alga, a blue-green alga, or a red alga. The descriptions of the various phyla given in the Introduction and the synoptic key to the classes on page 6 will be useful in making this first assignment. From here on to final analysis convenient signposts occur along the way in the form of order and family delimitations and of generic and specific keys. A final determination should not be accepted until both descriptions and diagrams are consulted, and whenever possible confirmed by comparison with authentic reference material.

A few species, reported or collected since Britton's *Catalog* appeared, are included with notes on their location within the state. Additional literature that has come to the attention of the authors and thought to be helpful to the student of algae is cited in the Bibliography. No attempt has been made to repeat the bibliography on distributional and habitat data cited in the *Catalog*.

In order to secure continuity of style and expression, the illustrations have been largely redrawn from authoritative sources by a single artist. None has been reproduced in facsimile. Some are original. Proper credit is given for each figure that is redrawn. The diagrams of most of the *Zygnemataceae* were made by Marie Wilson, a few species of the genus *Mougeotia* by Theodore Urban. The remaining illustrations were all executed by Jane W. Roller. We are further indebted to Miss Roller for her energy and persistence in ferreting out many of the scattered original papers in which some of the species were first described and figured. Our thanks are due Paul S. Conger of the Smithsonian Institution for making his library and collections of diatoms available for study. We are grateful to E. N. Transeau of The Ohio State University for permitting access to the manuscript of his monograph on the *Zygnemataceae*. The Chicago Natural History Museum generously allowed us access to the specimens in its Cryptogamic Herbarium. We are under obligations to Lenoir Britton, Margaret Cameron, Emily Caruthers, Tenta Winternitz, Nancy Gute and Loel Tiffany for aid in typing, editing and assembling the manuscript. We wish to thank the Graduate School of Northwestern University for certain grants-in-aid helpful in prosecuting the investigation.

Finally, we are especially grateful for the courtesy, guidance, and technical assistance afforded us, during the printing of the book, by the personnel of the University of Chicago Press.

L. H. TIFFANY

M. E. BRITTON

EVANSTON, ILLINOIS
January 1, 1951

TABLE OF CONTENTS

PAGE

INTRODUCTION 1

BRIEF SYNOPSIS OF THE ALGAL CLASSES 6

PHYLUM CHLOROPHYTA 7

Class Chlorophyceae 7

Key to the Genera 8

Order Volvocales 13
Family Polyblepharidaceae 13
Family Chlamydomonadaceae 13
Family Phacotaceae 14
Family Volvocaceae 16
Family Haematococcaceae 20

Order Tetrasporales 20
Family Palmellaceae 20
Family Tetrasporaceae 21

Order Ulotrichales 24
Family Ulotrichaceae 24
Family Microsporaceae 28
Family Cylindrocapsaceae 30
Family Chaetophoraceae 30
Family Protococcaceae 40
Family Coleochaetaceae 42

Order Cladophorales 44
Family Cladophoraceae 45

Order Oedogoniales 48
Family Oedogoniaceae 49

Order Ulvales 100
Family Schizomeridaceae 100

Order Chlorococcales 102
Family Chlorococcaceae 102
Family Micractiniaceae 104
Family Endosphaeraceae 106
Family Characiaceae 108
Family Protosiphonaceae 109
Family Hydrodictyaceae 109
Family Coelastraceae 112
Family Oocystaceae 113
Family Scenedesmaceae 120

PAGE

Order Siphonales 124
  Family Dichotomosiphonaceae 124

Order Zygnematales 124
  Family Zygnemataceae 126
  Family Mesotaeniaceae 164
  Family Desmidiaceae 167

PHYLUM CHRYSOPHYTA 206

Class Xanthophyceae 206
Key to the Genera 206
Order Heterococcales 206
  Family Botryococcaceae 207
  Family Chlorotheciaceae 207

Order Heterotrichales 210
  Family Tribonemataceae 210
Order Heterosiphonales 210
  Family Botrydiaceae 210
  Family Vaucheriaceae 211
Class Bacillariophyceae 214
Key to the Genera 215
Order Centrales 217
  Suborder Coscinodiscineae 217
    Family Coscinodiscaceae 217
    Family Eupodiscaceae 224
  Suborder Rhizosolenineae 226
    Family Rhizosoleniaceae 226
  Order Pennales 226
  Suborder Fragilarineae 227
    Family Tabellariaceae 227
    Family Meridionaceae 228
    Family Diatomaceae 228
    Family Fragilariaceae 231
    Family Eunotiaceae 237
  Suborder Achnanthineae 240
    Family Achnanthaceae 240
  Suborder Naviculineae 244
    Family Naviculaceae 244
    Family Gomphonemataceae 269
    Family Cymbellaceae 274
  Suborder Surirellineae 282
    Family Nitzschiaceae 282
    Family Surirellaceae 289

PAGE

Class Chrysophyceae 296
   Key to the Genera 297

   Order Chrysomonadales 297
     Family Mallomonadaceae 297
     Family Syncryptaceae 300
     Family Synuraceae 300
     Family Ochromonadaceae 300

   Order Rhizochrysidales 304
     Family Rhizochrysidaceae 304

PHYLUM PYRROPHYTA 306

   Class Dinophyceae 306
   Key to the Genera 306

   Order Peridiniales 307
     Family Glenodiniaceae 307
     Family Peridiniaceae 310
     Family Ceratiaceae 314

PHYLUM EUGLENOPHYTA 315

   Class Euglenophyceae 315
   Key to the Genera 315

   Order Euglenales 316
     Family Euglenaceae 316

   Order Colaciales 327
     Family Colaciaceae 327

PHYLUM MYXOPHYTA 328

   Class Myxophyceae 328
   Key to the Genera 329

   Order Chroococcales 330
     Family Chroococcaceae 330

   Order Chamaesiphonales 336
     Family Pleurocapsaceae 336

   Order Oscillatoriales 338
     Suborder Oscillatorineae 338
       Family Oscillatoriaceae 338

     Suborder Nostochineae 356
       Family Nostocaceae 356
       Family Scytonemataceae 366
       Family Stigonemataceae 370
       Family Rivulariaceae 372

TABLE OF CONTENTS

PAGE

PHYLUM RHODOPHYTA 379

  Class Rhodophyceae 379

    Key to the Genera 379

    Subclass Florideae 379

      Order Nemalionales 380

        Family Batrachospermaceae 380

        Family Thoreaceae 382

DOUBTFUL SPECIES 383

GLOSSARY 385

BIBLIOGRAPHY 391

INDEX 397

INTRODUCTION

THE algal habitats of the state of Illinois are many and diverse. Lake Michigan, one of the world's largest freshwater lakes, adjoins two of the northeastern counties, and the Mississippi River, one of the world's largest streams, forms the entire western boundary of the state. Two other large streams, the Ohio and Wabash rivers, form the southeastern boundary. The state is 216 miles in width and 385 miles in length, with an area of 56,043 square miles. Altitude varies from 268 feet above sea level at the confluence of the Ohio and Mississippi rivers at the southern end of the state to 1,241 feet in Jo Daviess County at the northwest. Approximately 88 per cent of the land has an altitude between 400 and 800 feet above sea level. Much of the state is a relatively flat plain and, except for a few areas in the extreme north, along the Mississippi River, and in the southern part, most of the counties have a slope of less than 2 per cent in from 30 to 80 per cent of their acreage.

About 56 per cent of the state was originally prairie grassland occupying land surfaces marked by their flatness of surface, poor drainage, and abundant standing waters. The prairie ponds and pools of the central part of the state have been rich sources of algae, at least for certain times during the growing season, but drainage of the highly fertile prairie soils for agricultural purposes has destroyed many of these habitats in recent years. About half of the land requires drainage for successful farming, and natural algal habitats have suffered from this activity, especially in the flat areas at the upper end of the watersheds in the east-central part of the state.

Lotic environments include very large rivers forming the state boundaries—the Illinois, Fox, Kaskaskia, Sangamon, Kankakee, and Rock rivers—and large numbers of smaller streams down to the smallest rivulets penetrating prairie and woodland. More than 40 per cent of the land surface is drained by the Illinois River and its tributaries, and 25 per cent by streams flowing directly into the Mississippi. Only about 1 per cent of the land surface drains into Lake Michigan, and the remainder is received by the Wabash and Ohio rivers. The depositional topography, a consequence of the multiple glaciations of the Pleistocene Period, has resulted in a large number of aquatic algal habitats. The areas of younger glacial drift in the northern part of the state abound in small lakes and ponds of

1

different depths, physical and chemical properties and floristic composition. In this area streams are poorly developed and there still remain thousands of acres of undrained swamps and marshes with varying amounts of water throughout the year. Occasional peat bogs occur, particularly in Lake and McHenry counties. Only a few counties in the extreme south, Calhoun County centrally located on the Mississippi River, and Jo Daviess County at the northwest corner of the state escaped glaciation and exhibit a more rugged terrain with well developed stream drainage and few standing waters.

Many of the smaller flowing waters become ponded during drouth periods of summer and autumn. Ox-bow ponds, bayous, and low areas subject to stream overflow furnish algal habitats of a permanent nature or only temporarily at certain seasons. Soil algae are numerous, subaerial species are few, and the absence of extremely elevated terrain excludes certain montane species.

Although human activities have made serious inroads on the algal habitats of the state, there remain sufficient bodies of water to permit extensive investigations of these plants. Much of the state remains unexplored with respect to the algal flora, there being no known records from 38 of the 102 counties. Of the 64 counties from which algal species have been collected, 40 are represented by collections largely from streams along which they lie. The number of known species from these counties is small. The areas of rougher terrain are least known and should provide a rewarding field for investigation. Despite the extensive drainage of the prairie areas, careful collecting in small pools and ponds during the wetter part of the growing season should add much to our knowledge of the algae in these areas where experience of the past has demonstrated the algal flora to be so rich.

For many years botanists have rather dubiously placed all algae and fungi in the *Thallophyta*, generally separable from other plants by their one-celled sporangia and their unicellular sex organs (or if multicellular, the gametes are not enclosed by a jacket of sterile cells). The validity of this grouping, or at least the wisdom of it, has been considerably lessened in recent years by the acceptance of the viewpoint that algae and fungi represent two phylogenetic series, each of considerable homogeneity. If emphasis is placed upon cell structure and behavior, it is evident that there are several series among the algae themselves. On the basis of kinds of motile cells, storage products, plastids, and other features, such groups as the diatoms, the greens, the blue-greens, and the reds, for example, are readily separable one from the other except in a relatively few forms whose complete life cycles are not known. The structural and physiological characteristics of each group remain remarkably constant throughout the assemblage.

Phycologists at the present time are in general agreement with suggestions of Pascher, Smith, Fritsch and others that the designation *Thallophyta* is scarcely tenable as a well-defined division or phylum of the plant kingdom. This interpretation would also lead to the discontinuance of the use of *Algae* and *Fungi* as subdivisions or classes of the *Thallophyta*. Several groups of algae are now considered to be sufficiently distinct from each other to constitute phyla in themselves. We may then accept some 7 phyla of the plant kingdom as entirely or essentially algal. These phyla will now be briefly characterized. The classes belonging to each phylum are briefly delimited on page 6 and more completely described in the body of the text.

CHLOROPHYTA, composed of 2 classes (*Chlorophyceae* and *Charophyceae*), are commonly green in color and are referred to as the grass-green algae. They contain chlorophyll *a* and *b*, alpha- and beta-carotenes, and 4 xanthophylls in about the same proportions as occur in the vascular plants. The pigments are located in definite chromatophores. Starch is the customary form of food storage, oil is generally present, and pyrenoids are usually well-defined. Cellulose and pectic substances are prominent constituents of the cell-walls. Motile vegetative and reproductive cells, occurring in many of the green algae, are generally bi-, quadri- or multi-flagellate, with the flagella of equal length. The *Zygnematales* have no flagellate cells and their gametes are amoeboid. Reproduction in the phylum is both sexual and asexual. Sexual fusion includes isogamy, anisogamy, and oogamy. Most of the vegetative cells are haploid with the zygote as the only diploid phase. A few species exhibit distinct alternation of haploid and diploid phases. In several anisogamous genera of the *Siphonales* the nuclei are diploid. The body-type ranges from unicellular to colonial and multicellular. Most of the *Chlorophyta* inhabit fresh water, although there are numerous marine and terrestrial representatives.

CHRYSOPHYTA include the *Xanthophyceae* (usually yellow-green), the golden-brown to yellow-brown *Chrysophyceae*, and the *Bacillariophyceae* (diatoms). There are definite chromatophores in which yellow and brown pigments predominate. These include 2 carotenes and 7 xanthophylls, variously distributed in the 3 classes. In addition to chlorophyll *a*, present in all *Chrysophyta*, chlorophyll *c* is reported for the diatoms and chlorophyll *e* for the *Xanthophyceae*. Starch has never been reported. Definite pyrenoids are rarely evident, although pyrenoid-like structures occur. Oil, together with such insoluble reserves as leucosin and volutin, is the chief storage product. The cell-wall is usually composed of 2 halves or overlapping parts, whose constituents are often largely pectic compounds and silica. Both flagellate and non-flagellate cells occur, and they may be solitary or united into definite colonies. Thick-walled resting spores (statospores) are common. Asexually formed spores may be flagellate or not. Gametes when present exhibit isogamy and may be flagellate or amoeboid. The vegetative cells of the diatoms are probably all diploid, those of the other 2 classes haploid. Diatoms are widely distributed in nearly all aquatic and terrestrial habitats, while the yellow-greens and the golden-browns are largely freshwater, the latter widely distributed in cold waters.

PYRROPHYTA are generally regarded as including the dinoflagellates (*Dinophyceae*), the *Desmokontae* and the cryptomonads (*Cryptophyceae*), the last of doubtful affinities. The discoid or parietal chromatophores are generally yellowish-green to golden-brown, although various dark-yellow, brown to dark-brown hues may be seen. The pigments of the *Dinophyceae* are chlorophyll *a* and *c*, beta-carotene, and 4 xanthophylls. Reserves are starch (or starch-like compounds) and oil. Cell walls, when present, are usually cellulose in composition and often highly sculptured. Most organisms are unicellular and biflagellate, with some algal-appearing forms non-flagellate and unicellular or multicellular. The 2 flagella exhibit the unusual features of dissimilar position, unlike motion, and different form. Asexual and sexual reproduction are known, but the latter is rare. The representatives of the phylum grow largely in the plankton of both freshwater and marine habitats. Some forms are rather abundant in sand pools. Only the *Dinophyceae* are currently known from Illinois.

EUGLENOPHYTA, or euglenoids, have colorless or grass-green chromatophores, with pigments of chlorophyll *a* and *b*, beta-carotene, and a xanthophyll present. Nutrition may be holozoic, holophytic or saprophytic with the reserve foods paramylum (an insoluble starch-like carbohydrate) and fats. Nearly all representatives of the division are unicellular with 1–3 anteriorly placed flagella on the motile cells. A definite palmelloid organization of cells is the dominant phase in at least one genus. The protoplast may be rigid or not. Cell division is the usual method of multiplication, with thick-walled cysts present in several genera. Sexual reproduction is rare. Most euglenoids occur in freshwater ponds and pools, some are sessile, and a few are endozoophytic. Perhaps it is best at present to recognize a single class, *Euglenophyceae*.

RHODOPHYTA possess olive-green, red, purple and blue chromatophores which contain chlorophyll *a* and *d*, alpha- and beta-carotene, and the xanthophyll lutein, all usually dominated by the phycobilins: r-phycoerythrin (red) and r-phycocyanin (blue). Pyrenoid-like bodies occur in some genera, and the chief reserve product is a polysaccharide similar to starch, known as floridean starch. The cell-wall contains cellulose and various pectic compounds. The plants range from a few unicellular, colonial or simple filamentous types to those of considerable complexity of body form and often of great beauty. There are no motile cells of any kind. Sexual reproduction is complex, involving the union of a male gamete nucleus with a carpogonial nucleus. The resulting zygote develops directly into carpospores or into a filamentous structure which forms carpospores. The germinating carpospores, if haploid, produce sexual plants; if diploid, asexual plants producing tetrasporangia, each of which forms 4 tetraspores. Thus the "plant" of the *Rhodophyta* is either haploid, or exhibits an alternation of similar haploid and diploid phases. Most members of the phylum are marine. The few freshwater genera are generally restricted to well-aerated, cool, rapidly flowing water. There is a single class, the *Rhodophyceae*.

PHAEOPHYTA, or brown algae, possess chromatophores containing chlorophyll *a* and *c*, usually masked by the predominant beta-carotene and at least 7 xanthophylls, especially fucoxanthin. The cell-walls are basically cellulose with peripheral pectic-like substances, commonly called algin. The food reserves are sugars of various kinds and polysaccharides such as laminarin. Life cycles are diverse: alternation of diploid asexual plants with haploid sexual plants, similar or dissimilar; and the presence of diploid plants only. The plant body is multicellular, often structurally complex, of considerable size (such as some of the seaweeds), and without locomotion. The motile spores and gametes are pear-shaped with 2 laterally placed flagella of unequal length. The brown algae are almost wholly marine. The 3 known freshwater genera are not recorded from Illinois. The division is described here merely to complete the algal groups.

MYXOPHYTA (CYANOPHYTA), containing the single class, *Myxophyceae*, are commonly known as the blue-green algae, although the colors are quite diverse. There are no definite chromatophores, but the pigments are diffused throughout the peripheral part of the cytoplasm. In addition to chlorophyll *a*, 2 carotenes, and at least 2 xanthophylls, there occur the phycobilins: c-phycocyanin and c-phycoerythrin. Reserve products are sugars and glycogen, with some oil and little understood granules which may be proteinaceous. The cell has a primitive type of nucleus, no flagellate cells of any kind are known, and sexual reproduction does not occur. The plant-body organization varies from the unicell and the colony to the branched and unbranched filament. The *Myxophyta* are world wide in distribution, occurring most abundantly in freshwater and terrestrial habitats. A few are endozoophytic.

BRIEF SYNOPSIS OF THE ALGAL CLASSES

A. Cell-walls composed of two overlapping siliceous halves (valves) fitting together like two parts of a pillbox; valves as seen in top view, with surface rows of punctae or striae in radial, transverse, longitudinal or sometimes irregular patterns

Bacillariophyceae (p. 214)

A. Cell-walls composed of a definite number of articulated plates, or cells naked; vegetative cell or zoospore with a transverse groove in which lies a flagellum

Dinophyceae (p. 306)

A. Cell-walls and cells not as above.. B

   B. Pigments localized in definite chromatophores; color not or rarely blue-green.. C

   B. Pigments not localized in definite chromatophores; color usually blue-green, sometimes masked by other pigments..........Myxophyceae (p. 328)

C. Chromatophores grass-green, rarely gray or colorless, sometimes encrusted with lime; food reserve starch or paramylum.................................... D

C. Chromatophores red, blue, yellow, yellow-green, golden-brown, or sometimes greenish; food reserve neither starch nor paramylum........................ F

   D. Plant always a multicellular, erect, branched thallus, differentiated into a regular succession of nodes and internodes, frequently encrusted with lime

Charophyceae*

   D. Plants unicellular, colonial or multicellular, lacking the regular succession of nodes and internodes, rarely encrusted with lime........................ E

E. Plants unicellular and solitary (colonial in *Colacium*); vegetative cells motile with 1, 2 or 3 flagella; sometimes colorless (rarely reddish); food reserve paramylum

Euglenophyceae (p. 315)

E. Plants unicellular to multicellular; solitary, colonial, filamentous or parenchymatous; vegetative cells not motile or motile with 2 flagella of equal length (4-6-8 in a few genera); chromatophores definite and of great variety, rarely colorless; food reserve starch.................................Chlorophyceae (p. 7)

   F. Chromatophores yellow-green; plants solitary, colonial or filamentous; filaments septate or non-septate (long and tubular in *Vaucheria*); motile cells with 2 flagella of unequal length, or with many flagella arranged in pairs; cell-walls often of two overlapping cylinders; food reserves leucosin and oils

Xanthophyceae (p. 206)

   F. Chromatophores golden-brown or yellowish; plants solitary or colonial, generally microscopic; motile cells with 1 flagellum, 2 flagella of equal or unequal length or rarely 3 flagella; some species dominantly amoeboid; food reserves leucosin and oils.............................Chrysophyceae (p. 296)

   F. Chromatophores red to blue, sometimes greenish; freshwater forms of one or few cells or macroscopic gelatinous or bristle-like thalli; devoid of flagella; cell-wall not of 2 pieces; food reserve floridean starch...Rhodophyceae (p. 379)

* Not treated in this book.

Phylum CHLOROPHYTA

Class *CHLOROPHYCEAE*

THE Chlorophyceae (grass-green algae) may be unicellular or form multicellular thalli varying from simple aggregations of cells in regular or irregular colonies to expanded sheets, branched or unbranched filaments, and hollow or solid cylinders. Vegetative cells are uni- or multinucleate, motile or immobile, free-floating or sessile, and usually contain one or more chromatophores that are highly variable among different species. Chromatophores are single to numerous in each cell, axial or parietal in position, entire or perforate, and may be cup-shaped, discoid, stellate, laminate or a variety of other shapes. Pigmentation is variable in amount but typically the chromatophores are bright green, the pigments being chlorophylls *a* and *b*, beta- and alpha-carotene, and at least 4 xanthophylls (among which lutein predominates) in about the same proportion as in vascular plants. Pyrenoids with starch sheaths are usually present, one or more in each chromatophore. Food reserves are typically starch although many species also contain oil droplets and in some species fats are the only foods accumulated.

Definite cell-walls are usually present and consist of an inner layer of cellulose, or rarely callose, and an outer layer of pectose that is sometimes impregnated with chitin or encrusted with lime. The cellulose layers are usually homogeneous but in some species are definitely stratified. Motile cells whether vegetative or reproductive bear anterior flagella usually of equal length and 2 in number, although they may be 2–8 or many. Motile cells usually have an orange-red light-sensitive eyespot near the base of the flagella, and a complex neuromotor apparatus. A pair of contractile vacuoles is present near the base of the flagella in some species.

Asexual reproduction may be by vegetative cell division, fragmentation, zoospores, aplanospores, or akinetes. Sexuality may be isogamous, anisogamous, or oogamous. Gametes are always formed within unicellular sex organs.

The Chlorophyceae are largely freshwater organisms although some orders have a few marine representatives and other orders are predominately marine. The freshwater species are mainly aquatics but many occur on a variety of moist terrestrial substrates.

7

KEY TO THE GENERA OF CHLOROPHYCEAE

1. Cells solitary (sometimes in *Palmella*-stages).......................... 2
1. Cells in colonies or aggregates, not filamentous................... 34
1. Cells forming filaments, sometimes plate-like or parenchymatous........... 65
   2. Vegetative cells flagellate......................... 3
   2. Vegetative cells not flagellate...................... 6
3. Cells with 2 flagella.............................. 4
3. Cells with 4 flagella...................... Carteria (p. 14)
3. Cells with 5 flagella...................... Chloraster (p. 13)
   4. Wall with broad, wing-like expansion........ Wislouchiella (p. 14)
   4. Wall without such expansion...................... 5
5. Protoplast adjoining cell-wall................. Chlamydomonas (p. 13)
5. Protoplast connected to wall by cytoplasmic
   strands.................................... Haematococcus (p. 20)
5. Protoplast surrounded by wall of 2 overlapping
   plates..................................... Phacotus (p. 14)
   6. Cells free-living.................................. 7
   6. Cells attached to aquatic plants or animals... Characium (p. 108)
   6. Cells endophytic........................ Chlorochytrium (p. 106)
   6. Cells growing on aerial substrates.......... Protococcus (p. 40)
   6. Cells growing on soil only (young plants).... Protosiphon (p. 109)
7. Cells without a median constriction................... 8
7. Cells with a median constriction: isthmus joining semicells................. 26
   8. Cells spherical.................................... 9
   8. Cells ovoid, ellipsoid or citriform........... Oocystis (p. 116)
   8. Cells reniform........................... Nephrocytium (p. 116)
   8. Cells irregularly shaped, wall locally thickened.............. 13
   8. Cells angular.................................. 14
   8. Cells fusiform to acicular, or setiferous.................. 15
   8. Cells cylindric, or nearly so.................. 22
9. Cell-wall smooth................................ 10
9. Cell-wall with spines, setae or appendages.................. 11
9. Cell-wall with warts, ridges or reticulations..... Trochiscia (p. 119)
   10. Cell with pyrenoids.................. Chlorococcum (p. 102)
   10. Cell without pyrenoids.................. Chlorella (p. 114)
11. Cell-wall with 3–8 spines or appendages........ Treubaria (p. 119)
11. Cell-wall with many spines or setae................. 12
   12. Spines not over 7 μ long................. Trochiscia (p. 119)
   12. Spines or setae over 7 μ long.......... Golenkinia (p. 104)
13. Thickenings irregular, lamellated.............. Kentrosphaera (p. 108)
13. Thickenings button-like, not lamellated........ Chlorococcum (p. 102)
   14. Angles of cells with short spines or setae, or
   none..................................... Tetraedron (p. 117)
   14. Angles of cells with long spines or setae..... Treubaria (p. 119)
15. Ends of cells setiferous...................... Schroederia (p. 109)
15. Ends of cells attenuate, not setiferous................................. 16

16. Poles of cells pointed   17
16. Poles of cells rounded or truncate   19
17. Protoplast one, sometimes fragmented   18
17. Protoplasts two, one in each semicell . . . .   Closterium (p. 167)
   18. Cell with one pyrenoid, or none . . . .   Ankistrodesmus (p. 113)
   18. Cell with a row of pyrenoids . . . .   Closteriopsis (p. 114)
19. Cells generally lunate or arcuate . . . .   Closterium (p. 167)
19. Cells generally straight, or slightly curved   20
   20. Chloroplast single, axial . . . .   Roya (p. 166)
   20. Chloroplasts two or more   21
21. Cell-wall with girdle pieces (obscure in some spe-
cies) . . . .   Penium (p. 176)
21. Cell-wall without girdle pieces . . . .   Netrium (p. 166)
   22. Chloroplasts spirally twisted . . . .   Genicularia (p. 164)
   22. Chloroplasts not spirally twisted   23
23. Chloroplast laminate . . . .   Gonatozygon (p. 166)
23. Chloroplast not laminate   24
   24. Chloroplast single, axial . . . .   Roya (p. 166)
   24. Chloroplasts two or more   25
25. Cell-wall with girdle pieces (obscure in some spe-
cies) . . . .   Penium (p. 176)
25. Cell-wall without girdle pieces . . . .   Netrium (p. 166)
   26. Length of cell much more than the breadth . . .   Pleurotaenium (p. 178)
   26. Length not more than four times the breadth (sometimes greater in Penium)   27
27. Cells compressed   28
27. Cells not compressed   33
   28. Apices of semicells notched   29
   28. Apices of semicells not notched   30
29. Apical and lateral incisions deep . . . .   Micrasterias (p. 194)
29. Apical and lateral incisions shallow . . . .   Euastrum (p. 180)
   30. Apex of semicell with processes . . . .   Staurastrum (p. 197)
   30. Apex of semicell without processes   31
31. Spines absent or not conspicuous . . . .   Cosmarium (p. 182)
31. Spines conspicuous   32
   32. Wall uniformly thick . . . .   Arthrodesmus (p. 196)
   32. Front of semicell thickened medianly . . . .   Xanthidium
33. End view of cell circular . . . .   Penium (p. 176)
33. End view of cell not circular . . . .   Staurastrum (p. 197)
   34. Cells with flagella or pseudocilia   35
   34. Cells with neither flagella nor pseudocilia   42
35. Cells in twos or fours in an envelope . . . .   Tetraspora (p. 22)
35. Cells uniformly distributed within an envelope   36
   36. Colony usually symmetric   37
   36. Colony asymmetric   41
37. Cells mutually compressed . . . .   Pandorina (p. 16)
37. Cells not mutually compressed   38

38. Cells in a flat, plate-like colony . . . . Gonium (p. 16)
38. Cells in a spherical or ovoid colony 39
39. Colony many-celled (256 or more) . . . . Volvox (p. 18)
39. Colony fewer-celled (16–256) 40
    40. Vegetative cells all of same size . . . . Eudorina (p. 17)
    40. Vegetative cells of two sizes . . . . Pleodorina (p. 17)
41. Colony pear-shaped, attached to other algae . . . . Apiocystis (p. 22)
41. Colony with posterior projections, not attached . . . Platydorina (p. 17)
    42. Cells with spines or setae 43
    42. Cells with neither spines nor setae 46
43. Cells pyramidately arranged . . . . Micractinium (p. 104)
43. Cells not pyramidately arranged 44
    44. Cells in a globose colony . . . . Sorastrum (p. 112)
    44. Cells in dense clusters . . . . Chaetosphaeridium (p. 44)
    44. Cells in a curved or flat plate 45
45. Cells in concentric rings, forming discs . . . . Pediastrum (p. 110)
45. Cells not in concentric rings . . . . Scenedesmus (p. 121)
    46. Cells 1–3 times as long as broad 47
    46. Cells 4–50 times as long as broad 61
47. Cells acicular to fusiform 48
47. Cells neither acicular nor fusiform 49
    48. Cells joined end to end . . . . Dactylococcus (p. 114)
    48. Cells joined laterally . . . . Scenedesmus (p. 121)
    48. Cells not joined, in a gelatinous envelope . . . . Kirchneriella (p. 115)
49. Cells forming a flat colony 50
49. Cells not forming a flat colony 51
    50. Cells always quadrately arranged . . . . Crucigenia (p. 120)
    50. Cells not, or very rarely, so arranged . . . . Pediastrum (p. 110)
51. Cells forming a hollow sphere . . . . Coelastrum (p. 113)
51. Cells not forming a hollow sphere 52
    52. Cells curved 53
    52. Cells not curved 55
53. Cells connected by remains of mother cell-wall 54
53. Cells not so connected . . . . Nephrocytium (p. 116)
    54. Cells of a colony all alike in shape . . . . Dictyosphaerium (p. 114)
    54. Cells of a colony of two different shapes . . . . Dimorphococcus (p. 115)
55. Cells enclosed by a colonial envelope* 56
55. Cells enclosed by remains of old mother cell-wall 60
55. Cells not so enclosed . . . . Protococcus (p. 40)
    56. Cells connected by gelatinous threads or bands 57
    56. Cells not so connected 58
57. Cells with median constriction . . . . Cosmocladium (p. 193)
57. Cells without a median constriction . . . . Dictyosphaerium (p. 114)
    58. Colonial envelope lamellated . . . . Gloeocystis (p. 20)
    58. Colonial envelope wholly or partially confluent 59
59. Colonies spherical, few-celled . . . . Sphaerocystis (p. 21)

* Cells of *Chlorococcum* (p. 102) sometimes embedded in gelatinous matrix.

59. Colonies amorphous, many-celled.............. Palmella (p. 21)
   60. Space between cells colorless.............. Oocystis (p. 116)
   60. Space between cells dark.................. Gloeotaenium (p. 115)
61. Colonial envelope present.................... Kirchneriella (p. 115)
61. Colonial envelope absent.. 62
   62. Cells radiating from a common center...... Actinastrum (p. 120)
   62. Cells not radiating from a common center.......................... 63
63. Colony a flat or curved plate................. Scenedesmus (p. 121)
63. Colony a definite, closed net................. Hydrodictyon (p. 109)
63. Colony neither plate-like nor net-like.................................. 64
   64. Cells slightly curved, or twisted, gradually
      tapering toward apices (rarely lunate)...... Ankistrodesmus (p. 113)
   64. Cells markedly lunate, apices acutely pointed. Selenastrum (p. 117)
65. Cells medianly constricted, with conspicuous semicells.................... 66
65. Cells not medianly constricted.. 71
   66. Length of cell up to 4 times the width............................ 67
   66. Length of cell 6 to 30 times the width...... Pleurotaenium (p. 178)
67. Apices of cells incised....................... Micrasterias (p. 194)
67. Apices of cells not incised.................................... 68
   68. Cells joined by apical processes........... Onychonema (p. 200)
   68. Cells not joined by apical processes............................... 69
69. Cells circular in end view.................... Hyalotheca (p. 202)
69. Cells elliptical or angular in end view................................. 70
   70. Median constriction deep................. Spondylosium (p. 201)
   70. Median constriction shallow............... Desmidium (p. 204)
71. Vegetative filaments without cross-walls......................... 72
71. Vegetative filaments with cross-walls........................... 73
   72. Transverse constrictions present.......... Dichotomosiphon (p. 124)
   72. Transverse constrictions absent........... Protosiphon (p. 109)
73. Filaments branched*... 74
73. Filaments unbranched.. 85
   74. Plants discoid or pulvinate............... Coleochaete (p. 42)
   74. Plants neither discoid nor pulvinate............................. 75
75. Plants with setae arising laterally from the cells......................... 76
75. Plants with setae terminating the branches............................ 78
75. Plants with setae absent from the cells............................... 80
   76. Setae basally bulbous... 77
   76. Setae basally ensheathed.................. Coleochaete (p. 42)
77. Plant prostrate........................... Aphanochaete (p. 40)
77. Plant erect............................... Bulbochaete (p. 49)
   78. Lateral branches markedly and abruptly dif-
      ferentiated from the main axis............. Draparnaldia (p. 36)
   78. Lateral branches little and gradually differentiated from the main axis... 79
79. Filaments in dense gelatinous masses.......... Chaetophora (p. 32)
79. Filaments not in dense gelatinous masses....... Stigeoclonium (p. 32)
   80. Akinetes usually present... 81

  * *Mougeotia* (p. 126) and *Zygogonium* (p. 134) may sometimes be sought here.

80. Akinetes usually absent.. 82
81. Thallus encrusted with lime................... Chlorotylium (p. 40)
81. Thallus not encrusted with lime............... Pithophora (p. 48)
  82. With a few short rhizoid-like branches, or un-
      branched............................... Rhizoclonium (p. 45)
  82. With well-developed branches... 83
83. Branching usually basal; growing only on turtles. Basicladia (p. 46)
83. Branching general throughout the plant.............................. 84
  84. Branches of same diameter throughout; mi-
      croscopic.............................. Microthamnion (p. 38)
  84. Branches of unequal diameter; plant macro-
      scopic................................. Cladophora (p. 45)
85. Chromatophores plate-like or ribbon-like.......................... 86
85. Chromatophores axial discs or pillow-shaped, or radially branched.......... 89
85. Chromatophores otherwise.. 91
  86. Chromatophore an axial plate or ribbon...................... 87
  86. Chromatophores ribbon-like, parietal, usually spiral, 1 to 16............ 88
87. Cell-walls usually spinescent.................. Gonatozygon (p. 166)
87. Cell-walls never spinescent................... Mougeotia (p. 126)
  88. Conjugation by tubes formed before union.. Spirogyra (p. 140)
  88. Conjugation by genuflexion; rarely, tubes
      formed after union...................... Sirogonium (p. 162)
89. Chromatophores a pair of axial, more or less stellate bodies............... 90
89. Chromatophores a pair of pillow-shaped bodies.. Zygogonium (p. 134)
  90. Gametangia appearing solid at conjugation... Zygnemopsis (p. 134)
  90. Gametangia not appearing solid at conjuga-
      tion................................... Zygnema (p. 136)
91. Cells bearing setae......................... Aphanochaete (p. 40)
91. Cells not bearing setae.. 92
  92. Filament with conspicuous gelatinous sheath..................... 93
  92. Filament without a conspicuous sheath......................... 96
93. Sheath tough, close fitting; cells often not in a
    single row............................... Cylindrocapsa (p. 30)
93. Sheath soft, broad; cells always in a single row..................... 94
  94. Ends of cells flat....................... Ulothrix (p. 24)
  94. Ends of cells broadly rounded.. 95
95. Cells always adjacent, end to end.............. Radiofilum (p. 26)
95. Cells usually separate and in pairs............. Geminella
  96. Chromatophores reticulate; with oogonia and
      antheridia............................. Oedogonium (p. 57)
  96. Chromatophores not reticulate; without oogonia and antheridia......... 97
97. Filaments composed of articulated H-pieces..... Microspora (p. 29)
97. Filaments without such H-pieces....................................... 98
  98. Plant multiseriate, except when young...... Schizomeris (p. 100)
  98. Plant uniseriate.. 99
99. Cells without pyrenoids and often in pairs...... Binuclearia (p. 28)
99. Cells with pyrenoids and not in pairs................................ 100

100. Chromatophore a transverse girdle; fragmen-
    tation rare........................... Ulothrix (p. 24)
100. Chromatophore at one side of cell; fragmentation common........... 101
101. Chromatophore as long as the cell............ Stichococcus (p. 26)
101. Chromatophore half as long as the cell........ Hormidium (p. 26)

Order VOLVOCALES

Vegetative cells motile, uninucleate, solitary or forming definite colonial aggregates, sometimes temporarily amorphous (*Palmella*-stages), usually biflagellate or in some genera with 4, 5, 6 or 8 flagella, all of equal length and anteriorly placed; cell-wall generally present, internally of cellulose and peripherally of pectic compounds; colonial envelope gelatinous; a single eyespot; one or more pyrenoids, green chromatophores rarely lacking; all cells of a colony, or only a portion of them, capable of reproduction; formation of daughter colonies; isogamy to oogamy.

Family **Polyblepharidaceae**

Vegetative cells always solitary, without cellulose wall, but with rather firm peripheral membrane which allows for some change of cell shape, with 2, 4, 5 or 8 flagella, rarely without green chromatophores; isogamy.

Chloraster Ehrenberg 1848

Vegetative cell naked, spindle-shaped, with four radial, mid-polar lobes, actively motile by five equal-lengthed flagella at the anterior end; two contractile vacuoles at base of flagella, conspicuous eyespot; chromatophore cup-shaped, toward posterior end of cell, with single pyrenoid.

1. *Chloraster gyrans* Ehrenberg. Cells up to 15 μ in diameter (including lobes) and 18 μ in length; flagella about the length of the cell. Pl. 1, figs. **7-9.**

Family **Chlamydomonadaceae**

Vegetative cells solitary, sometimes palmelloid, with a definite homogeneous cellulose wall, biflagellate or quadriflagellate; isogamy, anisogamy and oogamy.

Chlamydomonas Ehrenberg 1833

Vegetative cell unicellular, actively motile, ovoid, spherical, fusiform or ellipsoid, anterior end sometimes beaked between the 2 equal-lengthed flagella; uninucleate, with contractile vacuoles, with or without eyespot and pyrenoid, with cup-shaped chromatophore.

Longitudinal cell division; zoospores, aplanospores, akinetes; smooth or rough-walled zygotes; isogamy, anisogamy, oogamy.

1. *Chlamydomonas globosa* Snow. Cells 5-10 μ in diameter, spherical or

subellipsoid, without anterior beak; chromatophore cup-shaped, with 1 pyrenoid and eyespot; 1 contractile vacuole at the base of the flagella; *Palmella*-stages frequent and usually with 4–8 cells. Pl. 1, fig. 4.

Carteria Diesing 1866

Vegetative cell unicellular, actively motile by 4 flagella at the anterior end, spherical, ellipsoid or cordiform; zoospores and gametes with 4 flagella; otherwise as in *Chlamydomonas.*

1. *Carteria multifilis* (Fresenius) Dill. Vegetative cell 7–13 × 9–16 μ, broadly ellipsoid or nearly spherical, with large pyrenoid and apical papilla; zygotes spherical 12–16 μ in diameter. Pl. 1, fig. 3.

Family **Phacotaceae**

Vegetative cells solitary, rarely palmelloid, compressed, with or without wing-like expansions between the two overlapping halves of the cell-wall, biflagellate; isogamy.

Phacotus Perty 1852

Unicellular, biflagellate, flattened, round or oval in front view and biconvex in edge view; envelope thick, impregnated with calcium carbonate, rough, composed of 2 overlapping halves; protoplast ovoid.

Multiplication by longitudinal division of protoplast into 2–8 zoospores; *Palmella*-stages may contain the half-walls of several generations.

1. *Phacotus lenticularis* (Ehrenberg) Stein. Cells 13–20 × 13–20 μ, lenticular. Pl. 1, figs. 1, 2.

Wislouchiella Skvortzow 1925

Cell solitary, strongly compressed, wall with broad wing-like expansion; each compressed face with blunt cylindrical processes; outer surface with minute, brownish or colorless warts; protoplast pyriform to oval in front view, rhomboidal in vertical view, anteriorly biflagellate, with 2 contractile vacuoles; chromatophore massive and cup-shaped with a single submedian pyrenoid and with an anteriorly placed eyespot.

Multiplication by division into 4 daughter cells.

Figs. 1, 2.—*Phacotus lenticularis* (Ehrenberg) Stein, front and side view.

Fig. 3.—*Carteria multifilis* (Fresenius) Dill.

Fig. 4.—*Chlamydomonas globosa* Snow.

Figs. 5, 6.—*Wislouchiella planctonica* Skvortzow, front and side view.

Figs. 7–9.—*Chloraster gyrans* Ehrenberg.

Fig. 10.—*Gonium sociale* (Dujardin) Warming.

Fig. 11.—*Gonium formosum* Pascher.

Fig. 12.—*Gonium pectorale* Mueller.

Fig. 13.—*Pandorina morum* Bory.

(Fig. 3, Pascher; figs. 4, 11, 12, G. M. Smith; figs. 7–9, Stein; fig. 10, Chodat. Figs. 3, 4 ×*1000;* all others ×*500.*)

PLATE 1
(Figs. 1 to 13)

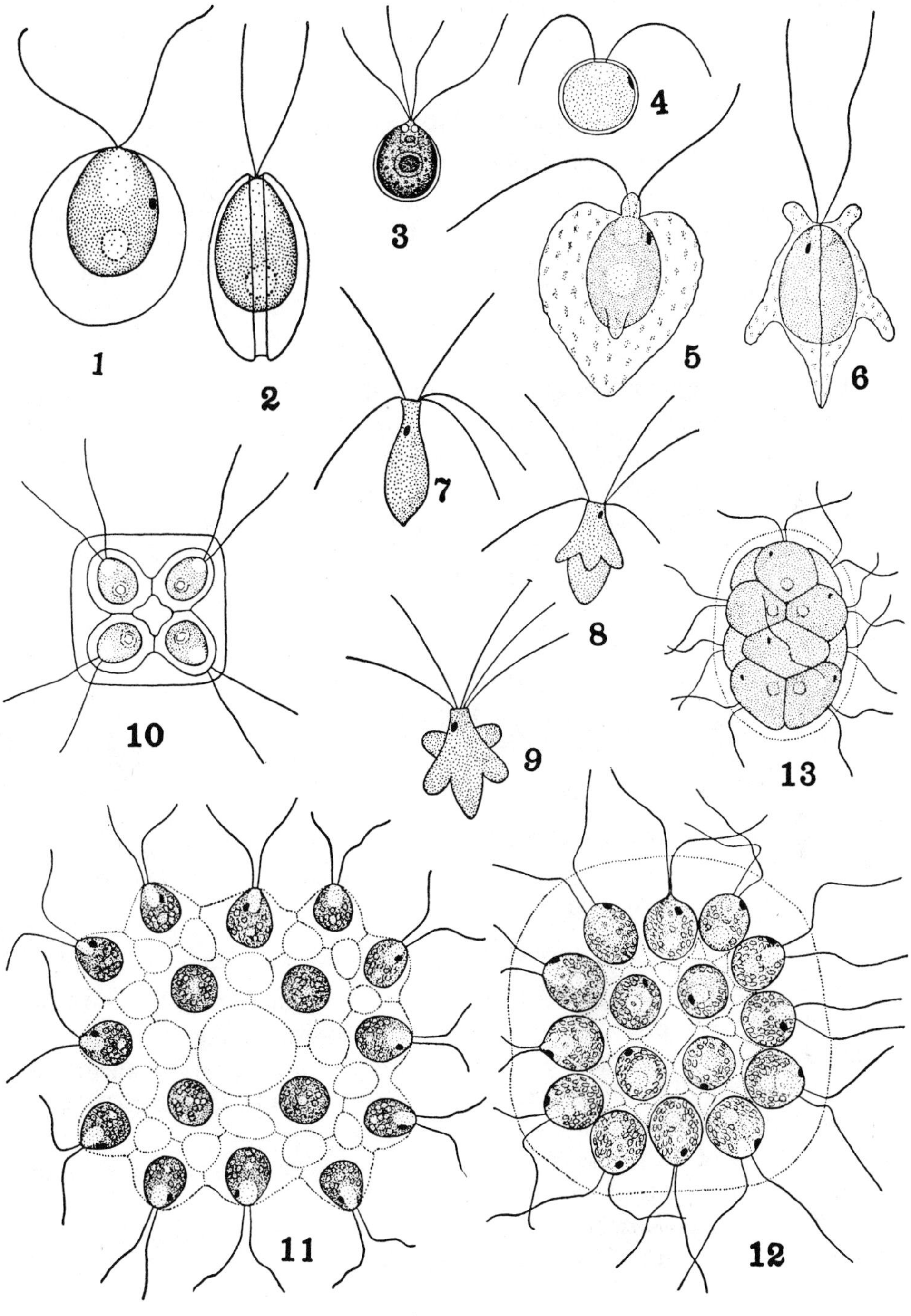

1. *Wislouchiella planctonica* Skvortzow. Cells 16–20 × 20–26 μ (with wings); processes up to 10 μ long.

Shallow pool near Charleston, Coles County. (Collected by K. E. Damann). Pl. 1, figs. 5, 6.

Family Volvocaceae

Cells in definite flat or spherical colonies, the individual cells peripherally arranged and with distinct or diffluent sheaths and biflagellate; cells in a colony all alike or not, sometimes consisting of large cells capable of reproduction and smaller cells purely vegetative in character; autocolonies, rarely akinetes and *Palmella*-stages, isogamy to oogamy.

Gonium Mueller 1773

Colony flat, quadrangular, motile with 4–16 cells in a common gelatinous matrix or connected by gelatinous strands; cell ovoid to pear-shaped, with 2 flagella of equal length, with contractile vacuoles and eyespot; chromatophore single, cup-shaped, with 1 pyrenoid.

Formation of autocolonies, akinetes, zoospores, and isogamous gametes.

KEY TO THE SPECIES

1. Colony of only 4 cells.. 1. G. sociale
1. Colony of 16 cells (rarely 8 or 4)...................................... 2. G. pectorale

1. *Gonium sociale* (Dujardin) Warming. Cells 6–16 × 10–22 μ, ovoid, 1.5–2.0 times as long as broad. Pl. 1, fig. 10.

2. *Gonium pectorale* Mueller. Cells 5–14 × 5–16 μ. ovoid; colonies 70–100 μ in diameter. Pl. 1, fig. 12.

It is quite likely that some of the records of *G. pectorale*, particularly the earlier ones, may refer to *G. formosum* Pascher (Pl. 1, fig. 11). The latter has distinctly pear-shaped cells, 7–11 × 10–25 μ.

Pandorina Bory 1824

Colony spherical, subspherical or nearly oblong, motile, with 4–8–16–32 cells mutually compressed in the periphery of colony, enclosed by a rather copious, hyaline envelope; envelope with or without protuberance; cell pyriform to angular, biflagellate; chromatophore single, cup-shaped, with 1 pyrenoid; 1 eyespot, and 2 contractile vacuoles.

Formation of autocolonies, zoospores, anisogamous gametes, and smooth-walled zygotes.

1. *Pandorina morum* Bory. Cell 8–16 μ in diameter; colony 20–45 × 20–50 μ, usually with 16 cells. Pl. 1, fig. 13.

Eudorina Ehrenberg 1832

Colony spherical, obovoid or ellipsoid, motile, with 16–32–64 cells at some distance from one another and near the periphery of the hyaline, gelatinous envelope; envelope symmetric or with posterior projections; cell biflagellate, spherical, with 1–2 anterior contractile vacuoles, with 1 eyespot; chromatophore single, cup-shaped, 1 to several pyrenoids.

Formation of autocolonies, zoospores, anisogamous gametes and smooth-walled zygotes.

1. *Eudorina elegans* Ehrenberg. Cell 12–24 μ in diameter; colony 50–200 μ in diameter, usually 32-celled. Pl. **2**, fig. **14.**

Pleodorina Shaw 1894

Colony spherical to subspherical, motile, with 32–128 cells at some distance from one another near the periphery of a hyaline, gelatinous envelope; cells spherical to ovoid, differentiated into purely vegetative and those capable of reproduction, biflagellate, with cup-shaped chromatophore, 1 pyrenoid (more in reproductive cells), 1 large anterior eyespot, 2 contractile vacuoles.

Formation of autocolonies; anisogamy and oogamy.

KEY TO THE SPECIES

1. Colony with half vegetative, half reproductive cells.............. 1. P. californica
1. Colony usually with 4 vegetative cells......................... 2. P. illinoisensis

1. *Pleodorina californica* Shaw. Vegetative cells 6–14 μ, reproductive cells 6–34 μ, in diameter; colony 40–400 μ in diameter, composed of 32–128 cells, about half vegetative and half reproductive; zygote spherical, 22–33 μ in diameter, reddish-brown, wall smooth, finely granulate or sometimes irregularly thickened. Pl. **2**, fig. **16.**

2. *Pleodorina illinoisensis* Kofoid. Vegetative cell 9–16 μ, reproductive cell 16–25 μ, in diameter; colony 130–175 $\times$ 150–200 μ, with 16–32 cells, usually 4 cells vegetative and the remainder reproductive. Pl. **2**, fig. **17.**

Platydorina Kofoid 1899

Colony flat, twisted, motile, with 16–32 cells (rarely less) in one layer but alternately pointing in opposite directions, enclosed in a horseshoe-shaped sheath with 3–5 posterior prolongations; cell oblately spheroid or angularly compressed, biflagellate, with eyespot and pyrenoid, parietal chromatophore, with 2 contractile vacuoles.

Formation of autocolonies; anisogamous gametes, and zygotes.

1. *Platydorina caudata* Kofoid. Cell 10–24 × 10–24 μ; 16-celled colonies 43 × 70 and 16 μ thick; 32-celled colonies 145 × 165 and 25 μ thick; zygote spherical, thick, with finely granulate wall. Pl. 2, fig. 15.

Volvox Linnaeus 1758

Colony spherical to ovoid, sometimes ellipsoid or pyriform, motile, with a large number (200–20,000) of cells peripherally arranged in a hyaline, colonial envelope; cells biflagellate, spherical, ovoid or disciform, differentiated into those potentially vegetative, asexual or sexual; a cup-shaped to disc-shaped chromatophore, 1 pyrenoid, 1 eyespot, and 2–6 contractile vacuoles; vegetative cells with or without cytoplasmic connections.

Formation of autocolonies, eggs and sperms, and zygotes.

KEY TO THE SPECIES

1. Zygote with smooth outer surface... 2
1. Zygote with spiny verrucose surface................... 1. V. globator
   2. Cells connected by protoplasmic strands................ 2. V. aureus
   2. Cells not so connected.............................. 3. V. spermatosphaera

1. *Volvox globator* Linnaeus. Cells pyriform, stellate in polar view, with a single flattened chromatophore, connected by stout protoplasmic strands, with well-defined, angular cell sheaths; mature asexual colonies broadly ellipsoid, 380–540 × 400–575 μ, composed of 8,000–20,000 cells; zygote 44–56 μ in diameter, with bluntly spiny to verrucose wall, without warts, 35–45 μ in diameter. Pl. 2, figs. 18, 19.

2. *Volvox aureus* Ehrenberg. Cells ovoid, with a spherical chromatophore, and connected by fine protoplasmic strands; mature asexual colonies ellipsoid, 300–475 × 340–510 μ, composed of 1,300–4,000 cells; zygote 38–62 μ in diameter, smooth-walled. Pl. 2, fig. 21.

3. *Volvox spermatosphaera* Powers. Cells ellipsoid, not connected by cytoplasmic strands; asexual colonies broadly ellipsoid, 245–415 × 275–

Fig. 14.—*Eudorina elegans* Ehrenberg.

Fig. 15.—*Platydorina caudata* Kofoid.

Fig. 16.—*Pleodorina californica* Shaw, part of colony.

Fig. 17.—*Pleodorina illinoisensis* Kofoid.

Fig. 18.—*Volvox globator* Linnaeus, part of colony.

Fig. 19.—*Volvox globator* Linnaeus, zygote.

Fig. 20.—*Volvox spermatosphaera* Powers, part of colony with daughter colony.

Fig. 21.—*Volvox aureus* Ehrenberg, part of colony with sex cells.

Fig. 22.—*Haematococcus lacustris* (Girod) Rostafinski.

(Figs. 14, 16–20, G. M. Smith; figs. 15, 22, Tiffany. Fig. 19 ×*750;* all others ×*400.*)

PLATE 2 (Figs. 14 to 22)

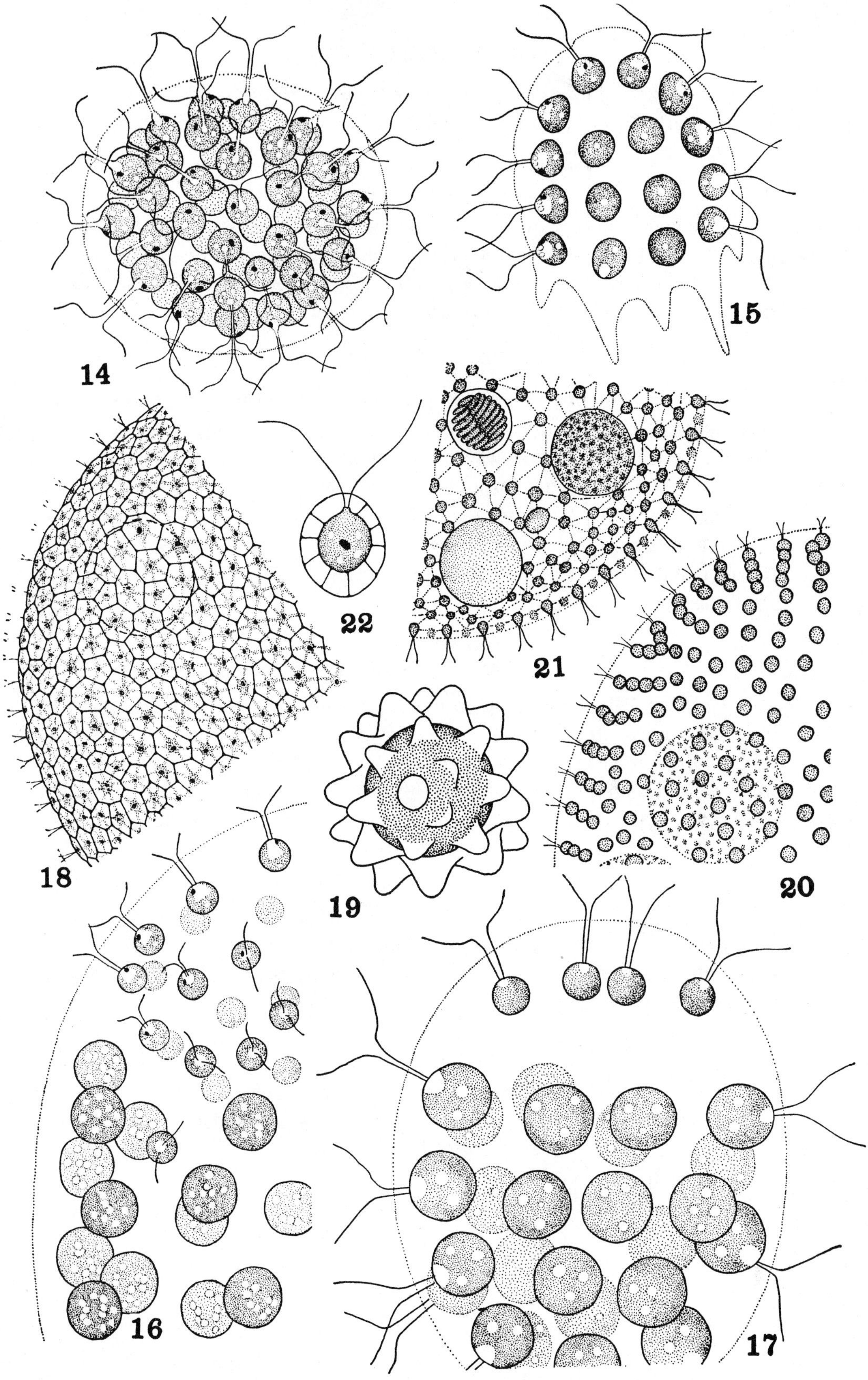

14

15

18

22

21

20

19

16

17

450 (–650) μ, composed of 1,000–3,000 cells; zygote 34–43 μ in diameter, with smooth outer surface: inner face of exospore with small pits. Pl. 2, fig. 20.

Family Haematococcaceae

Motile cells solitary or definitely colonial; protoplast connected to cell-wall by numerous cytoplasmic strands; biflagellate; green color frequently obscured by hematochrome; autocolonies, sometimes akinetes, aplano-spores and *Palmella*-stages; isogamy.

Haematococcus C. A. Agardh 1828

Cell solitary, ovoid, sometimes beaked between the 2 flagella; cell-wall peripherally firm and internally often wide and gelatinous, transversed by strands from the protoplast; chromatophore more or less reticulate, with 1 eyespot, 2–8 pyrenoids; bright red hematochrome often abundant.

Vegetative division, akinetes, isogamous gametes.

1. *Haematococcus lacustris* (Girod) Rostafinski [*Sphaerella lacustris* (Girod) Wittrock]. Cells 8–30 μ in diameter, often brick-red in color. Pl. 2, fig. 22.

Order Tetrasporales

Vegetative cells uninucleate, unicellular with gelatinous sheath or united into gelatinous microscopic or macroscopic colonies, with or without pseudocilia; cells capable of division, not mobile; eyespots present in some genera; cell-wall of cellulose and pectic compounds; chromatophores usually with pyrenoids and starch, sometimes only oil present as a food reserve; zoospores, akinetes, aplanospores; isogamy.

Family Palmellaceae

Vegetative cells forming small amorphous gelatinous colonies, some-times of definite shape, with cell sheaths remaining distinct or confluent; no pseudocilia; fragmentation of colony, zoospores; isogamy.

Gloeocystis Naegeli 1849

Cell globose or ellipsoid, solitary or embedded in large or small numbers in a gelatinous sheath, lamellose or without stratification, formed from the membranes of successive mother cells; chromatophore parietal, bell-shaped, with 1 pyrenoid.

Fragmentation of the colony and formation of zoospores and akinetes.

KEY TO THE SPECIES

1. Colonial sheath lamellose.. 2
1. Colonial sheath unstratified.............................. 1. G. ampla
   2. Solitary, or in groups of 2–8.......................... 2. G. gigas
   2. Not solitary, usually larger groups...................... 3. G. planctonica

1. *Gloeocystis ampla* Kuetzing. Cell 10–12 × 9–15 μ, ovoid, enclosed in unstratified gelatinous sheath; colonies, usually fragmenting, up to 15 mm. in diameter. Pl. **3,** fig. **23.**

2. *Gloeocystis gigas* (Kuetzing) Lagerheim. Cell 9–17 μ in diameter, spherical or very broadly ellipsoid, solitary or in families of 2–8, enclosed by distinctly lamellose sheath; colonies 45–100 μ (or more) in diameter. Pl. **3,** fig. **24.**

3. *Gloeocystis planctonica* (W. and G. S. West) Lemmermann. Cell 7.5–12 μ in diameter, spherical, embedded in angular free-floating, lamellose envelope; colony 120–135 μ in diameter. Pl. **3,** fig. **25.**

Palmella Lyngbye 1819; emend. Chodat 1902

Cells spherical to broadly ellipsoid, forming microscopic or macroscopic colonies amorphous in appearance; indefinite gelatinous matrix composed of partly or wholly confluent cell sheaths; cup-shaped chromatophore, with a single basal pyrenoid; chlorophyll sometimes masked by hematochrome.

Vegetative division; biflagellate zoospores, with or without eyespot; akinetes; isogamous gametes.

1. *Palmella miniata* Leiblein. Cell 3–40 μ in diameter, colored by hematochrome, solitary or in groups of 2–8 in irregular gelatinous masses; on damp soil. Pl. **3,** figs. **28, 29.**

Sphaerocystis Chodat 1897

Colony spherical with groups of 4–32 cells arranged toward the periphery of a hyaline, homogeneous envelope; cell spherical, sometimes with individual sheath, chromatophore cup-shaped or entirely filling the cell, with 1 pyrenoid.

Fragmentation of the colony and formation of zoospores.

1. *Sphaerocystis schroeteri* Chodat. Cell 6–22 μ in diameter; colony 50–500 μ in diameter; with characters of the genus. Pl. **3,** figs. **26, 27.**

Family **Tetrasporaceae**

Vegetative cells forming microscopic or macroscopic aggregates of definite shape or amorphous, rarely solitary; cells, enclosed by gelatinous matrix, often in twos or fours; pyrenoids present, sometimes absent;

2 pseudocilia anteriorly placed and often projecting beyond gelatinous envelope; daughter cells, colony fragmentation, zoospores, akinetes; isogamy.

Tetraspora Link 1809

Colony macroscopic or microscopic, attached or free-floating, spherical, elongate, or variously shaped, with copious, homogeneous envelope; cells spherical, with 2–4 pseudocilia, grouped in fours or rarely irregular; chromatophore cup-shaped, parietal, rarely diffuse, usually with 1 pyrenoid.

Zoospores, isogamous gametes, aplanospores, and akinetes.

KEY TO THE SPECIES

1. Gelatinous colony irregularly saccate........................ 1. T. gelatinosa
1. Gelatinous colony tubular.. 2
  2. Colony repeatedly split.................................. 2. T. lubrica
  2. Colony consistently cylindric............................ 3. T. cylindrica

1. *Tetraspora gelatinosa* (Vaucher) Desvaux. Cells varying in size in same colony, 3–13 μ in diameter, in irregularly inflated masses. Pl. 4, fig. 33.

2. *Tetraspora lubrica* (Roth) C. A. Agardh. Cells 7–11 μ in diameter, in long (1–30 cm. in running water) tubular, repeatedly split envelopes, usually attached to aquatic macrophytes. Pl. 3, figs. 30, 31.

3. *Tetraspora cylindrica* (Wahlenberg) C. A. Agardh. Cells 2–20 μ in diameter, in long tough cylindric envelopes reaching extreme lengths of a meter and diameters of 1–2 cm., usually attached. (Lawrence County, Tiffany.) Pl. 4, fig. 32.

Apiocystis Naegeli 1849

Colony microscopic, commonly pear-shaped and epiphytic on other algae, the envelope usually with a well-defined peripheral zone; cell spherical, with 2 pseudocilia; chromatophore parietal with pyrenoid.

Fig. 23.—*Gloeocystis ampla* Kuetzing.

Fig. 24.—*Gloeocystis gigas* (Kuetzing) Lagerheim.

Fig. 25.—*Gloeocystis planctonica* (W. & G. West) Lemmermann.

Figs. 26, 27.—*Sphaerocystis schroeteri* Chodat.

Fig. 28.—*Palmella miniata* Leiblein, part of colony.

Fig. 29.—*Palmella miniata*, zoospore.

Fig. 30.—*Tetraspora lubrica* (Roth) Agardh, entire colony.

Fig. 31.—*Tetraspora lubrica*, part of colony.

(Fig. 23, Cienkowski; figs. 24, 26, 27, by permission from *Fresh-water Algae of the United States* by G. M. Smith. Copyright 1933. McGraw-Hill Book Co., Inc.; fig. 25, G. S. West. Fig. 30 $\times\frac{1}{2}$; figs. 28, 29 $\times 600$; figs. 26, 27 $\times 1000$; all others $\times 400$.)

PLATE 3

(Figs. 23 to 31)

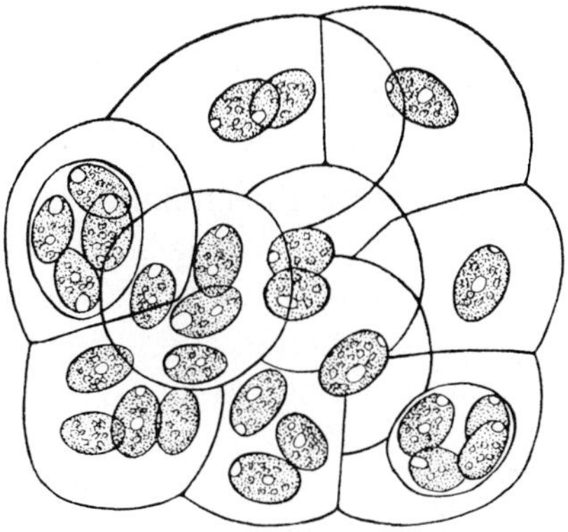

23

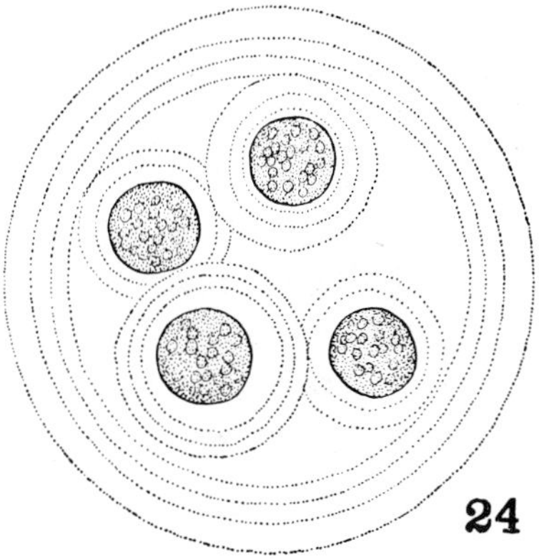

24

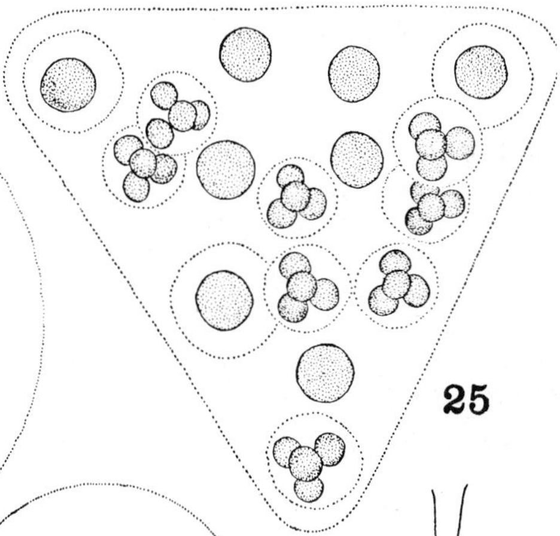

25

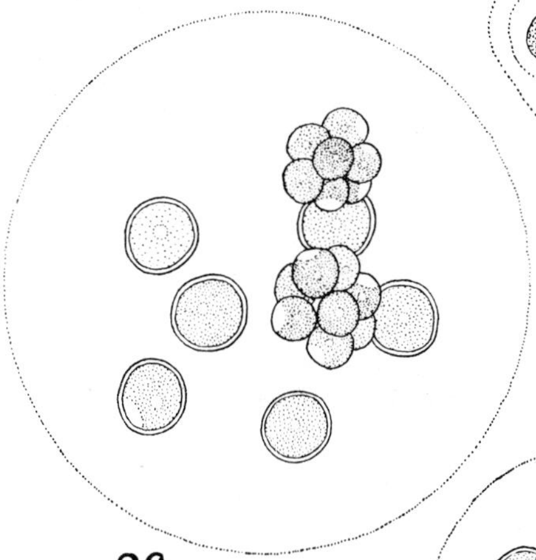

26

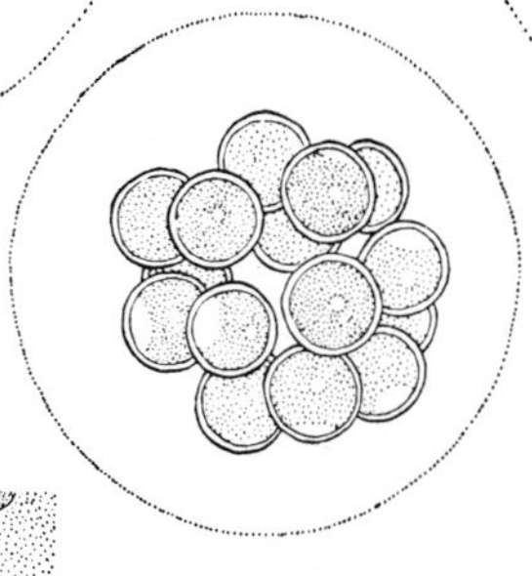

27

29

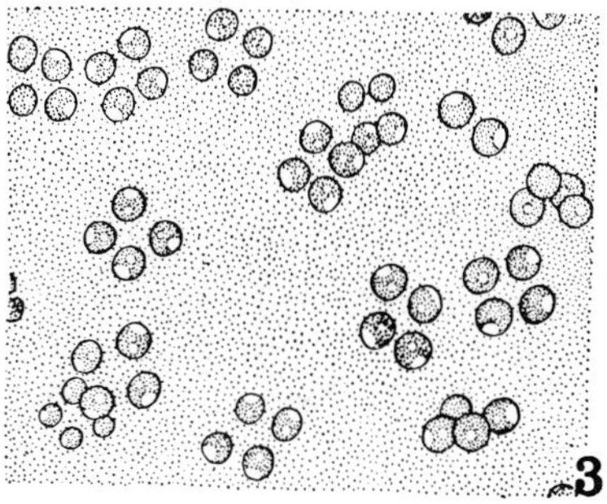

31 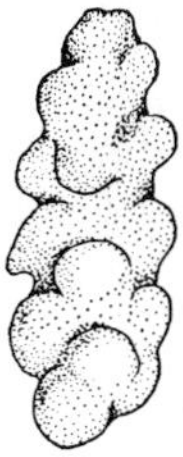   30 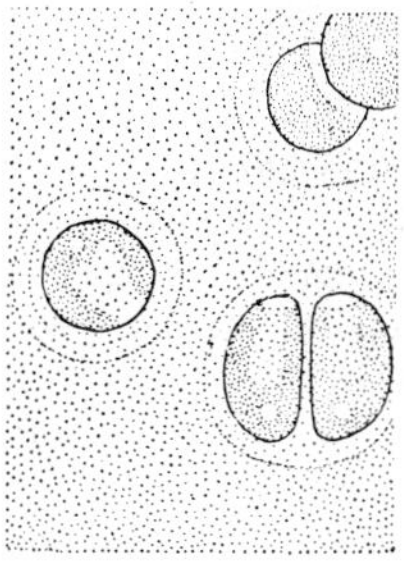   28

Zoospores, isogamous gametes.

1. *Apiocystis brauniana* Naegeli. Cell 6–8 μ in diameter; colony 12–1,000 μ (or more) in diameter. Pl. 4, fig. 34.

Order ULOTRICHALES

Cells forming simple or branched filaments (rarely unicellular or parenchyma-like), almost always uninucleate and generally with a single laminate chromatophore; pyrenoids usually present; starch the chief food reserve; cell-wall cellulose with peripheral pectic compounds; biflagellate or quadriflagellate zoospores, aplanospores, akinetes; isogamy to oogamy.

Family **Ulotrichaceae**

Unbranched filaments, with uninucleate cells, having parietal, band-shaped chromatophores; zoospores, akinetes, aplanospores; isogamy.

Ulothrix Kuetzing 1833

Filament unbranched, not apically attenuated, frequently attached basally; vegetative cell uninucleate, cylindric or sometimes barrel-shaped; chromatophore band-shaped, occupying part or the whole of cell circumference, with 1 or more pyrenoids.

Formation of quadriflagellate and biflagellate zoospores and of akinetes; biflagellate gametes; zygotes germinating into daughter protoplasts producing aplanospores or zoospores; haploid filaments producing either gametes only, gametes and zoospores, or zoospores only.

KEY TO THE SPECIES

1. Cell 5–9 μ in diameter, 1 pyrenoid 2
1. Cell 11–45 μ in diameter, several pyrenoids . . . . 1. U. zonata
   2. Cells 5–6 μ in diameter . . . . 2. U. variabilis
   2. Cells 7–9 μ in diameter . . . . 3. U. tenerrima

FIG. 32.—*Tetraspora cylindrica* (Wahlenberg) Agardh, entire colony and part of colony enlarged.

FIG. 33.—*Tetraspora gelatinosa* (Vaucher) Desvaux, part of colony.

FIG. 34.—*Apiocystis brauniana* Naegeli.

FIGS. 35, 36.—*Ulothrix zonata* (Weber & Mohr) Kuetzing, vegetative filament with holdfast cell; zoospores and gametes.

FIG. 37.—*Ulothrix variabilis* Kuetzing.

FIG. 38.—*Ulothrix tenerrima* Kuetzing, filament with zoospores.

FIGS. 39–41.—*Hormidium klebsii* G. M. Smith.

FIG. 42.—*Radiofilum irregulare* (Wille) Brunnthaler.

(Fig. 34, by permission from *Fresh-water Algae of the United States* by G. M. Smith. Copyright 1933. McGraw-Hill Book Co., Inc.; figs. 35–38, Tiffany. Fig. 32 (colony) $\times\frac{1}{2}$; figs. 34–36 $\times 300$; fig. 33 $\times 1200$; others $\times 400$.)

PLATE 4
(Figs. 32 to 42)

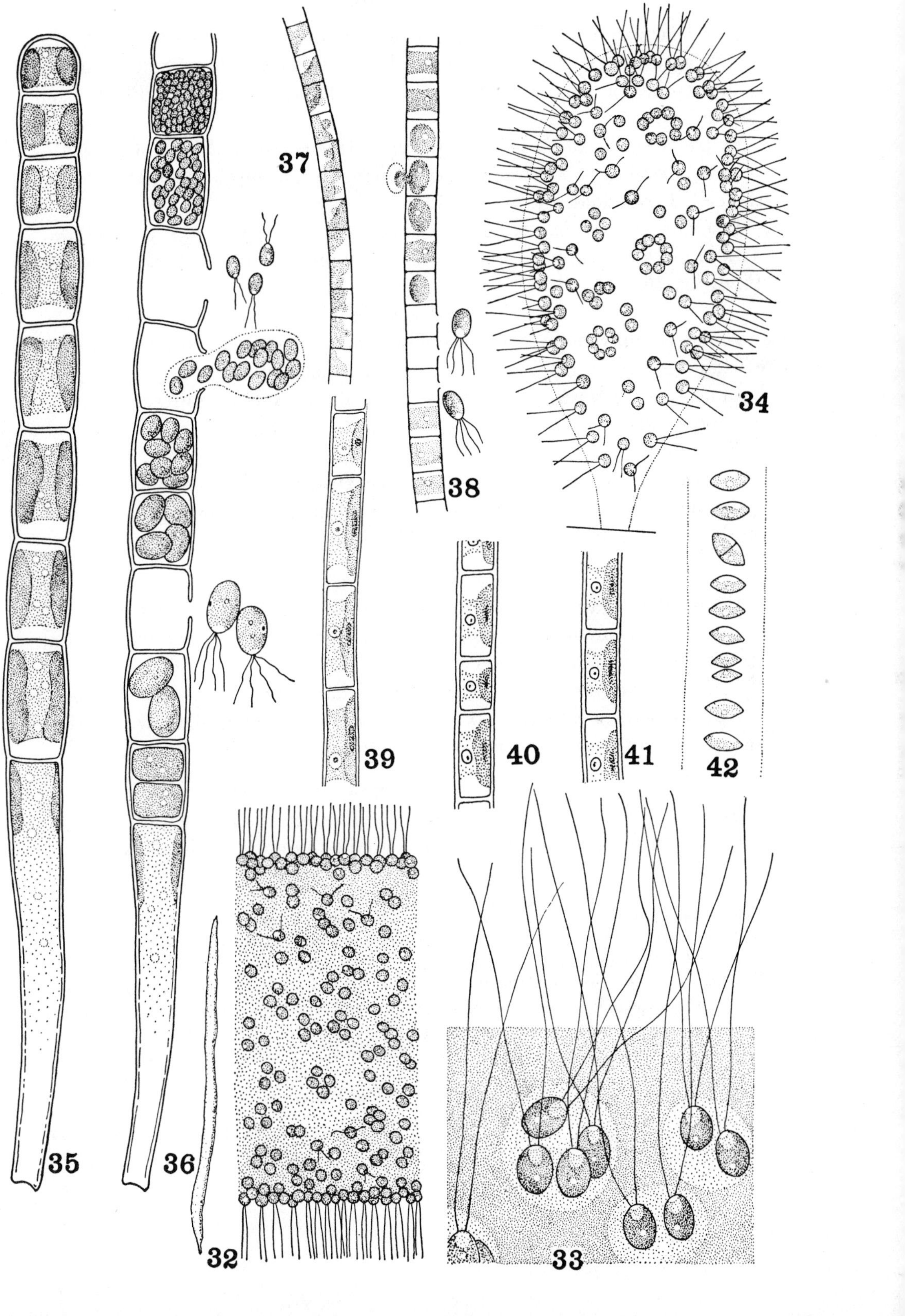

1. *Ulothrix zonata* (Weber and Mohr) Kuetzing. Vegetative cell cylindric or swollen, 11–45 × 10–100 μ; cell-wall thick at maturity; chromatophore usually a median band with several large pyrenoids. Pl. **4,** figs. **35, 36.**

2. *Ulothrix variabilis* Kuetzing. Vegetative cell cylindric, 5–6 × 3–9 μ, with thin walls; chromatophore, often irregular, occupying about one-half the cell, 1 pyrenoid. Pl. **4,** fig. **37.**

3. *Ulothrix tenerrima* Kuetzing. Vegetative cell cylindric, 7–9 × 6–12 μ, with thin walls; chromatophore zonate or on one side, with 1 pyrenoid. Pl. **4,** fig. **38.**

Stichococcus Naegeli 1849

Filament unbranched, consisting of a few (sometimes solitary) or many cells; vegetative cell uninucleate, cylindric; chromatophore parietal and laminate, not covering more than one-half the cell circumference; without pyrenoids.

Fragmentation.

1. *Stichococcus bacillaris* Naegeli. Vegetative cells 2.5–3.0 × 3–12 μ, cylindric, very readily separating; chromatophore thin and pale; usually on damp rocks and soil. Pl. **5,** fig. **45.**

Radiofilum Schmidle 1894

Filament unbranched, consisting of spherical to nearly lenticular cells, enclosed in a broad gelatinous sheath (sheath frequently with radial stratification); fragmentation.

1. *Radiofilum irregulare* (Wille) Brunnthaler. Vegetative cell 12–15 × 4–6 μ, enclosed in a sheath up to 30 μ in diameter; cells often arranged in an irregular row (or rows) and sheath often not cylindric. Pl. **4,** fig. **42.**

Hormidium Kuetzing 1843; emend. Klebs 1896

Filament unbranched, consisting of cylindric cells and without gelatinous sheath; cell uninucleate, with a single laminate parietal chromato-

---

Fig. 43.—*Hormidium flaccidum* (Kuetzing) A. Braun.

Fig. 44.—*Hormidium subtile* (Kuetzing) Heering, fragmentation of filament.

Fig. 45.—*Stichococcus bacillaris* Naegeli.

Fig. 46.—*Binuclearia tatrana* Wittrock.

Fig. 47.—*Microspora pachyderma* (Wille) Lagerheim, akinetes.

Figs. 48, 49.—*Microspora willeana* Lagerheim, vegetative filament and akinetes.

Figs. 50, 51.—*Microspora stagnorum* (Kuetzing) Lagerheim, vegetative filament and zoospore formation.

Fig. 52.—*Microspora quadrata* Hazen.

Fig. 53.—*Microspora tumidula* Hazen.

Fig. 54.—*Microspora floccosa* (Vaucher) Thuret, akinetes and dead cells.

Fig. 55.—*Cylindrocapsa geminella* Wolle.

Fig. 56.—*Cylindrocapsa geminella* var. *minor* Hansgirg.

(Figs. 43, 45, 48–54, Hazen; figs. 46, 55, 56, Tiffany. Fig. 45 ×*500;* all others ×*800.*)

PLATE 5

(Figs. 43 to 56)

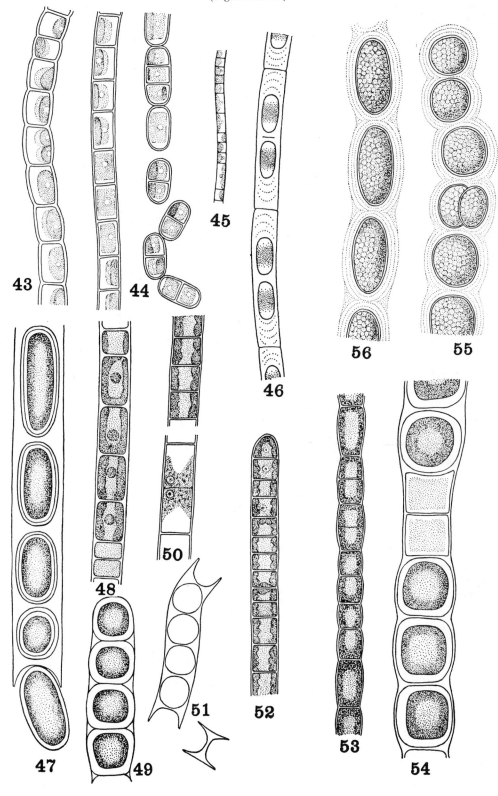

43   44   45   46   56   55

47   48   49   50   51   52   53   54

phore only partially encircling the cell; pyrenoid single, somewhat elongate, encompassed by many small starch grains.

Fragmentation; biflagellate zoospores; aplanospores; isogamy.

KEY TO THE SPECIES

1. Cells cylindric; unconstricted at cross-walls.................................. 2
1. Cells tumid; constricted at cross-walls....................... 1. H. flaccidum
   2. Vegetative cells 5.5–7.0 × 8–15 μ; pyrenoids 1.5–2.0 μ in diameter... 2. H. klebsii
   2. Vegetative cells 5–8 × 6–23 μ; pyrenoids smaller........... 3. H. subtile

1. *Hormidium flaccidum* (Kuetzing) A. Braun [*Stichococcus flaccidus* (Kuetzing) Gay]. Vegetative cell 6–10 × 2–10 μ, swollen up to 18 μ in diameter; cell-wall thick; chromatophore broad, with a single large pyrenoid; moist places, rarely submerged. Pl. **5**, fig. **43**.

2. *Hormidium klebsii* G. M. Smith. Vegetative cell 5.5–7.0 × 8–15 μ; zoospore asymmetric, pear-shaped, with chromatophore confined to one side, 2 contractile vacuoles, no eyespot; pyrenoid 1.5–2.0 μ in diameter. Pl. **4**, figs. **39–41**.

Pool on Northwestern University Campus, Cook County (Tiffany).

3. *Hormidium subtile* (Kuetzing) Heering [*Stichococcus subtilis* (Kuetzing) Klercker]. Vegetative cell 5–8 × 6–23 μ; filaments not constricted at cross-walls and not readily breaking up; aquatic; pyrenoids small. Pl. **5**, fig. **44**.

Binuclearia Wittrock 1886

Filaments unbranched and devoid of gelatinous sheath; cells cylindric with flattened poles and much shorter cylindric chromatophores with rounded ends; space between end of cell and chromatophore gelatinous and lamellose; daughter cells often in pairs, older cells becoming equidistant; chromatophore single, laminate, usually occupying the middle of the cell, without pyrenoid, and often with a prominent granule at each end.

Aplanospores, akinetes, and (?) zoospores; sexual reproduction unknown.

1. *Binuclearia tatrana* Wittrock. Vegetative cells 6–10 × 10–70 μ. Lake Zurich, Lake County (Tiffany). Pl. **5**, fig. **46**.

Family **Microsporaceae**

Unbranched filaments with uninucleate cells having a single variously lobed chromatophore lacking pyrenoids; each cell-wall consisting of 2 articulated H-shaped pieces enveloping the protoplast and composed of cellulose and pectic compounds; zoospores, aplanospores, akinetes.

Microspora Thuret 1850; emend. Lagerheim 1888

Filament unbranched, composed of articulated H-pieces; vegetative cell cylindric or swollen, uninucleate, walls thick or thin; chromatophore perforate, reticulate, and covering entire inner surface of cell-wall; pyrenoid none.

Fragmentation; akinetes, aplanospores, and biflagellate zoospores; sexual reproduction unknown.

KEY TO THE SPECIES*

1. Diameter of vegetative cell 5–7 μ......................... 1. M. quadrata
1. Diameter of vegetative cell 7–14 μ... 2
1. Diameter of vegetative cell 14–17 μ....................... 2. M. floccosa
    2. Cells thick-walled.................................... 3. M. pachyderma
    2. Cells thin-walled... 3
3. Cells 7–10 μ in diameter................................... 4
3. Cells 11–14 μ in diameter.............................. 4. M. willeana
    4. Filament cylindric................................... 5. M. stagnorum
    4. Filament constricted at cross-walls.................... 6. M. tumidula

1. *Microspora quadrata* Hazen. Vegetative cell 5–7 × 3–7 μ, wall thin; chromatophore internally covering entire cell-wall; akinete rounded, 5–7 μ in diameter. Pl. **5**, fig. **52**.

2. *Microspora floccosa* (Vaucher) Thuret. Vegetative cell 14–18 × 14–40 μ, wall thin; akinete variously shaped, 18–22 μ in diameter, filament cylindric or nearly so. Pl. **5**, fig. **54**.

3. *Microspora pachyderma* (Wille) Lagerheim. Vegetative cell 8–14 × 12–40 μ, wall up to 3 μ thick; akinetes quadrately rounded to ellipsoid, 8–14 × 10–18 μ. Pl. **5**, fig. **47**.

4. *Microspora willeana* Lagerheim. Vegetative cell 11–16 × 6–25 μ, wall thin; akinete spherical or nearly so, 14–18 μ in diameter; filament cylindric. Pl. **5**, figs. **48, 49**.

5. *Microspora stagnorum* (Kuetzing) Lagerheim. Vegetative cell (5–) 7–10 × 8–30 μ, wall thin; aplanospore ellipsoid or spherical. Pl. **5**, figs. **50, 51**.

6. *Microspora tumidula* Hazen. Vegetative cell 7–10 × 7–18 μ, with constrictions at the cross-wall; akinetes 8–11 μ in diameter, rounded or lenticular. Pl. **5**, fig. **53**.

* A preliminary analysis of the genus by Grace Scharf Phinney (1948) indicates that some of these species may not be valid.

Family Cylindrocapsaceae

Unbranched filaments, with cells having concentrically stratified cellulose walls surrounded by pectic sheath (sometimes filamentous nature obscured by development of *Palmella*-stages with irregular cell arrangement); chromatophore often massive with 1 pyrenoid, sometimes obscured by starch grains; fragmentation, zoospores; oogamy.

Cylindrocapsa Reinsch 1867

Filament unbranched, usually uniseriate within a pectic tubular envelope, cells sometimes irregularly arranged; vegetative cell ellipsoid, ovoid, subrectangular or spherical, each with a stratified gelatinous wall; chromatophore massive, pyrenoid single.

Fragmentation; biflagellate zoospores; eggs and biflagellate sperms; oospores; *Palmella*-stages.

KEY TO THE SPECIES

1. Vegetative cells globose, or nearly so.................... C. geminella
1. Vegetative cells ellipsoid.............................. C. geminella var. minor

1. *Cylindrocapsa geminella* Wolle. Vegetative cell globose or nearly so, 14–24 μ in diameter, with thick lamellose walls; oospore globose, 40–50 μ in diameter, with lamellose wall 10–15 μ thick. Pl. 5, fig. 55.

    a. Var. *minor* Hansgirg. Vegetative cell 12–25 × 15–50 μ, ellipsoid to cylindric; oospore globose, 18–25 μ in diameter, not filling oogonium. Pl. 5, fig. 56.

Family Chaetophoraceae

Branching filaments, free or forming a parenchyma-like tissue, the thallus of most genera partly prostrate and partly erect and freely branched, often accompanied with copious gelatinous matrix; composed of uninucleate cells, generally with a single laminate parietal chromatophore and may be terminated by one or more long colorless much attenuated cells; zoospores, akinetes, aplanospores; isogamy to oogamy.

Fig. 57.—*Aphanochaete repens* A. Braun.

Fig. 58.—*Protococcus viridis* Agardh.

Fig. 59.—*Chaetosphaeridium pringsheimii* Klebahn.

Fig. 60.—*Chaetosphaeridium globosum* (Nordstedt) Klebahn.

Fig. 61.—*Chaetophora incrassata* (Hudson) Hazen.

Fig. 62.—*Chaetophora elegans* (Roth) Agardh, terminal branches and basal portion of colony.

(Figs. 57, 59, Tiffany; fig. 60, by permission from *Fresh-water Algae of the United States* by G. M. Smith. Copyright 1933. McGraw-Hill Book Co., Inc.; figs. 61, 62, Hazen. Figs. 57, 59, 60 ×*50;* fig. 58 ×*1000;* figs. 61, 62 ×*300.*)

PLATE 6
(Figs. 57 to 62)

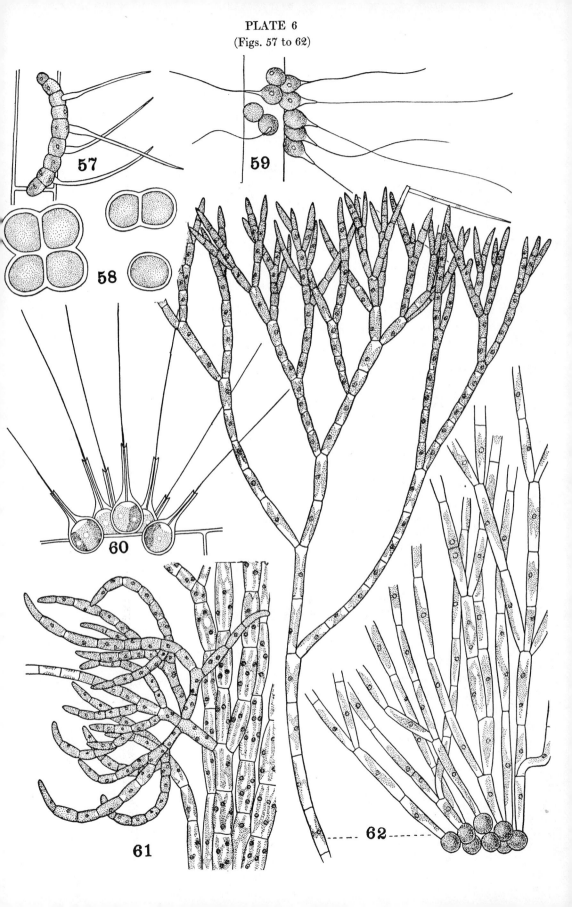

57

59

58

60

61

62

Chaetophora Schrank 1789

Filament branched, enclosed in a macroscopic, tough envelope that may be spherical, hemispherical, elongate, or irregularly tuberculate; fasciculate branching at the apices and ultimate branchlets often multicellularly setiferous; vegetative cell cylindric or somewhat swollen; chromatophore single, covering whole wall in young cells and then with 1 pyrenoid, becoming zonate in larger cells with several pyrenoids.

Quadriflagellate zoospores; akinetes, biflagellate gametes; zygotes.

KEY TO THE SPECIES

1. Colony globose or tuberculate.. 2
1. Colony elongate, irregularly laciniate........................ 1. C. incrassata
   2. Branching lax and spreading............................. 2. C. elegans
   2. Branching erect.. 3
3. Branches fascicled at the top............................. 3. C. pisiformis
3. Branches not fascicled at the top......................... 4. C. attenuata

1. *Chaetophora incrassata* (Hudson) Hazen. Gelatinous colonies elongate, irregularly lobed and laciniate; main filaments elongate, bearing densely fascicled and usually setiferous branchlets; vegetative cells of main filaments 8–16 × 8–90 μ, cylindric or swollen. Pl. 6, fig. 61.

2. *Chaetophora elegans* (Roth) C. A. Agardh. Gelatinous colonies globose or subglobose; filaments with lax branching, radiating from center of colony; vegetative cells of main filaments 6–11 × 20–100 μ. Pl. 6, fig. 62.

3. *Chaetophora pisiformis* (Roth) C. A. Agardh. Gelatinous colonies globose to tuberculate; filaments radiating from center of colony, branches with fasciculate and sometimes setiferous apices; vegetative cells of main filaments 5–8 × 15–40 μ, cylindric. Pl. 7, fig. 63.

4. *Chaetophora attenuata* Hazen. Gelatinous colony globose or nearly so; filaments branched, very erect, nearly parallel with each other, not apically fasciculate; vegetative cell of main filament 5–6 × 25–60 μ. Pl. 7, fig. 64.

Stigeoclonium Kuetzing 1843

Plant differentiated into an irregularly branched or somewhat parenchymatous prostrate system and a sparsely branched erect portion with obscure main axis and with lateral branches much attenuate; often en-

Fig. 63.—*Chaetophora pisiformis* (Roth) C. A. Agardh.   terminal branches and basal portion of colony.

Fig. 64.—*Chaetophora attenuata* Hazen,   (Both figs. from Hazen. ×*300*.)

PLATE 7

(Figs. 63 to 64)

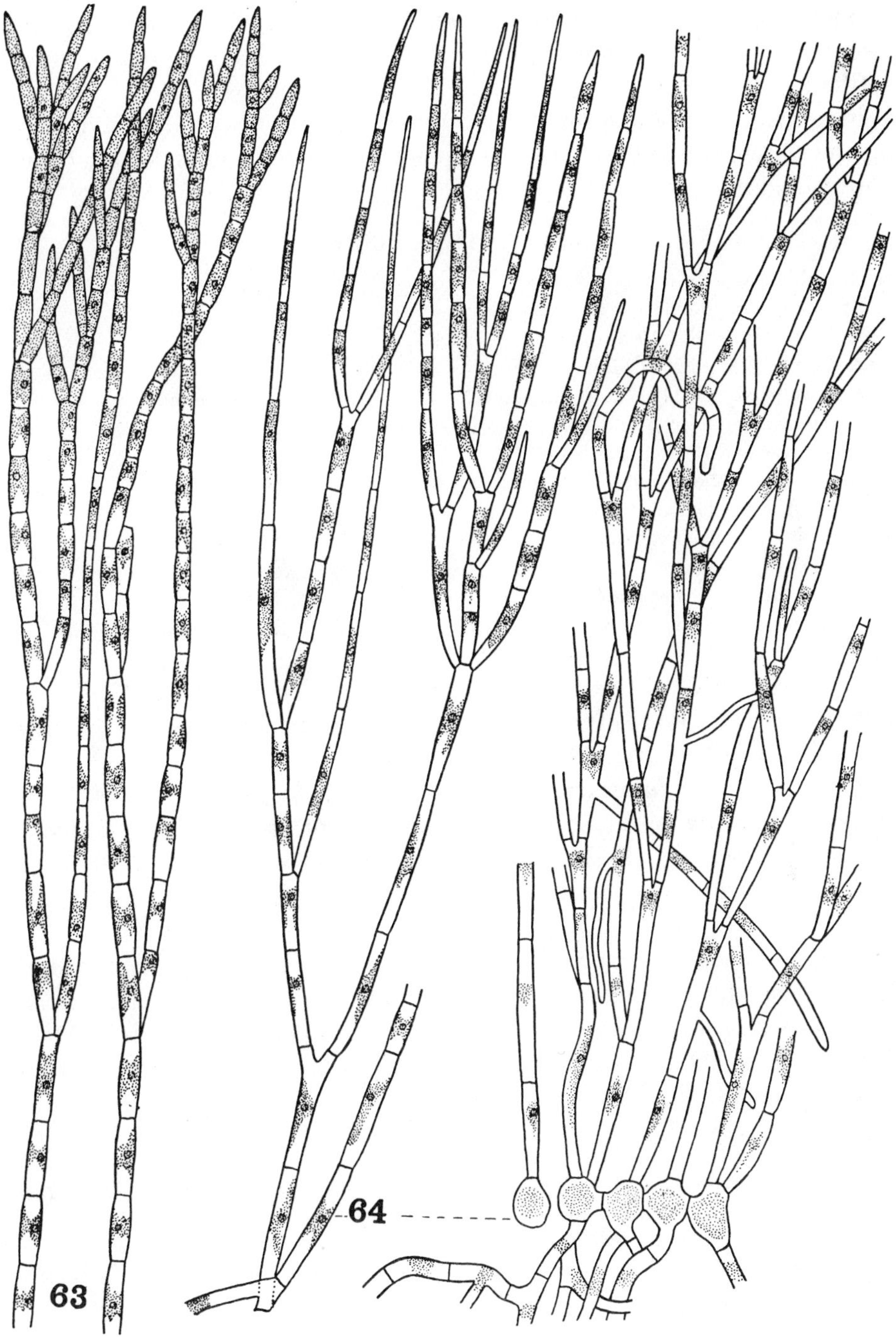

63

64

closed in a delicate gelatinous sheath; vegetative cells cylindric or slightly swollen, uninucleate; chromatophore transversely zonate with several pyrenoids, or (in young cells) a complete girdle with one pyrenoid, or in setiferous cells none.

Fragmentation; *Palmella*-stages; quadriflagellate zoospores; akinetes; aplanospores; biflagellate gametes (quadriflagellate in some species); zygotes; isogamy.

KEY TO THE SPECIES

1. Branching predominately opposite.................................... 2
1. Branching predominately alternate................................... 3
  2. Vegetative cell 5–10 μ in diameter.............. 1. S. tenue
  2. Vegetative cell 10–12 μ in diameter.............. 2a. S. lubricum v. varians
  2. Vegetative cell 14–17 μ in diameter.............. 2. S. lubricum
3. Vegetative cell 6–11 μ in diameter............................. 4
3. Vegetative cell 11–18 μ in diameter............................ 5
  4. Plant with short, tufted filaments............. 3. S. nanum
  4. Plant with elongate filaments.................... 4. S. stagnatile
5. Branches densely fasciculate......................... 5. S. glomeratum
5. Branches scattered....................................... 6
  6. Vegetative cell 1–2 diameters long............... 6. S. longipilum
  6. Vegetative cell 3–10 diameters long............. 7. S. subsecundum

1. *Stigeoclonium tenue* (Agardh) Kuetzing. Vegetative cell 5–10 $\times$ 7–30 μ; branches more often opposite, though some always solitary; tufts bright green. Pl. **10,** fig. **70.**

2. *Stigeoclonium lubricum* (Dillwyn) Kuetzing. Vegetative cell 14–17 $\times$ 10–30 μ, somewhat swollen; branching opposite or various. Pl. **8,** fig. **66.**

  a. Var. *varians* (Hazen) Collins. Vegetative cell 10–12 $\times$ 20–60 μ, with shorter tufts and more setiferous branches than the species. Pl. **8,** fig. **67.**

3. *Stigeoclonium nanum* (Dillwyn) Kuetzing. Vegetative cell 6–8 $\times$ 6–15 μ; branching alternate, branchlets tapering apically. Pl. **10,** fig. **71.**

4. *Stigeoclonium stagnatile* (Hazen) Collins. Vegetative cells 7–11 $\times$ 8–32 μ; filaments sparsely branched, solitary or opposite; forming floccose masses. Pl. **10,** fig. **72.**

Fig. 65.—*Stigeoclonium longipilum* Kuetzing.

Fig. 66.—*Stigeoclonium lubricum* (Dillwyn) Kuetzing.

Fig. 67.—*Stigeoclonium lubricum* var. *varians* (Hazen) Collins.

Fig. 68.—*Stigeoclonium subsecundum* Kuetzing.

(Fig. 65, Kuetzing; figs. 66, 67, Hazen; fig. 68, Tiffany. Fig. 65 $\times 300$; all others $\times 350$.)

PLATE 8

(Figs. 65 to 68)

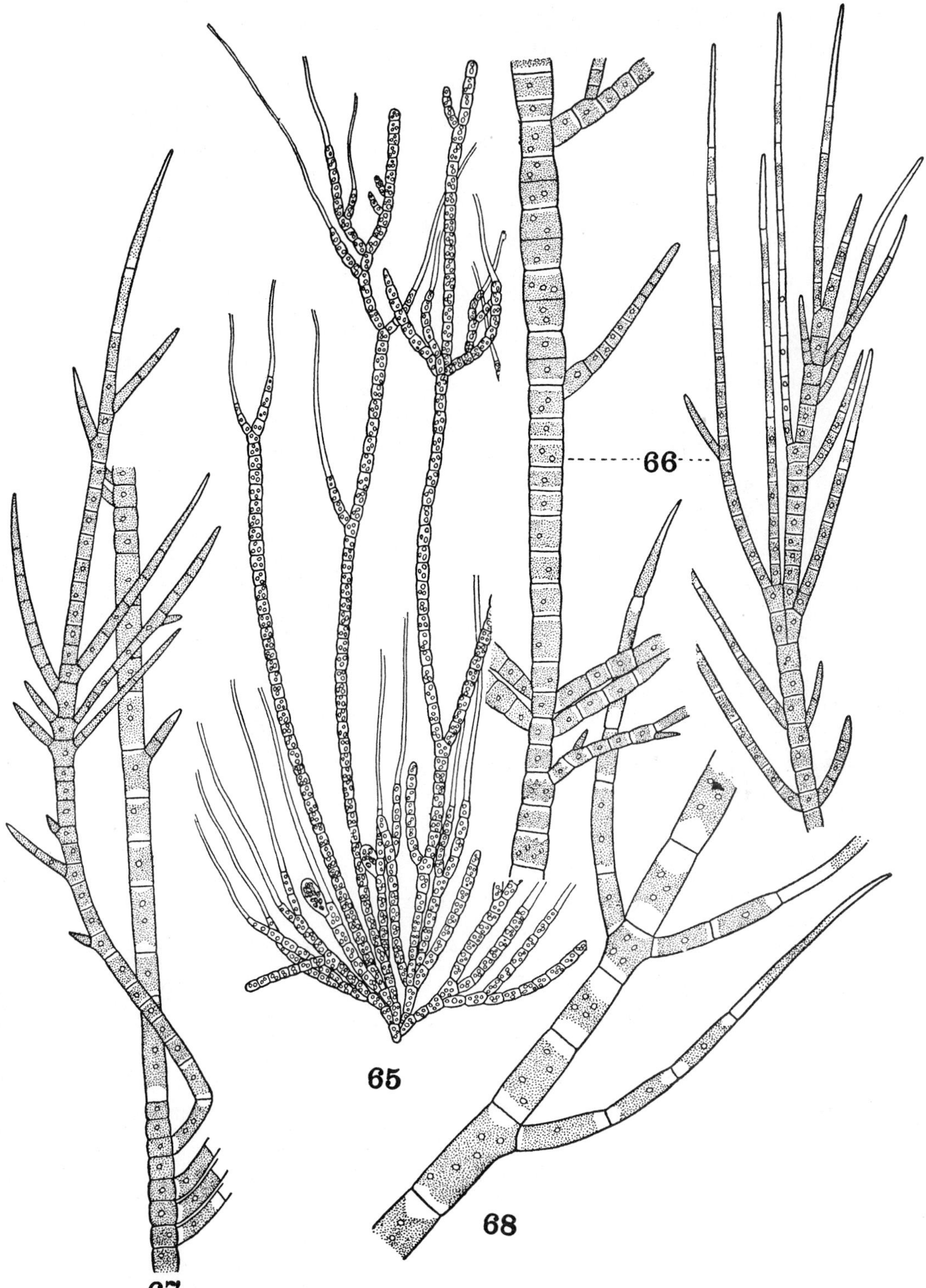

66

65

67

68

5. *Stigeoclonium glomeratum* (Hazen) Collins. Vegetative cell, cylindric or slightly swollen, 11–14 × 20–90 μ; branching usually opposite, generally densely fascicled at the top; branchlets often setiferous. Pl. **9**, fig. **69.**

6. *Stigeoclonium longipilum* Kuetzing. Vegetative cell 11–14 × 11–30 μ, opposite branching predominating; end cells generally setiferous. Pl. **8,** fig. **65.**

7. *Stigeoclonium subsecundum* Kuetzing. Vegetative cells 12–18 × 13–150 μ; branching sparse and solitary; tufts loose, pale green to yellowish. Pl. **8**, fig. **68.**

Draparnaldia Bory 1808

Filaments branched, attached by rhizoids, and enclosed in a soft gelatinous investment, with prostrate portion of plant not prominent; erect part of plant differentiated into large primary and smaller fasciculate branches, branchlets terminating in long hyaline setae; cells of primary branches cylindric or swollen, with a transversely zonate chloroplast: chromatophores of axial cells entire, toothed, or reticulate, with several pyrenoids; cells of branches usually cylindric with chromatophore covering entire wall and ordinarily with 1 pyrenoid.

Quadriflagellate zoospores, akinetes, quadriflagellate isogamous gametes; zygotes.

KEY TO THE SPECIES

1. Branchlets with a definite main axis.. 2
1. Branchlets without a definite main axis... 3
  2. Branchlets erect; branch cluster elongate................... 1. D. plumosa
  2. Branchlets spreading; branch cluster ovate................. 2. D. acuta
3. Branchlets in spherical clusters............................. 3. D. ravenelii
3. Branchlets in elongate clusters............................. 4. D. glomerata

1. *Draparnaldia plumosa* (Vaucher) C. A. Agardh. Cells of main axis subcylindric, 45–70 × 50–200 μ; branchlets erect, dense, with definite axes; chromatophores of cells of main axis usually occupying less than $\frac{1}{3}$ the length of the cells. Pl. **11**, fig. **82.**

2. *Draparnaldia acuta* (Agardh) Kuetzing. Cells of main axis somewhat inflated, 50–110 × 50–200 μ; branchlets spreading, dense, with definite axes, chromatophores of main axis usually occupying less than half of cell length. Pl. **11**, fig. **81.**

3. *Draparnaldia ravenelii* Wolle. Cells of main axis cylindric or somewhat constricted at both ends, 150–200 × 160–400 μ; branching frequent

FIG. 69.—*Stigeoclonium glomeratum* (Hazen) Collins. (Hazen. ×*350*.)

PLATE 9

(Fig. 69)

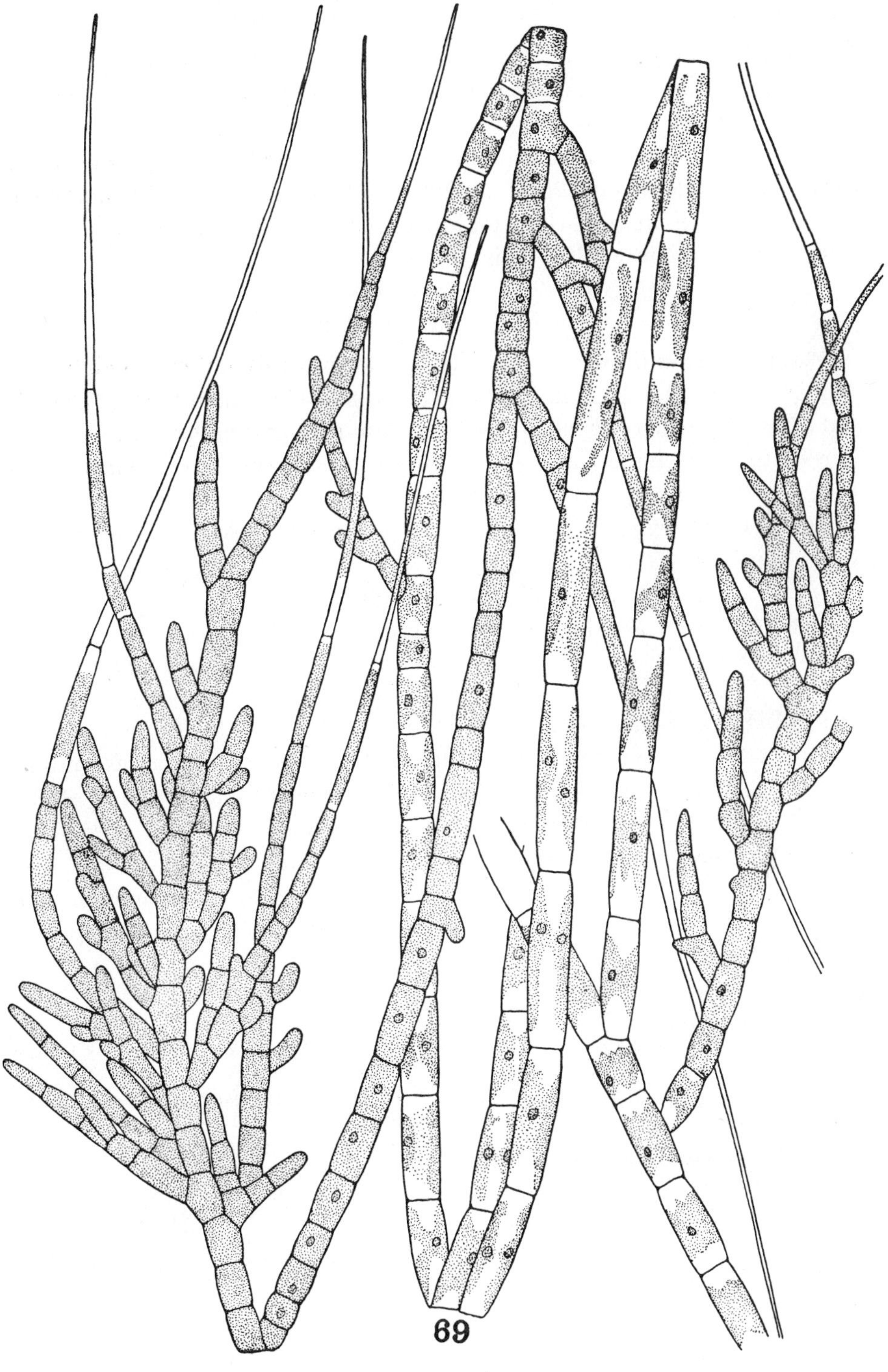

69

to sparse, cells seldom more than 100 μ in diameter; branchlets in sessile, spherical clusters, radiating and several times forked, branchlet cells 6–16 μ in diameter; chromatophore of main axis a narrow band with numerous, long, irregular marginal teeth. (Reported from Lawrence County, Tiffany.) Pl. 11, fig. **79.**

4. *Draparnaldia glomerata* (Vaucher) C. A. Agardh. Vegetative cells of main axis inflated, 50–125 × 30–200 μ; filaments repeatedly branched, branchlets without a distinct main axis; chromatophore of cells of main axis narrowly zonate. Pl. 11, fig. **80.**

Microthamnion Naegeli 1849

Plants densely branched, usually less than a millimeter in height, attached to substrate by bulbous basal cells; cells of same diameter throughout; terminal cells apically blunt to rounded; gelatinous matrix none; chromatophore single, laminate, occupying nearly the whole length of the cell, and devoid of pyrenoids.

Zoospores, 4 or 8 to a cell, pyriform, biflagellate; akinetes (rare).

KEY TO THE SPECIES

1. Main axis distinct, extending throughout plant . . . . 1. M. strictissimum
1. Main axis not distinct . . . . 2. M. kuetzingianum

1. *Microthamnion strictissimum* Rabenhorst. Plants with main axis extending to apex; branching usually alternate; branches erect or ascending; cells cylindric, 2–4 × 7–45 μ; found in streams firmly attached to sticks, etc., in pools and in greenhouses. Pl. 12, fig. **85.**

2. *Microthamnion kuetzingianum* Naegeli. Plants without a main axis, densely and irregularly branched; cells cylindric to somewhat clavate, 3–4 × 6–20 μ; found in habitats similar to those of the preceding species. Pl. 12, fig. **83.**

Fig. 70.—*Stigeoclonium tenue* (Agardh) Kuetzing.

Fig. 71.—*Stigeoclonium nanum* (Dillwyn) Kuetzing.

Fig. 72.—*Stigeoclonium stagnatile* (Hazen) Collins.

Fig. 73.—*Coleochaete soluta* (Brébisson) Pringsheim.

Fig. 74.—*Coleochaete scutata* Brébisson.

Fig. 75.—*Coleochaete orbicularis* Pringsheim.

Fig. 76.—*Coleochaete irregularis* Pringsheim.

Figs. 77, 78.—*Coleochaete nitellarum* Jost, oogonium and oospore.

(Figs. 70, 73–76, Tiffany; fig. 71, Fritsch; fig. 72, Hazen; figs. 77, 78, Prescott. Figs. 70–72 ×*350*; figs. 73, 74, 76–78 ×*500*; fig. 75 ×*1000*.)

PLATE 10
(Figs. 70 to 78)

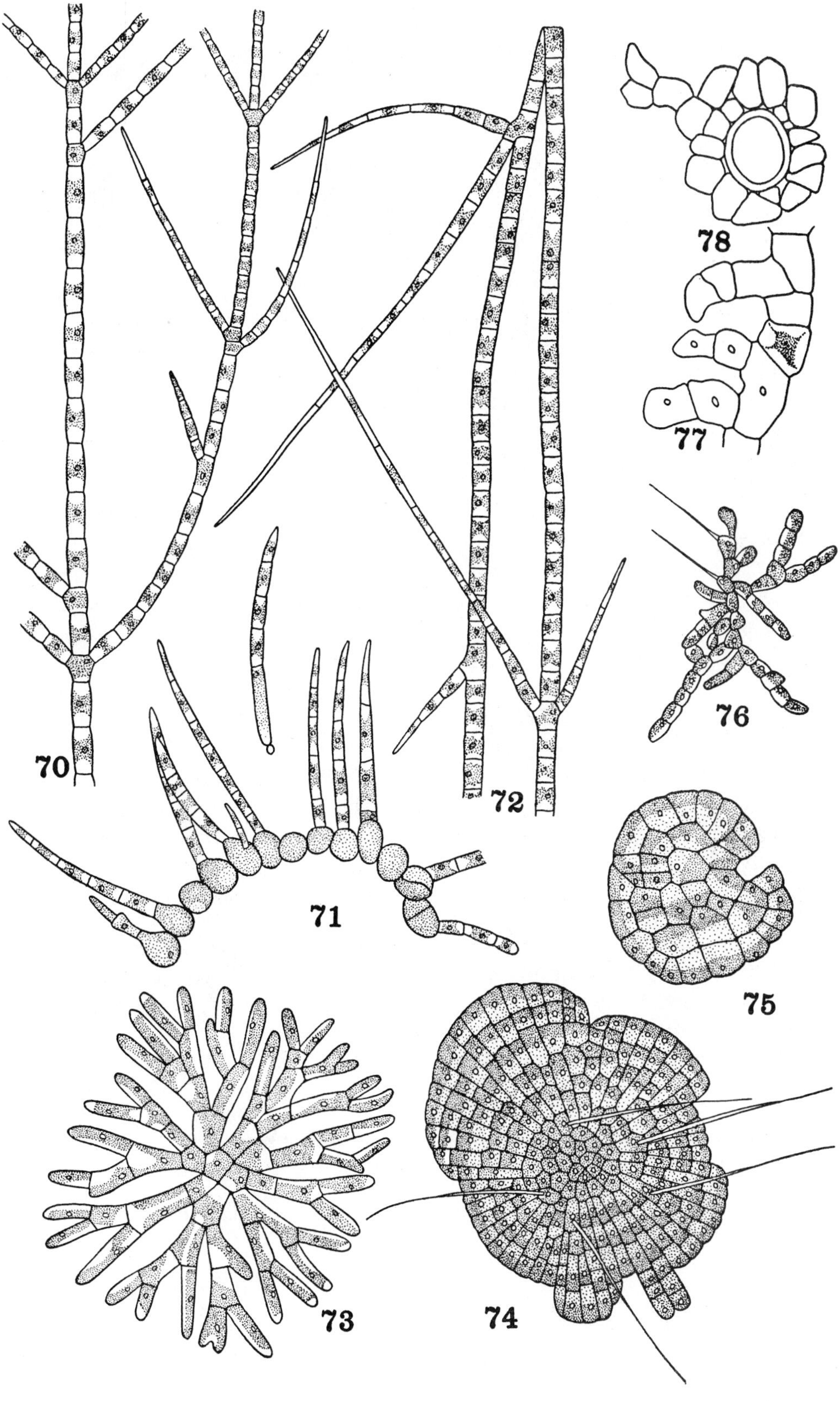

70

71

72

73

74

75

76

77

78

Chlorotylium Kuetzing 1843

Plant aggregate sessile, rounded to cushion-like, heavily encrusted with lime; filaments with nearly always unilateral branching and cylindric cells; longer cells with pale chromatophores alternate with more numerous shorter cells having conspicuous chromatophores; each chromatophore parietal, laminate, and with a single pyrenoid.

Biflagellate zoospores; *Palmella*-stages with zoospores; akinetes, often red in color, formed from small cells.

1. *Chlorotylium mammiforme* (Balbis) Kuetzing. Cells 7–10 μ in diameter; shorter cells about as long as broad, longer cells 3–10 times the diameter; thallus cushion-like, irregular, not in layers, bright green, encrusted with lime. Pl. 12, fig. 84.

Aphanochaete A. Braun 1851

Filaments simple or irregularly branched, prostrate on other algae; vegetative cells cylindric, barrel-shaped, globose, or cylindric-globose, bearing 1 or more long hyaline setae from their dorsal sides; chromatophore laminate, parietal, usually with several pyrenoids.

Quadriflagellate zoospores; aplanospores; heterogamous, quadriflagellate gametes.

1. *Aphanochaete repens* A. Braun. Vegetative cells subglobose to cylindric, 5–10 × 5–12 μ; setae 3–4 μ thick at base and up to 200 μ long, sometimes absent. Pl. 6, fig. 57.

Family **Protococcaceae**

Unicellular or with cells united into small aggregates, uninucleate, with a single laminate, often lobed and irregular chromatophore, generally without pyrenoids; probably a reduced derivative from filamentous ancestors; cell division; neither motile cells nor sexual reproduction.

Protococcus C. A. Agardh 1824

Cells solitary or in clumps of few cells, rounded or ellipsoid or angularly compressed, wall thick; chromatophore parietal, laminate, usually without pyrenoids; aerial on stones, sticks, and tree trunks.

Cell division; no other reproduction known.

Fig. 79.—*Draparnaldia ravenelii* Wolle.
Fig. 80.—*Draparnaldia glomerata* (Vaucher) C. A. Agardh.
Fig. 81.—*Draparnaldia acuta* (Agardh) Kuetzing.

Fig. 82.—*Draparnaldia plumosa* (Vaucher) C. A. Agardh.

(Figs. 80, 82, Hazen. Fig. 79 ×40 and ×200; all others ×250.)

PLATE 11

(Figs. 79 to 82)

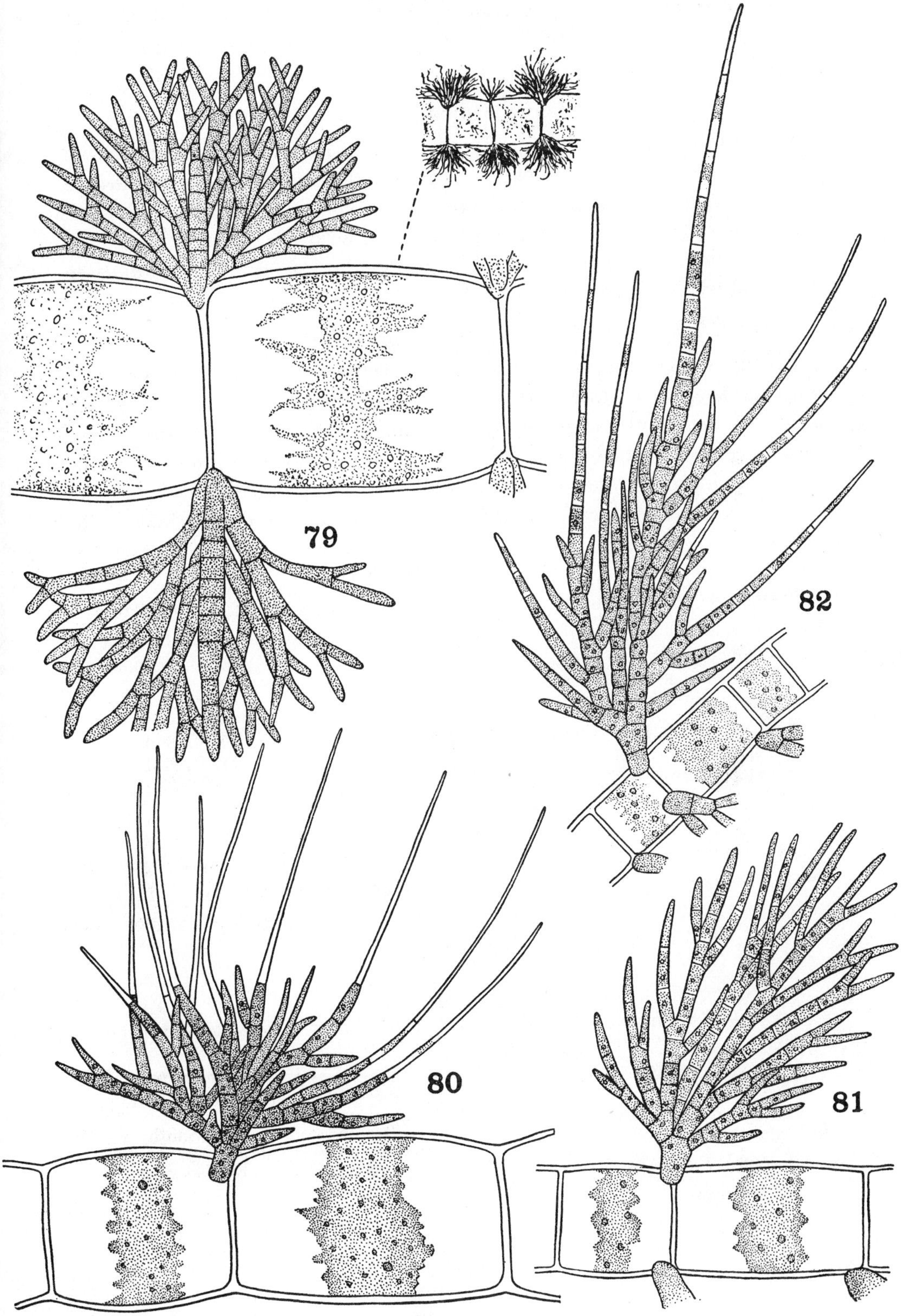

79

80

81

82

1. *Protococcus viridis* C. A. Agardh. Vegetative cells 4–10 × 4–12 μ. On barks of trees and occasionally on wood of docks and piers; never normally aquatic. Pl. **6**, fig. **58**.

Family **Coleochaetaceae**

Cells united into branching filaments, sometimes forming parenchyma-like discs, or solitary, uninucleate with a single laminate, parietal chromatophore, usually with a single pyrenoid; sessile and generally epiphytic, rarely endophytic, setae occurring on all or certain cells of a plant; zoospores, aplanospores; isogamy or oogamy, the oogonium sometimes ensheathed by a layer of cells.

Coleochaete Brébisson 1844

Filamentous, irregularly branched, erect and prostrate or prostrate only and then with branches distinct or laterally joined into a parenchymatous disc, epiphytic or endophytic; some cells with a single, unbranched seta basally ensheathed by a gelatinous cylinder; cells uninucleate with a single laminate chromatophore, usually with 1 pyrenoid.

Biflagellate zoospores; aplanospores, sperms and eggs; thick-walled oospore.

KEY TO THE SPECIES

1. Plants endophytic.. 1. C. nitellarum
1. Plants epiphytic, forming flat expansions................................. 2
  2. Filaments extended irregularly...................................... 2. C. irregularis
  2. Filaments more or less radiate...................................... 3
3. Filaments united laterally.. 4
3. Filaments not united laterally... 3. C. soluta
  4. Cells 8–16 × 16–30 μ.. 4. C. orbicularis
  4. Cells 25–45 × 25–120 μ... 5. C. scutata

1. *Coleochaete nitellarum* Jost. Found within walls of *Nitella* and *Chara*; filaments simple or branched, more or less united into a flat expansion; setae penetrating host walls; cells very irregular in form; oogonium somewhat corticate, spherical or flattened; antheridia in groups, cut off from vegetative cells. Pl. **10**, figs. **77, 78**.

Fig. 83.—*Microthamnion kuetzingianum* Naegeli.

Fig. 84.—*Chlorotylium mammiforme* (Balbis) Kuetzing.

Fig. 85.—*Microthamnion strictissimum* Rabenhorst.

Fig. 86.—*Pithophora oedogonia* (Montagne) Wittrock, vegetative filament with akinetes.

Figs. 87, 88.—*Pithophora varia* Wille, intercalary and terminal akinetes.

(Figs. 83, 85, G. M. Smith; fig. 84, Heering after Migula; figs. 87, 88, Tiffany. Figs. 83–85 ×*50;* all others ×*200.*)

PLATE 12

(Figs. 83 to 88)

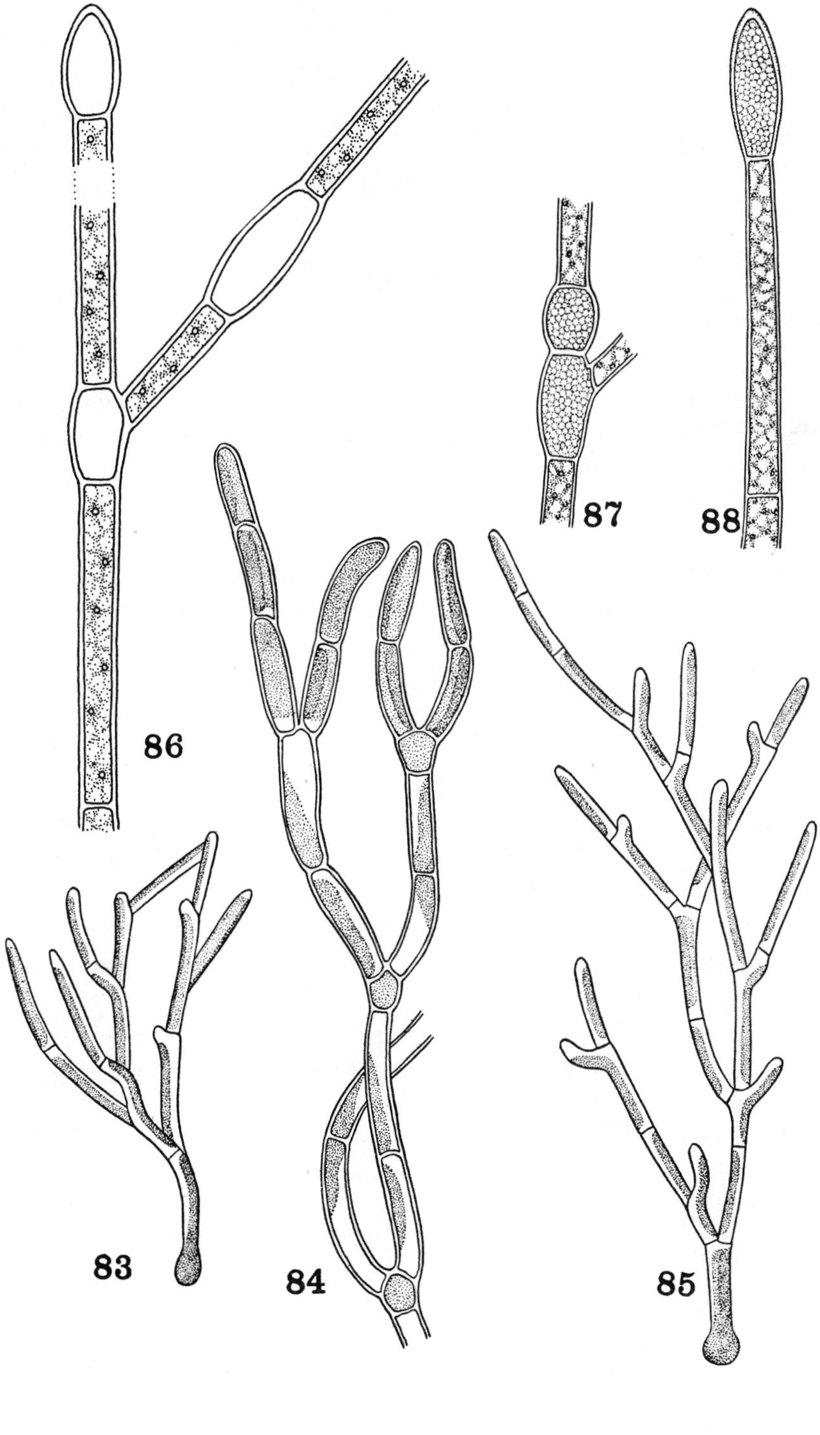

87

88

86

83

84

85

2. *Coleochaete irregularis* Pringsheim. Vegetative cells 18–25 × 18–40 μ, appearing quadrangular or polygonal; filaments irregularly branched, free or somewhat united, prostrate or nearly erect; oogonia ovoid, 60–100 × 60–120 μ, naked or corticate. Pl. **10**, fig. **76**.

3. *Coleochaete soluta* (Brébisson) Pringsheim. Vegetative cells 12–25 × 25–100 μ; filaments radiating from a common center, prostrate, not laterally united; oogonia corticate, usually globose, up to 200 μ in diameter; antheridia flask-shaped, 17–20 × 25–30 μ. Pl. **10**, fig. **73**.

4. *Coleochaete orbicularis* Pringsheim. Vegetative cells 8–16 × 16–30 μ, oblong to polygonal; filaments laterally united into a parenchymatous monostromatic frond; oogonia ovoid, 50–66 × 60–86 μ. Pl. **10**, fig. **75**.

5. *Coleochaete scutata* Brébisson. Vegetative cells 25–45 × 12–120 μ, appearing quadrangular; filaments laterally united into a parenchymatous disc and radiating from the center; oogonia subglobose, 120–140 × 140–160 μ, corticate. Pl. **10**, fig. **74**.

Chaetosphaeridium Klebahn 1892

Unicellular or in dense clumps or roughly filamentous, with or without a gelatinous envelope, epiphytic on other algae; vegetative cells ovoid to spherical, each bearing distally a long seta basally ensheathed, uninucleate; chromatophore 1 or 2, laminate and parietal.

Cell division; zoospores; sexual reproduction not known.

KEY TO THE SPECIES

1. Cells 9–12 μ in diameter, united by utricles...................... 1. C. pringsheimii
1. Cells 12–18 μ in diameter, densely aggregated.................. 2. C. globosum

1. *Chaetosphaeridium pringsheimii* Klebahn. Vegetative cells 9–12 × 9–14 μ, united by persistent utricles; sheaths 2 × 13–18 μ; setae up to 300 μ long. Pl. **6**, fig. **59**.

2. *Chaetosphaeridium globosum* (Nordstedt) Klebahn. Vegetative cells globose, 12–18 μ in diameter, densely aggregated, utricles not usually persistent; sheaths 2–3 × 16–17 μ. Pl. **6**, fig. **60**.

Order CLADOPHORALES

Simple or branching filaments made up of multinucleate cells with numerous discoid chromatophores united by cytoplasmic strands or not; zoospores, aplanospores, akinetes; isogamy, oogamy.

Family **Cladophoraceae**

Cells cylindric, multinucleate, forming simple or branching filaments, frequently rhizoidal; walls stratified: inner cellulose part covered by pectic compounds and peripherally by chitin-like material; zoospores, akinetes; isogamy; some genera with alternation of identical haploid and diploid phases.

Cladophora Kuetzing 1843

Filaments usually with profuse lateral branching, attached by well-defined rhizoidal cells or free-floating as entangled masses of indefinite shape; vegetative cells with thick stratified walls, multinucleate, much longer than broad; chromatophores single and reticulate or numerous and discoid, pyrenoids several.

Quadriflagellate zoospores; biflagellate gametes; most species with alternation of diploid asexual with a haploid sexual generation.

KEY TO THE SPECIES

1. Branches often in definite glomerate clusters.................... 1. C. glomerata
1. Branches sparingly distributed along main axis.................. 2. C. crispata

1. *Cladophora glomerata* (Linnaeus) Kuetzing. Cells of the main axis 45–150 (mostly 65–125) × 300–1,000 μ, of branches 35–60 × 150–360 μ; branches often in glomerate clusters; plants attaining lengths of 5–10 cm. or sometimes up to nearly 1 meter; transition from thick walls of main axis and primary branches to thin walls of branch clusters distinct; branching of main filament often Y-shaped; plant mass light green to dark green. [Includes *C. kuetzingianum* Grunow, *C. canalicularis* (Roth) Kuetzing, and *C. glomerata* var. *callicoma* Rabenhorst.] Pl. **13**, fig. **93.**

2. *Cladophora crispata* (Roth) Kuetzing. Cells 20–125 μ (usually over 40 μ in main axes) in diameter and 1–20 (usually 5–8) diameters long; filaments mostly long, slender and intricately entangled, free-floating or attached; main axis composed of relatively short cells with thick lamellose walls and quite dense chromatophores; branches long, slender with relatively thinner walls and more diffuse chromatophores, sparingly distributed along the main axis; plant mass dark-green, grass-green or yellow-green. [Includes *C. fracta* (Dillwyn) Kuetzing and *C. fracta* f. *flotowiana* Brand.] Pl. **13**, fig. **92.**

Rhizoclonium Kuetzing 1843

Filaments cylindric, slightly or not at all constricted at the cross-walls, with short, irregularly twisted and curved rhizoidal branches, 1–2-

celled, or unbranched; vegetative cells with walls up to 4 μ in thickness and generally lamellose, multinucleate; chromatophore parietal, reticulate, with several pyrenoids.

Fragmentation; irregularly shaped vegetative cells resembling akinetes; biflagellate zoospores.

KEY TO THE SPECIES

1. Rhizoidal branches multicellular, abundant   1. R. fontanum
1. Rhizoidal branches unicellular, or none.................................... 2
     2. Cell length 1–3 times the width........ 2.   R. hieroglyphicum
     2. Cell length 3–12 times the width....... 2a. R. hieroglyphicum var. macromeres

1. *Rhizoclonium fontanum* Kuetzing. Vegetative cells 22–27 $\times$ 55–310 μ, with thin walls and 2- or 3-celled rhizoidal branches, each separated from the parent cells by a cross-wall; filaments light-green or yellow-green, much entangled. Pl. **13**, fig. **90**.

2. *Rhizoclonium hieroglyphicum* (Agardh) Kuetzing. Vegetative cells 10–35 $\times$ 10–115 μ, usually simple, occasionally with 1-celled and nearly colorless rhizoidal branches; filaments slightly or not at all constricted at the cross-walls; cell-walls usually thin, but may be thick in terrestrial forms; plants unattached, aquatic, subaerial or terrestrial; floating forms grass-green or yellow-green, straight, thin-walled and without rhizoidal branches. Pl. **13**, fig. **91**.

     a. Var. *macromeres* Wittrock. Vegetative cells 19–30 $\times$ 40–350 μ, with thin walls, cylindric or slightly constricted at cross-walls; filaments straight or intricately tangled, without rhizoidal cells. Cook and Grundy Counties (Phinney, 1946).

Basicladia Hoffman and Tilden 1930

Filaments branched, sometimes only in the region of the basal cells, attached to freshwater turtles by rhizoidal outgrowths or by a coralloidal system of prostrate branches; erect filaments with shorter cells toward apex; vegetative cells multinucleate, chromatophore somewhat massive or scarcely reticulate, with pyrenoids.

FIG. 89.—*Basicladia chelonum* (Collins) Hoffman and Tilden, rhizoidal basal cell, basal branching, vegetative cells, and formation of zoospores.

FIG. 90.—*Rhizoclonium fontanum* Kuetzing.

FIG. 91.—*Rhizoclonium hieroglyphicum* (Agardh) Kuetzing.

FIG. 92.—*Cladophora crispata* (Roth) Kuetzing.

FIG. 93.—*Cladophora glomerata* (Linnaeus) Kuetzing.

(Figs. 89, 91, 93, Tiffany. Figs. 89, 90, 92 $\times$100; fig. 91 $\times$300; fig. 93 $\times$75.)

PLATE 13

(Figs. 89 to 93)

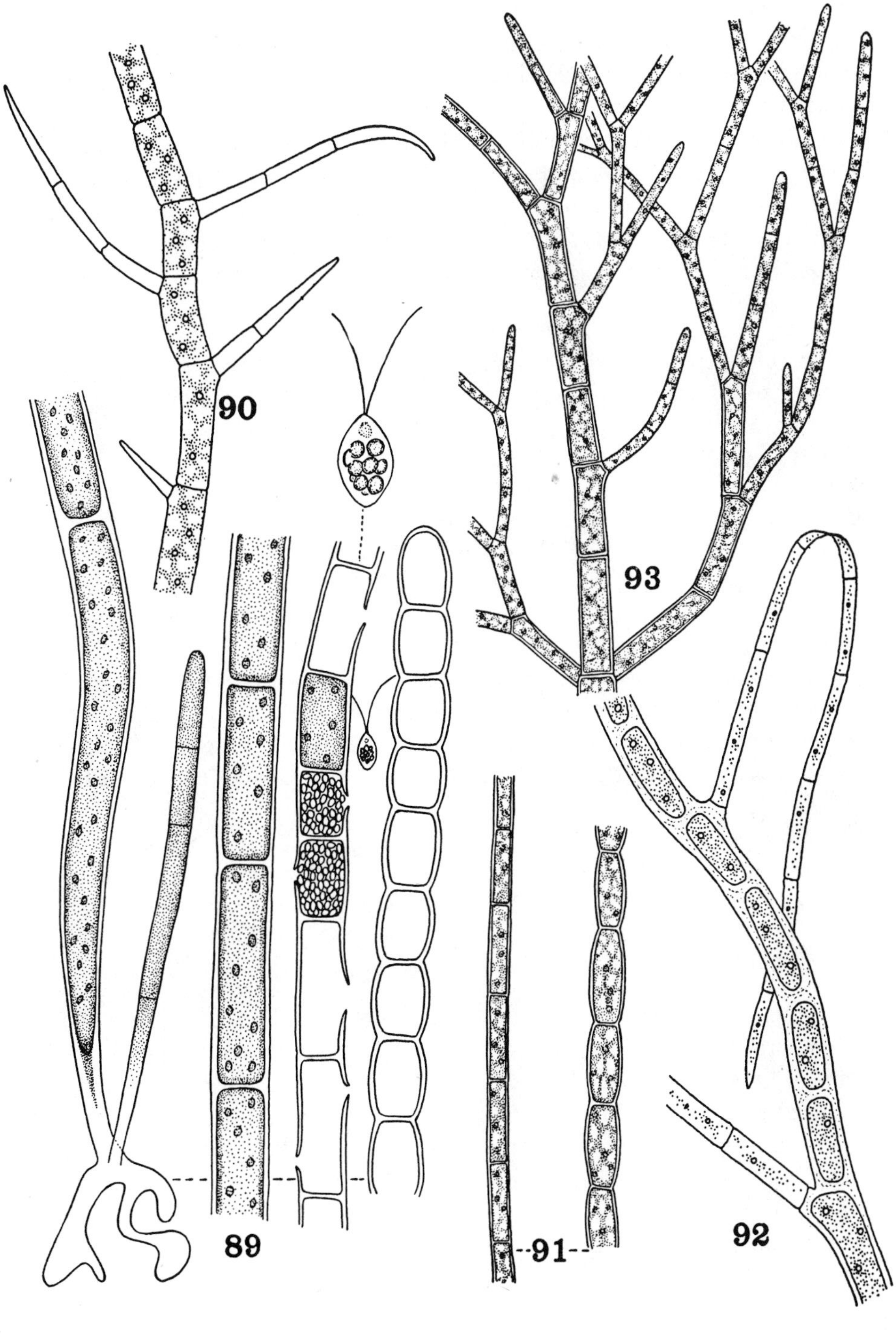

90

93

89

91

92

Fragmentation; zoospores or gametes from shortened cells of the filament; gametes, discharged from mother cell through a lateral pore, biflagellate, spindle-shaped, with numerous chromatophores and an eyespot; zygote at first spindle-shaped and quadriflagellate, later spherical, without flagella.

1. *Basicladia chelonum* (Collins) Hoffman and Tilden. Vegetative cells 30–65 (–120) × 40–500 μ, sporangia 30–50 × 30–200 μ; basal coenocyte 12–20 μ in diameter and up to 1,000 μ in length; branches usually in the vicinity of holdfast cells; filaments form dark-green matted tufts, 1–8 cm. in length; growing on carapaces of turtles. Pl. **13**, fig. **89**.

Pithophora Wittrock 1877

Filaments irregularly branched, with smaller branches toward the apex; cells up to 30 diameters long, with thin walls and bright-green or pale-green chromatophores; plants forming light-green to grass-green masses; akinetes terminal or intercalary, solitary or in series.

Fragmentation; akinetes.

KEY TO THE SPECIES

1. Akinetes generally more than 250 μ long...................... 1. P. oedogonia
1. Akinetes generally less than 250 μ long...................... 2. P. varia

1. *Pithophora oedogonia* (Montagne) Wittrock. Vegetative cells 40–120 × 200–3,000 μ; akinetes 80–115 (–160) × 232–375 μ: if intercalary, cask-shaped or lobed and variously distorted when formed at bases of branches, if terminal, ovoid to subconic. (Includes *P. kewensis* Wittrock.) Pl. **12**, fig. **86**.

2. *Pithophora varia* Wille. Vegetative cells 50–100 × 100–500 μ; akinetes 60–112 × 70–250 μ, ovoid to cylindric, or irregular and often angular at bases of branches. Pl. **12**, figs. **87, 88**.

Order OEDOGONIALES

Filaments simple or branched; cells uninucleate, chromatophores parietal, generally in the form of a reticulum with 1 or more pyrenoids; cell division by a rupture of the wall of each cell near its apex due to a ring-like thickening on the inner wall of each cell and formation of a new transverse septum between daughter nuclei; multiflagellate zoospores formed singly in the vegetative cells; advanced oogamy; monoecious or dioecious, and if the latter, either macrandrous or nannandrous; sperms 1 or 2 in each antheridium, eggs single in an oogonium.

Family **Oedogoniaceae**

With characteristics of the Order.

Bulbochaete Agardh 1817

Filaments usually attached, branched, the branches unilateral; vegetative cells uninucleate, normally widening upwards; chromatophore reticulate, with pyrenoids at intersections in reticulum; basal cell ordinarily the only one capable of division in formation of main axis, first new cell forming a long tubular bristle with swollen bulb-like base, subsequent cells intercalated between basal cell and next one above; division rarely intercalary; terminal cell of each branch always furnished with a bristle; oogonium arising by double division of a vegetative cell.

Multiflagellate zoospores; oogonia and eggs, antheridia and multiflagellate sperms, oospores; dwarf males and androsporangia, androspores.

KEY TO THE SPECIES

1. Monoecious... 2
1. Dioecious, nannandrous.. 3
    2. Oogonium 20–25 × 33–40 μ.............. 1. B. nana
    2. Oogonium 26–33 × 46–58 μ.............. 2. B. mirabilis
    3. Oospore-wall crenulate.................... 3. B. crenulata
    3. Oospore-wall smooth...................... 4. B. nordstedtii
    3. Oospore-wall reticulate-scrobiculate......... 5. B. gigantea
    3. Oospore-wall scrobiculate... 4
    3. Oospore-wall longitudinally costate.................................. 8
        4. Oogonium 60–78 μ in diameter........... 6. B. crassiuscula
        4. Oogonium 36–51 μ in diameter....................................... 5
    5. Vegetative cell 10–15 μ in diameter......... 7. B. furberae
    5. Vegetative cell 15–20 μ in diameter................................. 6
        6. Division of suffultory cell superior......... 4. B. nordstedtii
        6. Division of suffultory cell median, or nearly so...................... 7
        6. Division of suffultory cell basal.......... 8. B. brebissonii
    7. Length of oogonium 31–40 μ............... 9. B. intermedia
    7. Length of oogonium 39–44 μ............... 10. B. subintermedia
        8. Vegetative cell repand.................... 11. B. repanda
        8. Vegetative cell cylindric or nearly so................................. 9
        8. Vegetative cell neither repand nor cylindric......................... 10
    9. Diameter of oogonium 28–32 μ.............. 12. B. hiloensis
    9. Diameter of oogonium 32–39 μ.............. 13. B. rectangularis
        10. Length of oogonium more than 55 μ............................... 11
        10. Length of oogonium less than 55 μ............................... 12
    11. Costae smooth or finely scrobiculate........ 15. B. minor
    11. Costae broadly denticulate................. 16. B. insignis

11. Costae reticulate-dentate.................. 17. B. reticulata
  12. Oogonium 22–27 μ in diameter.......... 18. B. pygmaea
  12. Oogonium 26–30 μ in diameter...................................... 13
  12. Oogonium 30–36 μ in diameter.......... 14. B. varians
13. Dwarf male stipe 17–18 μ long............. 14a. B. varians var. hawaiensis
13. Dwarf male stipe 11–14 μ long............. 14b. B. varians var. subsimplex

1. *Bulbochaete nana* Wittrock. Monoecious; oogonium ellipsoid, patent, below terminal seta or vegetative cell; outer wall of oospore longitudinally costate; antheridia 1–2, erect (rarely patent), subepigynous or scattered; vegetative cell 10–16 × 10–22 μ; oogonium 20–25 × 33–40 μ; oospore 18–23 × 30–38 μ; antheridium 7–9 × 5–9 μ. Pl. **16**, fig. **112**.

2. *Bulbochaete mirabilis* Wittrock. Monoecious; oogonium cylindric-ellipsoid to sub-oblong-ellipsoid, patent (rarely erect), below terminal seta or vegetative cell; outer wall of oospore longitudinally costate; antheridia 1–4, erect or patent, subepigynous or scattered; vegetative cell 15–20 × 20–40 μ; oogonium 26–33 × 46–58 μ; oospore 25–31 × 44–56 μ; antheridium 9–12 × 6–9 μ. Pl. **14**, fig. **95**.

3. *Bulbochaete crenulata* Pringsheim. Dioecious, nannandrous, gynandrosporous; oogonium subdepressed-globose, patent, below terminal seta or androsporangium, or rarely vegetative cell; division of suffultory cell median or slightly below; spore-wall scrobiculate to crenulate; androsporangia epigynous or scattered, 1–5; dwarf male on or near oogonium, antheridium interior, stipe slightly curved, shorter than antheridium; vegetative cell 16–20 × 32–70 μ; oogonium 43–48 × 35–43 μ; oospore 40–46 × 33–40 μ; antheridium 10–15 × 7–10 μ; dwarf male 9–10 × 24–26 μ. Pl. **14**, fig. **98**.

4. *Bulbochaete nordstedtii* Wittrock. Dioecious, nannandrous, gynandrosporous; oogonium depressed-globose or subquadrangularly so, patent, below androsporangium or rarely terminal seta; division of suffultory cell superior (occasionally submedian); oospore-wall finely scrobiculate or nearly smooth; androsporangium unicellular, epigynous; dwarf male on oogonium, stipe slightly curved, shorter than antheridium; vegetative cell 14–18 × 28–85 μ; oogonium 36–43 × 29–36 μ; oospore 34–41 × 27–

FIG. 94.—*Bulbochaete brebissonii* Kuetzing.

FIG. 95.—*Bulbochaete mirabilis* Wittrock.

FIG. 96.—*Bulbochaete intermedia* DeBary.

FIG. 97.—*Bulbochaete gigantea* Pringsheim.

FIG. 98.—*Bulbochaete crenulata* Pringsheim.

FIGS. 99, 100.—*Bulbochaete crassiuscula* Nordstedt.

(Figs. 94, 95, 99, 100, Hirn; figs. 96, 97, 98, Tiffany. All ×300.)

PLATE 14

(Figs. 94 to 100)

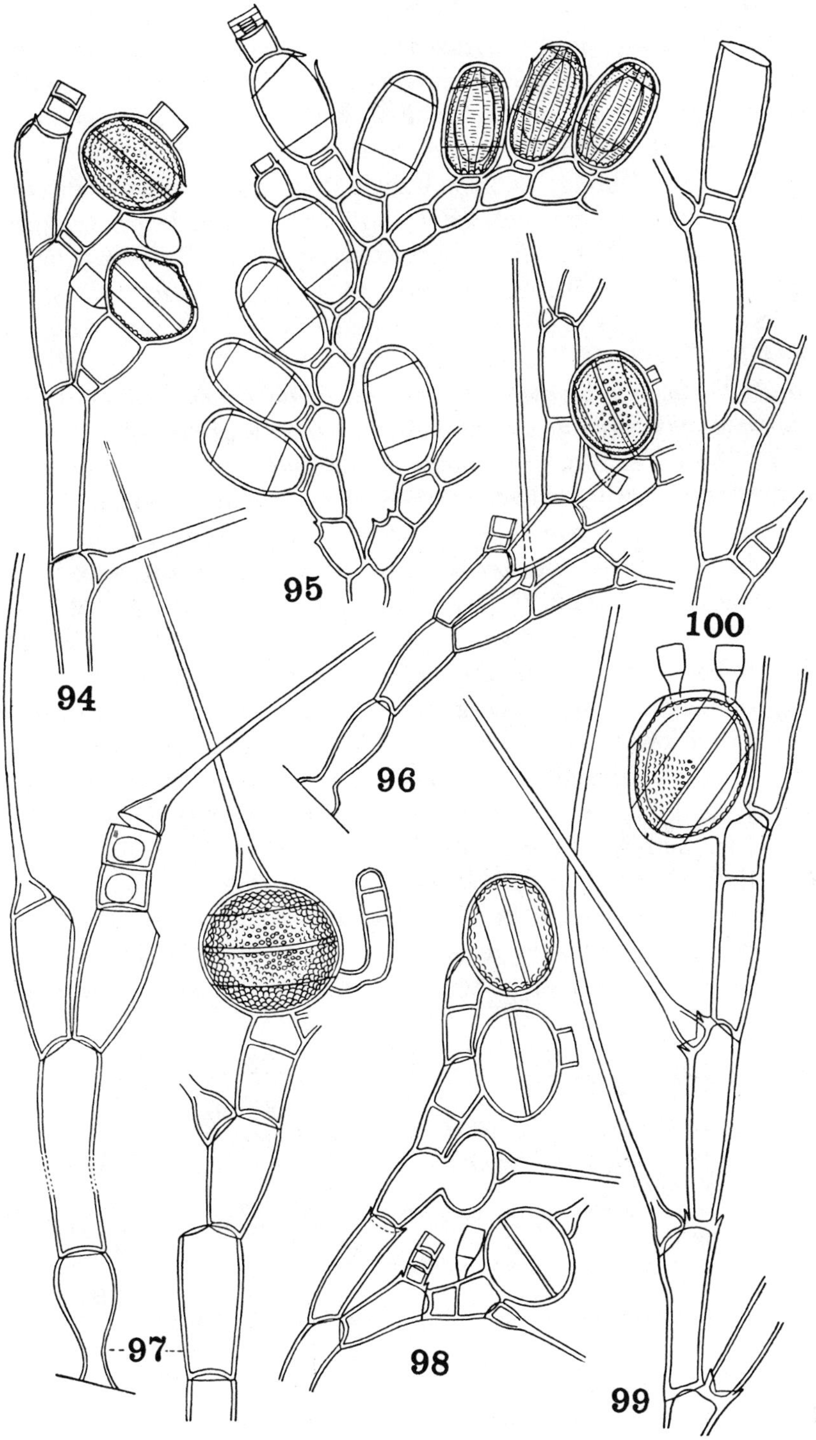

94

95

96

97

98

99

100

34 μ; androsporangium 10–12 $\times$ 9–12 μ; dwarf male 9–19 $\times$ 23–25 μ. Pl. 16, fig. 114.

5. *Bulbochaete gigantea* Pringsheim. Dioecious, nannandrous, idioandrosporous; oogonium subdepressed-globose or rarely depressed-oboviform-globose, patent, below terminal seta, rarely below vegetative cell; division of suffultory cell slightly below median; outer wall of oospore reticulate-scrobiculate; androsporangia 1–5; dwarf male slightly longer than the oogonium on which it develops; antheridium interior; stipe about twice as long as antheridium, curved; vegetative cell 24–32 $\times$ 50–112 μ; oogonium 60–70 $\times$ 50–58 μ; oospore 58–68 $\times$ 48–56 μ; androsporangial cell 18–20 $\times$ 10–14 μ; dwarf male stipe 10–13 $\times$ 28–45 μ; antheridial cell 13–14 $\times$ 20–30 μ. Pl. 14, fig. 97.

6. *Bulbochaete crassiuscula* Nordstedt. Dioecious, nannandrous, idioandrosporous; oogonium subquadrangularly depressed-globose, patent, below terminal seta or occasionally vegetative cell; division of suffultory cell superior (rarely submedian); outer oospore-wall scrobiculate; androsporangia 1–4; dwarf male on oogonium or near it; antheridium interior, stipe slightly curved, shorter than antheridium; vegetative cell 22–27 $\times$ 55–148 μ; oogonium 60–78 $\times$ 50–62 μ; oospore 58–76 $\times$ 48–60 μ; antheridium 16–19 $\times$ 10–13 μ; dwarf male 12–14 $\times$ 30–34 μ. Pl. 14, figs. 99, 100.

7. *Bulbochaete furberae* Collins. Dioecious, nannandrous, gynandrosporous; oogonium depressed-globose, below terminal seta, patent (rarely erect); division of suffultory cell inframedian; outer wall of oospore scrobiculate; androsporangia scattered, 1–9; dwarf male on oogonium, stipe strongly curved; antheridium interior; vegetative cell 10–15 $\times$ 30–75 μ; oogonium 36–43 $\times$ 27–34 μ; oospore 34–41 $\times$ 25–32 μ; androsporangium 9–10 $\times$ 8–9 μ; dwarf male 7–8 $\times$ 20–25 μ. Pl. 16, fig. 111.

8. *Bulbochaete brebissonii* Kuetzing. Dioecious, nannandrous, gynandrosporous; oogonium depressed-subquadrangular-globose, erect, below terminal seta or androsporangium; division of the suffultory cell basal;

Fig. 101.—*Bulbochaete repanda* Wittrock.

Fig. 102.—*Bulbochaete varians* Wittrock.

Fig. 103.—*Bulbochaete varians* var. *subsimplex* (Wittrock) Hirn.

Fig. 104.—*Bulbochaete varians* var. *hawaiensis* Nordstedt.

Fig. 105.—*Bulbochaete rectangularis* Wittrock.

Fig. 106.—*Bulbochaete pygmaea* Pringsheim.

Fig. 107.—*Bulbochaete minor* A. Braun.

Fig. 108.—*Bulbochaete hiloensis* (Nordstedt) Tiffany.

Fig. 109.—*Bulbochaete insignis* Pringsheim.

Fig. 110.—*Bulbochaete reticulata* Nordstedt.

(Figs. 101–107, 109, Tiffany; figs. 108, 110, Hirn. Fig. 106 $\times 200$; all others $\times 300$.)

PLATE 15

(Figs. 101 to 110)

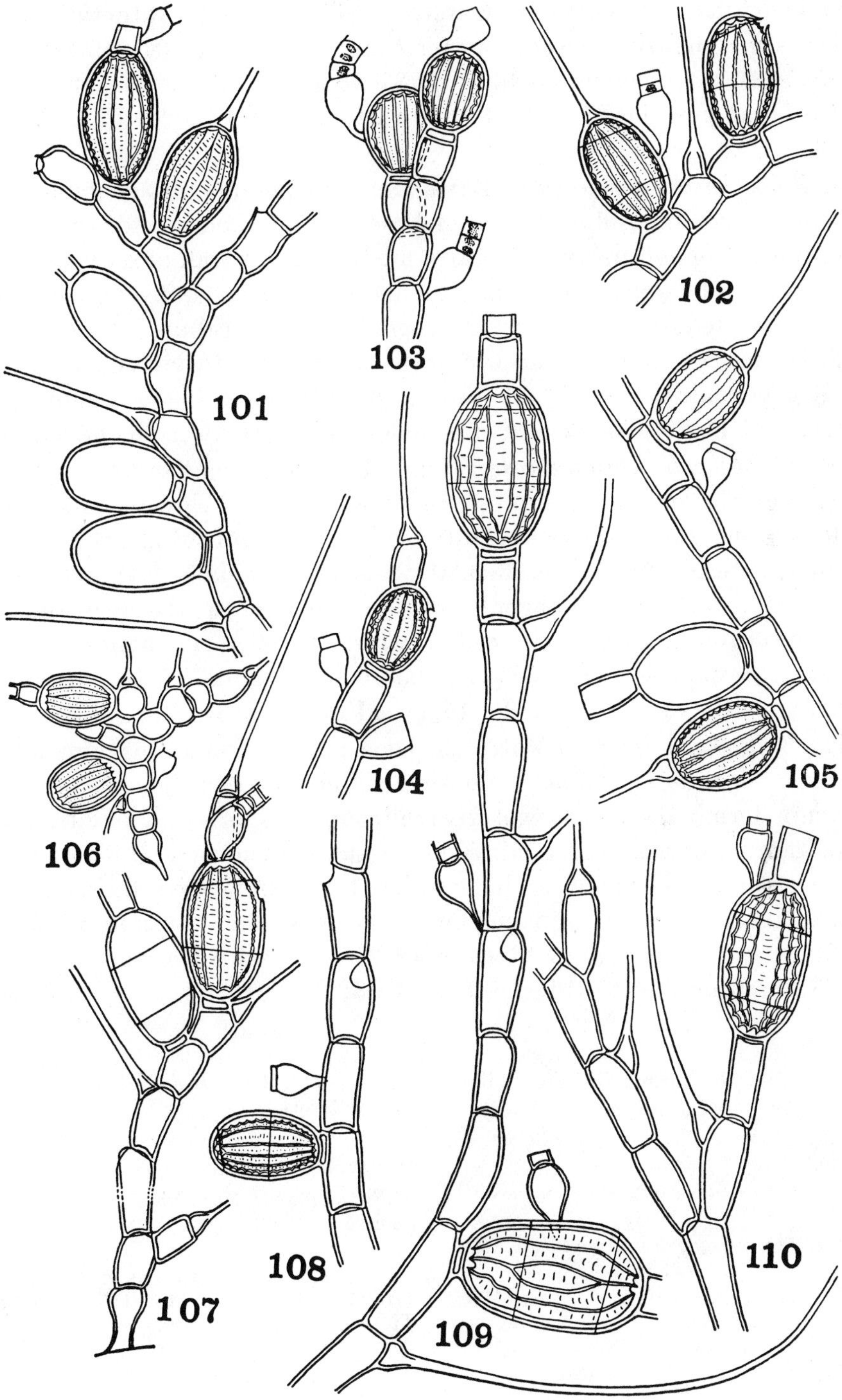

outer oospore-wall scrobiculate; androsporangia scattered or epigynous, 1–3; dwarf male on oogonium (rarely on adjacent cell), antheridium interior, stipe slightly curved, shorter than antheridium; vegetative cell 17–20 × 50–90 μ; oogonium 42–50 × 37–45 μ; oospore 40–48 × 35–43 μ; androsporangium 11–15 × 12–18 μ; dwarf male 10–12 × 28–33 μ. Pl. 14, fig. 94.

9. *Bulbochaete intermedia* DeBary. Dioecious, nannandrous, gynandrosporous; oogonium subdepressed-globose, patent, below androsporangium; division of suffultory cell nearly median; outer wall of oospore scrobiculate, rarely apparently smooth; androsporangia 1–2, epigynous or rarely scattered; dwarf male on the oogonium; antheridium interior, stipe slightly curved, shorter than the antheridium; vegetative cell 17–20 × 35–70 μ; oogonium 40–48 × 31–40 μ; oospore 38–46 × 30–38 μ; androsporangial cell 11–13 × 7–12 μ; dwarf male 9–10 × 21–26 μ. Pl. 14, fig. 96.

10. *Bulbochaete subintermedia* Elfving. Dioecious, nannandrous, gynandrosporous; oogonium subdepressed-globose, patent, below terminal seta, androsporangium, or rarely vegetative cell; division of suffultory cell submedian; outer spore-wall scrobiculate; androsporangia 1–?; epigynous or scattered; dwarf male on oogonium, stipe curved or nearly erect, shorter than the oogonium; vegetative cell 17–22 × 34–100 μ; oogonium 44–51 × 39–44 μ; oospore 42–48 × 37–41 μ; androsporangium 13–16 × 9–10 μ; dwarf male 10–12 × 25–30 μ. Pl. 16, fig. 113.

11. *Bulbochaete repanda* Wittrock. Dioecious, nannandrous, gynandrosporous; oogonium suboblong-ellipsoid, patent or erect, below androsporangium, terminal seta, or vegetative cell; outer oospore-wall longitudinally costate; androsporangia epigynous or subepigynous, 1–?; dwarf male near or on oogonium; antheridia exterior, 1–3; vegetative cell, frequently repand, 12–17 × 24–60 μ; oogonium 26–36 × 43–58 μ; oospore 21–33 × 40–50 μ; androsporangium 13–15 × 16–21 μ; dwarf male stipe 11–15 × 21–27 μ; antheridium 7–10 × 5–7 μ. Pl. 15, fig. 101.

Fig. 111.—*Bulbochaete furberae* Collins.

Fig. 112.—*Bulbochaete nana* Wittrock.

Fig. 113.—*Bulbochaete subintermedia* Elfving.

Fig. 114.—*Bulbochaete nordstedtii* Wittrock.

Fig. 115.—*Oedogonium suecicum* Wittrock.

Fig. 116.—*Oedogonium magnusii* Wittrock.

Figs. 117, 118.—*Oedogonium plusiosporum* Wittrock.

Fig. 119.—*Oedogonium franklinianum* Wittrock.

Fig. 120.—*Oedogonium curvum* Pringsheim.

(Fig. 111, Lewis in Collins; figs. 112, 113, 116–118, Hirn; figs. 114, 115, 119, 120, Tiffany. All figures ×*300*.)

PLATE 16

(Figs. 111 to 120)

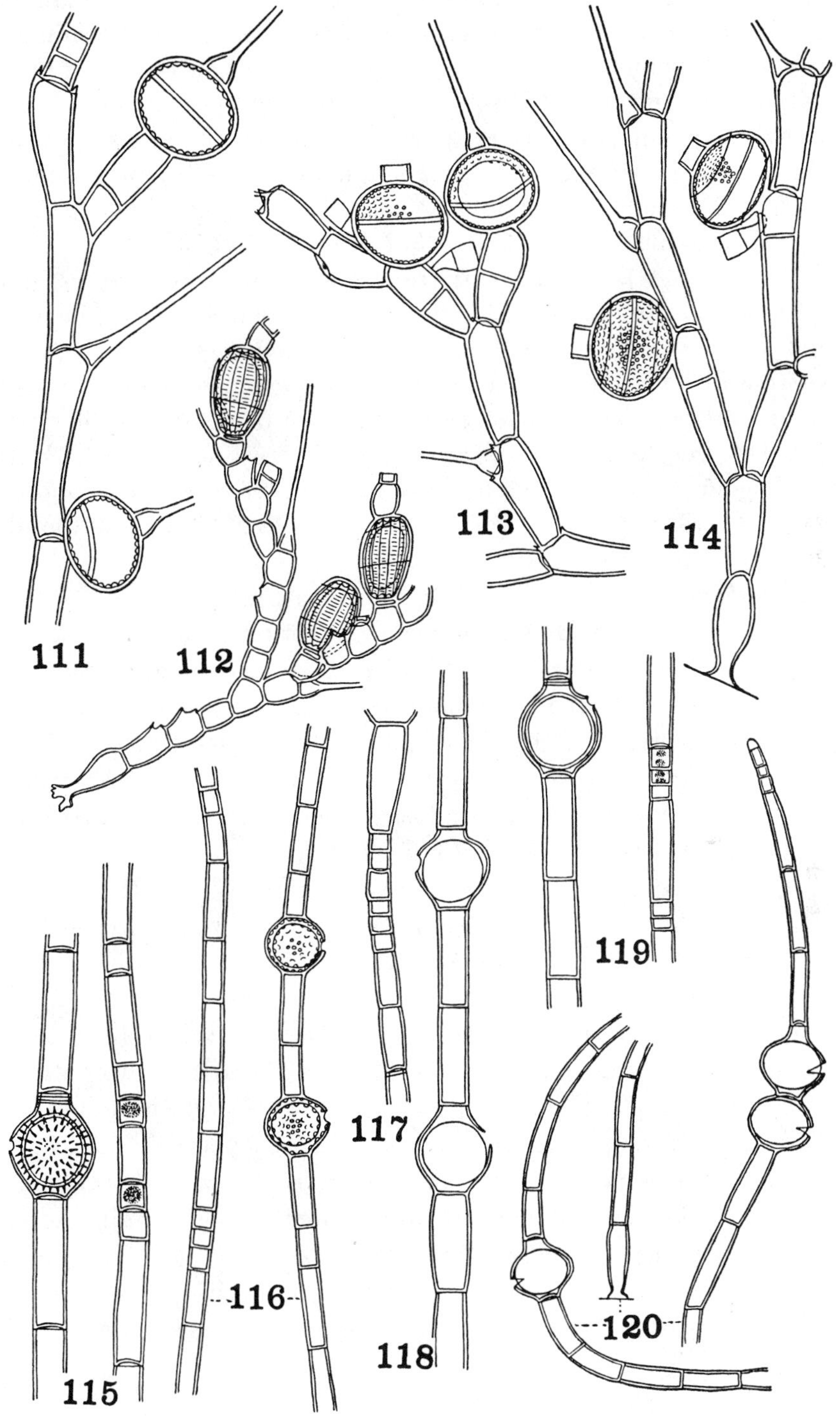

111 112 113 114 115 116 117 118 119 120

12. Bulbochaete hiloensis (Nordstedt) Tiffany. Dioecious, nannandrous, gynandrosporous; oogonium ellipsoid, patent or erect, below terminal seta or androsporangium or more rarely vegetative cell; outer wall of oospore longitudinally costate; androsporangia generally epigynous, 1–?; dwarf male near oogonium; antheridia exterior, 1–4; vegetative cell, subrectangular in section, 14–20 × 24–48 μ; oogonium 28–33 × 43–51 μ; oospore 26–30 × 38–45 μ; androsporangium 12–17 × 13–16 μ; dwarf male stipe 13–17 × 22–27 μ; antheridium 8–9.× 5–7 μ. Pl. **15**, fig. **108**.

13. Bulbochaete rectangularis Wittrock. Dioecious, nannandrous, gynandrosporous; oogonium ellipsoid, patent or more rarely erect, below terminal seta or androsporangium or more rarely vegetative cell; outer oospore-wall longitudinally costate; androsporangia scattered or epigynous, 1–?; dwarf male near or occasionally on oogonium; antheridia exterior, 1–4; vegetative cell, subrectangular in cross section, 16–23 × 20–46 μ; oogonium 32–39 × 45–63 μ; oospore 29–37 × 43–61 μ; androsporangium 13–16 × 10–27 μ; dwarf male stipe 14–18 × 22–27 μ; antheridium 8–10 × 5–7 μ. Pl. **15**, fig. **105**.

14. Bulbochaete varians Wittrock. Dioecious, nannandrous, gynandrosporous; oogonium ovoid, patent or erect, below terminal seta or below androsporangial cell; outer oospore-wall with serrate, longitudinal costae; androsporangia scattered, epigynous or hypogynous, 1–2; dwarf male on or near the oogonium, antheridia exterior, 1–3; vegetative cell 17–22 × 22–33 μ; oogonium 30–36 × 44–54 μ; oospore 28–34 × 42–52 μ; androsporangial cell 14–17 × 14–18 μ; dwarf male stipe 14–16 × 24–27 μ; antheridial cell 8–10 × 6–7 μ. Pl. **15**, fig. **102**.

a. Var. *hawaiensis* Nordstedt. Vegetative cell 13–18 × 17–36 μ; oogonium 27–30 × 44–54 μ; oospore 25–28 × 42–52 μ; androsporangium 12–16 × 13–14 μ; dwarf male stipe 17–18 × 28–31 μ; antheridium 10–11 × 6–7 μ. Pl. **15**, fig. **104**.

b. Var. *subsimplex* (Wittrock) Hirn. Vegetative cell 13–18 × 16–34 μ; oogonium 26–30 × 39–46 μ; oospore 24–28 × 37–44 μ; androsporangium 10–14 × 7–16 μ; dwarf male stipe 11–14 × 15–24 μ; antheridium 7–8 × 5–7 μ; costae of oospore serrulate or sometimes smooth. Pl. **15**, fig. **103**.

15. Bulbochaete minor A. Braun. Dioecious, nannandrous, gynandrosporous; oogonium ovoid, erect or rarely patent, below terminal seta, androsporangial cell, or more rarely vegetative cell; outer oospore-wall longitudinally costate; androsporangia epigynous, subepigynous, or scattered, 1–?; dwarf male on or near oogonia; antheridia exterior, 1–4; vegetative cell 18–25 × 27–50 μ; oogonium 32–42 × 59–69 μ; oospore 30–40 × 57–67 μ; androsporangium 15–16 × 16–21 μ; dwarf male stipe 12–15 × 22–24 μ; antheridium 6–10 × 6–7 μ. Pl. 15, fig. 107.

16. *Bulbochaete insignis* Pringsheim. Dioecious, nannandrous, gynandrosporous; oogonium ellipsoid, erect or patent, below androsporangium or terminal seta or vegetative cell; oospore ellipsoid with broadly denticulate, longitudinal costae on the outer oospore-wall; androsporangia epigynous or scattered, 1–?; dwarf male near or on oogonium; antheridia exterior, 1–3; vegetative cell 19–25 × 48–88 μ; oogonium 46–56 × 70–90 μ; oospore 44–54 × 68–88 μ; androsporangium 16–20 × 9–25 μ; dwarf male stipe 16–19 × 29–33 μ; antheridium 10–13 × 7–10 μ. Pl. 15, fig. 109.

17. *Bulbochaete reticulata* Nordstedt. Dioecious, nannandrous, gynandrosporous; oogonium ellipsoid, erect, below androsporangium or terminal seta or vegetative cell; outer wall of oospore reticulate-dentate, with doubly dentate, occasionally anastomosing, longitudinal ridges, the teeth united to one another by transverse ridges; androsporangia epigynous or scattered, 1–?; dwarf male on oogonium, antheridium exterior; vegetative cell 20–25 × 40–87 μ; oogonium 44–52 × 66–85 μ; oospore 42–50 × 64–83 μ; androsporangium 16–19 × 13–23 μ; dwarf male stipe 17–20 × 30–33 μ; antheridium 11–13 × 6–9 μ. Pl. 15, fig. 110.

18. *Bulbochaete pygmaea* Pringsheim. Dioecious, nannandrous, gynandrosporous; oogonium ellipsoid, patent, below terminal seta or vegetative cell; outer wall of oospore longitudinally costate; suffultory cell without division; androsporangia subepigynous or scattered, 1–?-celled; dwarf male near oogonium; antheridia exterior, 1–3; vegetative cell 11–15 × 8–15 μ; oogonium 22–27 × 32–40 μ; oospore 20–23 × 30–38 μ; androsporangium 7–10 × 6–9 μ; dwarf male stipe 11–12 × 15–19 μ; antheridium 7–8 × 7–8 μ. (Reported from Pope County by Phinney, 1946.) Pl. 15, fig. 106.

Oedogonium Link 1820

Filaments single, unbranched; vegetative cells uninucleate, cylindric, or sometimes capitellate, nodulose or undulate; chromatophore reticulate, with numerous pyrenoids at larger intersections of reticulum; basal cell with holdfast; terminal cell obtuse, apiculate, or hyaline; vegetative cells, except the basal one, capable of division; oogonia and antheridia produced by direct division of vegetative cells.

Multiflagellate zoospores; oogonia and eggs, antheridia and multiflagellate sperms, oospores; dwarf males, androsporangia, androspores.

KEY TO THE SPECIES

1. Plants without dwarf males. 2
1. Plants with dwarf males. 55
   2. Oogonium opening by a pore. 3
   2. Oogonium opening by a lid. 38
3. Pore median or supramedian. 4
3. Pore superior. 13
   4. Wall of oospore smooth. 5
   4. Wall of oospore scrobiculate. . . . . 1. O. magnusii
   4. Wall of oospore echinate. . . . . 2. O. suecicum
5. Monoecious. 6
5. Dioecious. 11
5. Both dioecious and monoecious. . . . . 3. O. varians
   6. Diameter of oogonium 18–29 μ. 7
   6. Diameter of oogonium 32–45 μ. 9
7. Filament irregularly curved. . . . . 4. O. curvum
7. Filament straight. 8
   8. Oogonium 18–24 $\times$ 18–26 μ. . . . . 5. O. vulgare
   8. Oogonium 24–29 $\times$ 26–31 μ. . . . . 6. O. cryptoporum
9. Length of oogonium 24–30 μ. 7. O. laeve
9. Length of oogonium 34–50 μ. 10
   10. Oospore depressed-globose. . . . . 8. O. obsoletum
   10. Oospore regularly globose. . . . . 9. O. plusiosporum
11. Diameter of oogonium 22–27 μ. . . . . 10. O. rufescens
11. Diameter of oogonium 26–31 μ. . . . . 11. O. franklinianum
11. Diameter of oogonium 30–45 μ. 12
11. Diameter of oogonium 48–70 μ. . . . . 12. O. cardiacum
   12. Diameter of vegetative cell 9–16 μ. . . . . 13. O. sociale
   12. Diameter of vegetative cell 16–28 μ. . . . . 14. O. lemmermannii
13. Wall of oospore smooth. 14
13. Wall of oospore longitudinally costate. 31
13. Wall of oospore scrobiculate. 36
   14. Plants monoecious. 15
   14. Plants dioecious. 20
15. Oogonium basally inflated. . . . . 15. O. pseudoboscii
15. Oogonium not basally inflated. 16
   16. Diameter of oogonium 31–40 μ. 17
   16. Diameter of oogonium 40–58 μ. 18
17. Diameter of vegetative cell 10–14 μ. . . . . 16. O. globosum
17. Diameter of vegetative cell 15–18 μ. . . . . 17. O. intermedium
   18. Length of oogonium 44–65 μ. 19
   18. Length of oogonium 66–100 μ. . . . . 18. O. upsaliense
19. Diameter of vegetative cell 12–17 μ. . . . . 19. O. fragile
19. Diameter of vegetative cell 20–30 μ. . . . . 20. O. vaucherii
   20. Oospore globose, subglobose, or cylindric-globose. 21
   20. Oospore ellipsoid, obovoid, subcylindric, or subellipsoid. 26

21. Oogonium scarcely exceeding vegetative cell in diameter.. 21. O. capillare
21. Oogonium noticeably exceeding vegetative cell in diameter................... 22
    22. Antheridial filament smaller than oogonial filament..................... 23
    22. Antheridial filament not smaller than oogonial filament.................. 25
23. Oogonium 42–56 μ in diameter... 24
23. Oogonium 70–85 μ in diameter................... 22. O. rivulare
    24. Diameter of male filament 25–30 μ............ 23. O. capilliforme
    24. Diameter of male filament 33–40 μ............ 24. O. diversum
25. Oogonium 36–42 μ in diameter.................. 25. O. gracilius
25. Oogonium 42–49 μ in diameter.................. 26. O. plagiostomum
    26. Diameter of oogonium 42–68 μ... 27
    26. Diameter of oogonium 63–78 μ................. 92. O. landsboroughi
    26. Diameter of oogonium 70–90 μ... 30
27. Diameter of cells of oogonial plant 19–37 μ........................... 28
27. Diameter of cells of oogonial plant 36–46 μ......... 27. O. majus
    28. Vegetative cell often 7–10 diameters long............................. 29
    28. Vegetative cell less than 7 diameters long...... 28. O. grande
29. Diameter of oogonium 42–52 μ.................. 29. O. angustum
29. Diameter of oogonium 55–65 μ.................. 30. O. oboviforme
    30. Length of oogonium 83–115 μ................. 31. O. amplum
    30. Length of oogonium 130–160 μ................ 22. O. rivulare
31. Monoecious... 32
31. Dioecious... 33
    32. Costae 18–22 in number..................... 32. O. paulense
    32. Costae 27–35 in number..................... 33. O. paludosum
33. Costae 12–20 in number... 34
33. Costae 27–35 in number... 35
    34. Costae crenulate........................... 34. O. crenulatocostatum
    34. Costae crenate or dentate................... 35. O. longiarticulatum
35. Oogonium 29–38 × 69–100 μ................... 36. O. occidentale
35. Oogonium 39–51 × 75–110 μ................... 37. O. boscii
    36. Diameter of vegetative cell 15–22 μ.......... 38. O. punctatum
    36. Diameter of vegetative cell 24–48 μ... 37
37. Length of oogonium 48–70 μ.................... 39. O. americanum
37. Length of oogonium 81–113 μ................... 40. O. taphrosporum
    38. Oospore-wall scrobiculate................... 41. O. stictospermum
    38. Oospore-wall longitudinally costate........... 42. O. paucocostatum
    38. Oospore-wall smooth... 39
39. Oogonium with median constriction.............. 43. O. pusillum
39. Oogonium without median constriction.. 40
    40. Division of oogonium median... 41
    40. Division of oogonium superior.. 44
41. Plants monoecious... 42
41. Plants dioecious.. 43
    42. Vegetative cell distinctly capitellate.......... 44. O. capitellatum
    42. Vegetative cell cylindric.................... 45. O. acmandrium
    42. Vegetative cell subhexagonal or ellipsoid....... 93. O. reinschii

43. Diameter of oogonium 23–33 μ . . . . 46. O. howardii
43. Diameter of oogonium 33–40 μ . . . . 47. O. pratense
43. Diameter of oogonium 48–55 μ . . . . 48. O. punctatostriatum
    44. Plants dioecious. 45
    44. Plants monoecious. 49
45. Diameter of oogonium 16–43 μ. 46
45. Diameter of oogonium 43–50 μ . . . . 49. O. welwitschii
    46. Oospore globose to depressed-globose. 47
    46. Oospore ovoid to ellipsoid. 48
47. Diameter of oogonium 18–27 μ . . . . 50. O. mitratum
47. Diameter of oogonium 28–36 μ . . . . 51a. O.   pringsheimii v.
                                                                     nordstedtii
47. Diameter of oogonium 35–43 μ . . . . 51. O. pringsheimii
    48. Diameter of oogonium 16–20 μ. . . . . 52. O. epiphyticum
    48. Diameter of oogonium 23–29 μ. . . . . 53. O. pisanum
49. Vegetative cell cylindric. 50
49. Vegetative cell capitellate. 54
    50. Oogonium obovoid-globose to subglobose. . . . . 54. O. crispum
    50. Oogonium oboviform-pyriform. . . . . 55. O. simplex
    50. Oogonium ellipsoid to oblong. 51
51. Oogonium 14–19 × 34–40 μ. 56. O. gracillimum
51. Oogonium 20–26 μ in diameter. 52
    52. Oospore nearly or quite filling oogonium. 53
    52. Oospore not filling oogonium longitudinally. . . . . 59. O. oblongum
53. Vegetative cell 7–9 × 11–36 μ. . . . . 57. O. oblongellum
53. Vegetative cell 8–15 × 16–60 μ. . . . . 58. O. kirchneri
    54. Oogonium 30–33 μ in diameter. . . . . 60. O. ouchitanum
    54. Oogonium 42–45 μ in diameter. . . . . 61. O. bohemicum
55. Vegetative cell undulate. . . . . 62. O. undulatum
55. Vegetative cell not undulate. 56
    56. Oogonium opening by a pore. 57
    56. Oogonium opening by a lid. 69
57. Pore median. 58
57. Pore superior. 62
    58. Wall of oospore echinate. 59
    58. Wall of oospore spirally echinate. . . . . 63. O. illinoisense
    58. Wall of oospore smooth. 61
59. Suffultory cell enlarged. . . . . 64. O. hystricinum
59. Suffultory cell not enlarged or only slightly so. 60
    60. Diameter of vegetative cell 7–13 μ. . . . . 65. O. aster
    60. Diameter of vegetative cell 12–16 μ. . . . . 66. O. pungens
    60. Diameter of vegetative cell 18–30 μ. . . . . 67. O. echinospermum
61. Diameter of oogonium 30–37 μ. . . . . 68. O. braunii
61. Diameter of oogonium 49–52 μ. . . . . 69. O. flavescens
    62. Oospore-wall pitted. . . . . 70. O. concatenatum
    62. Oospore-wall costate. 63
    62. Oospore-wall smooth. 65

63. Costae 16–25 in number.. 64
63. Costae 25–35 in number........................ 71. O. wolleanum
  64. Oogonium 57–66 μ in diameter............... 72. O. cyathigerum
  64. Oogonium 65–85 μ in diameter............... 73. O. perfectum
65. Suffultory cell enlarged......................... 74. O. borisianum
65. Suffultory cell not enlarged....................................... 66
  66. Diameter of oogonium 24–35 μ............... 75. O. multisporum
  66. Diameter of oogonium 35–45 μ............... 76. O. irregulare
  66. Diameter of oogonium 48–60 μ.................................. 67
67. Gynandrosporous............................. 77. O. crassiusculum
67. Idioandrosporous............................. 78. O. idioandrosporum
  68. Division of oogonium median....................................... 69
  68. Division of oogonium superior...................................... 72
  68. Division of oogonium supreme...................................... 74
69. Oogonium 13–16 μ in diameter.................. 79. O. longicolle
69. Oogonium 21–26 μ in diameter.................. 80. O. rothii
69. Oogonium 25–31 μ in diameter.................. 82a. O. decipiens v. afri-
                                                             canum
69. Oogonium 29–38 μ in diameter....................................... 70
69. Oogonium 39–46 μ in diameter................. 81. O. macrospermum
  70. Vegetative cell cylindric..................... 82. O. decipiens
  70. Vegetative cell capitellate....................................... 71
71. Division of oogonium narrow................... 82b. O. decipiens v. dis-
                                                             simile
71. Division of oogonium wide...................... 83. O. subplenum
  72. Oospore-wall longitudinally costate........... 84. O. croasdaleae
  72. Oospore-wall scrobiculate..................... 85. O. monile
  72. Oospore-wall smooth.. 73
73. Vegetative cell 4–8 μ in diameter.............. 86. O. rugulosum
73. Vegetative cell 15–20 μ in diameter............ 87. O. macrandrium
  74. Oospore-wall smooth.. 75
  74. Oospore-wall longitudinally costate............................... 76
75. Gynandrosporous............................. 88. O. obtruncatum
75. Idioandrosporous............................. 89. O. praticolum
  76. Costae 11–30 in number................... 90. O. acrosporum
  76. Costae 40–45 in number................... 91. O. tentoriale

1. *Oedogonium magnusii* Wittrock. Dioecious, macrandrous (perhaps monoecious also); oogonia 1–3, depressed-globose, pore median, rimiform; oospore depressed-globose, quite filling oogonium, spore-wall of 3 layers: outer layer smooth, middle layer scrobiculate, inner layer smooth; antheridia to 8-seriate, sperm 1; vegetative cell 7–10 $\times$ 12–40 μ; oogonium 24–27 $\times$ 21–26 μ; oospore 22–25 $\times$ 18–23 μ; antheridium 8–10 $\times$ 5–11 μ. Pl. **16,** fig. **116.**

2. *Oedogonium suecicum* Wittrock. Dioecious, macrandrous; oogonium 1, subglobose, pore median; oospore globose, nearly filling oogonium, outer

spore-wall echinate, inner smooth; antheridia 2–6; sperm 1; basal cell elongate, terminal cell apically obtuse; vegetative cell 9–14 $\times$ 30–90 μ; oogonium 32–38 $\times$ 34–41 μ; oospore 30–37 $\times$ 30–37 μ; antheridium 10–12 $\times$ 13–17 μ. Pl. **16**, fig. **115**.

3. *Oedogonium varians* Wittrock and Lundell. Monoecious (or sometimes dioecious); oogonium 1, rarely more, depressed- or subdepressed-pyriform-globose, pore nearly superior; oospore globose, not filling oogonium, spore-wall smooth; antheridia to 9-seriate, scattered; sperms 2, division horizontal; basal cell elongate; terminal cell apically obtuse; vegetative cell 12–16 $\times$ 35–144 μ; oogonium 34–50 $\times$ 34–55 μ; oospore 31–41 $\times$ 30–41 μ; antheridium 11–15 $\times$ 5–7 μ. Pl. **17**, fig. **135**.

4. *Oedogonium curvum* Pringsheim. Monoecious; oogonia 1–6, depressed-globose, pore median; oospore depressed-globose, filling or not filling oogonium, spore-wall smooth; antheridia hypogynous or epigynous or scattered, 1–7; sperm 1; basal cell elongate; filament usually irregularly curved; vegetative cell 5–10 $\times$ 10–40 μ; oogonium 21–25 $\times$ 18–24 μ; oospore 19–23 $\times$ 14–19 μ; antheridium 6–9 $\times$ 6–9 μ. Pl. **16**, fig. **120**.

5. *Oedogonium vulgare* (Wittrock) Tiffany. Monoecious; oogonia 1–5, subdepressed-obovoid-globose or subdepressed-globose, pore median; oospore subdepressed-globose, quite filling oogonium; spore-wall smooth; antheridia 1–4, subepigynous or hypogynous or scattered; sperm 1; vegetative cell 5–8 $\times$ 15–48 μ; oogonium 18–25 $\times$ 18–26 μ; oospore 16–23 $\times$ 15–19 μ; antheridium 5–7 $\times$ 9–12 μ. Pl. **17**, fig. **123**.

6. *Oedogonium cryptoporum* Wittrock. Monoecious; oogonium 1, subdepressed-obovoid-globose or subdepressed-globose, pore median; oospore subdepressed-globose, quite filling oogonium, spore-wall smooth; anther-

Fig. 121.—*Oedogonium obsoletum* Wittrock.

Fig. 122.—*Oedogonium cryptoporum* Wittrock.

Fig. 123.—*Oedogonium vulgare* (Wittrock) Tiffany.

Figs. 124–126.—*Oedogonium rufescens* Wittrock.

Fig. 127.—*Oedogonium rufescens* var. *exiguum* (Elfving) Tiffany.

Figs. 128, 129.—*Oedogonium rufescens* var. *lundellii* (Wittrock) Tiffany.

Fig. 130.—*Oedogonium laeve* Wittrock.

Fig. 131.—*Oedogonium cardiacum* (Hassall) Wittrock.

Fig. 132.—*Oedogonium cardiacum* var. *carbonicum* Wittrock.

Fig. 133.—*Oedogonium intermedium* Wittrock.

Fig. 134.—*Oedogonium globosum* Nordstedt.

Fig. 135.—*Oedogonium varians* Wittrock and Lundell.

Figs. 136, 137.—*Oedogonium sociale* Wittrock.

Fig. 138.—*Oedogonium lemmermannii* Tiffany.

(Figs. 121, 128, 129, 131, 134, 136, 137, Hirn; figs. 122–127, 130, 132–134, 138, Tiffany. All $\times 300$.)

PLATE 17

(Figs. 121 to 138)

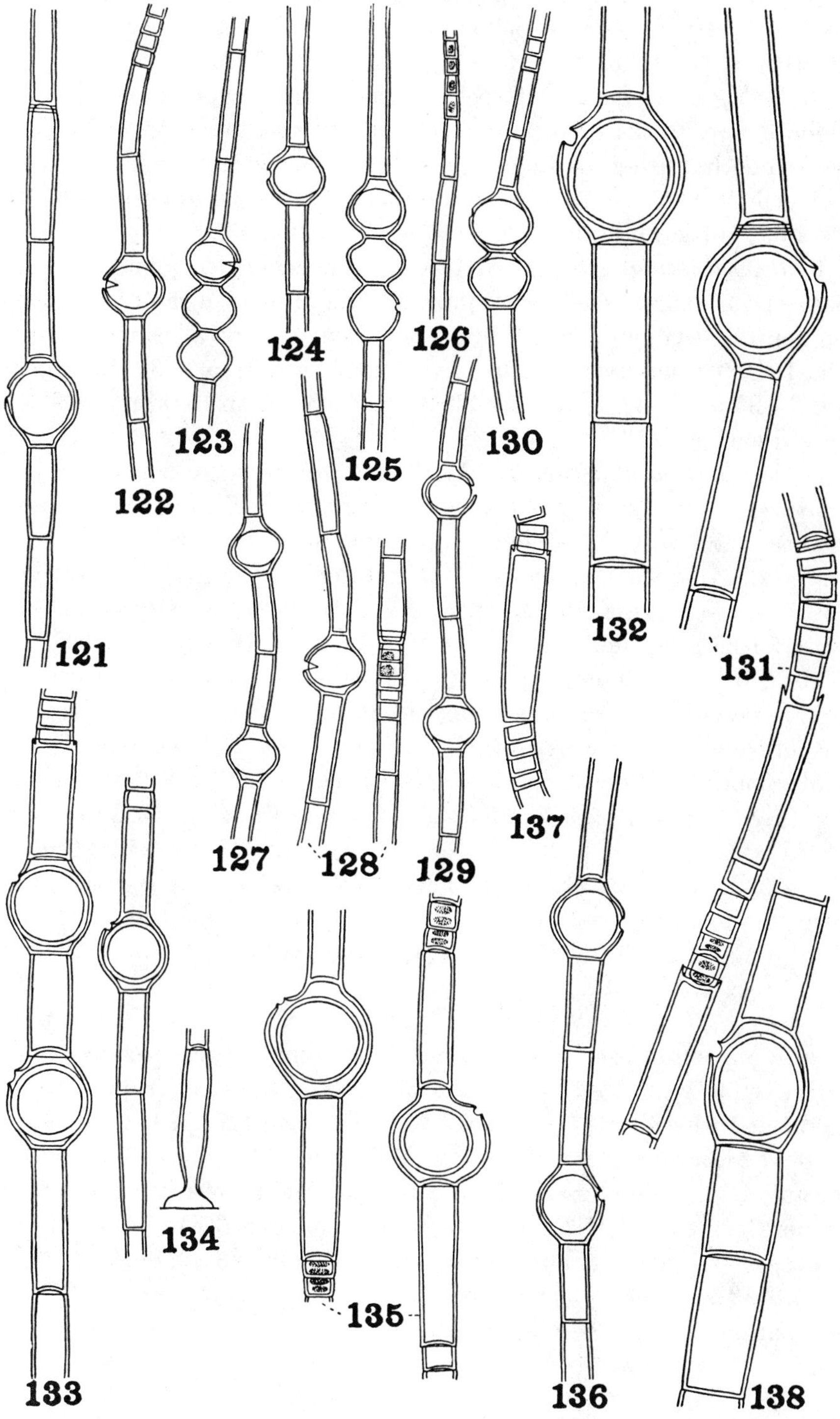

idia 1–7, scattered or subhypogynous or subepigynous; sperm 1; vegetative cell 7–10 × 28–60 μ; oogonium 23–28 × 26–31 μ; oospore 22–27 × 19–21 μ; antheridium 6–8 × 7–11 μ. Pl. **17**, fig. **122**.

7. *Oedogonium laeve* Wittrock. Monoecious; oogonium 1, depressed-globose, pore median; oospore depressed-globose, filling oogonium, spore-wall smooth; antheridia in groups of 1–2, subepigynous, sperm 1; vegetative cell 10–14 × 20–70 μ; oogonium 32–38 × 24–30 μ; oospore 30–35 × 23–26 μ; antheridium 9–10 × 9–13 μ. Pl. **17**, fig. **130**.

8. *Oedogonium obsoletum* Wittrock. Monoecious; oogonium 1, subglobose or subdepressed-globose, pore a little above supramedian; oospore subdepressed-globose, not filling oogonium, spore-wall smooth; antheridia 1–3, subepigynous; sperm 1; vegetative cell 9–15 × 30–75 μ; oogonium 34–39 × 34–43 μ; oospore 30–34 × 28–32 μ; antheridium 8–9 × 12–16 μ. Pl. **17**, fig. **121**.

9. *Oedogonium plusiosporum* Wittrock. Monoecious; oogonium 1, subglobose or subellipsoid-globose, with pore a little above median; oospore globose, rarely subglobose, not quite filling oogonium; spore-wall smooth; antheridia to 6-seriate; sperm 1(?); terminal cell obtuse; vegetative cell 12–19 × 24–77 μ; oogonium (28–) 34–45 × 35–50 μ; oospore (25–) 30–39 × 30–39 μ; antheridium 12–14 × 8–12 μ. Pl. **16**, figs. **117, 118**.

10. *Oedogonium rufescens* Wittrock. Dioecious, macrandrous; oogonia 1–3, obovoid- or depressed-obovoid-globose, pore median, rimiform; oospore globose or depressed-globose, filling oogonium or nearly so; spore-wall smooth; antheridia to 12-seriate; sperm 1; female vegetative cell 8–10 × 34–70 μ, male 7–9 × 30–54 μ; oogonium 22–24 × 22–30 μ; oospore 21–23 × 17–22 μ; antheridium 6–8 × 8–12 μ. Pl. **17**, figs. **124–126**.

a. Var. *exiguum* (Elfving) Tiffany. Vegetative cell a little smaller; oospore subdepressed-globose; antheridia 3; vegetative cell 5–9 × 22–88 μ; oogonium 22–24 × 20–28 μ; oospore 20–22 × 17–23 μ; antheridium 5 × 10–12 μ. Pl. **17**, fig. **127**.

b. Var. *lundellii* (Wittrock) Tiffany. Vegetative cell wider in proportion to oogonium than in the species; oogonium depressed-globose; vegetative cell 9–13 × 30–75 μ; oogonium 22–25 × 21–27 μ; oospore 19–23 × 15–22 μ; antheridium 7–9 × 6–12 μ. Pl. **17**, figs. **128, 129**.

11. *Oedogonium franklinianum* Wittrock. Dioecious, macrandrous; oogonium 1, subglobose, with a supramedian to nearly superior pore; oospore globose, almost filling oogonium, spore-wall smooth; antheridia 1–4; sperms 2, division horizontal; female vegetative cell 8–12 × 30–95 μ; male 8–10 × 25–90 μ; oogonium 26–31 × 29–41 μ; oospore 24–30 × 24–30 μ; antheridium 8–9 × 5–7 μ. Pl. **16**, fig. **119**.

12. *Oedogonium cardiacum* (Hassall) Wittrock. Dioecious, macrandrous; oogonium usually 1, subglobose to subcordiform-globose, with a supramedian pore; oospore globose, not filling the oogonium; spore-wall smooth; antheridia 1–10; sperms 2, division horizontal; basal cell elongate; terminal cell apically obtuse; female vegetative cell 18–30 × 60–200 μ, male 15–25 × 45–170 μ; oogonium 48–70 × 58–78 μ; oospore 42–60 × 42–60 μ; antheridium 15–21 × 10–14 μ. Pl. 17, fig. 131.

a. Var. *carbonicum* Wittrock. Oogonia 1 or 2, obovoid to globose-ovoid, pore nearly superior; oospore obovoid-ellipsoid to globose-ellipsoid; female vegetative cell 14–30 × 40–200 μ; male 14–25 × 40–150 μ; oogonium 42–56 × 50–80 μ; oospore 40–52 × 46–65 μ; antheridium 13–20 × 12–15 μ. Pl. 17, fig. 132.

13. *Oedogonium sociale* Wittrock. Dioecious, macrandrous; oogonium 1, subglobose, pore median; oospore globose (or subglobose), quite filling oogonium, spore-wall smooth; antheridia 1–5, sperms 2, division horizontal; vegetative cell 9–16 × 30–130 μ; oogonium 30–38 × 33–42 μ; oospore (26–) 28–35 × 28–35 μ; antheridium 12–14 × 8–11 μ. Pl. 17, figs. 136, 137.

14. *Oedogonium lemmermannii* Tiffany. Dioecious, macrandrous; oogonium usually 1, subglobose, pore supramedian; oospore globose, not filling oogonium; spore-wall smooth; antheridia 1–6; sperms 2, division horizontal; female vegetative cell 16–28 × 25–75 μ; male 14–23 × 25–75 μ; oogonium 30–45 (–50) × 35–59 μ; oospore 28–43 × 28–42 μ; antheridium 12–15 × 5–6 μ. Pl. 17, fig. 138.

15. *Oedogonium pseudoboscii* Hirn. Monoecious; oogonium 1, subobovoid, pore superior; oospore ellipsoid-ovoid or ellipsoid, inflating lower part of oogonium, otherwise not filling it, spore-wall smooth; antheridia 1–2, subepigynous; sperms 2, division horizontal; vegetative cell 8–14 × 64–275 μ; oogonium 41–50 × 75–105 μ; oospore 38–45 × 48–60 μ; antheridium 11–12 × 10–11 μ. Pl. 18, fig. 150.

16. *Oedogonium globosum* Nordstedt. Monoecious; oogonium 1, globose or subglobose, pore superior; oospore globose, quite filling oogonium, spore-wall smooth; antheridia 1–7, subepigynous or subhypogynous or scattered; sperms 2, division horizontal; basal cell elongate; terminal cell setiform; vegetative cell 10–14 × 40–95 μ; oogonium 32–40 × 32–46 μ; oospore 30–37 × 28–37 μ; antheridium 9–12 × 4–8 μ. Pl. 17, fig. 134.

17. *Oedogonium intermedium* Wittrock. Monoecious; oogonium 1, obovoid to obovoid-globose, pore superior; oospore globose or obovoid-globose, filling oogonium or nearly so, spore-wall smooth and thick; antheridia 1–4, epigynous or subepigynous or hypogynous or rarely scattered; sperms 2, division horizontal; vegetative cell 15–18 × 45–80 μ; oogonium 31–37 ×

34–45 μ; oospore 30–36 × 33–41 μ; antheridium 14–16 × 5–10 μ. Pl. **17**, fig. **133**.

18. *Oedogonium upsaliense* Wittrock. Monoecious; oogonium 1, obovoid or suboblong-ellipsoid, pore superior; oospore same form as oogonium and filling it, spore-wall smooth; antheridia 1–3, subhypogynous; antheridium, oogonium, and vegetative cell alternating; sperms 2, division vertical; vegetative cell varying much in same filament; suffultory cell up to 27 μ in diameter; basal cell elongate; terminal cell obtuse; vegetative cell 13–20 × 55–160 μ; oogonium 45–50 × 66–100 μ; oospore 42–47 × 60–75 μ; antheridium 15–18 × 7–10 μ. Pl. **18**, fig. **144**.

19. *Oedogonium fragile* Wittrock. Monoecious; oogonium 1, globose or subobovoid-globose, with superior pore; oospore globose, filling oogonium, spore-wall smooth; antheridia 1–3; sperms 2, division horizontal; basal cell elongate; vegetative cell 12–17 × 50–120 μ; oogonium 42–50 × 44–55 μ; oospore 39–46 × 39–46 μ; antheridium 12–15 × 10–12 μ. Pl. **18**, fig. **145**.

a. Var. *abyssinicum* Hirn. Oogonium smaller than the type; antheridia to 6-seriate; vegetative cell 12–17 × 25–100 μ; oogonium 38–45 × 40–50 μ; oospore 36–43 × 36–44 μ; antheridium 11–15 × 6–14 μ. Pl. **18**, fig. **141**.

20. *Oedogonium vaucherii* (Le Clerc) A. Braun. Monoecious; oogonium 1, usually ovoid, pore superior; oospore globose to subglobose, not filling oogonium; spore-wall smooth and sometimes thick; antheridia 1–4; sperms 2, division horizontal; basal cell elongate; vegetative cell 20–30 × 32–118 μ; oogonium 40–58 × 45–65 μ; oospore 35–54 × 35–55 μ; antheridium 17–30 × 6–15 μ. Pl. **18**, fig. **146**.

21. *Oedogonium capillare* (Linnaeus) Kuetzing. Dioecious, macrandrous; oogonium 1, not or scarcely exceeding the vegetative cell in diameter, cylindric to subcyclindric, pore superior; oospore globose to cylindric-globose to ovoid, not or completely filling oogonium, spore-wall smooth; antherid-

Figs. 139, 140.—*Oedogonium capillare* (Linnaeus) Kuetzing.

Fig. 141.—*Oedogonium fragile* var. *abyssinicum* Hirn.

Figs. 142, 143.—*Oedogonium plagiostomum* Wittrock.

Fig. 144.—*Oedogonium upsaliense* Wittrock.

Fig. 145.—*Oedogonium fragile* Wittrock.

Fig. 146.—*Oedogonium vaucherii* (Le Clerc) A. Braun.

Fig. 147.—*Oedogonium rivulare* (Le Clerc) A. Braun.

Fig. 148.—*Oedogonium gracilius* (Wittrock) Tiffany.

Fig. 149.—*Oedogonium reinschii* Roy.

Fig. 150.—*Oedogonium pseudoboscii* Hirn.

(Figs. 139, 140, 144–146, 148, 149, Tiffany; figs. 141–143, 147, Hirn; fig. 150, Silfvenius. All ×300.)

PLATE 18

(Figs. 139 to 150)

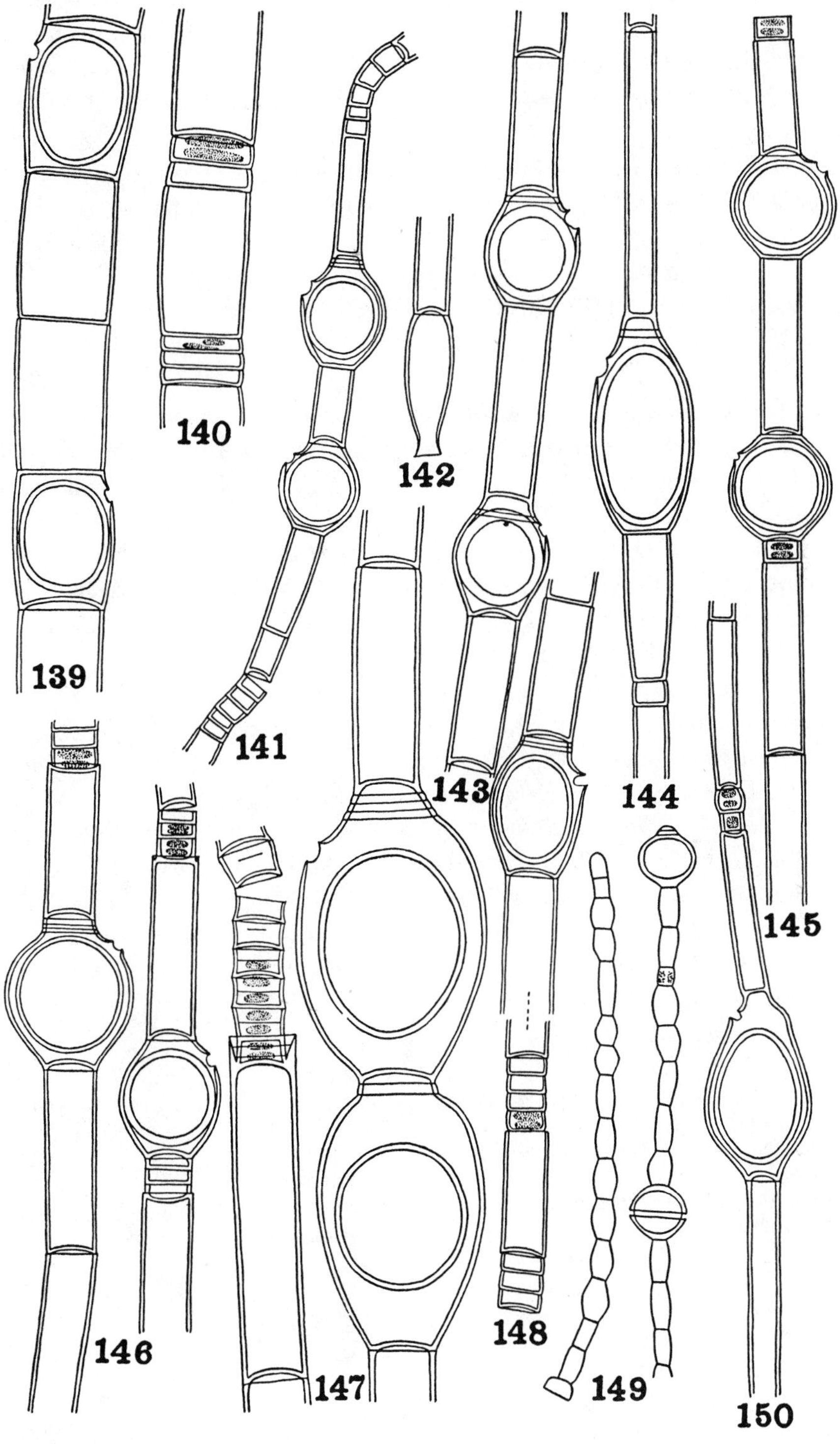

139

140

141

142

143

144

145

146

147

148

149

150

ia 1–4, often alternating with vegetative cell; sperms 2, division horizontal; basal cell elongate, terminal cell broadly apiculate to obtuse; female vegetative cell 35–56 × 36–120 μ, male 35–50 × 35–90 μ; oogonium 40–60 × 47–75 μ; oospore 30–52 × 35–65 μ; antheridium 30–48 × 5–10 μ. Pl. 18, figs. 139, 140.

22. *Oedogonium rivulare* (Le Clerc) A. Braun. Dioecious, macrandrous; oogonia 1–7, obovoid, pore superior; oospore obovoid, ellipsoid, or subglobose, not filling oogonium longitudinally, spore-wall smooth; antheridia to 13-seriate; sperms 2, division horizontal; basal cell elongate; female vegetative cell 35–45 × 110–350 μ, male 30–36 × 120–280 μ; oogonium 70–85 × 130–160 μ; oospore 55–70 × 65–100 μ; antheridium 21–28 × 14–26 μ. Pl. 18, fig. 147.

23. *Oedogonium capilliforme* Kuetzing. Dioecious, macrandrous; oogonium 1, obovoid to subovoid, with superior pore; oospore ovoid-globose, cylindric-globose, subglobose, or globose, not filling oogonium, spore-wall smooth; antheridia 2–8, often alternating with the vegetative cell; sperms 2, division horizontal; basal cell elongate, terminal cell apically obtuse or apiculate; female vegetative cell 28–38 × 42–120 μ, male 25–30 × 40–100 μ; oogonium 42–50 × 51–62 μ; oospore 37–45 × 40–50 μ; antheridium 20–25 × 8–10 μ. Pl. 19, figs. 153, 154.

24. *Oedogonium diversum* (Hirn) Tiffany. Dioecious, macrandrous; oogonium 1, obovoid to subovoid, with superior pore; oospore ovoid-globose, subglobose or globose, not filling oogonium; spore-wall smooth; antheridia 2–5; sperms 2, division horizontal; female vegetative cell 34–46 × 45–130 μ, male 33–40 × 50–120 μ; oogonium 46–56 × 46–70 μ; oospore 43–52 × 40–58 μ; antheridium 30–37 × 6–11 μ. Pl. 19, figs. 151, 152.

25. *Oedogonium gracilius* (Wittrock) Tiffany. Dioecious, macrandrous; oogonium 1, obovoid-globose, with superior pore; oospore globose to subglobose, usually filling oogonium, spore-wall smooth; antheridia 1–8, often alternating with vegetative cell; basal cell elongate; vegetative cell

FIGS. 151, 152.—*Oedogonium diversum* (Hirn) Tiffany.

FIGS. 153, 154.—*Oedogonium capilliforme* Kuetzing.

FIGS. 155–157.—*Oedogonium occidentale* (Hirn) Tiffany.

FIGS. 158, 159.—*Oedogonium crenulatocostatum* Wittrock.

FIG. 160.—*Oedogonium crenulatocostatum* var. *cylindricum* (Hirn) Tiffany.

FIGS. 161, 162.—*Oedogonium paulense* Nordstedt and Hirn.

FIG. 163.—*Oedogonium paludosum* (Hassall) Wittrock.

FIG. 164.—*Oedogonium paludosum* var. *parvisporum* Hirn.

(Figs. 151, 152, 155–157, Hirn; figs. 153, 154, 158–160, 162–164, Tiffany; fig. 161, Schmidle. All ×300.)

PLATE 19

(Figs. 151 to 164)

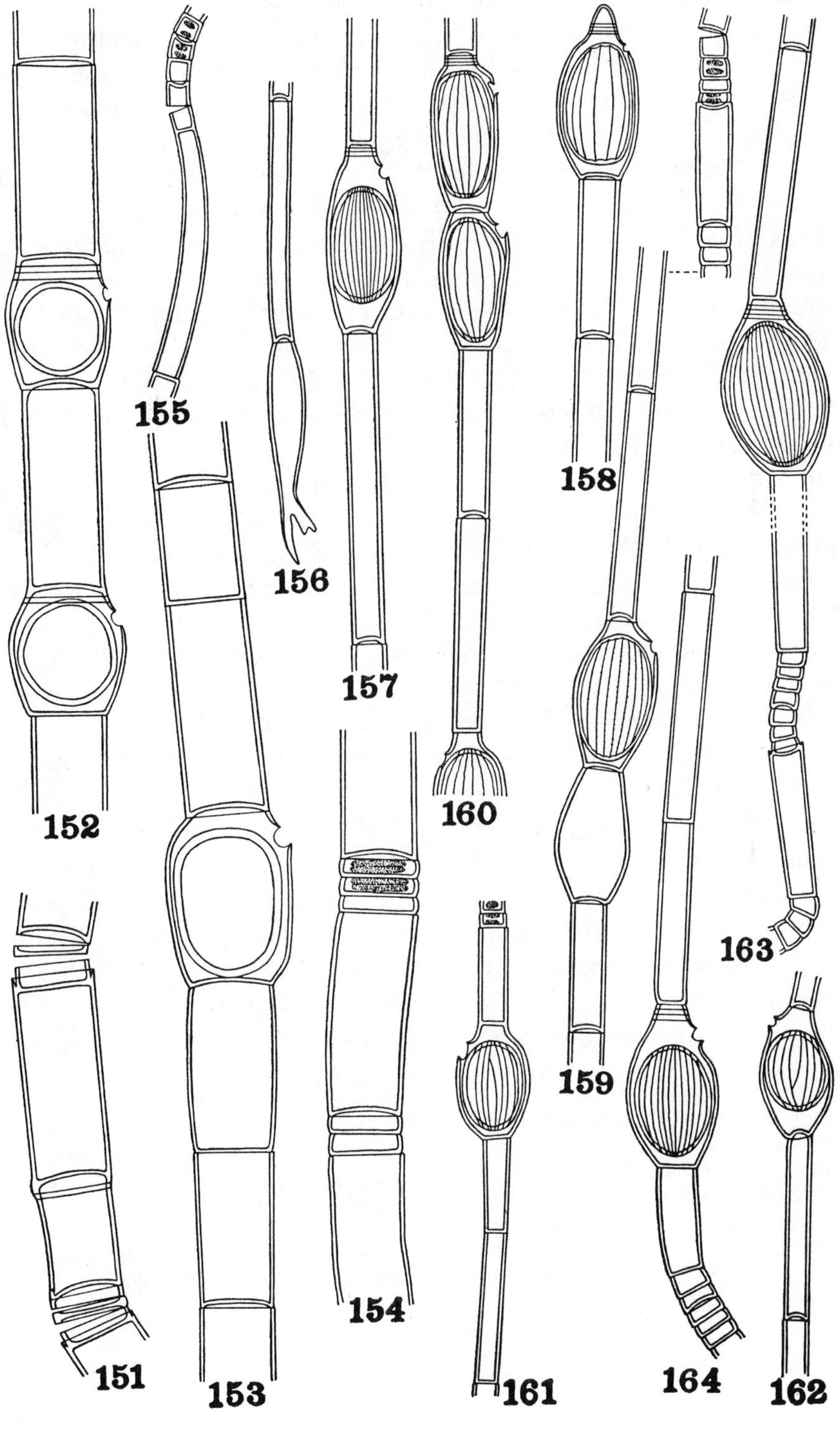

151
152
153
154
155
156
157
158
159
160
161
162
163
164

20–25 × 40–100 μ; oogonium 36–42 × 46–57 μ; oospore 34–39 × 36–44 μ; antheridium 19–22 × 7–10 μ. Pl. **18**, fig. **148.**

26. *Oedogonium plagiostomum* Wittrock. Dioecious, macrandrous; oogonium 1, obovoid-globose, with superior pore; oospore globose to subglobose, usually filling oogonium, spore-wall smooth and thick; antheridia 1–6, often alternating with vegetative cell; basal cell elongate; vegetative cell 22–27 × 65–120 μ; oogonium 42–49 × 50–60 μ; oospore 41–47 × 42–49 μ; antheridium 20–24 × 8–10 μ. Pl. **18**, figs. **142, 143.**

27. *Oedogonium majus* (Hansgirg) Tiffany. Dioecious, macrandrous; oogonia 1–3, subobovoid (sometimes nearly ellipsoid), pore superior; oospore similar in shape to oogonium and usually filling it; spore-wall smooth; antheridia 1–5; sperms 2, division vertical; basal cell elongate; female vegetative cell 36–46 × 80–200 μ, male 32–42 × 80–200 μ; oogonium 52–68 × 75–90 μ; oospore 50–64 × 68–88 μ; antheridium 30–36 × 10–16 μ. Pl. **20**, figs. **167, 168.**

28. *Oedogonium grande* Kuetzing. Dioecious, macrandrous; oogonia 1–5, subobovoid, pore superior; oospore of the same form as oogonium which it completely fills or not, spore-wall smooth; antheridia 1–10; sperms 2, division vertical; basal cell elongate; female vegetative cell 28–37 × 70–210 μ; male 28–33 × 70–175 μ; oogonium 49–60 × 86–110 μ; oospore 47–58 × 60–94 μ; antheridium 25–33 × 11–18 μ. Pl. **20**, figs. **169–171.**

a. Var. *aequatoriale* Wittrock. Male vegetative cell 22–28, female 26–33 × 70–165 μ; oogonium 44–51 × 75–100 μ; oospore 42–49 × 50–81 μ. Pl. **20**, fig. **172.**

29. *Oedogonium angustum* (Hirn) Tiffany. Dioecious, macrandrous; oogonia 1–4, subobovoid, pore superior; oospore similar in shape to oogonium and nearly filling it; spore-wall smooth; antheridia to 36-seriate; sperms 2, division vertical; female vegetative cell 19–30 × 70–330 μ; male 19–25 × 80–225 μ; oogonium 42–52 × 62–110 μ; oospore 40–50 × 60–89 μ; antheridium 18–22 × 7–15 μ. Pl. **20**, figs. **173, 174.**

30. *Oedogonium oboviforme* Wittrock. Dioecious, macrandrous; oogonium

Figs. 165, 166.—*Oedogonium oboviforme* Wittrock.

Figs. 167, 168.—*Oedogonium majus* (Hansgirg) Tiffany.

Figs. 169–171.—*Oedogonium grande* Kuetzing.

Fig. 172.—*Oedogonium grande* var. *aequatoriale* Wittrock.

Figs. 173, 174.—*Oedogonium angustum* (Hirn) Tiffany.

Figs. 175, 176.—*Oedogonium amplum* Magnus and Wille.

(Figs. 165, 166, 172–176, Hirn; figs. 167–171, Tiffany. All ×300.)

PLATE 20

(Figs. 165 to 176)

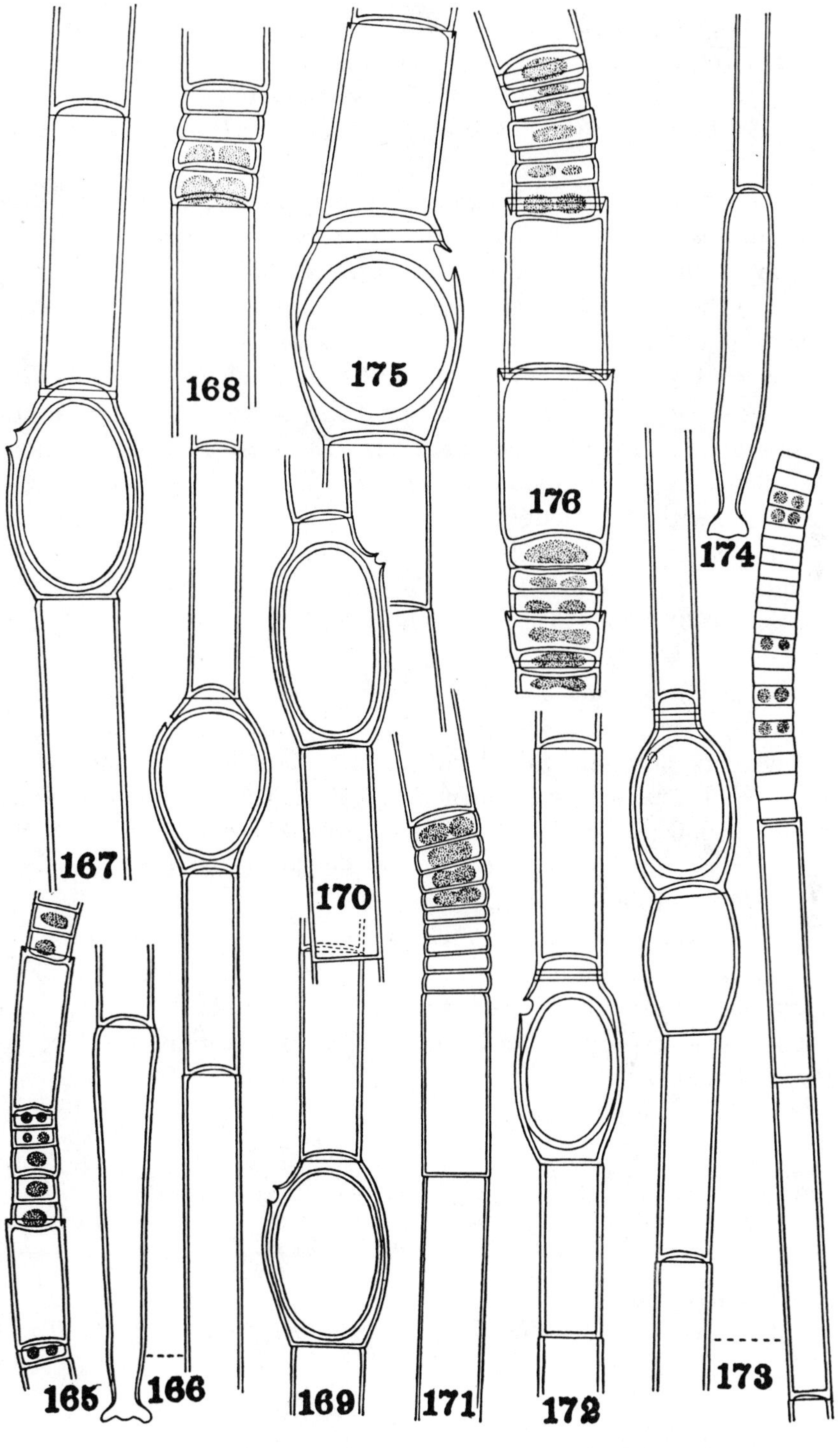

1, obovoid, pore superior; oospore obovoid (rarely ellipsoid-obovoid), about filling oogonium, spore-wall smooth; antheridia to 19-seriate, sperms 2, division vertical; basal cell elongate; female vegetative cell 21–33 × 72–280 μ; male 21–31 × 72–270 μ; oogonium 55–65 × 80–107 μ; oospore 54–61 × 70–85 μ; antheridium 21–28 × 5–13 μ. Pl. 20, figs. 165, 166.

31. *Oedogonium amplum* Magnus and Wille. Dioecious, macrandrous; oogonia 1 or 2, ovoid to obovoid-ellipsoid, pore superior; oospore ellipsoid to broadly ellipsoid (or nearly globose) nearly filling oogonium, its wall smooth; antheridia 2–20, division vertical; female vegetative cell 46–54 × 70–160 μ, male 42–50 × 65–200 μ; oogonium 75–90 × 83–115 μ; oospore 72–85 × 77–100 μ; antheridium 40–50 × 8–20 μ. Pl. 20, figs. 175, 176.

32. *Oedogonium paulense* Nordstedt and Hirn. Monoecious; oogonium 1, subellipsoid or ellipsoid-ovoid, pore superior; oospore ellipsoid, not or quite filling oogonium, spore-wall of three layers: outer layer smooth, middle layer with 18–22 longitudinal ribs, entire and sometimes anastomosate, inner layer smooth; antheridia 1–2, subepigynous; sperms 2, division horizontal; vegetative cell 10–15 × 50–120 μ; oogonium 33–38 × 43–68 μ; oospore 30–36 × 38–45 μ; antheridium 10–14 × 6–8 μ. Pl. 19, figs. 161, 162.

33. *Oedogonium paludosum* (Hassall) Wittrock. Monoecious; oogonium 1, ellipsoid, pore superior; oospore ellipsoid, filling oogonium, spore-wall in three layers: outer and middle layers with 27–35 longitudinal ribs, continuous, rarely anastomosate; antheridia 1–8, scattered, often in the upper part of the filament; sperms 2, division vertical; vegetative cell 15–20 × 50–140 μ; oogonium 39–48 × 66–84 μ; oospore 36–45 × 54–63 μ; antheridium 14–16 × 6–13 μ. Pl. 19, fig. 163.

a. Var. *parvisporum* Hirn. Oogonium subellipsoid or suboblong-ellipsoid; oospore not filling oogonium; antheridium subepigynous or sub-hypogynous or scattered; vegetative cell 15–20 × 45–120 μ; oogonium 38–44 × 70–86 μ; oospore 35–41 × 54–60 μ; antheridium 15–17 × 7–12 μ. Pl. 19, fig. 164.

FIGS. 177, 178.—*Oedogonium paucocostatum* Transeau.

FIGS. 179, 180.—*Oedogonium punctatum* Wittrock.

FIGS. 181, 182.—*Oedogonium longiarticulatum* (Hansgirg) Tiffany.

FIG. 183.—*Oedogonium boscii* (Le Clerc) Wittrock.

FIGS. 184, 185.—*Oedogonium taphrosporum* Nordstedt and Hirn.

FIGS. 186, 187.—*Oedogonium americanum* Transeau.

(Figs. 177, 178, 181–183, 186, 187, Tiffany; figs. 179, 180, 184, 185, Hirn. All ×*300*.)

PLATE 21

(Figs. 177 to 187)

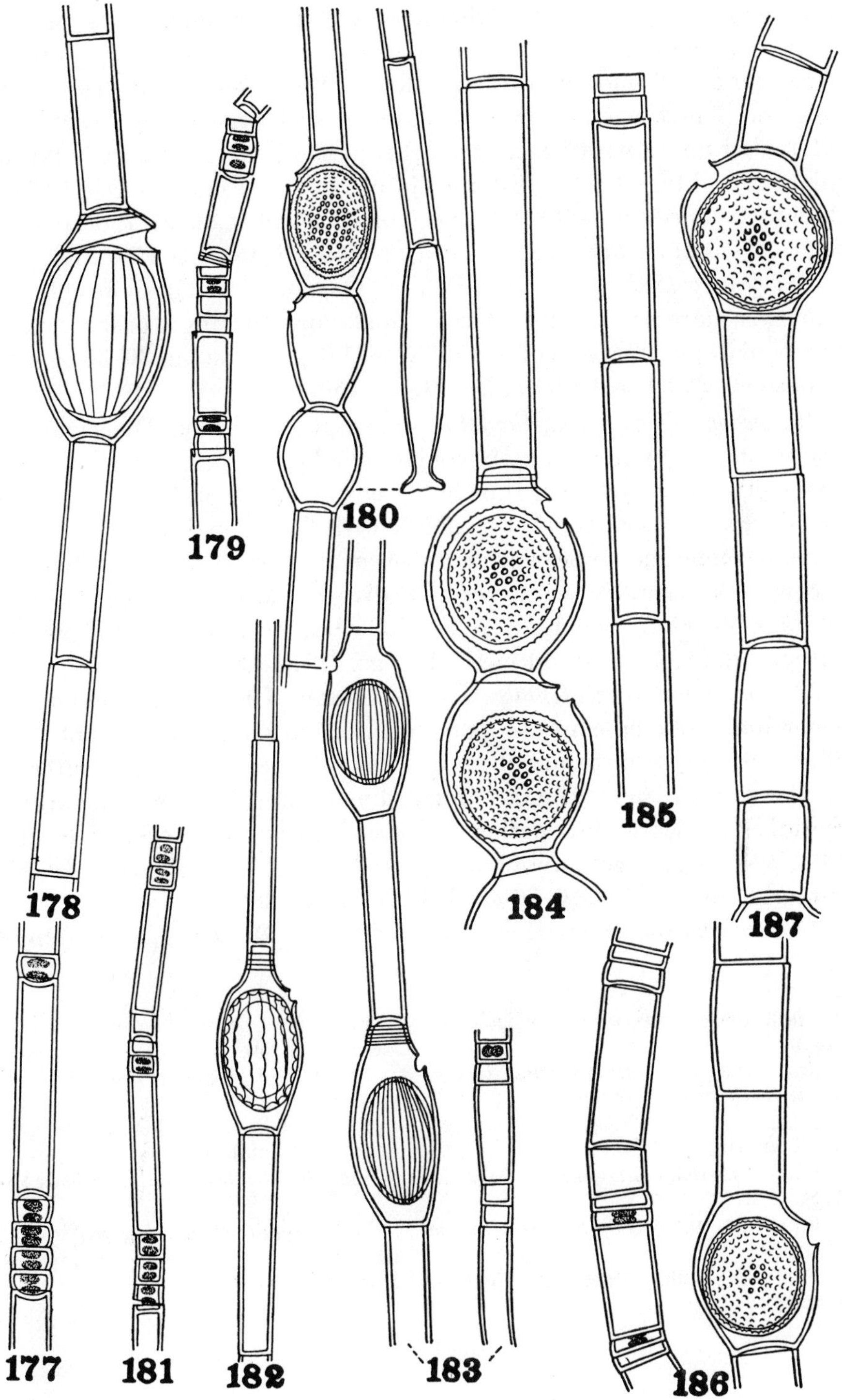

179

180

178

185

184

187

177   181   182   183   186

34. *Oedogonium crenulatocostatum* Wittrock. Dioecious, macrandrous; oogonium 1–6, obovoid to subellipsoid, often terminal, pore superior; oospore of the same form as the oogonium, which it nearly or quite fills, outer spore-wall smooth, median wall with 14–20 longitudinal ribs, crenulate and sometimes anastomosing, inner wall smooth; antheridia 2–6, often alternating with vegetative cell; sperms 2, division horizontal; terminal cell obtuse to broadly apiculate; female vegetative cell 10–18 × 25–125 μ, male 9–13 × 32–80 μ; oogonium 30–36 × 40–65 μ; oospore 28–34 × 37–55 μ; antheridium 9–12 × 32–80 μ. Pl. **19**, figs. **158, 159.**

a. Var. *cylindricum* (Hirn) Tiffany. Oogonium and oospore cylindric-oblong or more rarely ellipsoid or obovoid-ellipsoid; ribs of oospore scarcely crenulate; vegetative cell 11–16 × 44–150 μ; oogonium 30–36 × 42–81 μ; oospore 27–34 × 40–65 μ. Pl. **19**, fig. **160.**

35. *Oedogonium longiarticulatum* (Hansgirg) Tiffany. Dioecious, macrandrous; oogonium single, obovoid to subellipsoid, pore superior; oospore obovoid to nearly ellipsoid, not filling oogonium, its wall of three layers: the outer and inner smooth, the middle with 12–18 longitudinal, distinctly crenate (sometimes appearing dentate) costae; antheridia 2–5, often alternating with vegetative cell; sperms 2, division horizontal; vegetative cell 12–15 × 60–90 μ; oogonium 27–32 × 58–60 μ; oospore 24–30 × 44–52 μ; antheridium 8–11 × 10–14 μ. Pl. **21**, figs. **181, 182.**

36. *Oedogonium occidentale* (Hirn) Tiffany. Dioecious, macrandrous; oogonium 1, oblong-ellipsoid, pore superior; oospore ellipsoid, not nearly filling oogonium longitudinally, its walls of three layers: the outer and middle with 27–35 continuous longitudinal costae, the inner smooth; antheridia 1–6, scattered; sperms 2, division horizontal; vegetative cell 8–16 × 50–165 μ; oogonium 29–38 × 69–100 μ; oospore 27–37 × 42–50 μ; antheridium 12–13 × 10–16 μ. Pl. **19**, figs. **155–157.**

37. *Oedogonium boscii* (Le Clerc) Wittrock. Dioecious, macrandrous;

Fig. 188.—*Oedogonium pringsheimii* Cramer.

Figs. 189, 190.—*Oedogonium pringsheimii* var. *nordstedtii* Wittrock.

Figs. 191, 192.—*Oedogonium epiphyticum* Transeau and Tiffany.

Figs. 193–195.—*Oedogonium howardii* G. S. West.

Figs. 196, 197.—*Oedogonium pisanum* Wittrock.

Figs. 198, 199.—*Oedogonium pratense* Transeau.

Fig. 200.—*Oedogonium welwitschii* W. and G. S. West.

Fig. 201.—*Oedogonium acmandrium* Elfving.

Figs. 202, 203.—*Oedogonium stictospermum* (Skuja) Tiffany.

Fig. 204.—*Oedogonium bohemicum* Hirn.

(Figs. 188–192, 195, 198–204, Tiffany; figs. 193, 194, G. S. West; figs. 196, 197, Hirn. All ×*300*.)

PLATE 22

(Figs. 188 to 204)

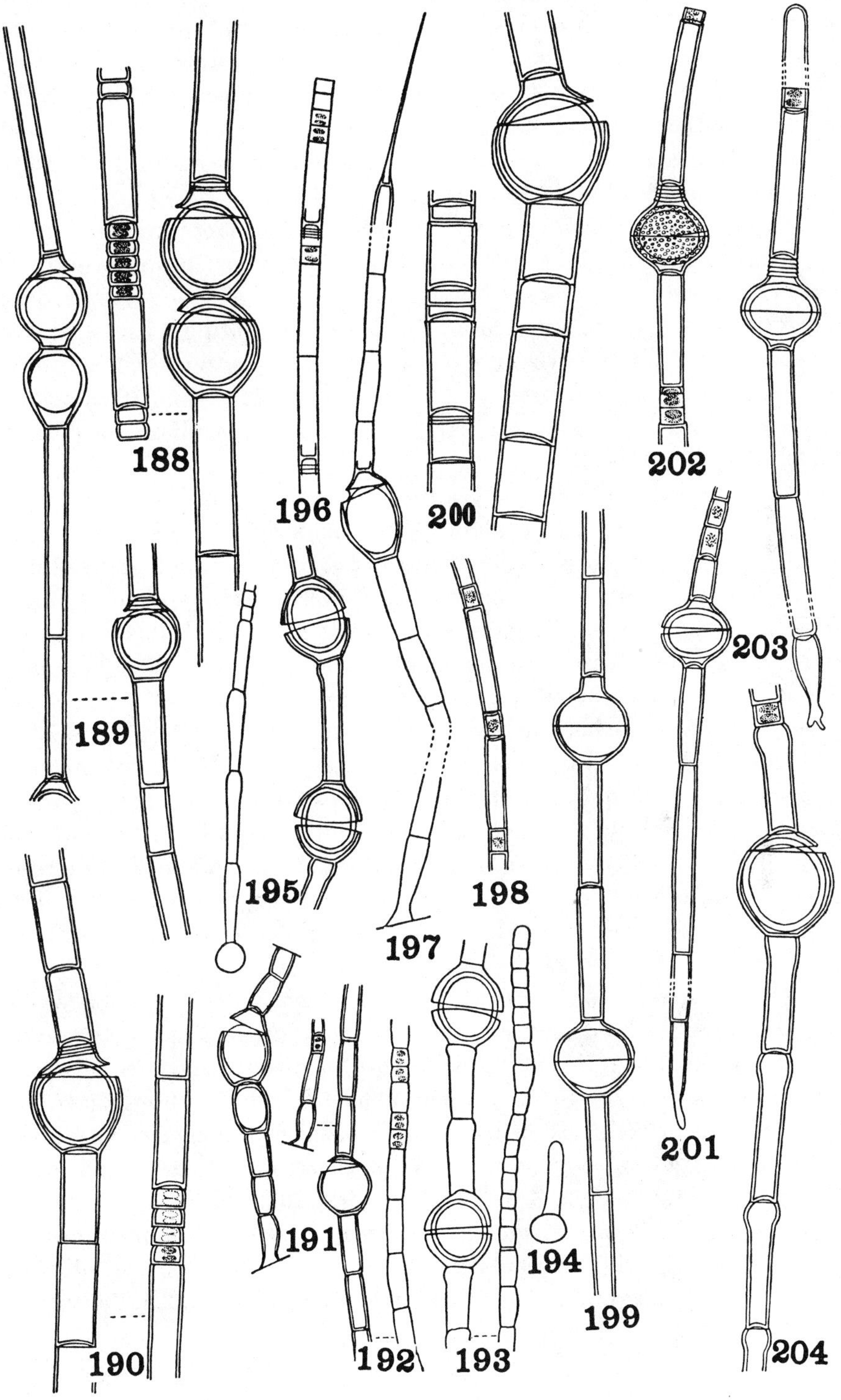

188

196 200 202

189

195 198

197 203

201

190 191 192 193 199 204

194

oogonium 1 (rarely 2), oblong-ellipsoid, pore superior; oospore ellipsoid, not nearly filling oogonium longitudinally, spore-wall of three layers: outer and middle layers with 27–35 continuous, rarely anastomosate, longitudinal ribs; antheridia 1–8, scattered, often in upper part of filament; sperms 2, division vertical; vegetative cell, female 14–23 × 45–135 μ, male 13–18 × 52–108 μ; oogonium 39–51 × 75–110 μ; oospore 36–43 × 56–70 μ; antheridium 13–14 × 6–16 μ. Pl. 21, fig. 183.

38. *Oedogonium punctatum* Wittrock. Dioecious, macrandrous; oogonia 1–4, obovoid (rarely globose-obovoid), pore superior; oospore obovoid, nearly filling oogonium (rarely subglobose and not filling oogonium), outer spore-wall scrobiculate; antheridia 1–5, often alternating with vegetative cell; sperms 2, division horizontal; basal cell elongate; terminal cell (often an oogonium) apically obtuse; vegetative cell 15–22 × 42–128 μ; oogonium 38–45 × 52–65 μ; oospore 37–43 × 43–55 μ; antheridium 15–17 × 6–10 μ. Pl. 21, figs. 179, 180.

39. *Oedogonium americanum* Transeau. Dioecious, macrandrous; oogonium 1, globose to depressed-globose, pore superior; oospore globose, ellipsoid-globose, or depressed-globose, filling oogonium or not, spore-wall of three layers: median layer scrobiculate; antheridia 1–5, frequently alternating with vegetative cell; sperms 2, division horizontal; basal cell elongate; terminal cell obtuse; female vegetative cell 28–48 × 40–100 μ, male vegetative cell 24–30 × 40–100 μ; oogonium 40–76 × 48–70 μ; oospore 38–74 × 46–56 μ; antheridium 20–28 × 4–12 μ. Pl 21, figs. 186, 187.

40. *Oedogonium taphrosporum* Nordstedt and Hirn. Dioecious, macrandrous; oogonia 1–6, obovoid or obovoid-ellipsoid, pore superior; oospore globose or ellipsoid-globose, not filling oogonium, outer layer of spore-wall scrobiculate, inner layer smooth; antheridia 2–?; terminal cell, sometimes an oogonium, obtuse; basal cell elongate; vegetative cell 25–39 × 100–375 μ; oogonium 70–83 × 81–113 μ; oospore 58–65 × 62–70 μ; antheridium 24–32 × 8–12 μ. Pl. 21, figs. 184, 185.

41. *Oedogonium stictospermum* (Skuja) Tiffany. Monoecious; oogonium 1 (rarely 2) depressed-globose, with median operculum; oospore depressed-globose, not quite filling oogonium longitudinally, median spore-wall scrobiculate, light brown; antheridia 1–4, subepigynous or subhypogynous; sperms 2, division horizontal; basal cell elongate; vegetative cell 7–14 × 25–140 μ; oogonium 28–39 × 29–38 μ; oospore 27–36 × 26–32 μ; antheridium 8–11 × 8–14 μ. Pl. 22, figs. 202, 203.

42. *Oedogonium paucocostatum* Transeau. Dioecious, macrandrous; oogonium 1, ellipsoid, operculate, division superior; oospore ellipsoid, nearly filling the oogonium, the inner and outer walls smooth, the median

with 15–19 longitudinal costae; antheridia 2–8, sperms 2, division horizontal; terminal cell obtuse; basal cell usually elongate; vegetative cell (15–) 19–25 × 70–160 μ; oogonium 54–60 × 70–104 μ; oospore 50–56 × 66–90 μ; antheridium 18–23 × 8–12 μ. Pl. **21**, figs. **177, 178.**

43. *Oedogonium pusillum* Kirchner. Monoecious; oogonium 1 (rarely 2), subbiconic-ellipsoid or subbiconic-globose, seen from above circular, margin even, operculate, division wide (usually up to 2.5 μ); oospore ellipsoid or globose, generally constricted at the middle, not quite filling oogonium, spore-wall smooth; antheridia 1 or 2, subepigynous, sperm (?)1; basal cell subhemispherical; terminal cell obtuse or obtusely conical; vegetative cell 3–6 × 10–60 μ; oogonium 14–16 × 15–25 μ; oospore 11–13 × 13–15 μ; antheridium 3–4 × 5–6 μ; basal cell 7–8 × 7–8 μ. Pl. **23**, fig. **210.**

44. *Oedogonium capitellatum* Wittrock. Monoecious; oogonium 1, subdepressed- or depressed-globose, operculate, division median; oospore depressed-globose completely filling oogonium, or nearly so, walls smooth; antheridia 1–3, subepigynous or hypogynous or rarely scattered, sperm 1; basal cell subhemispherical or broadly ellipsoid; terminal cell piliform; vegetative cells capitellate, 6–9 × 20–60 μ, oogonium 20–26 × 17–23 μ; oospore 18–23 × 15–19 μ; antheridium 6–7 × 5–9 μ; basal cell 16–18 × 6–10 μ. Pl. **23**, figs. **213, 214.**

45. *Oedogonium acmandrium* Elfving. Monoecious; oogonia 1–2, depressed-globose or subglobose, operculate, division median and narrow; oospore depressed-globose or subglobose, filling oogonium, wall smooth; antheridia 1–3, subepigynous, epigynous, or hypogynous, often terminal; sperm 1; basal cell elongate; vegetative cell 7–10 × 30–80 μ; oogonium 30–35 × 28–38 μ; oospore 28–33 × 25–29 μ; antheridium 8–10 × 10–15 μ. Pl. **22**, fig. **201.**

46. *Oedogonium howardii* G. West. Dioecious, macrandrous; oogonia 1 or 2, globose or subglobose with broad median operculum; oospore globose filling oogonium, its wall smooth; antheridia to 16-seriate; sperm 1; vegetative cell broadly capitellate; basal cell subhemispheric to nearly spheric; vegetative cell 7–12 × 18–42 μ; oogonium 26–33 × (23–) 26–33 μ; oospore 21–30 × 24–30 μ; antheridium 7–9 × 5–14 μ; basal cell 12–20 × 10–13 μ. Pl. **22**, figs. **193–195.**

47. *Oedogonium pratense* Transeau. Dioecious, macrandrous; oogonium 1 (rarely 2), subdepressed-globose or broadly pyriform-globose, operculate, division median, narrow but distinct; oospore depressed-globose or subglobose, filling or nearly filling oogonium, spore-wall smooth; antheridia 1–2, usually alternating with vegetative cell; sperm 1; basal cell elongate; vegetative cell, female 10–17 × 35–95 μ; male 8–15 × 32–82 μ; oogonium

33-40 × 35-50 μ; oospore 32-38 × 28-35 μ; antheridium 10-14 × 13-18 μ. Pl. 22, figs. **198, 199.**

48. *Oedogonium punctatostriatum* DeBary. Dioecious, macrandrous; oogonium 1, depressed-globose, operculate, division median, rather wide and distinct; oospore depressed-globose, not filling oogonium, spore-wall smooth; antheridium to 10-seriate; sperm 1; wall of vegetative cell and oogonium spirally punctate; basal cell depressed-globose or subhemispheric, wall vertically plicate; female vegetative cell 18-22 × 38-128 μ, male 16-19 × 33-108 μ; oogonium 48-55 × 38-48 μ; oospore 40-51 × 35-42 μ; antheridium 16-19 × 6-12 μ; basal cell 28-31 × 21-25 μ. Pl. **23,** fig. **221.**

49. *Oedogonium welwitschii* West and West. Dioecious, macrandrous; oogonia 1-3, subovoid-globose, operculate, division superior; oospore globose, filling or not filling oogonium, spore-wall smooth; antheridia 2; female vegetative cell 20-28 × 25-84 μ; male 17-20 × 35-80 μ; oogonium 43-50 × 43-52 μ; oospore 35-43 × 35-42 μ; antheridium 16-18 × 7-9 μ. Pl. **22,** fig. **200.**

50. *Oedogonium mitratum* Hirn. Dioecious, macrandrous; oogonia 1-4, globose or subglobose, operculate, division supramedian or superior, narrow but distinct; oospore globose (rarely subglobose), filling oogonium; spore-wall smooth; antheridia 1-5, subepigynous; sperms 2, division horizontal; vegetative cell, often capitellate, 4-10 × 18-80 μ; oogonium 18-27 × 20-35 μ; oospore 17-23 × 17-23 μ; antheridium 6-9 × 6-8 μ. Pl. **23,** figs. **208, 209.**

51. *Oedogonium pringsheimii* Cramer. Dioecious, macrandrous; oogonia 1-6, subovoid-globose, operculate, division superior; oospore globose,

Figs. 205, 206.—*Oedogonium crispum* (Hassall) Wittrock.

Fig. 207.—*Oedogonium crispum* var. *gracilescens* Wittrock.

Figs. 208, 209.—*Oedogonium mitratum* Hirn.

Fig. 210.—*Oedogonium pusillum* Kirchner.

Fig. 211.—*Oedogonium simplex* Hirn.

Fig. 212.—*Oedogonium kirchneri* Wittrock.

Figs. 213, 214.—*Oedogonium capitellatum* Wittrock.

Fig. 215.—*Oedogonium rothii* Pringsheim.

Fig. 216.—*Oedogonium ouchitanum* Taft.

Fig. 217.—*Oedogonium gracillimum* Wittrock and Lundell.

Fig. 218.—*Oedogonium oblongum* Wittrock.

Fig. 219.—*Oedogonium oblongum* var. *majus* Nordstedt.

Fig. 220.—*Oedogonium oblongellum* Kirchner.

Fig. 221.—*Oedogonium punctatostriatum* DeBary.

(Figs. 205, 206, 208-210, 214, 217, 218, Tiffany; figs. 207, 211-213, 219, 221, Hirn; fig. 215, Pringsheim; fig. 220, G. S. West; fig. 216, Taft. All ×*300*.)

PLATE 23

(Figs. 205 to 221)

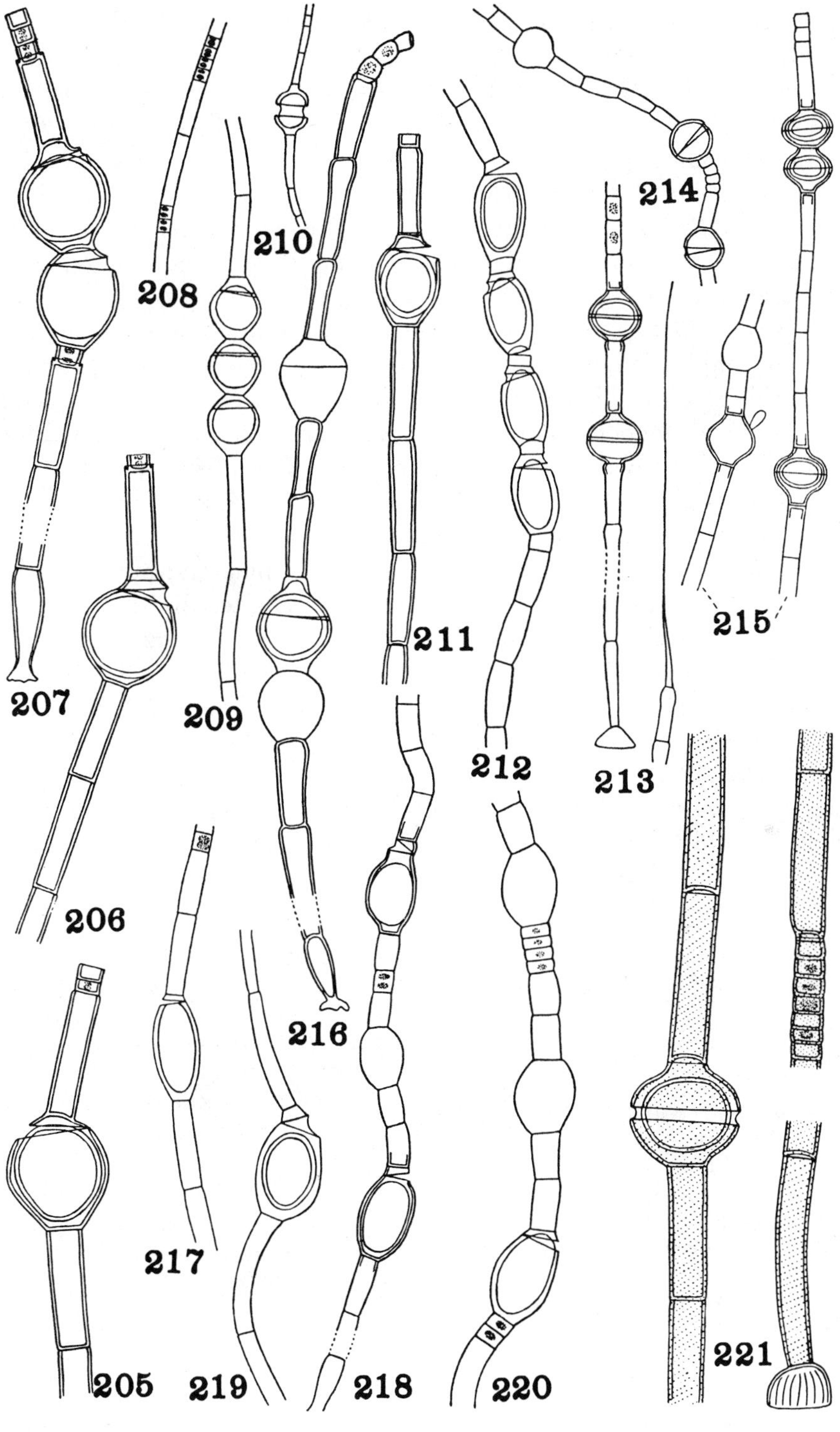

nearly filling oogonium, spore-wall smooth, often thickened; antheridia to 10-seriate, often alternating with vegetative cell; sperms 2, division horizontal; basal cell elongate; terminal cell broadly apiculate or obtuse; female vegetative cell 14–20 × 28–100 μ, male 12–16 × 24–64 μ; oogonium 35–43 × 36–46 μ; oospore 30–37 × 30–37 μ; antheridium 10–15 × 6–9 μ. Pl. 22, fig. **188.**

a. Var. *nordstedtii* Wittrock. Smaller than the type, oogonia 1–2, oospore not filling oogonium; female vegetative cell 10–16 × 20–76 μ, male 9–15 × 18–68 μ; oogonium 28–39 × 36–45 μ; oospore 26–34 × 27–34 μ; antheridium 9–12 × 8–9 μ. Pl. 22, figs. **189, 190.**

52. *Oedogonium epiphyticum* Transeau and Tiffany. Dioecious, macrandrous; oogonia 1–3, ellipsoid to ellipsoid-ovoid, with superior operculum; oospore ellipsoid to ellipsoid-ovoid to nearly globose, almost filling oogonium; spore-wall smooth; antheridia 1–2; sperms 2, division horizontal; basal cell elongate; female vegetative cell 6–9 × 18–48 μ, male 5–8 × 16–45 μ; oogonium 16–20 × 20–30 μ; oospore 15–18 × 18–28 μ; antheridium 5–7 × 5–10 μ. Pl. 22, figs. **191, 192.**

53. *Oedogonium pisanum* Wittrock. Dioecious, macrandrous; oogonium 1 (rarely 2–3), ellipsoid-ovoid to ovoid, operculate, division superior; oospore ovoid to ellipsoid, nearly filling oogonium, spore-wall smooth; antheridia 1–4; sperms 2, division horizontal; basal cell elongate; terminal cell piliferous; vegetative cell 5–12 × 12–72 μ; oogonium 23–29 (–32) × 23–43 (–45) μ; oospore 21–25 × 27–37 μ; antheridium 4–9 × 5–9 μ. Pl. 22, figs. **196, 197.**

54. *Oedogonium crispum* (Hassall) Wittrock. Monoecious; oogonium usually 1, obovoid-globose, operculate, division superior; oospore globose

FIGS. 222, 223.—*Oedogonium monile* Berkeley and Harvey.

FIGS. 224, 225.—*Oedogonium longicolle* Nordstedt.

FIG. 226.—*Oedogonium macrandrium* Wittrock.

FIG. 227.—*Oedogonium macrandrium* var. *propinquum* (Wittrock) Hirn.

FIG. 228.—*Oedogonium macrandrium* var. *aemulans* Hirn.

FIG. 229.—*Oedogonium undulatum* (Brébisson) A. Braun.

FIG. 230.—*Oedogonium obtruncatum* Wittrock.

FIG. 231.—*Oedogonium rugulosum* Nordstedt.

FIG. 232.—*Oedogonium rugulosum* var. *minutum* (Hansgirg) Tiffany.

FIG. 233.—*Oedogonium decipiens* Wittrock.

FIGS. 234, 235.—*Oedogonium decipiens* var. *dissimile* (Hirn) Tiffany.

FIG. 236.—*Oedogonium decipiens* var. *africanum* Tiffany.

FIGS. 237, 238.—*Oedogonium macrospermum* W. and G. S. West.

(Figs. 222, 223, 228, 229, 236, Hirn; figs. 224, 225, Nordstedt; figs. 226, 227, 230–232, 234, 235, Tiffany; fig. 233, Wittrock. All ×*300*.)

PLATE 24

(Figs. 222 to 238)

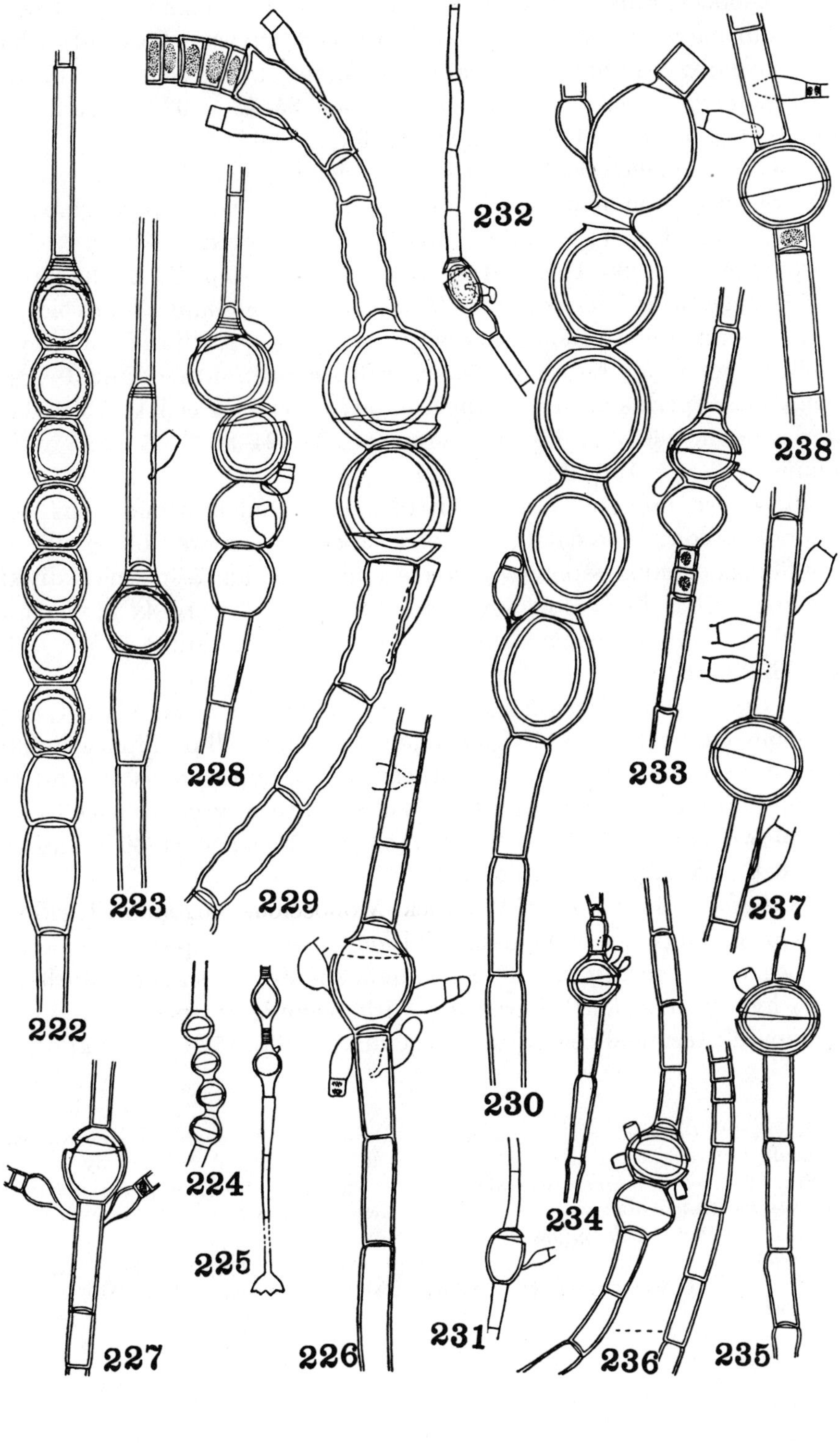

232

238

228

233

223

229

237

222

224

230

234

225

231

227

226

236

235

or subglobose, quite filling the oogonium, spore-wall smooth; antheridia 1–5, subepigynous or hypogynous; sperms 2, division horizontal; basal cell elongate; terminal cell apically obtuse; vegetative cell (10–) 12–16 × 35–80 μ; oogonium 37–45 × 41–53 μ; oospore 35–43 × 37–43 μ; antheridium 8–14 × 7–12 μ. Pl. **23**, figs. **205, 206.**

a. Var. *gracilescens* Wittrock. More slender than the species; oogonium varying from obovoid-globose to subellipsoid; oospore globose to ovoid; vegetative cell 10–14 × 30–70 μ; oogonium 33–39 × 33–51 μ; oospore 32–37 × 33–42 μ; antheridium 9–10 × 7–9 μ. Pl. **23**, fig. **207.**

55. *Oedogonium simplex* Hirn. Monoecious; oogonium 1, obovoid-pyriform, operculate, division superior; oospore globose, ellipsoid or obovoid-globose, not filling oogonium, spore-wall smooth; antheridium 1–?, subepigynous; sperms 2, division horizontal; vegetative cell 11–13 × 35–58 μ; oogonium 26–32 × 33–40 μ; oospore (22–) 24–30 × 23–30 μ; antheridium 8–10 × 7–10 μ. Pl. **23**, fig. **211.**

56. *Oedogonium gracillimum* Wittrock and Lundell. Monoecious; oogonium 1, oblong, operculate, division superior; oospore oblong-ellipsoid, not filling oogonium, spore-wall smooth; antheridium 1, sperms 2, division horizontal; basal cell elongate; vegetative cell 4–7 × 16–42 μ; oogonium 14–19 × 34–40 μ; oospore 13–17 × 24–32 μ; antheridium 3–5 × 4–7 μ. Pl. **23**, fig. **217.**

57. *Oedogonium oblongellum* Kirchner. Monoecious; oogonium 1, ellipsoid-obovoid, operculate, division superior; oospore ellipsoid, nearly filling oogonium, spore-wall smooth; antheridia 1–2, hypogynous or scattered; sperms 2, division horizontal; terminal cell obtuse; vegetative cell 7–9 × 14–35 μ; oogonium 20–24 × 25–33 μ; oospore 18–22 × 24–30 μ; antheridium 6–8 × 4–12 μ. Pl. **23**, fig. **220.**

58. *Oedogonium kirchneri* Wittrock. Monoecious; oogonium 1, ellipsoid or obovoid-ellipsoid, operculate, division superior; oospore of same form as oogonium, nearly filling oogonium, spore-wall smooth; antheridia 1–2, hypogynous and alternating with oogonium; sperms 2, division horizontal; terminal cell obtuse; vegetative cell 8–15 × 16–60 μ; oogoni-

FIG. 239.—*Oedogonium concatenatum* (Hassall) Wittrock.

FIG. 240.—*Oedogonium concatenatum* var. *superornatum* Tiffany.

FIGS. 241–243.—*Oedogonium illinoisense* Transeau.

FIG. 244.—*Oedogonium crassiusculum* Wittrock.

FIG. 245.—*Oedogonium crassiusculum* var. *cataractum* (Wolle) Tiffany.

FIG. 246.—*Oedogonium borisianum* (Le Clerc) Wittrock.

(Figs. 239, 240, 244–246, Tiffany; figs. 241–243, Transeau. All ×*300*.)

PLATE 25

(Figs. 239 to 246)

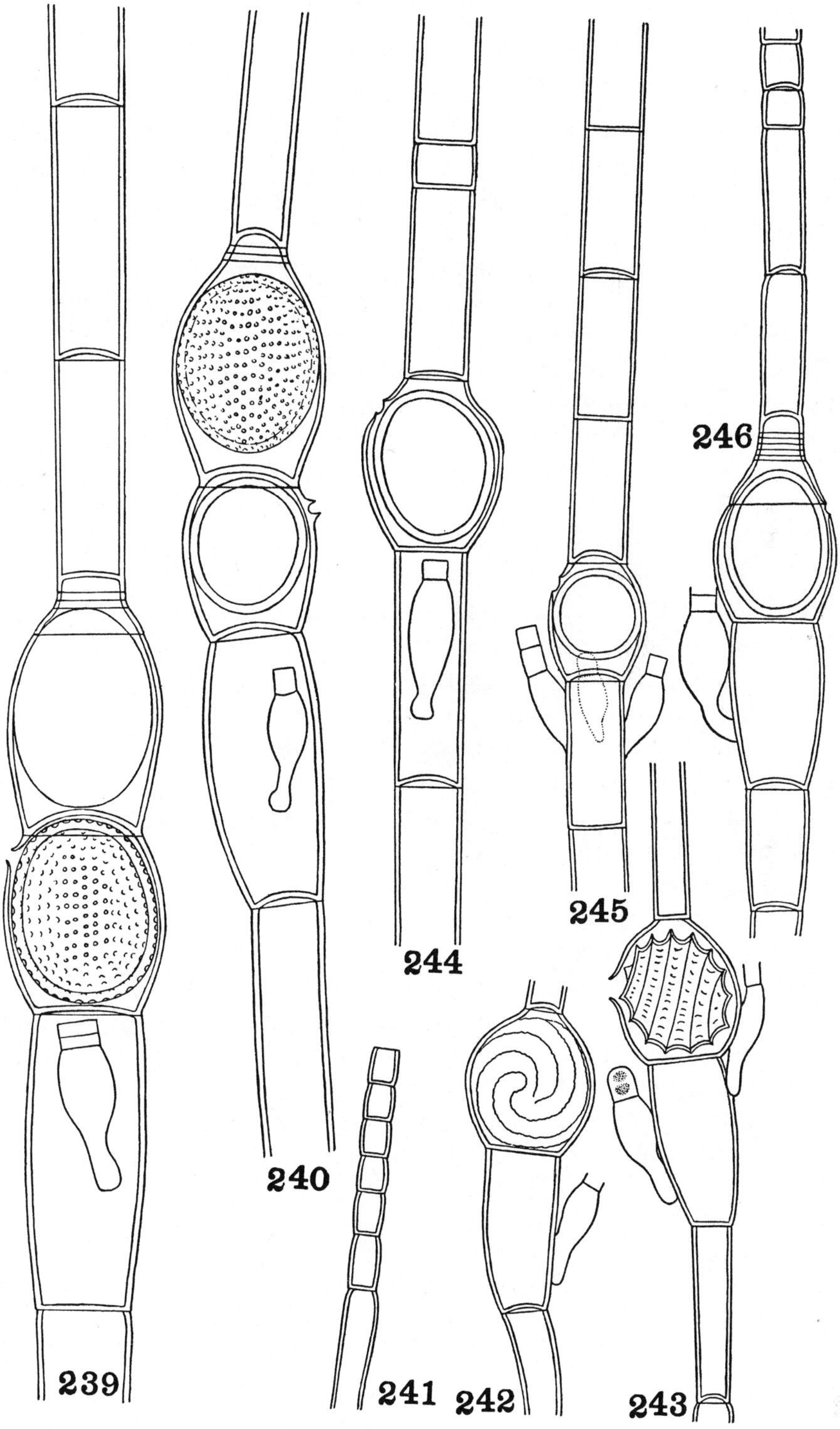

239 240 241 242 243 244 245 246

um 20–24 × 34–48 μ; oospore 19–23 × 32–41 μ; antheridium 9–13 × 4–7 μ. Pl. 23, fig. 212.

59. *Oedogonium oblongum* Wittrock. Monoecious; oogonium 1, oblong, operculate, division superior; oospore ellipsoid to ovoid, not filling oogonium longitudinally, spore-wall smooth; antheridia 1–3; sperms 2, division horizontal; basal cell elongate; vegetative cell 6–11 × 20–86 μ; oogonium 20–26 × 41–60 μ; oospore 19–23 × 30–36 μ; antheridium 6–9 × 7–9 μ. Pl. 23, fig. 218.

     a. Var. *majus* (Nordstedt) Hirn. Vegetative cell 8–11 × 35–75 μ; oogonium 26–28 × 42–50 μ; oospore 22–26 × 31–34 μ; antheridium 8–9 × 9–10 μ. Pl. 23, fig. 219.

60. *Oedogonium ouchitanum* Taft. Monoecious; oogonia 1–2, pyriform to subpyriform, opening by a superior operculum; oospore globose (rarely subglobose), not filling the oogonium longitudinally, its wall smooth; antheridia ?–3, scattered; vegetative cell capitellate; basal cell elongate; terminal cell obtuse; vegetative cell 5–13 × 33–50 μ; oogonium 30–33 × 33–40 μ; oospore 26–30 × 23–30 μ; antheridium 8–9 × 10–13 μ. Pl. 23, fig. 216.

61. *Oedogonium bohemicum* Hirn. Monoecious; oogonium 1, globose, operculate, division superior; oospore globose, filling oogonium, spore-walls smooth; antheridia 1–4, subepigynous; sperms 2, division horizontal; vegetative cell capitellate, 10–16 × 21–66 μ; oogonium 42–45 × 46–49 μ; oospore 40–43 × 40–43 μ; antheridium 9–10 × 5–7 μ. Pl. 22, fig. 204.

62. *Oedogonium undulatum* (Brébisson) A. Braun. Dioecious, nannandrous, gynandrosporous or idioandrosporous; oogonium 1 or 2, subglobose or ellipsoid-globose, operculate, division inferior, wide; oospore globose or subglobose, quite filling oogonium, spore-wall smooth, sometimes thick; androsporangia to 7-seriate; vegetative cell undulate (4 undulate constrictions); basal cell elongate, not undulate; terminal cell (sometimes oogonium) apically obtuse; dwarf male elongate-obconic, usually on suffultory cell, rarely on other vegetative cell near oogonium, antheridium interior; vegetative cell 15–22 × 45–110 μ; oogonium 48–56 × 50–75 μ; oospore 42–50 × 42–52 (–60) μ; androsporangium 15–21 × 7–14 μ; dwarf male 8–10 × 48–65 (–70) μ. Pl. 24, fig. 229.

FIGS. 247, 248.—*Oedogonium landsboroughi* (Hassall) Wittrock.

FIGS. 249, 250.—*Oedogonium wolleanum* Wittrock.

FIGS. 251, 252.—*Oedogonium cyathigerum* Wittrock.

FIGS. 253, 254.—*Oedogonium perfectum* (Hirn) Tiffany.

(Figs. 247, 248, 251, 252, Tiffany; figs. 249, 250, 253, 254, Hirn. All ×300.)

PLATE 26

(Figs. 247 to 254)

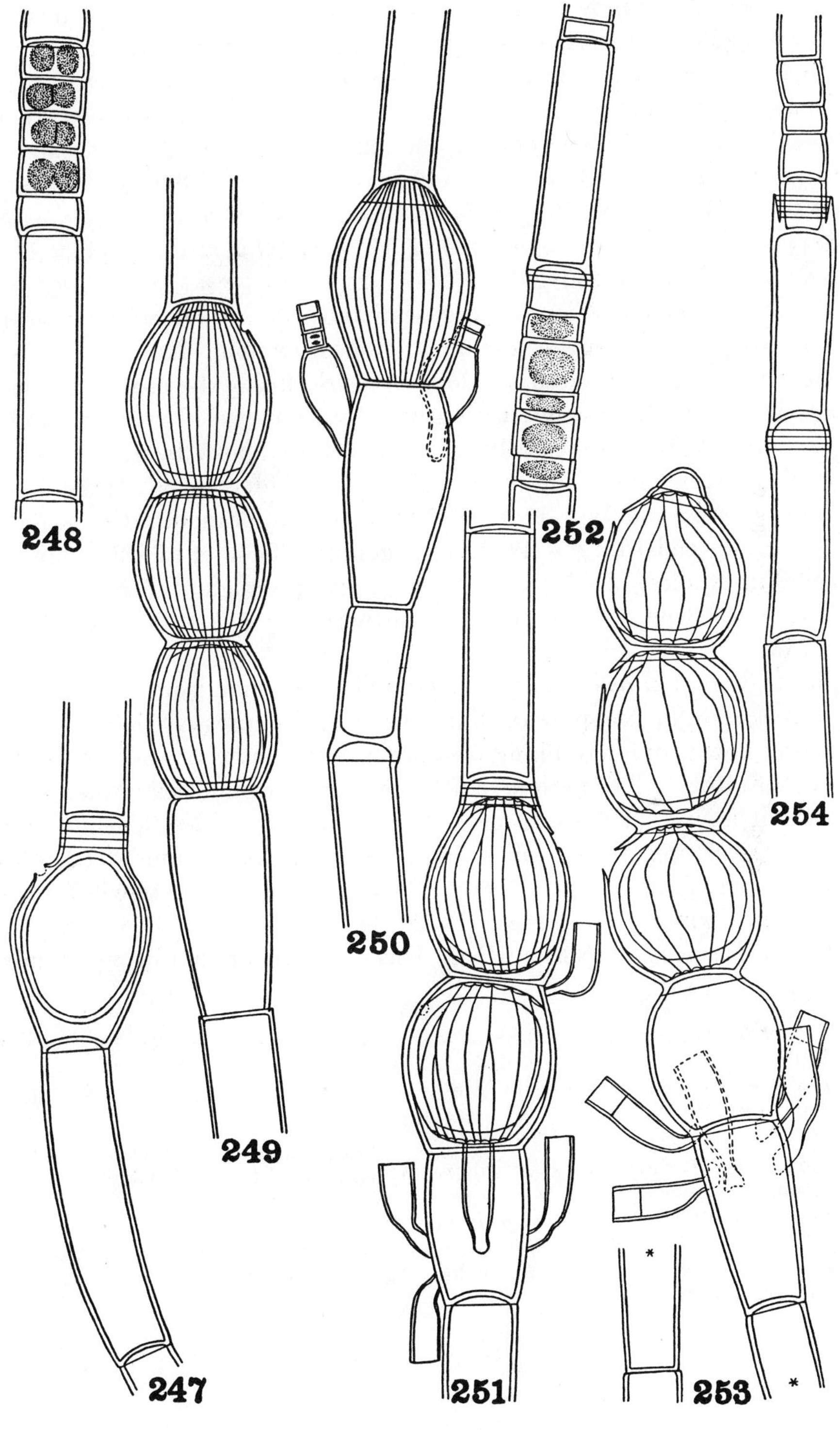

248

249

247

250

251

252

253

254

63. *Oedogonium illinoisense* Transeau. Dioecious, nannandrous, gynandrosporous; oogonium 1, subglobose to obovoid-globose, pore median; oospore globose or subglobose, nearly filling oogonium, outer spore-wall with 4–7 spiral ribs, uniting at poles, polar axis always transverse to axis of filament; suffultory cell enlarged; androsporangia 1–5; basal cell elongate; dwarf male slightly curved, on suffultory cell; antheridia exterior, 1–4; vegetative cell 13–18 × 80–140 μ; suffultory cell 32–40 × 50–80 μ; oogonium 51–60 × 60–70 μ; oospore 45–56 × 48–66 μ; androsporangium 13–17 × 17–22 μ; dwarf male stipe 14–17 × 37–57 μ; antheridium 9–12 × 15–23 μ. Pl. 25, figs. 241–243.

64. *Oedogonium hystricinum* Transeau and Tiffany. Dioecious, nannandrous, idioandrosporous; oogonium 1, globose or somewhat obovoid, pore median; oospore globose to subglobose, nearly filling the oogonium, outer spore-wall densely covered with spines; suffultory cell swollen; androsporangia 3–6; terminal cell obtuse; basal cell elongate; dwarf male nearly straight, resting on the suffultory cell, antheridium exterior, 1; vegetative cell of oogonial plants 8–15 × 42–100 μ; androsporangium 6–9 × 50–67 μ; suffultory cell 16–19 × 42–70 μ; oogonium 30–40 × 36–53 μ; oospore (including spines) 23–38 × 28–43 μ; androsporangium 6–8 × 8–15 μ; dwarf male stipe 6–10 × 20–32 μ; antheridium 5–6 × 6–10 μ. Pl. 27, fig. 258.

65. *Oedogonium aster* Wittrock. Dioecious, nannandrous; oogonium 1, subdepressed-globose, pore median; oospore subdepressed-globose or subglobose, not completely filling oogonium; outer layer of spore-wall echinate; suffultory cell sometimes a little swollen; terminal cell obtuse; dwarf male a little curved, on suffultory cell, stipe sometimes 2-celled, antheridia exterior, 1–2; vegetative cell 7–13 × 50–110 μ; oogonium 33–35 × 34–39 μ; oospore (with spines) 31–32 × 25–30 μ; dwarf male stipe 6–7 × 20–25 μ; antheridium 5–6 × 7–8 μ. Pl. 27, fig. 257.

66. *Oedogonium pungens* Hirn. Dioecious, nannandrous, gynandro-

Fig. 255.—*Oedogonium echinospermum* A. Braun.

Fig. 256.—*Oedogonium flavescens* (Hassall) Wittrock.

Fig. 257.—*Oedogonium aster* Wittrock.

Fig. 258.—*Oedogonium hystricinum* Transeau and Tiffany.

Figs. 259, 260.—*Oedogonium pungens* Hirn.

Figs. 261, 262.—*Oedogonium multisporum* H. C. Wood.

Fig. 263.—*Oedogonium irregulare* Wittrock.

Fig. 264.—*Oedogonium braunii* Kuetzing.

Figs. 265, 266.—*Oedogonium idioandrosporum* (Nordstedt and Wittrock) Tiffany.

(Figs. 255, 256, 258, 261–266, Tiffany; figs. 257, 259, 260, Hirn. All ×*300*.)

PLATE 27

(Figs. 255 to 266)

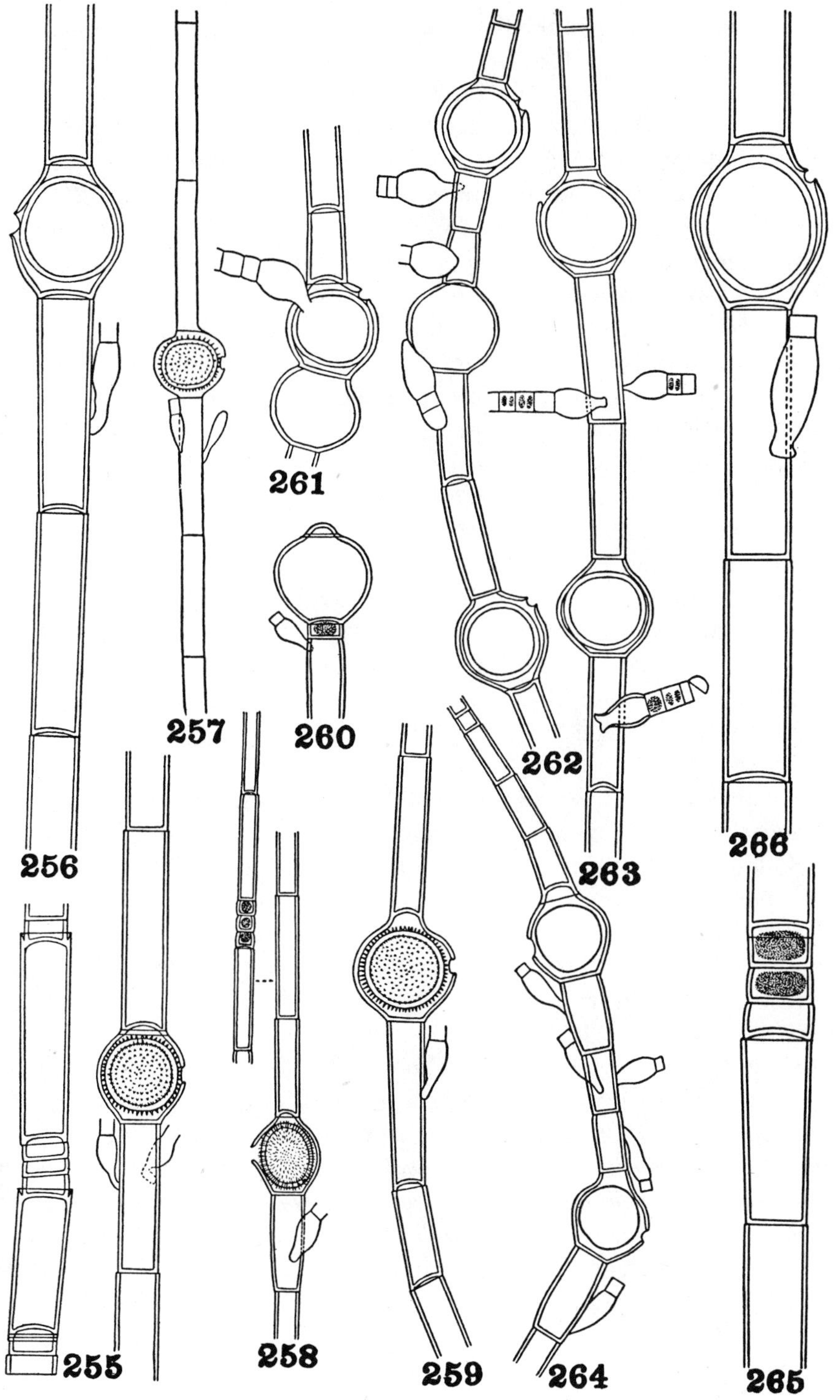

255 256 257 258 259 260 261 262 263 264 265 266

sporous; oogonium 1, subdepressed-globose (or nearly subglobose), pore median or a little above median; oospore subglobose, almost filling oogonium, outer spore-wall echinate; androsporangium 1–?, hypogynous; dwarf male a little curved, on suffultory cell, antheridia exterior, 1–2; vegetative cell 12–16 × 50–94 μ; oogonium 40–48 × 40–50 μ; oospore (with spines) 37–44 × 35–43 μ; androsporangium 14–16 × 10–15 μ; dwarf male stipe 9–12 × 20–30 μ; antheridium 6–7 × 8–12 μ. Pl. 27, figs. **259, 260.**

67. *Oedogonium echinospermum* A. Braun. Dioecious, nannandrous, gynandrosporous or idioandrosporous; oogonium 1, ellipsoid-globose or subglobose, pore median; oospore globose, quite filling oogonium, outer layer of spore-wall echinate; androsporangia 1–5; dwarf male a little curved, on suffultory cell, antheridia exterior, 1–2; vegetative cell 18–30 × 45–130 μ; oogonium 39–50 × 41–57 μ; oospore (with spines) 38–47 × 38–49 μ; androsporangium 21–25 × 9–15 μ; dwarf male stipe 10–15 × 26–35 μ; antheridium 6–12 × 6–15 μ. Pl. 27, fig. **255.**

68. *Oedogonium braunii* Kuetzing. Dioecious, nannandrous, gynandrosporous; oogonium 1, ovoid to subglobose, pore median; oospore globose, not filling oogonium, spore-wall smooth; androsporangia 1–2; basal cell elongate; terminal cell apically obtuse; dwarf male, usually on suffultory cell, stipe somewhat curved; antheridium exterior, 1; vegetative cell 13–15 × 25–60 μ; suffultory cell 16–20 × 28–50 μ; oogonium 30–37 × 33–43 μ; oospore 27–33 × 27–33 μ; androsporangium 13–15 × 11–12 μ; dwarf male stipe 7–12 × 20–28 μ; antheridium 5–8 × 9–10 μ. Pl. 27, fig. **264.**

69. *Oedogonium flavescens* (Hassall) Wittrock. Dioecious, nannandrous, idioandrosporous or gynandrosporous; oogonium 1, ellipsoid-globose to subglobose, pore median; oospore globose, not quite filling oogonium, spore-wall smooth; androsporangia 1–9; dwarf male somewhat curved, on the suffultory cell; antheridia 1–2; vegetative cell 18–23 × 72–140 μ; oogonium 49–52 × 51–60 μ; oospore 45–49 × 45–49 μ; androsporangium 17–20 × 8–18 μ; dwarf male stipe 11–12 × 36–45 μ; antheridium 9–10 × 15–20 μ. Pl. 27, fig. **256.**

70. *Oedogonium concatenatum* (Hassall) Wittrock. Dioecious, nannandrous, gynandrosporous; oogonia 1–6, subovoid or quadrangular-ellipsoid, pore superior; oospore of same form as oogonium, nearly filling it, outer layer of spore-wall smooth, middle layer with pits, more or less distinctly arranged in 30–35 longitudinal series, inner wall smooth; suffultory cell swollen; androsporangia 1–4; basal cell elongate; terminal cell obtuse; dwarf male curved, on suffultory cell; antheridia exterior, 1–4; vegetative cell 25–40 × 75–400 μ; suffultory cell 50–62 × 88–155 μ; oogonium 63–

83 × 76–105 μ; oospore 60–75 × 67–95 μ; androsporangium 25–28 × 15–36 μ; dwarf male stipe 17–25 × 50–75 μ; antheridium 13–15 × 12–25 μ. Pl. **25**, fig. **239**.

    a. Var. *superornatum* Tiffany. Smaller; oospore ellipsoid to globose; longitudinally arranged pits in 40–62 series; vegetative cell (19–) 25–45 × 64–160 μ; suffultory cell 51–61 × 115–134 μ; oogonium 56–77 × 68–112 μ; oospore 57–74 × 64–83 μ; androsporangium 27–32 × 12–32 μ; dwarf male stipe 16–22 × 52–73 μ; antheridium 9–13 × 11–22 μ. Pl. **25**, fig. **240**.

    71. *Oedogonium wolleanum* Wittrock. Dioecious, nannandrous, gynandrosporous or idioandrosporous; oogonia 1–4, subobovoid or quadrangular-ellipsoid, pore superior, wall with raised longitudinal lines on the inner surface; oospore of same form as oogonium, quite filling it, outer layer of spore-wall with 25–35 entire longitudinal ribs, rarely anastomosing, inner layer smooth; androsporangia 1–3, often subepigynous or scattered in the upper part of the filament; basal cell elongate; terminal cell, sometimes an oogonium, short-acute or acuminate; dwarf male on suffultory cell, stipe slightly curved; antheridia exterior, 1–3; vegetative cell 21–30 × 65–235 μ; suffultory cell 45–56 × 68–110 μ; oogonium 58–68 × 69–89 μ; oospore 56–66 × 65–83 μ; androsporangium 21–30 × 18–25 μ; dwarf male stipe 15–24 × 54–60 μ; antheridium 9–14 × 7–11 μ. Pl. **26**, figs. **249, 250**.

    72. *Oedogonium cyathigerum* Wittrock. Dioecious, nannandrous, idioandrosporous; oogonia 1–3, subobovoid or quadrangular-ellipsoid, pore superior; oospore same form as oogonium, filling it, outer layer of spore-wall smooth, the median with 16–25 longitudinal, continuous, rarely anastomosing, often curved, ridges—the inner smooth; basal cell elongate; terminal cell, often an oogonium, obtuse; dwarf male goblet-shaped, curved, on the suffultory cell or oogonium; antheridium interior; vegetative cell 21–30 × 40–300 μ; suffultory cell 42–48 × 75–110 μ; oogonium 57–66 × 70–100 μ; oospore 51–62 × 60–75 μ; androsporangium 23–30 × 12–30 μ; dwarf male cell 12–15 × 50–58 μ. Pl. **26**, figs. **251, 252**.

    73. *Oedogonium perfectum* (Hirn) Tiffany. Dioecious, nannandrous, idioandrosporous; oogonia 1–4, subobovoid to quadrangular-ellipsoid, pore superior; oospore of same form as oogonium and filling it; outer layer of spore-wall smooth, middle layer with 16–24 longitudinal, continuous, sometimes anastomosing, often curved ridges, inner layer smooth; androsporangia to 23-seriate; dwarf male goblet-shaped, curved, on suffultory cell or oogonium, antheridium interior; basal cell elongate; vegetative cell 22–35 × 65–350 μ; suffultory cell 37–56 × 56–152 μ; oogonium 65–85 × 72–111 μ; oospore 61–80 × 65–85 μ; androsporangium 21–30 × 15–30 μ; dwarf male 12–16 × 55–80 μ. Pl. **26**, figs. **253, 254**.

74. *Oedogonium borisianum* (Le Clerc) Wittrock. Dioecious, nannandrous, gynandrosporous; oogonia 1–5, obovoid or quadrangular-ellipsoid, pore superior; oospore ovoid to obovoid (often quadrangular-ovoid), not filling oogonium, spore-wall smooth; androsporangia 1–7, usually in the upper part of the filament; basal cell elongate; terminal cell, often an oogonium, broadly apiculate, obtuse, or sometimes setiferous; dwarf male, somewhat curved, on suffultory cell; antheridia 2; vegetative cell 15–23 × 45–140 μ; suffultory cell 31–38 × 50–92 μ; oogonium (33–) 40–50 × 55–90 μ; oospore 35–46 × 48–60 μ; androsporangium 16–19 × 15–23 μ; dwarf male stipe 12–18 × 35–47 μ; antheridium 7–10 × 11–16 μ. Pl. 25, fig. 246.

75. *Oedogonium multisporum* Wood. Dioecious, nannandrous; oogonia 1–3, subovoid or subglobose, pore superior; oospore globose, nearly filling oogonium, spore-wall smooth; dwarf male a little curved or nearly erect, near or on oogonium, antheridia exterior, 1–4; vegetative cell 10–15 × 10–30 μ; oogonium 24–35 × 27–33 μ; oospore 27–30 × 24–30 μ; dwarf male stipe 10–11 × 26–30 μ; antheridium 7–9 × 7–9 μ. Pl. 27, figs. 261, 262.

76. *Oedogonium irregulare* Wittrock. Dioecious, nannandrous; oogonium 1, globose or rarely subdepressed-globose, pore superior; oospore globose, completely filling oogonium, spore-wall smooth; dwarf male erect, on or near oogonium, antheridia exterior, 1–4; vegetative cell 15–20 × 40–80 μ; oogonium 37–45 × 36–47 μ; oospore 36–42 × 34–41 μ; dwarf male stipe 12–15 × 20–24 μ; antheridium 10–12 × 6–8 μ. Pl. 27, fig. 263.

77. *Oedogonium crassiusculum* Wittrock. Dioecious, nannandrous, gynandrosporous; oogonia 1–2, globose-obovoid or subglobose, pore superior; oospore ellipsoid-globose or globose, spore-wall smooth and thickened, quite filling oogonium; androsporangia 2–5; dwarf male suberect, on or near suffultory cell, antheridium exterior, 1–?; vegetative cell 27–30 × 95–105 μ; oogonium 54–60 × 60–75 μ; oospore 51–57 × 52–63 μ; androsporangium 26–28 × 10–18 μ; dwarf male 13–60 μ; antheridium 7–9 × 9–16 μ. Pl. 25, fig. 244.

a. Var. *cataractum* (Wolle) Tiffany. Idioandrosporous; oogonia 1–2, often terminal, obovoid-globose or subglobose or broadly ovoid, pore superior; oospore globose or obovoid-globose, nearly filling oogonium; androsporangia 1–6; dwarf male curved, on suffultory cell or below; vegetative cell 28–38 × 42–112 μ; oogonium 55–60 × 60–75 μ; oospore 50–55 × 50–60 μ; androsporangium 26–30 × 10–15 μ; dwarf male 10–65 μ. Pl. 25, fig. 245.

78. *Oedogonium idioandrosporum* (Nordstedt and Wittrock) Tiffany. Dioecious, nannandrous, idioandrosporous; oogonia 1–3, globose-obovoid to globose, pore superior; oospore ellipsoid-globose, ovoid, or angu-

lar-globose (rarely globose), nearly filling the oogonium, spore-wall smooth and thick; androsporangia 1–4; dwarf male straight or slightly curved, on or near the suffultory cell; antheridium exterior, 1 or 2; vegetative cell 25–36 × 65–200 μ; oogonium 48–59 × 57–90 μ; oospore 42–57 × 50–66 μ; androsporangium 30–34 × 12–21 μ; dwarf male stipe 14–16 × 60–70 μ; antheridium 8–10 × 10–18 μ. Pl. 27, figs. 265, 266.

79. *Oedogonium longicolle* Nordstedt. Dioecious, nannandrous; oogonia 1–7, pyriform, often vertically elongate, operculate, division median and narrow; oospore subdepressed-globose or subglobose, inflating oogonium medianly, not filling it longitudinally, spore-wall smooth; basal cell subhemispheric; dwarf male unicellular, obovoid, minute, on oogonium; vegetative cell 4–6 × 16–45 μ; oogonium 13–16 × 16–32 μ; oospore 12–15 × 10–16 μ; dwarf male 2 × 4 μ; basal cell 14 × 6 μ. Pl. 24, figs. 224, 225.

80. *Oedogonium rothii* Pringsheim. Dioecious, nannandrous, gynandrosporous; oogonia 1–3, subdepressed-globose, operculate, division median, narrow; oospore depressed-globose, almost filling oogonium, spore-wall smooth; androsporangia 1–4, subhypogynous, hypogynous, subepigynous, or scattered; vegetative cell 6–10 × 20–76 μ; oogonium 20–27 × 16–27 μ; oospore 17–25 × 14–20 μ; androsporangium 6–8 × 5–10 μ; dwarf male 4 × 11–12 μ. Pl. 23, fig. 215.

81. *Oedogonium macrospermum* West and West. Dioecious, nannandrous, gynandrosporous; oogonium 1 (rarely 2), subdepressed- to depressed-globose, operculate, division median, narrow; oospore subdepressed-globose, filling the oogonium, spore-wall smooth; dwarf male slightly curved or straight, not infrequently at right angles to the filament, on suffultory cell or on oogonium or scattered; antheridia exterior, 1–4; basal cell elongate; androsporangium 1–?; vegetative cell 10–16 × 30–80 μ; oogonium 39–46 × 34–44 μ; oospore 36–44 × 32–42 μ; dwarf male stipe 9–14 × 16–30 μ; androsporangium 14–15 × 10–11 μ; antheridium 7–10 × 6–16 μ. Pl. 24, figs. 237, 238.

82. *Oedogonium decipiens* Wittrock. Dioecious, nannandrous, gynandrosporous; oogonia 1–3, subdepressed-globose, operculate, division median, rather narrow; oospore subdepressed- or depressed-globose, almost filling the oogonium, spore-wall smooth; androsporangia 1–6, subepigynous, hypogynous, or scattered; dwarf male unicellular, usually on the oogonium; vegetative cell 9–12 × 28–80 μ; oogonium 30–38 × 27–40 μ; oospore 25–34 × 23–38 μ; androsporangium 9–10 × 8–15 μ; dwarf male 6–7 × 13–15 μ. Pl. 24, fig. 233.

a. Var. *africanum* Tiffany. Smaller and idioandrosporous; vegetative cell 8–13 × 25–60 μ; oogonium 25–32 × 24–32 μ; oospore 24–30 × 23–28 μ; androsporangium 7–11 × 9–13 μ; dwarf male 6–7 × 9–12 μ. Pl. 24, fig. 236.

b. Var. *dissimile* (Hirn) Tiffany. Gynandrosporous; vegetative cells, evidently capitellate, 8–14 × 20–65 μ; oogonium 28–35 × 23–38 μ; oospore 23–34 × 21–30 μ; androsporangium 8–9 × 6–10 μ; dwarf male 5–6 × 11–14 μ. Pl. 24, figs. 234, 235.

83. *Oedogonium subplenum* Tiffany. Dioecious, nannandrous, idioandrosporous and gynandrosporous; oogonia 1–3, depressed-globose to depressed-pyriform-globose, division median and wide; oospore globose, not filling oogonium, its wall smooth; androsporangia to 11-seriate; dwarf male obovoid, 1-celled, on oogonium; vegetative cell, capitellate, 7–12 × 23–80 μ; oogonium 29–38 × 26–41 μ; oospore 21–28 × 19–26 μ; androsporangium 7–10 × 7–11 μ; dwarf male 6–7 × 6–10 μ. Pl. 28, fig. 269.

84. *Oedogonium croasdaleae* Jao. Dioecious, nannandrous, gynandrosporous; oogonia 1–7, generally on the upper portion of the filament, quadrangular-ellipsoid, subovoid, or subellipsoid, operculate, division superior, sometimes wide; oospore of the same form as the oogonium and filling it, rarely not reaching the lower end; spore-membrane of three layers, the outer smooth, the median thick and lamellose, with 16–30 anastomosing, irregularly undulate, longitudinal ribs, the inner granulate; suffultory cell tumid; androsporangia to 8-seriate, epigynous, rarely hypogynous or subhypogynous; dwarf male goblet-shaped, curved, on the suffultory cell, occasionally on the oogonium, antheridium 1, interior; filaments tapering toward the base; terminal cell obtuse, often an oogonium or androsporangium; vegetative cell 20–30 × 95–230 μ; oogonium 56–77 × 88–116 μ; oospore 54–73 × 77–105 μ; suffultory cell 39–72 × 70–147 μ; androsporangium 10–55 × 7–77 μ; dwarf male 10–15 × 55–63 μ. Pl. 28, figs. 272–275.

85. *Oedogonium monile* Berkeley and Harvey. Dioecious, nannandrous; oogonia 1–8, subovoid or subglobose, operculate, division superior, very broad; oospore globose or subglobose, quite filling oogonium (except in length), spore-wall of three layers: outer layer smooth, middle layer scro-

Figs. 267, 268.—*Oedogonium praticolum* Transeau.

Fig. 269.—*Oedogonium subplenum* Tiffany.

Fig. 270.—*Oedogonium acrosporum* De-Bary.

Fig. 271.—*Oedogonium tentoriale* Nordstedt and Hirn.

Figs. 272–275.—*Oedogonium croasdaleae* Jao.

(Figs. 267–271, Tiffany; figs. 272–275, Jao. All ×*300*.)

PLATE 28

(Figs. 267 to 275)

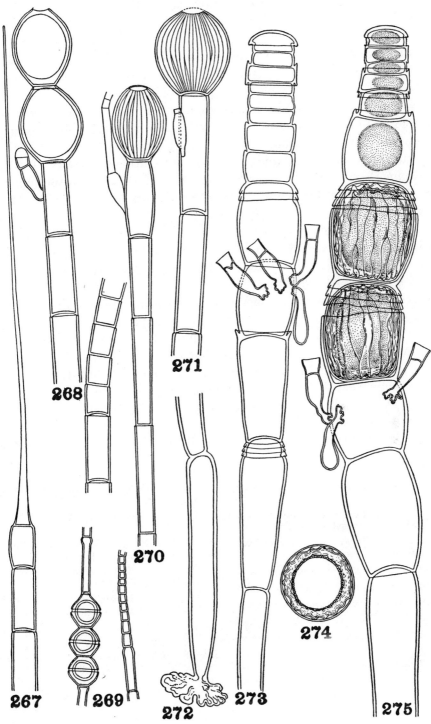

267   268   269   270   271   272   273   274   275

biculate, inner layer smooth; vegetative cell sometimes capitellate; basal cell elongate; terminal cell obtuse; dwarf male a little curved, near oogonium, antheridium exterior, 1–?; vegetative cell 9–15 × 50–160 μ; suffultory cell 21–29 × 40–57 μ; oogonium 30–39 × 30–56 μ; oospore 28–38 × 28–38 μ; dwarf male stipe 9 × 25 μ; antheridium 7 × 7 μ. Pl. 24, figs. 222, 223.

86. *Oedogonium rugulosum* Nordstedt. Dioecious, nannandrous, gynandrosporous; oogonia 1 or 2, obovoid or obovoid-ellipsoid, operculate, division superior; oospore ellipsoid, nearly filling oogonium (or rarely globose-ellipsoid, not filling oogonium), spore-wall smooth; dwarf male on or near oogonium; androsporangium usually 1, hypogynous; antheridium exterior, 1–?, curved; terminal cell apically obtuse; vegetative cell 4–8 × 10–35 μ; oogonium 16–20 × 22–29 μ; oospore 15–18 × 19–25 μ; androsporangium 6–8 × 10–11 μ; antheridium 4–5 × 5–6 μ; dwarf male 5–7 × 11–14 μ. Pl. 24, fig. 231.

a. Var. *minutum* (Hansgirg) Tiffany. Smaller; median spore-wall distinctly crenulate; vegetative cell 3–7 × 12–40 μ; oogonium 13–18 × 18–24 μ; oospore 12–17 × 15–20 μ; dwarf male 4–6 × 13–16 μ; antheridium 5–6 × 6–9 μ. Pl. 24, fig. 232.

87. *Oedogonium macrandrium* Wittrock. Dioecious, nannandrous; oogonia 1–4, globose-ovoid, operculate, division superior; oospore globose, rarely ovoid-globose, not completely filling the oogonium, spore-wall smooth; terminal cell obtuse or very shortly apiculate; dwarf male on or near the oogonium, stipe much curved, sometimes 2–3-celled; antheridia 1–7; vegetative cell 15–20 × 45–100 μ; oogonium 36–42 × 43–54 μ; oospore 31–37 × 33–39 μ; dwarf male stipe 12–13 × 24–33 μ; antheridium 9–10 × 7–10 μ. Pl. 24, fig. 226.

a. Var. *aemulans* Hirn. Vegetative cell 10–16 × 22–90 μ; oogonia 2–9–

Fig. 276.—*Schizomeris leibleinii* Kuetzing.

Fig. 277.—*Chlorococcum humicola* (Naegeli) Rabenhorst, vegetative cells.

Fig. 278.—*Chlorococcum humicola* (Naegeli) Rabenhorst, zoospore.

Fig. 279.—*Golenkinia radiata* Chodat.

Fig. 280.—*Chlorella vulgaris* Beijerinck.

Fig. 281.—*Chlorella parasitica* Brandt.

Fig. 282.—*Chlorella conductrix* Brandt.

Fig. 283.—*Sorastrum spinulosum* Naegeli.

Fig. 284.—*Characium naegelii* A. Braun.

Fig. 285.—*Characium pringsheimii* A. Braun.

Fig. 286.—*Characium ambiguum* Hermann.

Fig. 287.—*Kentrosphaera facciolae* Borzi, vegetative cell and zoospores.

Fig. 288.—*Chlorochytrium lemnae* Cohn, within tissues of *Lemna*.

Fig. 289.—*Hydrodictyon reticulatum* (Linnaeus) Lagerheim.

(Figs. 276, 279, 280, 283, 284, 286, Tiffany; figs. 277, 278, Smith; fig. 287, Borzi; fig. 288, Klebs. Figs. 276, 280–283, 287 ×600; figs. 277–279, 284–286 ×1000.)

PLATE 29

(Figs. 276 to 289)

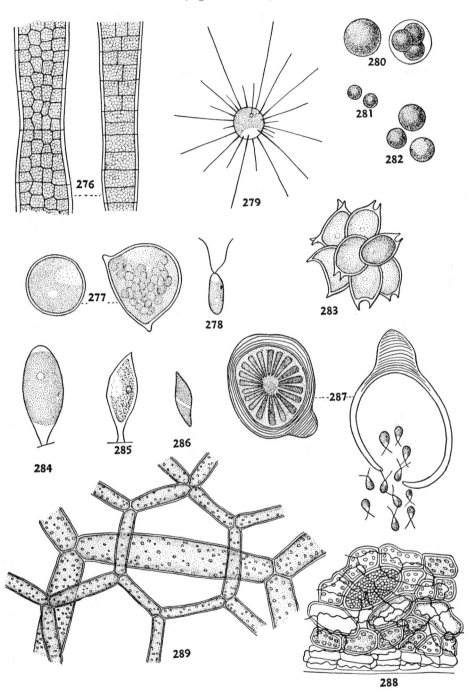

276

279

280

281

282

277

278

283

284

285

286

287

288

289

seriate, 28–42 × 33–45 μ; oospore 26–36 × 26–36 μ; dwarf male stipe 9–12 × 20–25 μ; antheridium 6–9 × 7–10 μ. Pl. 24, fig. 228.

b. Var. *propinquum* (Wittrock) Hirn. Smaller; oogonia 1–3; vegetative cell 8–14 × 18–70 μ; oogonium 28–36 × 28–45 μ; oospore 24–31 × 24–31 μ; dwarf male stipe 11–14 × 20–35 μ; antheridium 7–12 × 6–8 μ. Pl. 24, fig. 227.

88. *Oedogonium obtruncatum* Wittrock. Dioecious, nannandrous, gynandrosporous; oogonia 1–6, ellipsoid or globose-ellipsoid, operculate, division supreme, operculum small and deciduous; oospore of same form as oogonium, nearly filling it, spore-wall smooth; vegetative cell evidently capitellate; basal cell elongate, terminal cell (often the oogonium) apically obtuse; dwarf male oblong-pyriform, curved, unicellular, on oogonium; vegetative cell 18–22 × 56–110 μ; oogonium 45–55 × 56–68 μ; oospore 43–53 × 52–66 μ; androsporangium 20 × 24 μ; dwarf male stipe 17–20 × 36–40 μ; antheridium 6–8 × 4–6 μ. Pl. 24, fig. 230.

89. *Oedogonium praticolum* Transeau. Dioecious, nannandrous, idioandrosporous; oogonia 1–7, ellipsoid to globose-ellipsoid, often terminal, sometimes scattered, wall sometimes rather thick, operculate, division supreme, lid small and deciduous; oospore ellipsoid to globose-ellipsoid, quite filling the oogonium, wall smooth; androsporangia 1–20; vegetative cell slightly capitellate; basal cell usually elongate; terminal cell apiculate or extended into a long hyaline seta; antheridium exterior, 1; vegetative cell, female 16–26 × 65–130 μ; vegetative cell of androsporangial filament 14–22 × 56–110 μ; oogonium 48–60 × 62–74 μ; oospore 46–58 × 60–72 μ; androsporangium 20–24 × 18–22 μ; dwarf male stipe 8–14 × 21–28 μ; antheridium 6–10 × 7–12 μ. Pl. 28, figs. 267, 268.

90. *Oedogonium acrosporum* DeBary. Dioecious, nannandrous, gynandrosporous (or idioandrosporous); oogonium 1, terminal, ellipsoid, operculate, division supreme, operculum small and deciduous; wall of oogonium

FIGS. 290, 291.—*Pediastrum simplex* Meyen.

FIG. 292.—*Pediastrum simplex* var. *duodenarium* (Bailey) Rabenhorst.

FIG. 293.—*Pediastrum tetras* (Ehrenberg) Ralfs.

FIG. 294.—*Pediastrum tetras* var. *tetraodon* (Corda) Hansgirg.

FIGS. 295, 296.—*Pediastrum boryanum* (Turpin) Meneghini.

FIG. 297.—*Pediastrum boryanum* var. *longicorne* Raciborski.

FIG. 298.—*Pediastrum integrum* Naegeli.

FIG. 299.—*Pediastrum angulosum* (Ehrenberg) Meneghini, part of colony.

FIG. 300.—*Pediastrum duplex* Meyen.

FIG. 301.—*Pediastrum duplex* var. *clathratum* (A. Braun) Lagerheim.

FIG. 302.—*Pediastrum duplex* var. *rotundatum* Lucks.

(Figs. 290, 291, 293, 298, 302, Tiffany; figs. 294, 295–297, 300, 301, Smith; fig. 299, Taft. All ×600.)

PLATE 30

(Figs. 290 to 302)

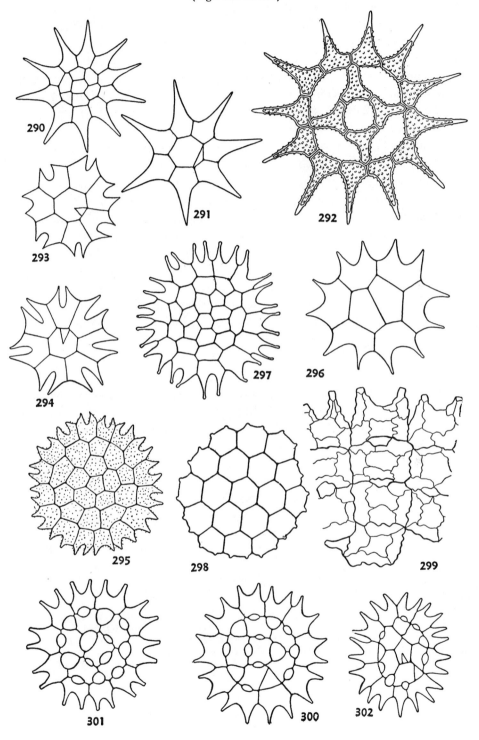

with longitudinal, sometimes anastomosing, ridges on the inner surface; oospore quite filling the oogonium, outer layer of spore-wall with 23–30 longitudinal ridges, closely fitting in between the ridges of the oogonium, the inner smooth; basal cell elongate; terminal cell obtuse; androsporangia 1–8, hypogynous or scattered; dwarf male curved, on the suffultory cell, stipe sometimes 2–3-celled, upper cells long, antheridia exterior, 1 or 2; vegetative cell 12–21 × 40–125 μ; suffultory cell 16–25 × 26–76 μ; oogonium 35–48 × 50–63 μ; androsporangium 16–21 × 12–15 μ; upper cell of dwarf male stipe 6–8 × 55–71 μ; the lower cell 9–12 × 30–38 μ; antheridium 6–8 × 9–15 μ. Pl. **28**, fig. **270**.

91. *Oedogonium tentoriale* Nordstedt and Hirn. Dioecious, nannandrous; oogonium 1, terminal, broadly ellipsoid or obovoid-globose, division supreme, lid small, deciduous, oogonium-wall longitudinally ribbed on the inner surface, ribs often anastomosate; oospore quite filling oogonium, outer layer of the spore-wall with 40–45 longitudinal, very finely crenulate ribs, closely filling in between the ribs of the oogonium, connected by delicate transverse lines, the inner layer smooth; basal cell elongate; terminal cell obtuse; dwarf male suberect, on suffultory cell, antheridium exterior, 1–?; vegetative cell 20–33 (–37) × 60–225 μ; oogonium 66–82 × 73–88 μ; oospore 64–80 × 70–83 μ; dwarf male stipe 10–15 × 37–48 μ; antheridium 9–12 × 7 μ. Pl. **28**, fig. **271**.

92. *Oedogonium landsboroughi* (Hassall) Wittrock. Dioecious, macrandrous; oogonia 1 or 2 (rarely 3), obovoid to ovoid, pore superior; oospore ovoid to ellipsoid, filling or not filling the oogonium; spore-wall smooth; antheridia up to 30-seriate; sperms 2, division vertical; basal cell elongate;

FIG. 303.—*Dactylococcus infusionum* Naegeli.

FIG. 304.—*Dictyosphaerium ehrenbergianum* Naegeli.

FIG. 305.—*Dictyosphaerium pulchellum* Wood.

FIG. 306.—*Closteriopsis longissima* Lemmermann.

FIG. 307.—*Ankistrodesmus falcatus* (Corda) Ralfs.

FIG. 308.—*Kirchneriella lunaris* (Kirchner) Moebius.

FIG. 309.—*Kirchneriella obesa* (W. West) Schmidle var. *major* (Bernard) G. M. Smith.

FIG. 310.—*Coelastrum cambricum* Archer, coenobium with daughter colony.

FIG. 311.—*Coelastrum reticulatum* (Dangeard) Senn, coenobium with daughter colony.

FIG. 312.—*Coelastrum microporum* Naegeli.

FIG. 313.—*Coelastrum sphaericum* Naegeli.

FIG. 314.—*Dimorphococcus lunatus* A. Braun.

(Figs. 303, 304, 308–311, G. M. Smith; figs. 312, 313, Tiffany; fig. 314, by permission from *Fresh-water Algae of the United States.* Copyright 1933. McGraw-Hill Book Co., Inc. Fig. 314 ×*1000;* all others ×*600*.)

PLATE 31

(Figs. 303 to 314)

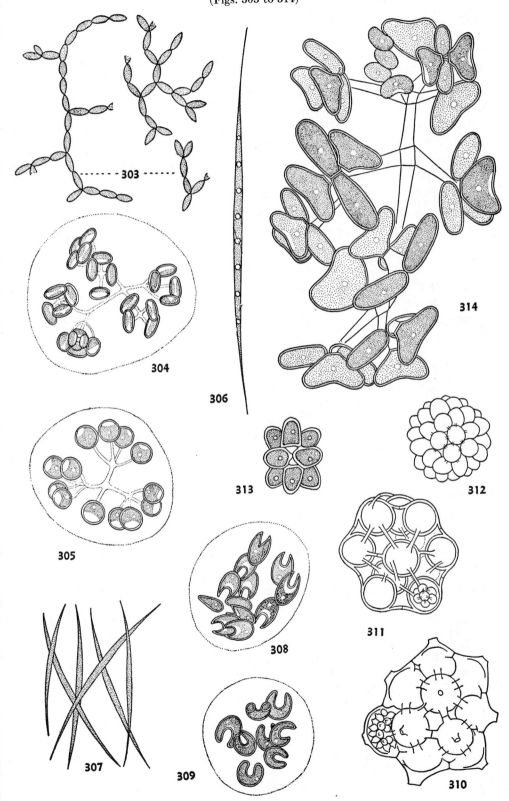

303

304

305

306

307

308

309

310

311

312

313

314

terminal cell obtuse; female vegetative cell 31–40 × 90–240 μ, male 30–37 × 120–225 μ; oogonium 63–78 × 85–115 μ; oospore (55–) 59–70 × 73–102 μ; antheridium 27–35 × 9–20 μ. (Reported from Pope County by Phinney, 1946.) Pl. 26, figs. 247, 248.

93. *Oedogonium reinschii* Roy. Monoecious; oogonia 1 or 2, globose or depressed-globose, rarely terminal, with wide median operculum; oospore similar in shape to oogonium, filling it or not, its wall smooth; antheridium subepigynous or subhypogynous; sperms 2, division vertical; vegetative cell often subhexagonal or subellipsoid, sometimes cylindric or subcylindric; basal cell subhemispheric; terminal cell apically obtuse; vegetative cell 5–11 × 9–24 μ; oogonium 17–20 × 15–21 μ; oospore 13–18 × 14–17 μ; antheridium 4–5 × 4–5 μ; basal cell 8–16 × 5–10 μ. (Reported from Pope County by Phinney, 1946.) Pl. 18, fig. 149.

Order ULVALES

Uninucleate cells forming flat sheets, hollow tubes or solid cylinders and having a single laminate, parietal chromatophore; zoospores, aplanospores, akinetes; isogamy or anisogamy; some genera with similar haploid and diploid alternating phases; largely marine.

Family Schizomeridaceae

At first a simple uniseriate filament apically acuminate and with a basal holdfast; at maturity a solid cylinder, multiseriate, sometimes irregularly constricted; chromatophores band-like or massive, usually with several pyrenoids; fragmentation, zoospores: sexual reproduction reported.

Schizomeris Kuetzing 1843

Filamentous; uniseriate with apical cell somewhat acuminate and with holdfast cell when young; older filaments solid cylinders of brick-like cells; filaments cylindrical or constricted at intervals; cells with ring-like

FIG. 315.—*Nephrocytium agardhianum* Naegeli.

FIG. 316.—*Nephrocytium lunatum* W. West, side and end views.

FIG. 317.—*Gloeotaenium loitlesbergerianum* Hansgirg.

FIG. 318.—*Oocystis elliptica* W. West.

FIG. 319.—*Oocystis solitaria* Wittrock.

FIG. 320.—*Oocystis naegelii* A. Braun.

FIG. 321.—*Oocystis gigas* Archer.

FIG. 322.—*Oocystis borgei* Snow.

FIG. 323.—*Oocystis crassa* Wittrock.

FIG. 324.—*Schroederia setigera* (Schroeder) Lemmermann.

FIG. 325.—*Selenastrum bibraianum* Reinsch.

FIG. 326.—*Selenastrum bibraianum* var. *gracile* Tiffany and Ahlstrom.

(Figs. 315–317, 324–326, Tiffany; figs. 318, 319, 322, 323, G. M. Smith; fig. 321, G. S. West. All ×*600*.)

PLATE 32

(Figs. 315 to 326)

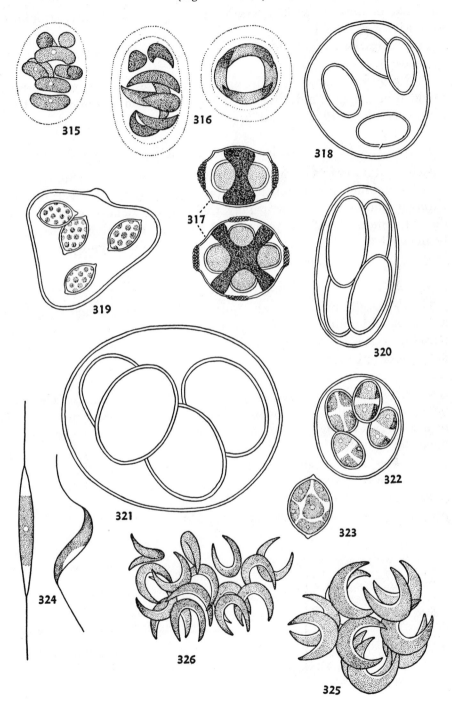

transverse walls, sometimes not extending to the surface; chromatophore band-like or massive with several pyrenoids or several chromatophores, each with a pyrenoid.

Fragmentation; quadriflagellate zoospores; aplanospores; biflagellate gametes(?).

1. *Schizomeris leibleinii* Kuetzing. Vegetative cell 10–20 × 10–30 μ, rounded or angular; older filaments up to 150 μ in diameter and 10–20 centimeters long. Pl. **29,** fig. **276.**

Order CHLOROCOCCALES

Cells solitary or in a colonial aggregate of a definite or indefinite number of cells, uninucleate or multinucleate, without vegetative cell division; chromatophores varied but usually well-defined: band-like, cup-shaped, discoid, sometimes diffuse; pyrenoids 1 to many in a cell; zoospores usually biflagellate, aplanospores (in some genera only aplanospores occur); isogamy, anisogamy, oogamy.

Family **Chlorococcaceae**

Cells generally unicellular and uninucleate, sometimes aggregated into a stratum and multinucleate at maturity; chromatophore cup-shaped and parietal or stellate and axial, with 1 to many pyrenoids; zoosporic or aplanosporic; isogamy.

Chlorococcum Fries 1820

Cells spherical, or angular in masses, terrestrial or aquatic; chromatophore parietal, bell-shaped or spherical, with 1 pyrenoid when young, diffuse with several pyrenoids when older; cells uninucleate; later multinucleate.

Zoospores, aplanospores, isogamous gametes, *Palmella*-stages.

1. *Chlorococcum humicola* (Naegeli) Rabenhorst. Cell 3–25 μ in diameter; solitary or in small aggregates; forming thin coatings on moist places, especially on damp soil. Pl. **29,** figs. **277, 278.**

FIG. 327.—*Actinastrum hantzschii* Lagerheim.

FIG. 328.—*Actinastrum hantzschii* var. *fluviatile* Schroeder.

FIG. 329.—*Micractinium pusillum* Fresenius.

FIG. 330.—*Micractinium quadrisetum* (Lemmermann) G. M. Smith.

FIG. 331.—*Crucigenia tetrapedia* (Kirchner) W. and G. S. West.

FIG. 332.—*Crucigenia lauterbornei* Schmidle.

FIG. 333.—*Crucigenia rectangularis* (Naegeli) Gay.

FIG. 334.—*Crucigenia irregularis* Wille.

(Figs. 327, 328, 331, 332, Smith; figs. 329, 330, 334, Tiffany. All ×600.)

PLATE 33

(Figs. 327 to 334)

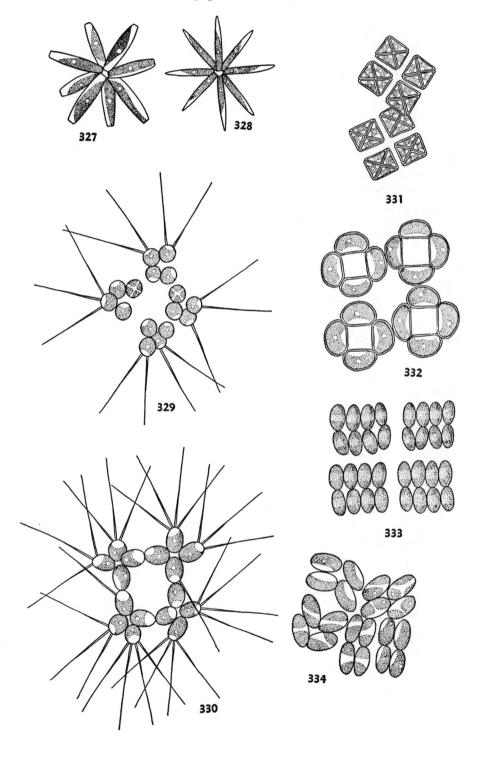

Family Micractiniaceae

Cells spherical to ellipsoid, solitary or united into coenobia of definite shape, sometimes surrounded by hyaline gelatinous sheaths, and bearing 1 or more setae; without vegetative cell division; chromatophores cup-shaped, with a single pyrenoid; zoospores, autospores; oogamy.

Golenkinia Chodat 1894

Cells spherical, solitary or rarely in temporary colonies, with hyaline, slightly tapering setae; chromatophore single, parietal and cup-shaped or entirely filling cell, with 1 pyrenoid.

Zoospores, autospores; oogamy.

1. *Golenkinia radiata* Chodat. Cells 7–15 μ in diameter, chromatophore single, cup-shaped, parietal, 1 pyrenoid; setae 24–45 μ long. Pl. **29**, fig. **279.**

Micractinium Fresenius 1858

Cells spherical to broadly ellipsoid, in colonies of 4–32, quadrately arranged or tetrahedrically disposed; cell-wall with 1–7 setae, not thickened at the base, on the free surface of the cell; chromatophore single, parietal, cup-shaped, with 1 pyrenoid.

Formation of autospores, liberated as an autocolony by division of cell contents and rupture of old mother-cell wall into 4 parts; oogamy (single egg partly protruding from female cell at fertilization).

KEY TO THE SPECIES

1. Cells spherical... 1. M. pusillum
1. Cells ovoid.. 2. M. quadrisetum

FIG. 335.—*Tetraedron minimum* (A. Braun) Hansgirg.

FIG. 336.—*Tetraedron minimum* f. *tetralobulatum* Reinsch.

FIG. 337.—*Tetraedron muticum* (A. Braun) Hansgirg.

FIG. 338.—*Tetraedron muticum* f. *punctulatum* (Reinsch) DeToni.

FIG. 339.—*Tetraedron gracile* (Reinsch) Hansgirg.

FIG. 340.—*Tetraedron trigonum* (Naegeli) Hansgirg.

FIG. 341.—*Tetraedron trigonum* var. *tetragonum* (Naegeli) Rabenhorst.

FIG. 342.—*Tetraedron trigonum* var. *minus* Reinsch.

FIG. 343.—*Tetraedron gigas* (Wittrock) Hansgirg.

FIG. 344.—*Tetraedron lobulatum* (Naegeli) Hansgirg.

FIG. 345.—*Tetraedron regulare* Kuetzing.

FIG. 346.—*Tetraedron bifurcatum* (Wille) Lagerheim.

FIG. 347.—*Tetraedron limneticum* Borge.

FIG. 348.—*Tetraedron quadratum* (Reinsch) Hansgirg.

FIG. 349.—*Tetraedron quadratum* f. *minus-acutum* Reinsch.

FIG. 350.—*Treubaria crassispina* G. M. Smith.

FIG. 351.—*Trochiscia reticularis* (Reinsch) Hansgirg.

FIG. 352.—*Trochiscia arguta* (Reinsch) Hansgirg.

(Figs. 335–340, 344, 345, 347, 350, 351, Smith; fig. 343, Wittrock; fig. 346, West. All ×600.)

PLATE 34

(Figs. 335 to 352)

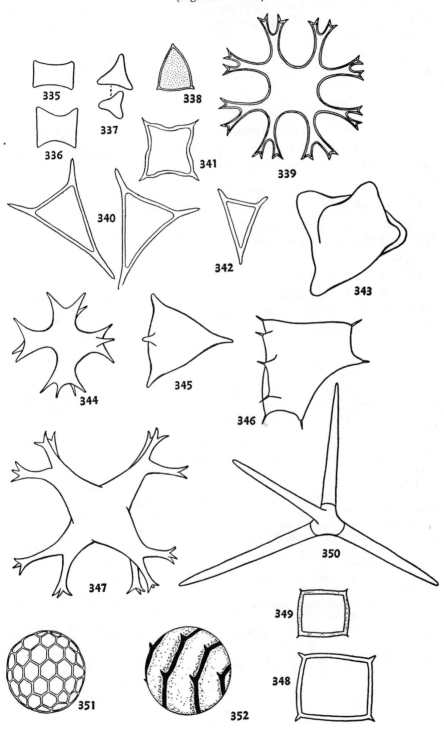

1. *Micractinium pusillum* Fresenius. Cells 3–7 μ in diameter, spherical, quadrately or pyramidately arranged, with 1–5 setae; setae 20–35 μ long. Pl. **33**, fig. **329**.

2. *Micractinium quadrisetum* (Lemmermann) G. M. Smith. Cells 4–7 × 8–10 μ, ovoid, with 1–4 setae, 23–40 μ long. Pl. **33**, fig. **330**.

Family **Endosphaeraceae**

Cells solitary, usually irregularly shaped, with parietal or central chromatophores having 1 or more pyrenoids; gamete-like zoospores; cells may be diploid; largely endophytic.

Chlorochytrium Cohn 1872

Cell rounded or irregular, with a parietal and cup-shaped chromatophore and 1 or more pyrenoids; chromatophore of older cells often vacuolate and filling cell lumen; endophytic within tissues of mosses and flowering plants.

Biflagellate gametes; zygotes; akinetes.

1. *Chlorochytrium lemnae* Cohn (*C. knyanum* Cohn and Szymanski). Cell spherical, ellipsoid, irregular, lobed or bent, sometimes elongate with a neck-like prolongation, up to 100 μ in length; endophytic in leaves and stems of various aquatics. Pl. **29**, fig. **288**.

FIG. 353.—*Scenedesmus armatus* (Chodat) G. M. Smith.

FIG. 354.—*Scenedesmus protuberans* Fritsch and Rich.

FIG. 355.—*Scenedesmus opoliensis* Richter.

FIG. 356.—*Scenedesmus acutiformis* Schroeder.

FIG. 357.—*Scenedesmus quadricauda* (Turpin) Brébisson.

FIG. 358.—*Scenedesmus quadricauda* var. *quadrispina* (Chodat) G. M. Smith.

FIG. 359.—*Scenedesmus quadricauda* var. *westii* G. M. Smith.

FIG. 360.—*Scenedesmus arcuatus* Lemmermann.

FIG. 361.—*Scenedesmus arcuatus* var. *platydisca* G. M. Smith.

FIG. 362.—*Scenedesmus carinatus* (Lemmermann) Chodat.

FIG. 363.—*Scenedesmus brasiliensis* Bohlin.

FIG. 364.—*Scenedesmus longus* Meyen.

FIG. 365.—*Scenedesmus abundans* (Kirchner) Chodat.

FIG. 366.—*Scenedesmus abundans* var. *longicauda* G. M. Smith.

FIG. 367.—*Scenedesmus denticulatus* Lagerheim.

FIG. 368.—*Scenedesmus acuminatus* (Lagerheim) Chodat.

FIG. 369.—*Scenedesmus obliquus* (Turpin) Kuetzing.

FIG. 370.—*Scenedesmus dimorphus* (Turpin) Kuetzing.

FIG. 371.—*Scenedesmus bijuga* (Turpin) Lagerheim.

FIG. 372.—*Scenedesmus bijuga* var. *alternans* (Reinsch) Borge.

FIG. 373.—*Scenedesmus longus* var. *minutus* G. M. Smith.

(Figs. 353–372, Smith. All ×600.)

PLATE 35

(Figs. 353 to 373)

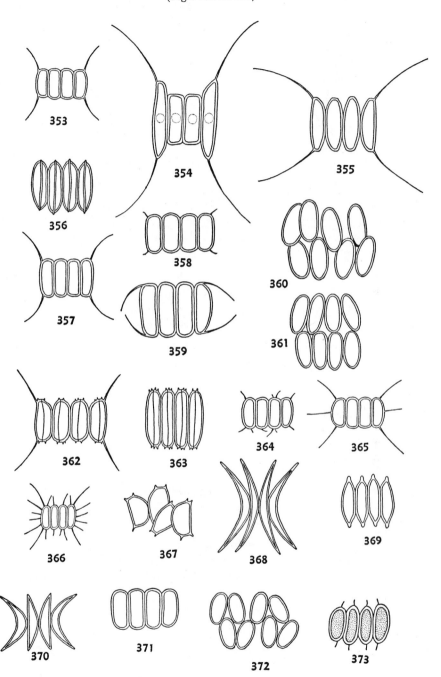

Kentrosphaera Borzi 1883

Cell globose to irregularly elongate with irregular wall thickenings, uninucleate (but becoming multinucleate just before reproduction), with axial chromatophores; free-living, aquatic or on moist soil, or in gelatinous envelopes of other algae.

Zoospores and aplanospores.

1. *Kentrosphaera facciolae* Borzi. Cell globose to ellipsoid, 26–43 μ in diameter, with unipolar thickening; aquatic. Pl. **29,** fig. **287.**

Family **Characiaceae**

Solitary cells growing on other algae, or forming star-like clusters, elongate, generally multinucleate, sometimes uninucleate, with a parietal laminate chromatophore with 1 or more pyrenoids (chromatophores sometimes diffuse, rarely absent); zoospores; akinetes; isogamy, anisogamy.

Characium A. Braun 1849

Cells solitary or aggregate, epiphytic or epizoophytic; generally stipitate or sometimes nearly sessile, pyriform, ovoid, subspherical, cylindric or fusiform; chromatophore 1 or several, parietal and laminate to cup-shaped, with 1 or more pyrenoids; uninucleate or multinucleate.

Formation of zoospores and gametes.

KEY TO THE SPECIES

1. Stipe with expanded base.................................... 1. C. pringsheimii
1. Stipe without expanded base.. 2
    2. Cell 4–8 μ in diameter.................................... 2. C. ambiguum
    2. Cell 7–18 μ in diameter.................................... 3. C. naegelii

1. *Characium pringsheimii* A. Braun. Cell 6–10 $\times$ 20–25 μ, erect, oblique, ovoid or short-acuminate, with short stipe having basal disc. Pl. **29,** fig. **285.**

2. *Characium ambiguum* Hermann. Cell 4–8 $\times$ 24–32 μ, straight, asymmetric, oblique or somewhat lanceolate, with pointed, somewhat bent apex; stipe short, without basal thickening; epiphytic on other algae. Pl. **29,** fig. **286.**

3. *Characium naegelii* A. Braun. Cell 7–18 $\times$ 20–42 μ, ellipsoid, lanceolate, pyriform or ovoid, with rounded apex and short stipe, without basal thickening. This alga is perhaps better referred to *Characiopsis naegelii* (A. Braun) Lemmermann. Pl. **29,** fig. **284.**

Schroederia Lemmermann 1899

Cells solitary, acicular to fusiform, straight or slightly curved; apices produced into setae which may be fine and tapering or 1 slightly broader, occasionally bifurcate, and sometimes ending in a disc; chromatophore single with 1–3 pyrenoids; eyespot present in one species.

Formation of biflagellate zoospores.

1. *Schroederia setigera* (Schroeder) Lemmermann. Cells 2.5–10.0 × 22.5–52.5 μ (without spines); spines 13–45 μ long. Pl. **32**, fig. **324**.

Family **Protosiphonaceae**

Cells multinucleate, coenocytic, terrestrial, with a green aerial part and a colorless underground rhizoidal part; aplanospores; isogamy.

Protosiphon Klebs 1896

Plants coenocytic, terrestrial: aerial part green, tubular when young or bladder-like in older plants; subterranean part narrowly rhizoidal, colorless; chromatophore single, parietal, reticulate, with several pyrenoids in mature cells; starch present.

Formation of proliferous outgrowths, thick-walled aplanospores with hematochrome; biflagellate isogamous gametes developed from vegetative plant or from aplanospores; zygotes; parthenogenesis.

1. *Protosiphon botryoides* (Kuetzing) Klebs. Plant unicellular, multinucleate; rhizoidal portion of older plants simple or branched; aerial portion globose to ovoid, green, up to 50 μ in diameter. (Reported from Pope County by Phinney, 1946.) Pl. **36**, fig. **374**.

Family **Hydrodictyaceae**

Cells united in radiate, plate-like or saccate colonies with a definite number of cells, mostly multinucleate; chromatophores parietal, entire or reticulate when young—diffuse in older cells; pyrenoids single or many in a cell; zoospores form new colony (coenobium) by apposition, either in old mother cell or in a vesicle after the swarming period; aplanospores; isogamous gametes uniting outside the parent cell.

Hydrodictyon Roth 1800

Cells macroscopic, usually elongate-cylindric (occasionally branched), united into a free-floating, saccate, reticulate coenobium; cells coenocytic with parietal chromatophores, reticulate at first and later diffuse, with pyrenoids; mesh of nets 3–12-sided (generally 4–7).

Formation of zoospores within the old coenobial wall and liberation of young coenobia; isogametes, zygotes, zoospores, polyhedral aplanospores.

1. *Hydrodictyon reticulatum* (Linnaeus) Lagerheim. Cells 5–250 μ in diameter and up to 1.5 cm. long. Pl. 29, fig. 289.

Pediastrum Meyen 1829

Coenobia free-floating, flat, composed of a single layer of cells (4–8–16–32–64–128–256), compact or perforate; cells coenocytic, with smooth or rough walls, marginal cells usually differently shaped from those of the interior, with processes; chromatophores parietal discs, later filling entire cell, 1–4 pyrenoids.

Zoospores, aplanospores, isogametes, and zygotes.

KEY TO THE SPECIES

1. Cell with a single projection.................................. 1. P. simplex
1. Cell with 2 or more projections, or bilobed................................ 2
  2. Projections simple...................................... 3
  2. Projections emarginate or bidentate..................... 2. P. tetras
3. Coenobium perforate...................................... 3. P. duplex
3. Coenobium entire.. 4
  4. Projections scarcely noticeable......................... 4. P. integrum
  4. Projections very pronounced............................ 5
5. Projections ending in linear teeth......................... 5. P. boryanum
5. Projections ending in broadly triangular teeth............... 6. P. angulosum

1. *Pediastrum simplex* Meyen. Cells 7–20 $\times$ 15–30 μ, walls smooth or punctate, projections of marginal cells single; coenobia 8–64-celled, compact or perforate. Pl. 30, figs. 290, 291.

  a. Var. *duodenarium* (Bailey) Rabenhorst. Cells 10–24 $\times$ 20–45 μ, with smooth or finely punctate walls; perforations of coenobia large. Pl. 30, fig. 292.

2. *Pediastrum tetras* (Ehrenberg) Ralfs. Cells 8–15 μ in diameter, with smooth walls, marginal cells with 4 projections and a deep linear incision; coenobia rectangular, oval or circular, 4–32-celled, without perforations. Pl. 30, fig. 293.

Fig. 374.—*Protosiphon botryoides* (Kuetzing) Klebs, mature and young plants.

Figs. 375–377.—*Dichotomosiphon tuberosus* (A. Braun) Ernst: fig. 375, oogonia and antheridia; fig. 376, akinete; fig. 377, vegetative portion.

Fig. 378.—*Vaucheria sessilis* (Vaucher) De Candolle.

Fig. 379.—*Vaucheria ornithocephala* Agardh.

(Figs. 375–377, by permission from *Freshwater Algae of the United States* by G. M. Smith. Copyright 1933. McGraw-Hill Book Co., Inc.; fig. 378, Couch; fig. 379, West. Fig. 374 $\times$*225;* fig. 375 $\times$*500;* figs. 376, 377 $\times$*5;* figs. 378, 379 $\times$*160.*)

PLATE 36

(Figs. 374 to 379)

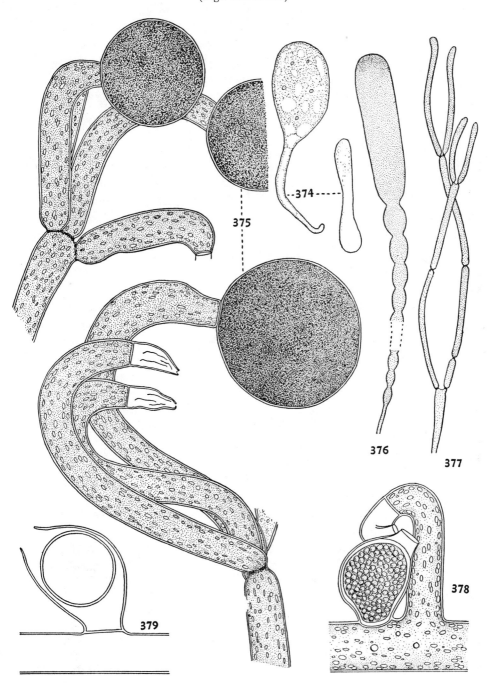

a. Var. *tetraodon* (Corda) Hansgirg. Cells 8–15 × 12–18 μ, with deep incisions and pronounced projections. Pl. **30**, fig. **294**.

3. *Pediastrum duplex* Meyen. Cells 11–21 μ in diameter, with smooth walls, outer half of marginal cells with 2 short projections; coenobia 8–128-celled, with lens-shaped perforations among cells. Pl. **30**, fig. **300**.

a. Var. *rotundatum* Lucks. Projections of marginal cells convex and capitate. Pl. **30**, fig. **302**.

b. Var. *clathratum* (A. Braun) Lagerheim. Projections of marginal cells deeply emarginate. Pl. **30**, fig. **301**.

4. *Pediastrum integrum* Naegeli. Cells 15–30 μ in diameter, marginal cells sometimes with 2 scarcely noticeable processes, but generally entire, wall smooth or punctate; coenobia 8–64-celled, nearly circular, without perforations. Pl. **30**, fig. **298**.

5. *Pediastrum boryanum* (Turpin) Meneghini. Cells 7–30 μ in diameter, with smooth or granulate walls, outer half of marginal cells with 2 short processes ending in short spines; coenobia 4–256-celled, usually compact. Pl. **30**, figs. **295, 296**.

a. Var. *longicorne* Raciborski. Cells up to 40 μ in diameter, with horns at end of processes 12–30 μ long; otherwise like the type. Pl. **30**, fig. **297**.

6. *Pediastrum angulosum* (Ehrenberg) Meneghini. Cells 15–50 μ in diameter, angular; marginal cells wider above, truncate at base, with a more or less deep sinus; coenobia 16–128-celled, reaching diameters of 400 μ. Pl. **30**, fig. **299**.

Sorastrum Kuetzing 1845

Coenobia more or less globose, made up of 8–16–32–64–128 cells; cells broadly sublunate, reniform, pyriform or subtriangular, with 1–4 spines on the distal ends, multinucleate when mature; chromatophore parietal or diffuse, 1 pyrenoid.

Formation of zoospores, which are liberated in a vesicle, as in *Pediastrum*.

1. *Sorastrum spinulosum* Naegeli. Cells 8–20 × 6–18 μ and 5–8 μ thick, broadly reniform to cuneate, with 4 horns (4–8 μ long on mature cells) at corners; stipe short. Pl. **29**, fig. **283**.

Family Coelastraceae

Cells united in definite hollow or solid colonies, ranging in number from 2 to 128 and usually radiate; reproduction solely by aplanospores (autospores).

Coelastrum Naegeli 1849

Coenobium a hollow sphere of 2–4–8–16–32–64–128 cells, daughter coenobia often remaining joined into a multiple colony; cells spherical, ovoid or pyramidal, compact or much perforate, united by short or long processes; sheath very delicate.

KEY TO THE SPECIES

1. Cell with truncate projection on outer face.................. 1. C. cambricum
1. Cell without such projection... 2
   2. Cells connected by long processes...................... 2. C. reticulatum
   2. Cells connected by short processes................................ 3
3. Cells ovoid.. 3. C. sphaericum
3. Cells spherical, or nearly so............................. 4. C. microporum

1. *Coelastrum cambricum* Archer. Cells 5–18 μ in diameter (or 6–20 μ with sheath), spherical, with a single truncate projection on outer face; coenobia 20–100 μ in diameter, spherical, composed of 8–128 cells joined to one another by short, somewhat flattened projections. Pl. 31, fig. 310.

2. *Coelastrum reticulatum* (Dangeard) Senn. Cells 6–24 μ in diameter, spherical; coenobia 10–65 μ in diameter, spherical or nearly so, of 8–32 cells joined by 6–9 long, slender, firm, gelatinous processes; coenobia generally multiple, rarely solitary. Pl. 31, fig. 311.

3. *Coelastrum sphaericum* Naegeli. Cells 3.5–7.5 (at base) × 6–12 μ, ovoid; coenobia, composed of 4–16 cells, 15–32 μ in diameter in 8-celled colonies. Pl. 31, fig. 313.

4. *Coelastrum microporum* Naegeli. Cells 3–20 μ in diameter (or 4–23 μ with sheath), spherical or sometimes ovoid; coenobia 20–90 μ in diameter, spherical to ovoid, of 8–64 cells joined to one another by short, stout gelatinous processes. Pl. 31, fig. 312.

Family **Oocystaceae**

Cells very variable in shape, sometimes ornamented, usually uninucleate with a single chromatophore that generally contains 1 pyrenoid; autospores not united into colonies at time of liberation from mother-cell wall; colonies due to entangling, gelatinous adhesions, or to a matrix formed by the gelatinization of the mother-cell wall; aplanospores (autospores); oogamy reported in *Dictyosphaerium*.

Ankistrodesmus Corda 1838; Ralfs 1848

Cells acicular to fusiform (sometimes with acute apices and considerably attenuate), straight, curved or sigmoid, solitary or loosely aggregate; chromatophore single, parietal, often without pyrenoids.

1. *Ankistrodesmus falcatus* (Corda) Ralfs. Cells 1.5–4.0 × 20–80 μ, curved, with acute apices, solitary or in loose fasciculate bundles. Pl. **31**, fig. **307.**

Closteriopsis Lemmermann 1898

Cells differing from those of *Ankistrodesmus* in their great length and in the presence of an axial row of 12 or more pyrenoids; considerable superficial resemblance to *Closterium*.

1. *Closteriopsis longissima* Lemmermann [*Ankistrodesmus longissimus* (Lemmermann) Wille]. Cells 4.0–7.5 × 225–530 μ, ending in hair-like apices. Pl. **31**, fig. **306.**

Chlorella Beyerinck 1890

Cells small, globose or rarely ellipsoid, solitary or aggregated into a thin mucous layer; chromatophore single, parietal, often cup-shaped, usually without pyrenoid.

Formation of autospores.

KEY TO THE SPECIES

1. Free-living... 1. C. vulgaris
1. Endozoophytic.. 2
   2. Cells 1.5–3.0 μ in diameter............................. 2. C. parasitica
   2. Cells 3–6 μ in diameter................................ 3. C. conductrix

1. *Chlorella vulgaris* Beyerinck. Cells 5–10 μ in diameter, spherical, forming 2–8 autospores. Pl. **29**, fig. **280.**

2. *Chlorella parasitica* Brandt. Cells 1.5–3.0 μ in diameter; found in *Spongilla, Ophrydium*, and other freshwater organisms. Pl. **29**, fig. **281.**

3. *Chlorella conductrix* Brandt. Cells 3–6 μ in diameter; found in *Hydra, Stentor, Paramecium.* Pl. **29**, fig. **282.**

Dactylococcus Naegeli 1849

Solitary or joined end to end in branching colonies devoid of a gelatinous envelope; cells more or less fusiform with attenuated ends; chromatophore at one side of the cell, laminate, parietal when young (fills cell in old plants), pyrenoid sometimes evident.

Autospores (usually 4) liberated by rupture of mother-cell wall.

1. *Dactylococcus infusionum* Naegeli. Cells 3–4 × 6–8 μ, fusiform with attenuated apices, joined end to end in branching chains. Pl. **31**, fig. **303.**

Dictyosphaerium Naegeli 1849

Cells spherical, ovoid, ellipsoid, or reniform, connected by branching threads; colonies enclosed by a hyaline, homogeneous sheath (sometimes inconspicuous), spherical or ovoid or irregular; chromatophore 1 (or 2), parietal, cup-shaped, with 1 pyrenoid.

Formation of 2–4 autospores, remaining connected to the colony by the branching threads formed from the old mother-cell walls; fragmentation of the colony; oogamy (female cell with 2 eggs; fertilization after extrusion from parent cell).

KEY TO THE SPECIES

1. Cells ovoid to ellipsoid.................................. 1. D. ehrenbergianum
1. Cells nearly spherical................................... 2. D. pulchellum

1. *Dictyosphaerium ehrenbergianum* Naegeli. Cells 4–7 × 6–10 μ, ovoid to ellipsoid, with 1–2 chromatophores; colonies spherical to ovoid. Pl. 31, fig. 304.

2. *Dictyosphaerium pulchellum* Wood. Cells 3–10 μ in diameter, spherical to ovoid, with 1 chromatophore (4 just before formation of daughter cells); colonies spherical to broadly ovoid, 4- to many-celled. Pl. 31, fig. 305.

Dimorphococcus A. Braun 1855

Cells in groups of 4, forming irregular free-floating colonies, held in position by the branching fragments of the mother cell, 2 cells in each group ellipsoid or oblong and the other 2 cells reniform to cardioid; chromatophores parietal, single, with 1 pyrenoid; enveloping mucus inconspicuous.

Formation of autospores that remain connected to old mother-cell wall.

1. *Dimorphococcus lunatus* A. Braun. Cells 4–15 × 9–25 μ; colonies 50–150 μ in diameter. Pl. 31, fig. 314.

Gloeotaenium Hansgirg 1890

Cells spherical to ellipsoid or flattened; solitary or united within a closely fitting mother-cell wall into colonies of 2–4–8 cells; cells separated and sometimes capped by dark-colored gelatinous masses impregnated with calcium carbonate; cell-wall thick, lamellose; mother-cell wall frequently folded; chromatophore filling cell, with or without pyrenoid.

Formation of 2–4–8 autospores; akinetes.

1. *Gloeotaenium loitlesbergerianum* Hansgirg. Cells 20–30 μ in diameter; 2-celled colonies 22–40 × 40–70 μ and 20–30 μ thick; 4-celled colonies 40–70 × 40–80 μ. Pl. 32, fig. 317.

Kirchneriella Schmidle 1893

Cells arcuate or lunate, attenuate or subcylindric, apices often nearly touching, loosely arranged in a wide gelatinous envelope; chromatophore single, parietal on convex side of cell or entirely filling cell, with or without pyrenoid.

Formation of 4–8 autospores.

1. *Kirchneriella lunaris* (Kirchner) Moebius. Cells 3–8 × 6–15 μ, crescent-shaped, bluntly pointed, irregularly in groups of 4–8; chromatophore nearly entire, 1 pyrenoid; colonies up to 250 μ in diameter. Pl. **31**, fig. **308**.

2. *Kirchneriella obesa* (W. West) Schmidle var. *major* (Bernard) G. M. Smith. Cells 3–5 × 8–21 μ, inner sides curved; chromatophore nearly filling cell, with 1 pyrenoid. Pl. **31**, fig. **309**.

Nephrocytium Naegeli 1849

Cells ovoid, reniform, oblong or ellipsoid, usually in colonies of 2–4–8–16 cells, with a usually well-defined colonial envelope; chromatophore at first a curved plate, later diffuse, 1 pyrenoid.

Formation of 2–4–8–16 autospores in each cell.

KEY TO THE SPECIES
1. Cells reniform or nearly so.................................... 1. N. agardhianum
1. Cells crescent-shaped....................................... 2. N. lunatum

1. *Nephrocytium agardhianum* Naegeli. Cells 2–13 × 6–28 μ, reniform or nearly so, with rounded ends. Pl. **32**, fig. **315**.

2. *Nephrocytium lunatum* W. West. Cells 4–7 × 14–18 μ, crescent-shaped, with pointed ends. Pl. **32**, fig. **316**.

Oocystis Naegeli 1845

Cells ovoid, ellipsoid or cylindric, with smooth walls and sometimes polar nodules, solitary or in colonies of 2–4–8–16 (or more) surrounded by the greatly swollen and partially gelatinized old mother-cell wall; chromatophores 1 to many, parietal, disciform, stellate or reticulate; with or without pyrenoids.

Formation of 2–16 autospores; aplanospores.

KEY TO THE SPECIES
1. Cells with polar nodules.. 2
1. Cells without polar nodules... 3
  2. Cells 7–10 μ in diameter.................................... 1. O. solitaria
  2. Cells 10–20 μ in diameter.................................. 2. O. crassa
3. Cells 9–21 μ in diameter... 4
3. Cells 32–40 μ in diameter................................... 3. O. gigas
  4. Chromatophore single...................................... 4. O. naegelii
  4. Chromatophores 1–4 in number............................. 5. O. borgei
  4. Chromatophores 10–20 in number...........................6. O. elliptica

1. *Oocystis solitaria* Wittrock. Cells 7–10 × 14–35 μ, ovoid to ellipsoid, solitary or 2–8, with conspicuous polar nodules; chromatophores usually 12–25, parietal, disciform to polygonal, with or without pyrenoids. Pl. **32**, fig. **319**.

a. Forma *major* Wille. Cells 22–25 × 40–48 μ, with punctate, thick walls; often in colonies of 4 cells.

2. *Oocystis crassa* Wittrock. Cells 10–20 × 14–26 μ, ovoid, with polar nodules, solitary or 2–8; chromatophores 4–10, parietal, disciform to angular, usually with pyrenoids. Pl. **32**, fig. **323**.

3. *Oocystis gigas* Archer. Cells 32–40 × 41–50 μ, broadly ellipsoid, poles broadly rounded without nodules, solitary or 2–4. Pl. **32**, fig. **321**.

4. *Oocystis naegelii* A. Braun. Cells 10–20 × 22–40 μ, ovoid-oblong, without polar nodules, solitary or 2–8; chromatophore single, parietal, plate-like. Pl. **32**, fig. **320**.

5. *Oocystis borgei* Snow. Cells 9–13 × 9–17 μ, usually broadly ellipsoid, without polar nodules, solitary or 2–8 within the old mother-cell wall; chromatophores 1–4, parietal, laminate, with 1 pyrenoid. Pl. **32**, fig. **322**.

6. *Oocystis elliptica* W. West. Cells 11–13 × 20–25 μ, oblong-ellipsoid, without polar nodules, generally in groups of 4–8, rarely solitary; chromatophores 10–20, parietal, disciform. Pl. **32**, fig. **318**.

Schroederia Lemmermann 1899

The genus *Schroederia* has long been classified with those genera of the Chlorococcales in which the only method of reproduction is by the formation of autospores (splanospores) (G. M. Smith, 1933; Tiffany, 1934; Prescott, 1951). The reports in the last decade of zoospore formation in the genus necessitates its transfer to the Characiaceae (p. 109).

Selenastrum Reinsch 1867

Cells arcuate to lunate, attenuate, their convex surfaces apposed into aggregates of 4–8–16 or more cells, without a gelatinous envelope; chromatophore single, parietal, with or without pyrenoids.

Formation of autospores.

1. *Selenastrum bibraianum* Reinsch. Cells 5–8 × 20–38 μ, crescent-shaped to sickle-shaped, in spherical to ovoid colonies of 4–16 or more cells; 5–25 μ between apices. Pl. **32**, fig. **325**.

a. Var. *gracile* (Reinsch) Tiffany and Ahlstrom. Cells 3–5 × 15–30 μ; otherwise like the type. Pl. **32**, fig. **326**.

Tetraedron Kuetzing 1845

Cells solitary (or rarely in temporary aggregates when young), flat and angular (triangular, quadrangular or polygonal) or polyhedral, with angles simple or produced into simple or furcate spines; wall smooth or not; chromatophores 1 to many, parietal or filling the cell, with or without pyrenoids.

Formation of 4–32 autospores.

KEY TO THE SPECIES

1. Cells flattened.. 2
1. Cells tetragonal.. 6
  2. Angles simple, not armed.................................... 3
  2. Angles spinous or forked.................................... 4
3. Cells quadrangular in flat view.................... 1. T. minimum
3. Cells triangular in flat view...................... 2. T. muticum
  4. Angles ending in many fine divisions.............. 3. T. gracile
  4. Angles without such divisions............................. 5
5. Cells triangular (sometimes quadrate)................... 4. T. trigonum
5. Cells regularly quadrate............................... 5. T. quadratum
  6. Angles simple...................................... 6. T. gigas
  6. Angles forked... 7
7. Angles spinous.. 8
7. Angles with 1–2 short processes.......................... 7. T. lobulatum
  8. Cells 10–40 μ in diameter........................ 8. T. regulare
  8. Cells 40–46 μ in diameter........................ 9. T. bifurcatum
  8. Cells 45–85 μ in diameter....................... 10. T. limneticum

1. *Tetraedron minimum* (A. Braun) Hansgirg. Cells 5–8 μ thick and 6–20 μ long, flat view square or oblong with concave sides and slightly rounded corners, side view fusiform-elliptic, wall smooth or granulate. Pl. 34, fig. 335.

  a. Forma *tetralobulatum* Reinsch. Sides more deeply concave; cells 10–12 μ in diameter. Pl. 34, fig. 336.

2. *Tetraedron muticum* (A. Braun) Hansgirg. Cells 5–8 μ thick and 8.5–15.0 μ long, triangular, with concave sides, angles truncate and rounded. Pl. 34, fig. 337.

  a. Forma *punctulatum* (Reinsch) DeToni. Sides slightly convex, walls finely punctate; cells 18–21 μ in diameter. Pl. 34, fig. 338.

3. *Tetraedron gracile* (Reinsch) Hansgirg. Cells 15–30 μ in diameter, 4-angled, sides emarginate or incised, angles 3-forked, ultimate divisions slender and acute up to 40 μ in length. Pl. 34, fig. 339.

4. *Tetraedron trigonum* (Naegeli) Hansgirg. Cells without spines 20–40 μ in diameter and 6–16 μ thick, triangular or sometimes 4-sided; angles rounded with mucronate tip, or stout spine 8–10 μ long. Pl. 34, fig. 340.

  a. Forma *majus* Bruegger. Larger, with stout spines.

  b. Var. *minus* Reinsch. Cells 10–14 μ in diameter, 3-sided, with straight sides, angles gradually tapering. Pl. 34, fig. 342.

  c. Var. *tetragonum* (Naegeli) Rabenhorst. Cells 18–30 μ in diameter, 4-sided; each angle with 1 or more spines. Pl. 34, fig. 341.

5. *Tetraedron quadratum* (Reinsch) Hansgirg. Cells 17–34 μ in diameter, regularly quadrate; sides straight or slightly convex; angles obtuse, each with a single spine; cell-wall of 2 layers, 2–5 μ thick. Pl. 34, fig. 348.

a. Forma *minus-acutum* Reinsch. Cells 17–18 μ in diameter, angles subacute, wall indistinctly lamellose. Pl. 34, fig. 349.

6. *Tetraedron gigas* (Wittrock) Hansgirg. Cells 35–45 $\times$ 65–75 μ, irregularly 5–6-angled; sides somewhat concave; angles unarmed. Pl. 34, fig. 343.

7. *Tetraedron lobulatum* (Naegeli) Hansgirg. Cells (without processes) 30–40 μ in diameter, tetragonal, flat or pyramidate, with concave sides, 1–2 short, dichotomous, usually spineless processes at the angles. Pl. 34, fig. 344.

8. *Tetraedron regulare* Kuetzing. Cells (with spines) 14–45 μ in diameter, tetragonal, pyramidal; sides convex, straight or concave, each angle with a short blunt spine. Pl. 34, fig. 345.

9. *Tetraedron bifurcatum* (Wille) Lagerheim. Cells 38–46 μ (without spines) in diameter, tetragonal; angles 3 or 4, bifurcate, with sharp tips. Pl. 34, fig. 346.

10. *Tetraedron limneticum* Borge. Cells (with processes) 45–85 μ in diameter, tetragonal, pyramidal, the angles dichotomously branched and terminating in 2 or 3 short spines; processes 8–12 μ in diameter at base. Pl. 34, fig. 347.

Treubaria Bernard 1908

Cells 3–8-angled, pyramidulate to quadrate in shape, sides of cells concave or straight; angles broadly rounded, each bearing a single hyaline spine that gradually tapers, or with subparallel sides but terminating abruptly in a sharp point; chromatophores 1–4, massive, completely or nearly filling the cell, with 1–4 pyrenoids.

Formation of 4 autospores, liberated by splitting of the cell-wall in 2 or more pieces.

1. *Treubaria crassispina* G. M. Smith. Cells (without spines) 12–15 μ, (with spines) 100–115 μ, in diameter; spines 45–60 μ long, 4–6 μ broad at the base. Pl. 34, fig. 350.

Trochiscia Kuetzing 1845

Cells spherical or nearly so, solitary or aggregate, with walls variously ornamented or areolate, usually containing several parietal chromatophores, each with a pyrenoid.

Vegetative division and formation of 4–16 autospores.

KEY TO THE SPECIES

1. Cells 24–32 μ in diameter.................................... 1. T. reticularis
1. Cells 31–43 μ in diameter.................................... 2. T. arguta

1. *Trochiscia reticularis* (Reinsch) Hansgirg. Cells 24–32 μ in diameter, with reticulate wall. Pl. 34, fig. **351.**

2. *Trochiscia arguta* (Reinsch) Hansgirg. Cells 31–43 μ in diameter, cell-walls 12–15 μ thick; acutely tipped prominences connected by parallel ridges. Pl. 34, fig. **352.**

Family **Scenedesmaceae**

Two, 4, 8 or occasionally more uninucleate cells united into a definitely arranged colony: in the same plane and parallel, quadrately disposed, pyramidal or radiating; cells spherical, ellipsoidal, acicular, angular and irregular, with walls ornamented or not; chromatophores 1 or more, parietal, longitudinal or occupying entire cell, generally with 1 pyrenoid; aplanospores (autospores), rarely akinetes.

Actinastrum Lagerheim 1882

Cells ovoid, oblong or club-shaped, generally radiating from a common center in 4–8–16-celled coenobia; chromatophore parietal, with or without pyrenoid.

Formation of 4–8–16 autospores by transverse and longitudinal division of the cell contents, the young colony being freed by a transverse rupture of the old mother-cell wall.

1. *Actinastrum hantzschii* Lagerheim. Cells 3–6 × 10–26 μ, ovoid-cylindric, with truncate ends, 3–6 times as long as broad; chromatophore single, with 1 pyrenoid. Pl. 33, fig. **327.**

a. Var. *fluviatile* Schroeder. Cells 1.5–5 × 16–32 μ, with free ends pointed. Pl. 33, fig. **328.**

Crucigenia Morren 1830

Coenobia of 4 cells, or multiples of 4 by daughter coenobial aggregates in a more or less conspicuous gelatinous envelope, forming a flat or slightly curved plate; cells flat, appearing ovoid, angular or semicircular in front view, quadrately arranged with a quadrate or rhomboidal space in the center; cell-wall smooth; chromatophores 1–4, cup-shaped, with or without a pyrenoid.

Formation of 4 autospores; akinetes.

KEY TO THE SPECIES

1. Cells ovoid to ellipsoid.. 2
1. Cells triangular.. 1. C. tetrapedia
1. Cells subhemispherical................................... 2. C. lauterbornei
   2. Coenobium generally regular....................... 3. C. rectangularis
   2. Coenobium often irregular......................... 4. C. irregularis

1. *Crucigenia tetrapedia* (Kirchner) W. and G. S. West. Cells 5–10 μ in diameter, flat, triangular, with rounded corners, with a very small rectangular opening at the center of the coenobium; cell contents homogeneous or with 1 chromatophore, with or without pyrenoids. Pl. 33, fig. 331.

2. *Crucigenia lauterbornei* Schmidle. Cells 4.5–9.0 × 8–15 μ, flat, subhemispherical in front view, with the flat side toward the center of the coenobium, in contact at the apices only; chromatophore single, with 1 pyrenoid. Pl. 33, fig. 332.

3. *Crucigenia rectangularis* (Naegeli) Gay. Cells 4–7 × 5–10 μ, ovoid to elongate-ovoid, in mutual contact at the poles and sides with a small rectangular opening at the center of the coenobium; chromatophores 1–4, each with a single pyrenoid; multiple coenobia common. Pl. 33, fig. 333.

4. *Crucigenia irregularis* Wille. Cells 4–9 × 6–14 μ, ovoid, with cells in contact at sides and poles or without definite arrangement; 1–4 parietal chromatophores, with or without pyrenoids. Pl. 33, fig. 334.

Scenedesmus Meyen 1829

Coenobia generally flat plates of ellipsoid, oblong, fusiform, acicular or ovoid cells in multiples of 2; cells laterally in contact or rarely connected by short processes, in 1 or 2 rows (sometimes with quadrate arrangement); cell-wall smooth or variously ornamented, with or without terminal or lateral spines or teeth; chromatophore single, parietal, often occupying the whole cell, pyrenoid generally single.

Formation of 2–32 autospores.

KEY TO THE SPECIES

1. Cells with spines or teeth.................................... 2
1. Cells without spines or teeth................................ 11
   2. Spines on terminal cells only........................... 3
   2. Spines on both terminal and interior cells............. 6
3. With longitudinal ridges on cells.......................... 4
3. Without longitudinal ridges on cells....................... 5
   4. Cells 7–16 μ long............................. 1. S. armatus
   4. Cells 25–34 μ long.......................... 2. S. protuberans
5. Cells naviculoid..................................... 3. S. opoliensis
5. Cells cylindric-ovoid to ellipsoid................. 4. S. quadricauda

6. Cells with longitudinal ridges.. 7
6. Cells without longitudinal ridges... 8
7. Cells fusiform.................................. 5. S. carinatus
7. Cells cylindric to ovoid-ellipsoid...................... 6. S. brasiliensis
   8. Pole of cell with single spine... 9
   8. Pole of cell with 1–4 spines... 10
9. Cells 8–11 μ long.............................. 7. S. longus
9. Cells 12–28 μ long............................. 3. S. opoliensis
   10. Polar spines as long as cells.................. 8. S. abundans
   10. Polar spines very short......................... 9. S. denticulatus
11. Cells fusiform... 12
11. Cells not fusiform... 15
   12. Cells 10–23 μ long.. 13
   12. Cells 30–40 μ long........................... 10. S. acuminatus
13. Cells with longitudinal ridges................. 11. S. acutiformis
13. Cells without longitudinal ridges.. 14
   14. Cell sides in contact straight.................... 12. S. obliquus
   14. Cell sides in contact not straight................ 13. S. dimorphus
15. Coenobium usually straight...................... 14. S. bijuga
15. Coenobium curved.............................. 15. S. arcuatus

1. *Scenedesmus armatus* (Chodat) G. M. Smith. Cells 4–7 × 7–16 μ, ovoid to oblong-ellipsoid with rounded apices, in a linear or subalternating series; a longitudinal ridge on each side of cell (often not prominent in median portion); terminal cells with a spine at each pole. Pl. **35**, fig. **353**.

2. *Scenedesmus protuberans* Fritsch and Rich. Cells 6–7 × 25–34 μ, fusiform, with a longitudinal ridge on each side of the cell; spines 25–35 μ long; coenobium of 4, or rarely 8, cells, external cells with protruded apices. Pl. **35**, fig. **354**.

3. *Scenedesmus opoliensis* P. Richter. Cells 5–8 × 12–28 μ, inner cells naviculoid, free faces of outer cells straight or convex, joined together in median position only; terminal cells with a long spine at each pole; inner cells with or without spines. Pl. **35**, fig. **355**.

4. *Scenedesmus quadricauda* (Turpin) Brébisson. Cells 3.5–6.0 × 11–16 μ, cylindric-ovoid, with rounded ends, in a linear or subalternating series; poles of outer cells with spines, inner cells without spines; spines 10–12 μ long. Pl. **35**, fig. **357**.

   a. Var. *quadrispina* (Chodat) G. M. Smith. Cells 3.5–8.0 × 8.5–15.0 μ, broadly ovoid, about twice as long as wide; 4-celled coenobia 8.5–15.0 × 16–32 μ; spines 2.5–5.5 μ long. Pl. **35**, fig. **358**.

   b. Var. *westii* G. M. Smith. Cells 4.5–8.0 × 16–22 μ; 4-celled coenobia 16–22 × 25–35 μ; spines 12–16 μ long. Pl. **35**, fig. **359**.

5. *Scenedesmus carinatus* (Lemmermann) Chodat. Cells 6–9 × 15–17 μ, fusiform, with a longitudinal ridge on each side of the cell; each pole with 2–3 teeth. Pl. **35**, fig. **362**.

6. *Scenedesmus brasiliensis* Bohlin. Cells 3–6 × 11–24 μ, cylindric to ovoid-ellipsoid, with a longitudinal ridge on each side of the cell; poles with 1–4 teeth. Pl. **35,** fig. **363.**

7. *Scenedesmus longus* Meyen. Cells 4–5 × 8–11 μ, oblong-cylindric with rounded ends each bearing a single spine. Pl. **35,** fig. **364.**

    a. Var. *minutus* G. M. Smith. Smaller than the type. Pl. **35,** fig. **373.**

8. *Scenedesmus abundans* (Kirchner) Chodat. Cells 4–7 × 7–12 μ, ovoid to oblong-ellipsoid, with 1–2 spines at each pole (sometimes terminal cells only) and additional spines on outer face of terminal cells. Pl. **35,** fig. **365.**

    a. Var. *longicauda* G. M. Smith. Cells 3–6 × 7–9 μ, spines 6–10 μ long; 4-celled coenobia 7–9 × 10–15 μ. Pl. **35,** fig. **366.**

9. *Scenedesmus denticulatus* Lagerheim. Cells 5–11 × 7–15 μ, ovoid to ovoid-ellipsoid, in a linear or subalternating series, poles with 1–4 short spines. Pl. **35,** fig. **367.**

10. *Scenedesmus acuminatus* (Lagerheim) Chodat. Cells 3–7 × 30–40 μ, fusiform, arcuate or lunate, with pointed ends; cell-wall smooth and without spines; coenobia curved. Pl. **35,** fig. **368.**

11. *Scenedesmus acutiformis* Schroeder. Cells 5–8 × 16–22 μ, fusiform, with acute apices, without spines or teeth; terminal cells with 2–4 longitudinal ridges, interior cells with 1 longitudinal ridge on each side. Pl. **35,** fig. **356.**

12. *Scenedesmus obliquus* (Turpin) Kuetzing. Cells 3–9 × 10–21 μ, fusiform, with acute apices, in a linear or sublinear series; cell sides in contact straight, free sides of terminal cells various; cell-wall smooth, without teeth or spines. Pl. **35,** fig. **369.**

13. *Scenedesmus dimorphus* (Turpin) Kuetzing. Cells 2–5 × 18–23 μ, fusiform with delicately pointed apices, in a linear or alternating series; inner cells asymmetric, outer cells lunate or symmetric; cell-wall smooth, without teeth or spines. Pl. **35,** fig. **370.**

14. *Scenedesmus bijuga* (Turpin) Lagerheim. Cells 4–7 × 7–18 μ, oblong-ellipsoid to ovoid with broadly rounded ends, usually in a single series; cell-wall smooth, without teeth or spines. Pl. **35,** fig. **371.**

    a. Var. *alternans* (Reinsch) Borge. Cells 4–8 × 6–15 μ, alternately arranged. Pl. **35,** fig. **372.**

15. *Scenedesmus arcuatus* Lemmermann. Cells 3–9 × 9–17 μ, ovoid or angular, in a double row, forming a curved coenobium with small interstices between cells; cell-wall smooth, without teeth or spines. Pl. **35,** fig. **360.**

    a. Var. *platydisca* G. M. Smith. Cells 4.5–7.5 × 8–17 μ, oblong-ellipsoid; coenobium flat. Pl. **35,** fig. **361.**

Order SIPHONALES

Unicellular, multinucleate, elongate, branched tubes; thallus sparingly branched or with definitely arranged branches upon an axis or intertwined into a macroscopic plant; chromatophores discoid or lenticular, each with a single pyrenoid, or pyrenoids lacking; food reserve usually starch; nuclei of vegetative cells of many genera known to be diploid; largely marine, some freshwater; zoospores, aplanospores, akinetes; anisogamy to oogamy.

Family **Dichotomosiphonaceae**

Tubular coenocytic filaments, dichotomously branched, constricted at and between the dichotomies, free-living, aquatic; food reserve starch; akinetes; oogamy.

Dichotomosiphon Ernst 1902

Dichotomously branched, coenocytic filaments, transversely constricted at each dichotomy and less commonly between branches, with colorless rhizoids; chromatophores numerous, lens-shaped, without pyrenoids, starch accumulation in the leucoplasts.

Tuberous starch-filled akinetes; biflagellate sperms in antheridia, and eggs in oogonia.

1. *Dichotomosiphon tuberosus* (A. Braun) Ernst. Filaments 40–110 μ in diameter and up to 10 centimeters long; akinetes straight and elongate or clavate and curved, 200–400 $\times$ 500–5000 μ; antheridia and oogonia at the ends of ultimate branches; antheridium 35–50 $\times$ 130–170 μ; oogonium globose, 290–320 μ in diameter; oospore of same shape, dark green, 250–280 μ in diameter. Pl. **36**, figs. **375–377**.

Order ZYGNEMATALES

Cells uninucleate, solitary or united into cylindric unbranched filaments; cell-wall generally cellulose with peripheral pectic compounds; chromatophores varied, but generally spiral bands, axial plates, or more

---

FIG. 380.—*Vaucheria hamata* (Vaucher) De Candolle.

FIG. 381.—*Vaucheria aversa* Hassall.

FIG. 382.—*Vaucheria polysperma* Hassall.

Fig. 383.—*Vaucheria repens* Hassall.

FIG. 384.—*Vaucheria gardneri* Collins.

FIG. 385.—*Vaucheria geminata* (Vaucher) De Candolle.

FIG. 386.—*Vaucheria longipes* Collins.

FIG. 387.—*Vaucheria terrestris* (Vaucher) De Candolle.

(Figs. 380, 385, Tiffany; figs. 381–383, 387, Goetz; figs. 384, 386, Collins. All $\times 160$.)

PLATE 37

(Figs. 380 to 387)

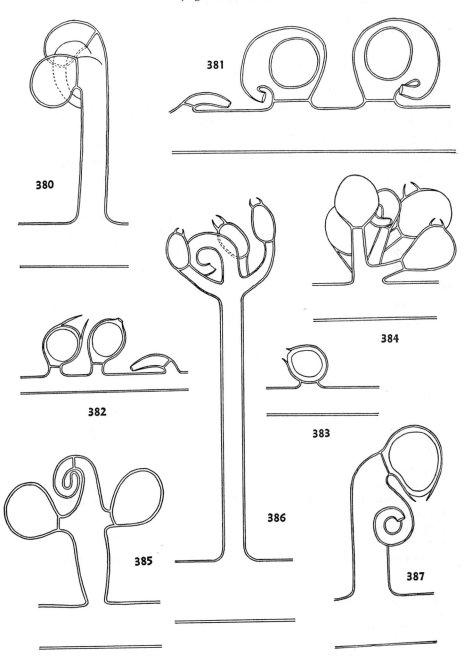

or less stellate bodies with or without pyrenoids, with starch the usual food reserve; no flagellate cells; amoeboid gametes usually fusing through regularly formed conjugation tubes or within gelatinous matrices; plants haploid, meiosis occurring at the germination of the zygote.

Family Zygnemataceae

Unbranched filaments with cylindric uninucleate cells containing 1 or more stellate, pillow-shaped, plate-like, disc-shaped or ribbon-like chromatophores, with or without pyrenoids; vegetative cell division; formation of zygotes in conjugation tubes (isogamy) or in 1 of the gametangia (anisogamy) by fusion of amoeboid gametes; parthenospores, aplanospores and akinetes.

Mougeotia C. A. Agardh 1824

Filaments simple or rarely with 1- or 2-celled branches, with cylindric cells, rhizoids common; chromatophores 1 or 2 axial plates with several pyrenoids in a single row or irregularly distributed; zygotes usually formed in the conjugating tubes, cytoplasmic residues remaining in the gametangia.

Fragmentation; aplanospores; zygotes of various shapes and colors, and with outer walls variously ornamented or not.

KEY TO THE SPECIES

1. Vegetative cell 3.5–5.5 μ in diameter 2
1. Vegetative cell 5–9 μ in diameter 3
1. Vegetative cell 9–38 μ in diameter 4
  2. Spore-wall smooth . . . . 1. M. elegantula
  2. Spore-wall punctate . . . . 2. M. boodlei
3. Spore-wall smooth . . . . 3. M. viridis
3. Spore-wall coarsely punctate . . . . 4. M. tumidula
3. Spore-wall verrucose . . . . 5. M. gracillima
  4. Conjugation generally scalariform 5
  4. Conjugation lateral, very rarely scalariform . . . . 6. M. reinschii
5. Sporangium not dividing either gametangium 6
5. Sporangium dividing only 1 gametangium 11
5. Sporangium dividing both gametangia . . . . 7. M. quadrangulata
5. Sporangium dividing 1 or both gametangia, or neither . . 8. M. calcarea

Fig. 388.—*Mougeotia nummuloides* (Hassall) DeToni, showing vegetative cells, zygotes and aplanospores.

Figs. 389–393.—*Mougeotia sphaerocarpa* Wolle; fig. 391 with two parthenospores.

Figs. 394–396.—*Mougeotia robusta* (DeBary) Wittrock.

Figs. 397–402.—*Mougeotia calcarea* (Cleve) Wittrock.

(All figures from Transeau ×300.)

PLATE 38

(Figs. 388 to 402)

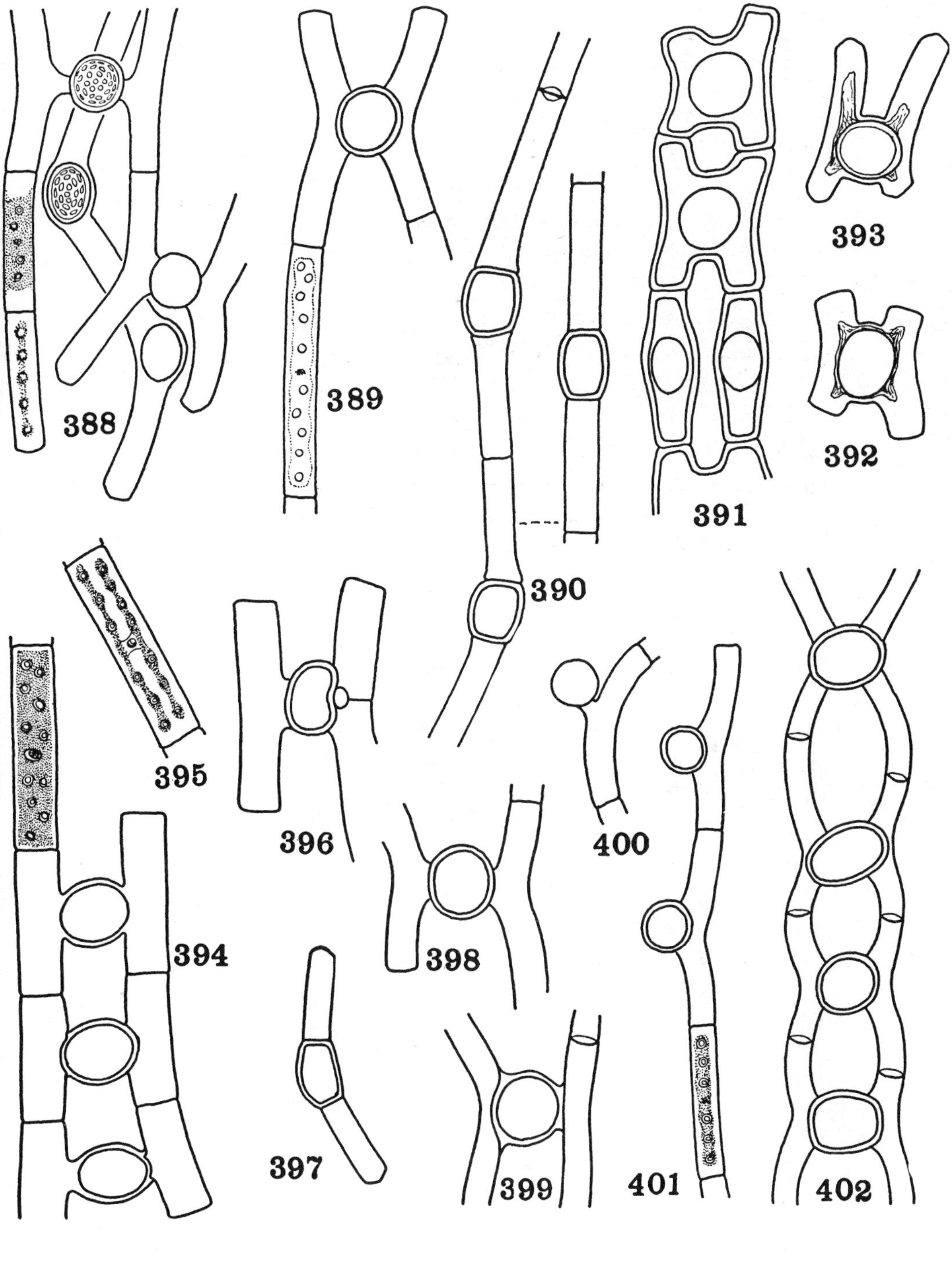

388

389

390

391

392

393

394

395

396

397

398

399

400

401

402

6. Spore-wall scrobiculate.. 7
6. Spore-wall smooth... 8
7. Vegetative cell 8–16 μ in diameter.................. 9. M. nummuloides
7. Vegetative cell 25–33 μ in diameter................. 10. M. robusta
   8. Zygote 13–25 μ in diameter...................... 11. M. parvula
   8. Zygote more than 25 μ in diameter.................................. 9
9. Vegetative cell often geniculate.................... 12. M. genuflexa
9. Vegetative cell not geniculate....................................... 10
   10. Zygote ovoid to subglobose, 36–40 × 40–55 μ...... 13. M. sphaerocarpa
   10. Zygote ovoid to globose, 30–38 × 30–38 μ......... 14. M. scalaris
11. Vegetative cell 9–13 μ in diameter.................. 15. M. transeaui
11. Vegetative cell 14–20 μ in diameter................. 16. M. floridana

1. *Mougeotia elegantula* Wittrock. Vegetative cells 3.5–4.5 × 50–135 μ; chromatophores with 4–8 pyrenoids; conjugating cells geniculate, sporangium adjoined by 4 cells; zygotes cruciate-quadrate, 18–24 μ across, with smooth hyaline walls, the corners rounded; aplanospores ellipsoid, 6–9 × 20–24 μ, otherwise similar to the zygotes. Pl. **39**, figs. **405–408**.

2. *Mougeotia boodlei* (W. and G. S. West) Collins. Vegetative cells 4.0–5.5 × 25–225 μ; chromatophores 0.5 to 0.8 the length of the cell, with 4–6 pyrenoids; zygotes quadrate, 15–18 × 15–23 μ, corners somewhat rounded; aplanospores ellipsoid, 12–15 × 23–35 μ, projecting slightly on the convex side of the slightly curved sporangia; spore-wall punctate, yellow-brown. Pl. **39**, figs. **403, 404**.

3. *Mougeotia viridis* (Kuetzing) Wittrock. Vegetative cells 6–9 × 40–160 μ; chromatophores occupying most of the cell, with 2–6 pyrenoids; zygotes adjoined by 4 cells, quadrate with concave sides and retuse angles, 20–32 μ on the side; aplanospores oblique-ellipsoid, 14–16 × 30–36 μ; spore-wall smooth, colorless. Pl. **39**, figs. **409, 410**.

4. *Mougeotia tumidula* Transeau. Vegetative cells 6.0–8.5 × 70–120 μ, chromatophore with 4–8 pyrenoids; sporangia dividing both gametangia; zygote quadrangular, with convex walls, 22–26 × 26–30 μ, angles retuse, walls colorless and coarsely punctate; aplanospores obliquely ellipsoid,

Figs. 403, 404.—*Mougeotia boodlei* (W. and G. S. West) Collins.

Figs. 405–408.—*Mougeotia elegantula* Wittrock.

Figs. 409, 410.—*Mougeotia viridis* (Kuetzing) Wittrock.

Figs. 411, 412.—*Mougeotia quadrangulata* Hassall.

Fig. 413.—*Mougeotia genuflexa* (Dillwyn) C. A. Agardh.

Fig. 414.—*Mougeotia tumidula* Transeau.

Figs. 415, 416.—*Mougeotia gracillima* (Hassall) Wittrock.

(All figures from Transeau. Figs. 411–413 ×200; all others ×400.)

PLATE 39
(Figs. 403 to 416)

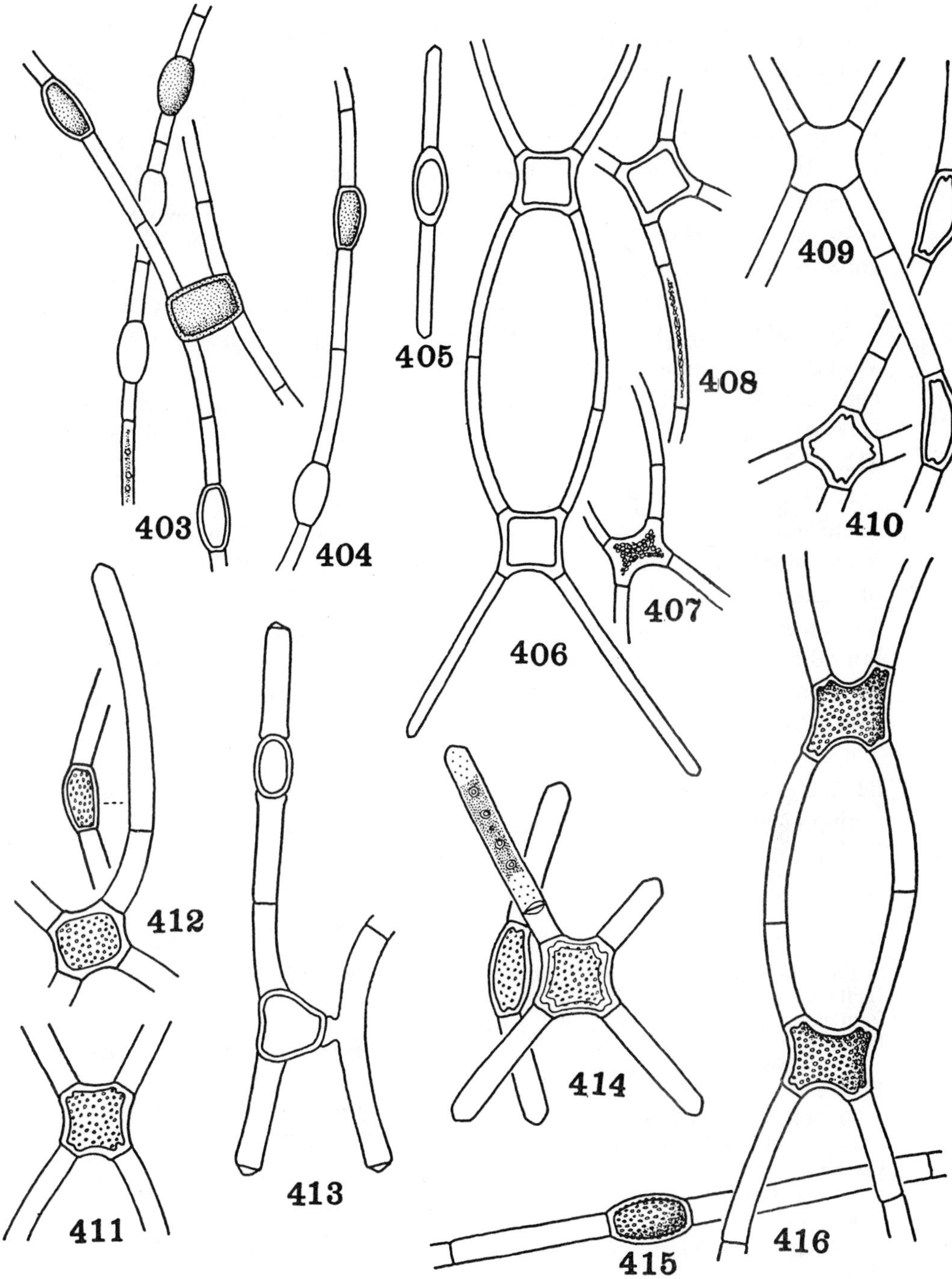

12–14 $\times$ 28–32 μ, with retuse ends and coarsely punctate wall. Pl. **39**, fig. **414**.

5. *Mougeotia gracillima* (Hassall) Wittrock. Vegetative cells 5–7 $\times$ 55–140 μ; sporangia dividing both gametangia (rarely only 1); zygote quadrate, with deeply concave sides, 20–25 $\times$ 20–28 μ, angles retuse, wall minutely verrucose; aplanospores spindle-shaped. Pl. **39**, figs. **415, 416**.

6. *Mougeotia reinschii* Transeau. Vegetative cells 15–24 $\times$ 75–170 μ, chromatophores with 4–8 pyrenoids in a single row; conjugation lateral, very rarely scalariform; zygote quadrately ovoid, 24–30 $\times$ 26–32 μ, spore-wall brown, smooth. Pl. **40**, fig. **421**.

7. *Mougeotia quadrangulata* Hassall. Vegetative cells 8–13 $\times$ 50–140 μ, with 8–16 pyrenoids in a line; conjugating cells geniculate; sporangia dividing both gametangia; zygote quadrate with straight sides and truncate corners or rarely with angles retuse, 28–40 μ on a side, with colorless punctate wall; aplanospores obliquely ovoid, 20–21 $\times$ 36–44 μ. Pl. **39**, figs. **411, 412**.

8. *Mougeotia calcarea* (Cleve) Wittrock. Vegetative cells 8–14 $\times$ 40–280 μ, chromatophore 0.5 to 0.8 the cell length, cells elongating and becoming geniculate before the spore formation; zygote globose, 25–30 μ in diameter or angular-globose, 22–28 $\times$ 30–50 μ, wholly in the tube, or extending into 1 or both gametangia, spore-wall smooth, colorless; aplanospores globose, lateral to the sporogenous wall or extending into the sporogenous cell, 17–21 μ in diameter, or rarely trapezoid-ovoid, dividing the sporogenous wall, 15–20 $\times$ 20–28 μ. Pl. **38**, figs. **397–402**.

9. *Mougeotia nummuloides* (Hassall) DeToni. Vegetative cells 8–16 $\times$ 32–160 μ; chromatophores with 2–6 pyrenoids in a row; sporangia not dividing either gametangium; zygote globose to ovoid, (17–) 22–32 (–37) μ in diameter; aplanospore ovoid within the angled sporogenous cell; spore-wall brown, scrobiculate. Pl. **38**, fig. **388**.

Figs. 417, 418.—*Mougeotia genuflexa* (Dillwyn) C. A. Agardh, showing scalariform and lateral conjugation, and genuflexing.

Figs. 419, 420.—*Mougeotia scalaris* Hassall.

Fig. 421.—*Mougeotia reinschii* Transeau.

Figs. 422–424.—*Mougeotia transeaui* Collins.

Fig. 425.—*Mougeotia parvula* Hassall.

Fig. 426.—*Zygnema sterile* Transeau.

Fig. 427.—*Zygnema cylindricum* Transeau.

Figs. 428, 429.—*Zygnema collinsianum* Transeau; fig. 428 with aplanospore and rhizoid.

Fig. 430.—*Zygnema insigne* (Hassall) Kuetzing.

Fig. 431.—*Zygnema tenue* Kuetzing.

Fig. 432.—*Zygnema azureum* Taft.

(Figs. 417–429, Transeau; figs. 430, 431, Jao; fig. 432, Transeau *et al.* Figs. 417, 418, 421 $\times$*150;* figs. 419, 420, 422–424, 426–429 $\times$*225;* fig. 425 $\times$*375;* figs. 430–432 $\times$*300.*)

PLATE 40

(Figs. 417 to 432)

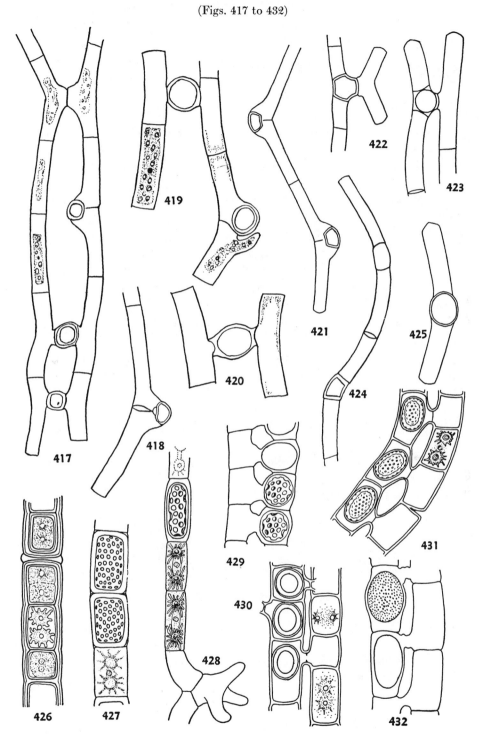

417 418 419 420 421 422 423 424 425 426 427 428 429 430 431 432

10. *Mougeotia robusta* (DeBary) Wittrock. Vegetative cells 25–33 ×75–260 μ, chromatophores with 10–20 irregularly distributed pyrenoids; sporangia not dividing either gametangium; zygotes ovoid to subglobose, 35–41 × 47–58 μ, spore-wall brown, scrobiculate; pits 1.0–1.6 μ in diameter, scattered. Pl. **38**, figs. **394–396.**

11. *Mougeotia parvula* Hassall. Vegetative cells 8–13 × 30–140 μ; chromatophores usually occupying $\frac{2}{3}$ of the cell, with 4–8 pyrenoids; conjugation scalariform; zygotes formed wholly in the conjugation tube, globose, 13–25 μ in diameter; spore-wall thick, brown, smooth; aplanospores obliquely ovoid, 16–20 × 20–24 μ. Pl. **40**, fig. **425.**

12. *Mougeotia genuflexa* (Dillwyn) C. A. Agardh. Vegetative cells 25–38 × 50–225 μ, often geniculate and attached to other similar cells, forming extensive nets, sometimes with rhizoidal branches; conjugation lateral, much less frequently scalariform; sporangia not dividing either gametangium; zygotes quadrately ovoid to globose, 30–40 μ in diameter, spore-wall smooth, brown. Pl. **39**, fig. **413;** pl. **40**, figs. **417, 418.**

13. *Mougeotia sphaerocarpa* Wolle. Vegetative cells 19–24 × 60–120 (–240) μ, usually with 4–6 pyrenoids, gametangia curved; zygote in the greatly enlarged conjugating tube or extending into the gametangia, ovoid or subglobose, 36–40 × 40–55 μ in diameter, spore-wall smooth, brown; aplanospores ovoid to obliquely ovoid, 24–30 × 35–50 μ. Pl. **38**, figs. **389–393.**

14. *Mougeotia scalaris* Hassall. Vegetative cells 20–34 × 40–180 μ; chromatophores with 4–10 pyrenoids in a single row, fertile cells straight or slightly curved; sporangia dividing neither gametangium; zygotes ovoid to globose, 30–38 (–40) μ in diameter; spore-wall smooth, yellow-brown, occupying the conjugating tube. Pl. **40**, figs. **419, 420.**

15. *Mougeotia transeaui* Collins. Vegetative cells 9–13 × 50–150 μ;

Fig. 433.—*Zygnema conspicuum* (Hassall) Transeau.

Fig. 434.—*Zygnema neopectinatum* Transeau.

Fig. 435.—*Zygnema excrassum* Transeau.

Fig. 436.—*Zygnema subtile* Kuetzing, a single zygote.

Fig. 437.—*Zygnema stellinum* (Vaucher) C. A. Agardh.

Fig. 438.—*Zygnema subcruciatum* Transeau.

Fig. 439.—*Zygnema cruciatum* (Vaucher) C. A. Agardh.

Fig. 440.—*Zygnema neocruciatum* Transeau, a single zygote.

Fig. 441.—*Zygnema vaucherii* C. A. Agardh.

Fig. 442.—*Zygnema chalybeospermum* Hansgirg.

Fig. 443.—*Zygnema leiospermum* DeBary.

(Figs. 433–435, Transeau *et al.*; figs. 437, 438, Jao; figs. 439, 441, Transeau; fig. 442, Czurda; fig. 443, Borge. Figs. 433–435 ×*500;* figs. 436, 439, 440 ×*350;* figs. 437, 438, 442, 443 ×*300;* fig. 441 ×*200.*)

PLATE 41

(Figs. 433 to 443)

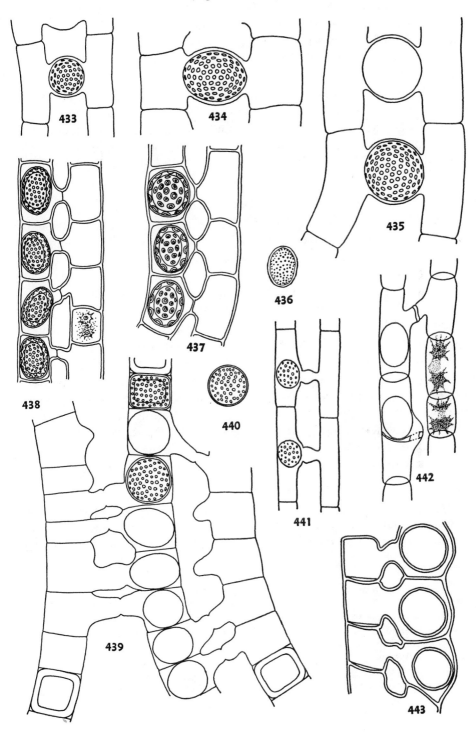

chromatophore with 4–8 pyrenoids in a single row; conjugation scalariform; zygotes globose to triangular-ovoid, 20–30 × 26–36 μ, occupying the middle of the receptive gametangium and the tube; spore-wall smooth; aplanospores obliquely ovoid, 12–20 × 20–32 μ. Pl. 40, figs. 422–424.

16. *Mougeotia floridana* Transeau. Vegetative cells 14–20 × 60–200 μ; chromatophores with 6–8 pyrenoids in a single row; zygote occupying the middle of the receptive gametangium and the tube, globose to triangular-ovoid, 30–40 × 36–48 μ, spore-wall yellow, smooth; aplanospores 18–24 × 30–45 μ, obliquely ovoid, occupying the middle of the cell, spore-wall yellow, smooth.

Zygnemopsis (Skuja) Transeau 1934

Filaments simple, cells 2–5 (–10) diameters long, with 2, occasionally 3–6 stellate or pillow-shaped chromatophores, each with a pyrenoid, connected by a cytoplasmic isthmus in which the nucleus occurs; cells lengthening at time of conjugation; separated from *Zygnema* by the swelling and filling of the gametangia with a dense lamellose pectic and cellulose colloid as the gametes pass into the conjugating tubes.

Reproduction by zygotes, parthenospores and aplanospores; several species known only from vegetative characteristics and aplanospores.

1. *Zygnemopsis decussata* (Transeau) Transeau. Vegetative cells 16–20 × 24–50 μ, chromatophores 2 and radiate, each with 1 pyrenoid; zygote ovoid to quadrate-ovoid, and irregular, 24–30 × 30–48 μ, angles rounded, retuse or produced; aplanospores unilaterally ovoid, the plane of the convex side changing with successive cells, 17–25 × 20–40 μ; parthenospores 15–20 × 20–30 μ; median wall in all the spores scrobiculate; akinetes with smooth heavy walls, 18–20 × 20–36 μ. Pl. 42, fig. 450.

Zygogonium Kuetzing 1843

Filaments with cylindric cells containing 2 axillary disc-shaped or pillow-shaped chromatophores with rounded or irregular margins, each with a central pyrenoid, and connected by a cytoplasmic isthmus to which the

FIG. 444.—*Zygnema adpectinatum* Transeau.

FIG. 445.—*Zygnema decussatum* (Vaucher) C. A. Agardh.

FIG. 446.—*Zygnema pectinatum* (Vaucher) C. A. Agardh.

FIGS. 447–449.—*Zygogonium ericetorum* Kuetzing, showing various stages in conjugation, formation and germination of aplanospores, and rhizoidal branches.

FIG. 450.—*Zygnemopsis decussata* (Transeau) Transeau, showing both zygotes and parthenospores.

(Fig. 444, Transeau *et al.*; fig. 445, Transeau. Figs. 444, 445 ×*350;* figs. 446, 450 ×*225;* figs. 447–449 ×*400.*)

PLATE 42

(Figs. 444 to 450)

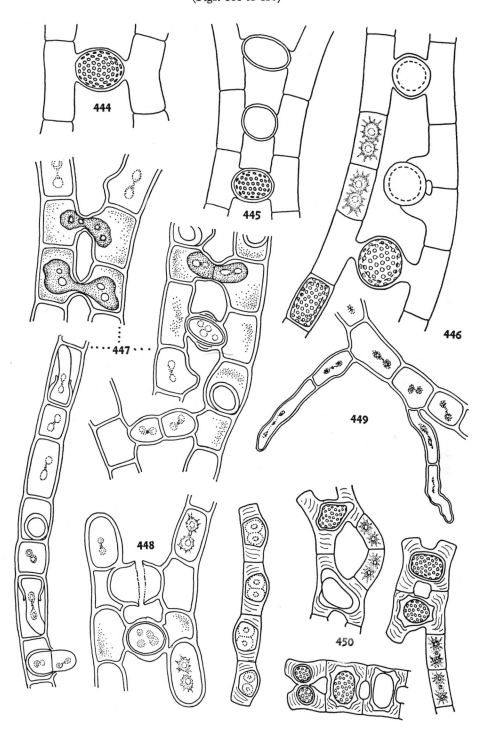

nucleus is laterally attached; plants usually unbranched, but sometimes with lateral branches of several to many cells; cell-wall thin, or greatly thickened and lamellose, often yellowish or brownish in color, cell-sap sometimes purple.

Reproduction by akinetes and aplanospores, and by zygotes formed by lateral or scalariform conjugation of isogamous gametes developing from only a portion of the cell contents; zygote enclosed in a sporangial wall which dehisces by an equatorial suture; aplanospores with cytoplasmic residue outside the spore-wall.

1. *Zygogonium ericetorum* Kuetzing. Vegetative cells 12–33 × 10–100 μ, with 2 axillary chromatophores, disc-shaped, pillow-shaped or indefinite, each with a central pyrenoid; conjugation scalariform; zygote 15–26 × 20–36 μ, thick-walled, smooth, ovoid or ellipsoid, in a sporangium formed by the conjugating tube and cut off from the adjoining gametangia; aplanospore globose or ovoid, occupying only a part of the cell, 15–20 × 15–40 μ, spore-wall smooth; terrestrial or submerged, with terrestrial forms frequently having purple cell-sap, thick lamellose walls colored yellow or brown; filaments branched or unbranched. Pl. 42, figs. 447–449.

Zygnema C. A. Agardh 1824

Filaments simple, with cells 1–9 diameters long, usually with 2 distinctly stellate chromatophores (rarely in some cells 1–4), each with a prominent central pyrenoid, connected by a cytoplasmic isthmus containing the nucleus.

Reproduction by zygotes, each formed largely or wholly in the tube (isogamy) or in 1 of the gametangia (anisogamy), parthenospores and aplanospores; conjugation scalariform, rarely lateral; spores with 3 (rarely 4) layers making up the wall: inner and outer usually thin and colorless, median layer chitinous, usually thick, varying in color from pale yellow to chestnut-brown or to bright blue or blue-black (blue spores are at first yellow, then brown, finally blue).

KEY TO THE SPECIES

1. Reproduction by zygotes (sometimes by aplanospores also) 2
1. Reproduction by aplanospores (zygotes rare or none) . . 1. Z. cylindricum
1. Reproduction mostly by akinetes . . . . 2. Z. sterile
   2. Zygote wholly or largely in conjugating tubes 3
   2. Zygote mostly in 1 of the gametangia 5
3. Vegetative cell 16–20 μ in diameter . . . . 3. Z. decussatum
3. Vegetative cell 22–27 μ in diameter . . . . 4. Z. conspicuum
3. Vegetative cell 25–30 μ in diameter . . . . 5. Z. adpectinatum
3. Vegetative cell 30–36 μ in diameter 4
3. Vegetative cell 40–45 μ in diameter . . . . 6. Z. neopectinatum

4. Zygote 35–40 × 36–45 μ........................ 7. Z. pectinatum
4. Zygote 45–50 × 50–70 μ........................ 8. Z. excrassum
5. Median wall of zygote smooth.. 6
5. Median wall of zygote not smooth................................... 8
  6. Median wall of zygote blue at maturity......... 9. Z. chalybeospermum
  6. Median wall of zygote brown at maturity............................ 7
7. Diameter of vegetative cell 20–24 μ .... 10. Z. leiospermum
7. Diameter of vegetative cell 26–32 μ .... 11. Z. insigne
  8. Median wall of zygote yellow to brown at maturity..................... 9
  8. Median wall of zygote blue to blue-black at maturity................... 13
9. Receptive gametangium cylindric or slightly enlarged.................... 10
9. Receptive gametangium greatly enlarged or inflated..................... 11
  10. Diameter of vegetative cell 24–30 μ............. 12. Z. subcruciatum
  10. Diameter of vegetative cell 30–36 μ............. 13. Z. cruciatum
  10. Diameter of vegetative cell 40–50 μ............. 14. Z. neocruciatum
11. Median wall of zygote punctate................... 15. Z. subtile
11. Median wall of zygote scrobiculate.................................... 12
  12. Vegetative cell 18–24 μ in diameter............. 16. Z. tenue
  12. Vegetative cell 24–28 μ in diameter............. 17. Z. vaucherii
  12. Vegetative cell 28–38 μ in diameter............. 18. Z. stellinum
13. Receptive gametangium cylindric or slightly enlarged. 19. Z. catenatum
13. Receptive gametangium greatly enlarged or inflated...................... 14
  14. Median wall of spore finely punctate........... 20. Z. azureum
  14. Median wall of spore pitted.................... 21. Z. collinsianum

1. *Zygnema cylindricum* Transeau. Vegetative cells 28–33 × 28–66 μ; aplanospores cylindric or tumid-cylindric, 30–33 × 24–54 μ, median spore-wall brown, scrobiculate, pits about 3 μ in diameter, suture irregular, filling the sporangia; zygotes not known. Pl. 40, fig. 427.

2. *Zygnema sterile* Transeau. Vegetative cells 44–54 × 22–69 μ, with heavy cell-walls, often with an outer pectic layer 6–15 μ in thickness; usually passing the dormant season as heavy-walled akinetes; rarely reproducing by aplanospores; median spore-wall brown and often distinctly colligate; zygotes not known. Pl. 40, fig. 426.

3. *Zygnema decussatum* (Vaucher) C. A. Agardh. Vegetative cells 16–20 × 35–100 μ; zygote globose to ovoid, 24–33 × 26–36 μ, median spore-wall finely scrobiculate, brown, forming in the conjugating tube. Pl. 42, fig. 445.

4. *Zygnema conspicuum* (Hassall) Transeau. Vegetative cells 22–27 × 50–90 μ; conjugation scalariform, zygote globose to ovoid, in the conjugating tubes, 24–32 × 26–33 μ, with median spore-wall brown, scrobiculate: pits about 1.5–2.0 μ in diameter and the same distance apart. Pl. 41, fig. 433.

5. *Zygnema adpectinatum* Transeau. Vegetative cells 25–30 × 30–100 μ;

zygote ovoid to globose, $36-40 \times 40-50 \mu$, in the conjugation tubes, with median spore-wall yellow-brown, scrobiculate: pits 2μ in diameter. Pl. 42, fig. 444.

6. *Zygnema neopectinatum* Transeau. Vegetative cells $40-45 \times 40-85 \mu$; zygote ovoid to globose, $45-54 \times 55-60 \mu$, in the conjugating tubes, with median spore-wall brown, scrobiculate: pits about 3μ in diameter. Pl. 41, fig. 434.

7. *Zygnema pectinatum* (Vaucher) C. A. Agardh. Vegetative cells $30-36 \times 25-120 \mu$, often with thick outer mucilaginous wall; zygote globose to ovoid, $35-44 \times 40-54 \mu$, in the conjugating tube, with median spore-wall brown, scrobiculate: pits about $2-3 \mu$ in diameter; aplanospores ovoid or cylindric, $30-38 \times 30-60 \mu$. Pl. 42, fig. 446.

8. *Zygnema excrassum* Transeau. Vegetative cells $32-36 \times 32-80 \mu$; conjugation scalariform; zygote $(40-) 50-60 \times 50-70 (-80) \mu$, in the tubes, usually ovoid, rarely globose, median spore-wall brown, scrobiculate: pits $3-4 \mu$ in diameter and about $3-4 \mu$ apart; aplanospores cylindric-ovoid, nearly filling the sporogenous cells. Pl. 41, fig. 435.

9. *Zygnema chalybeospermum* Hansgirg. Vegetative cells $24-27 \times 24-84 \mu$; conjugation scalariform or lateral; zygote in 1 of the gametangia, receptive gametangia cylindric or enlarged; zygote globose to ovoid, $30-33 \times 30-38 \mu$, median spore-wall blue, thick, smooth. Pl. 41, fig. 442.

10. *Zygnema leiospermum* DeBary. Vegetative cells $20-24 \times 20-40 \mu$; conjugation scalariform; zygote globose to ovoid, $23-30 \times 23-32 \mu$, in 1 somewhat swollen gametangium, median spore-wall thick, brown, and smooth. Pl. 41, fig. 443.

11. *Zygnema insigne* (Hassall) Kuetzing. Vegetative cells $26-32 \times 26-60 \mu$; conjugation scalariform or lateral; zygote globose or subglobose, $27-33 \times 27-35 \mu$, in 1 of the gametangia, receptive gametangia cylindric or enlarged, median wall yellow-brown and smooth; aplanospores $28-33 \mu$, ovoid to cylindric-ovoid, otherwise similar to zygotes. Pl. 40, fig. 430.

12. *Zygnema subcruciatum* Transeau. Vegetative cells $24-30 \times 26-60 \mu$; conjugation scalariform; receptive gametangium cylindric or enlarged mostly on the inner side; zygote globose to ovoid, $25-32 \times 28-40 \mu$, median spore-wall brown, finely scrobiculate. Pl. 41, fig. 438.

13. *Zygnema cruciatum* (Vaucher) C. A. Agardh. Vegetative cells $30-36 \times 30-60 \mu$; conjugation scalariform; zygote globose to ovoid, $30-38 \times 32-40 \mu$, in 1 of the gametangia, receptive gametangia cylindric or enlarged, median spore-wall brown and scrobiculate: pits about $1.5-2.0 \mu$ in diameter, $3-5 \mu$ apart; aplanospores cylindric-ovoid, $30-35 \times 30-60 \mu$, filling the cells, otherwise similar to zygotes. Pl. 41, fig. 439.

14. *Zygnema neocruciatum* Transeau. Vegetative cells 40–50 × 30–100 μ; conjugation scalariform; zygote globose or cylindric-ovoid, 40–45 × 40–50 μ, in 1 of the cylindric or slightly enlarged gametangia, median spore-wall brown and scrobiculate: pits about 2 μ in diameter and 3–4 μ apart; aplanospores common and similar to zygotes, rarely attaining lengths of 80 μ. Pl. 41, fig. 440.

15. *Zygnema subtile* Kuetzing. Vegetative cells 14–20 × 30–85 μ; conjugation scalariform or rarely lateral; zygote formed in 1 of the enlarged or sometimes inflated gametangia; zygote 20–29 × 22–30 μ, ovoid to subglobose, median spore-wall brown, punctate. Pl. 41, fig. 436.

16. *Zygnema tenue* Kuetzing. Vegetative cells 18–24 × 20–70 μ; conjugation scalariform; zygote globose to ovoid, often somewhat compressed, 25–30 × 25–40 μ, in 1 of the gametangia; median spore-wall brown, scrobiculate: pits 2–3 μ in diameter and 3–4 μ apart; receptive gametangia greatly enlarged or inflated toward the middle. Pl. 40, fig. 431.

17. *Zygnema vaucherii* C. A. Agardh. Vegetative cells 24–28 × 50–180 μ; conjugation scalariform; zygote ovoid, in 1 of the gametangia, 24–36 × 26–45 μ, median spore-wall brown and scrobiculate: pits about 3 μ in diameter; receptive gametangia gradually or abruptly inflated toward the middle. Pl. 41, fig. 441.

18. *Zygnema stellinum* (Vaucher) C. A. Agardh. Vegetative cells 28–38 × 27–100 μ; conjugation scalariform, rarely lateral; zygote ovoid, in 1 of the gametangia, 30–42 × 35–48 (–57) μ, median spore-wall yellow-brown, thick and scrobiculate: pits 3–4 μ in diameter and 3–4 μ apart; aplanospores common, usually cylindric, very rarely globose, walls similar to those of zygotes. Pl. 41, fig. 437.

19. *Zygnema catenatum* Transeau. Vegetative cells 30–36 × 35–80 μ; conjugation scalariform; zygote in 1 of the gametangia; receptive gametangium slightly enlarged on the conjugating side; zygote globose to ovoid, slightly compressed, 30–36 × 30–46 μ, median spore-wall blue, scrobiculate: pits 1.5–2.0 μ in diameter, 2–4 μ apart; aplanospores similar, 30–34 × 30–80 μ, filling the cells.

20. *Zygnema azureum* Taft. Vegetative cells 26–29 × 46–66 μ; conjugation scalariform, spores formed in 1 of the gametangia, receptive gametangium slightly to greatly enlarged; zygote ovoid to cylindric-ovoid, 27–33 × 33–50 μ, median spore-wall blue, finely punctate. Pl. 40, fig. 432.

21. *Zygnema collinsianum* Transeau. Vegetative cells 18–25 × 32–80 μ; conjugation scalariform, receptive gametangia inflated on the inner side near the middle; zygote globose, 26–40 μ in diameter to ovoid and 26–40 × 30–47 μ, median spore-wall blue, thick and marked by pits 4–5 μ in

diameter and 1–2 μ apart; aplanospores cylindric-ovoid, 18–24 $\times$ 40–76 μ, similar to the zygotes in color and markings. Pl. **40,** figs. **428, 429.**

Spirogyra Link 1820

Simple filaments with cylindric cells, 0.5–30.0 diameters long, end walls plane, colligate, semireplicate, replicate; chromatophores 1–16, straight or spirally arranged parietal ribbon-like bodies embedded in the cytoplasm, each with several to many more or less distinct pyrenoids; nucleus centrally placed, supported by several strands of cytoplasm which terminate near pyrenoids.

Reproduction by zygotes, aplanospores, parthenospores, akinetes and fragmentation; conjugation usually scalariform, sometimes lateral; tubes formed by both gametangia or by the male gametangium, before movement of the gametes; zygote walls layered, with chitinous median layer variously colored, smooth or ornamented.

KEY TO THE SPECIES

1. End walls of cells all plane.. 2
1. End walls of cells replicate*.. 39
1. End walls of cells semireplicate...................... 1. S. narcissiana
    2. Conjugating tubes formed by projections of both gametangia.............. 3
    2. Conjugating tubes formed wholly, or nearly so, from the male gametangium 36
3. Cells with 1 chromatophore (rarely 2)..................................... 4
3. Cells with 2–16 chromatophores (rarely 1)............................... 19
    4. Median spore-wall smooth†.. 5
    4. Median spore-wall variously ornamented........................... 18
5. Spores evidently polymorphic........................ 2. S. pratensis
5. Spores generally quite uniform in shape............................... 6
    6. Spores ellipsoid‡.. 7
    6. Spores ovoid to cylindric-ovoid (rarely globose or ellipsoid)............... 14
    6. Spores varying from ellipsoid to cylindric-ovoid....... 7. S. silvicola
7. Receptive gametangia cylindric or enlarged by spore...................... 8
7. Receptive gametangia inflated... 11
    8. Vegetative cell more than 44 μ in diameter........... 3. S. condensata
    8. Vegetative cell less than 44 μ in diameter............................ 9
9. Diameter of vegetative cell 18–26 μ.................... 4. S. communis
9. Diameter of vegetative cell 24–30 μ..................... 5. S. juergensii
9. Diameter of vegetative cell 29–42 μ................................... 10
    10. Spores 27–36 μ in diameter....................... 6. S. singularis
    10. Spores 36–43 μ in diameter....................... 7. S. silvicola
11. Inflation usually on the conjugating side only.......................... 12
11. Inflation usually on outer side only.................... 8. S. borgeana
11. Inflation usually on both sides... 13

   * At time of fruiting, some or many walls may be plane.
   † Second outer spore-wall scrobiculate in *S. velata* (no. 18).
   ‡ *S. mirabilis* (no. 16) and *S. velata* (no. 18) may occasionally be sought here.

12. Vegetative cell 16–24 μ in diameter.................. 9. S. gracilis
12. Vegetative cell 24–30 μ in diameter................. 10. S. teodoresci
12. Vegetative cell 30–40 μ in diameter............... 11. S. varians
12. Vegetative cell 40–48 μ in diameter................ 12. S. circumlineata
13. Diameter of vegetative cell 20–24 μ.................. 13. S. parvula
13. Diameter of vegetative cell 24–32 μ.................. 14. S. catenaeformis
    14. Vegetative cell usually less than 40 μ in diameter..................... 15
    14. Vegetative cell 40–50 μ in diameter................ 15. S. porticalis
15. Spores usually less than 29 μ in diameter............... 16. S. mirabilis
15. Spores usually more than 29 μ in diameter............................... 16
    16. Receptive gametangia cylindric or enlarged by spore................... 17
    16. Receptive gametangia inflated on inner side........ 11. S. varians
17. All walls of zygote smooth........................... 17. S. longata
17. Outer zygote-wall scrobiculate....................... 18. S. velata
    18. Median spore-wall irregularly corrugate............. 19. S. daedalea
    18. Median spore-wall irregularly reticulate............ 20. S. daedaleoides
    18. Median spore-wall finely punctate.................. 21. S. lagerheimii
    18. Median spore-wall scrobiculate.................... 22. S. scrobiculata
19. Median spore-wall smooth.. 20
19. Median spore-wall not smooth..................................... 31
    20. Spores laterally compressed.................................... 21
    20. Spores not laterally compressed................................ 23
21. Spores compressed-ellipsoid.......................... 23. S. crassoidea
21. Spores compressed-spheroid (lenticular)............................ 22
    22. Spores 57–62 μ in diameter.................... 24. S. majuscula
    22. Spores 70–110 μ in diameter..................... 25. S. submaxima
23. Receptive gametangia cylindric or enlarged by spore..................... 24
23. Receptive gametangia inflated.................................... 30
    24. Spores ellipsoid or cylindric-ellipsoid............................ 25
    24. Spores ovoid or cylindric-ovoid, rarely globose........................ 26
25. Vegetative cell 32–37 μ in diameter.................... 26. S. irregularis
25. Vegetative cell 70–80 μ in diameter.................... 27. S. nitida
25. Vegetative cell 90–115 μ in diameter.................... 28. S. setiformis
25. Vegetative cell 125–150 μ in diameter.................... 29. S. ellipsospora
    26. Chromatophores 2.......................... 30. S. distenta
    26. Chromatophores 3... 27
    26. Chromatophores 1–3.. 28
    26. Chromatophores 2–5.. 29
27. Spores 34–48 × 48–54 μ.................... 31. S. triplicata
27. Spores 54–64 × 75–100 μ.................... 32. S. neglecta
    28. Vegetative cell 32–42 μ in diameter.................. 33. S. decimina
    28. Vegetative cell 40–50 μ in diameter.................. 34. S. occidentalis
29. Diameter of spores 60–76 μ.......................... 27. S. nitida
29. Diameter of spores 87–108 μ.......................... 35. S. jugalis
    30. Vegetative cell 40–50 μ in diameter.................. 36. S. dubia
    30. Vegetative cell 55–67 μ in diameter.................. 32. S. neglecta
31. Spores laterally compressed... 32
31. Spores not laterally compressed... 34

32. Median spore-wall reticulate .... 37. S. maxima
32. Median spore-wall pitted 33
33. Vegetative cell 80–95 μ in diameter.................... 38. S. formosa
33. Vegetative cell 140–165 μ in diameter.................. 39. S. crassa
   34. Spores ellipsoid............................... 40. S. propria
   34. Spores ovoid.. 35
35. Vegetative cell 30–45 μ in diameter.................... 41. S. fluviatilis
35. Vegetative cell 48–60 μ in diameter.................... 42. S. novae-angliae
35. Vegetative cell 70–85 μ in diameter.................... 43. S. diluta
   36. Vegetative cell 27–30 μ in diameter.............. 44. S. punctiformis
   36. Vegetative cell 30–40 (–44) μ in diameter........... 37
   36. Vegetative cell 40–100 μ in diameter............... 38
37. Median spore-wall smooth.................... 45. S. reflexa
37. Median spore-wall punctate.................... 46. S. micropunctata
37. Median spore-wall corrugate.................... 47. S. corrugata
   38. Chromatophore 1.................... 48. S. rugulosa
   38. Chromatophores 2–4.................... 49. S. wabashensis
   38. Chromatophores 7–10.................... 50. S. hydrodictya
39. Chromatophore single in a cell.................... 40
39. More than 1 chromatophore in a cell (rarely 1)............ 48
   40. Receptive gametangia cylindric or enlarged by spore*.......... 41
   40. Receptive gametangia inflated.................... 43
41. Spores 21–30 μ in diameter........................... 51. S. weberi
41. Spores 29–60 μ in diameter.................... 42
   42. Vegetative cell 20–25 μ in diameter................. 52. S. latviensis
   42. Vegetative cell 28–34 μ in diameter................. 60. S. protecta
   42. Vegetative cell 34–40 μ in diameter................. 61. S. cleveana
   42. Vegetative cell 42–56 μ in diameter................. 62. S. denticulata
43. Inflation of gametangium fusiform.................... 44
43. Inflation of gametangium cylindric (quadrate)............ 45
   44. Median spore-wall scrobiculate.................... 46
   44. Median spore-wall smooth.................... 47
45. Diameter of vegetative cell 8–13 μ.................... 53. S. tenuissima
45. Diameter of vegetative cell 15–20 μ.................... 54. S. inflata
45. Diameter of vegetative cell 18–24 μ.................... 55. S. spreeiana

Figs. 451, 452.—*Spirogyra narcissiana* Transeau, showing vegetative cell, semi-replicate septa, and aplanospores.

Fig. 453.—*Spirogyra gracilis* (Hassall) Kuetzing.

Fig. 454.—*Spirogyra singularis* Nordstedt.

Fig. 455.—*Spirogyra communis* (Hassall) Kuetzing.

Fig. 456.—*Spirogyra silvicola* M. E. Britton.

Fig. 457.—*Spirogyra pratensis* Transeau, showing scalariform and lateral conjugation, aplanospores, normal and bullate vegetative cells.

(Figs. 451, 452, 457, Transeau; fig. 453, Borge; figs. 454, 455, Jao; fig. 456, M. E. Britton. Figs. 451–453, 456, 457 ×225; figs. 454, 455 ×300.)

* S. *tenuissima* (no. 53) may sometimes be sought here.

PLATE 43

(Figs. 451 to 457)

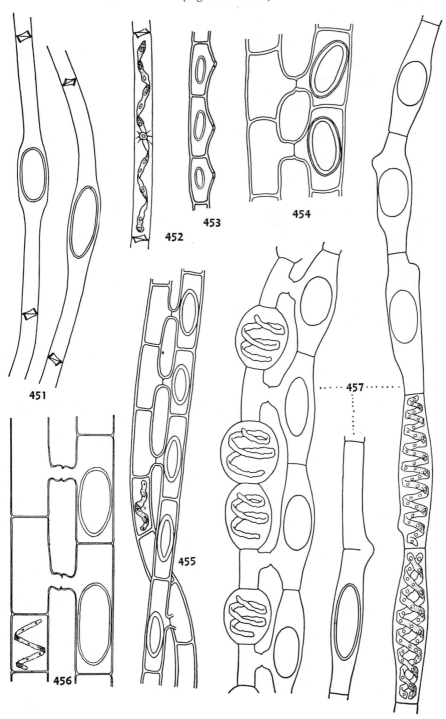

451

452

453

454

455

456

457

46. Vegetative cell 10–13 μ in diameter................ 56. S. rugosa
46. Vegetative cell 16–20 μ in diameter................ 57. S. discreta
47. Diameter of vegetative cell 18–24 μ.................. 58. S. groenlandica
47. Diameter of vegetative cell 24–30 μ.................. 59. S. quadrata
   48. Median spore-wall smooth........................ 49
   48. Median spore-wall not smooth.................... 54
49. Receptive gametangia cylindric or enlarged............ 50
49. Receptive gametangia inflated...................... 51
   50. Vegetative cell 20–25 μ in diameter............... 52. S. latviensis
   50. Vegetative cell 28–34 μ in diameter............... 60. S. protecta
   50. Vegetative cell 34–40 μ in diameter............... 61. S. cleveana
   50. Vegetative cell 42–56 μ in diameter............... 62. S. denticulata
51. Inflation of gametangia cylindric (quadrate)............ 63. S. rectangularis
51. Inflation of gametangia fusiform...................... 52
   52. Chromatophores 1–2 in each cell................... 53
   52. Chromatophores regularly 2 in each cell........... 64. S. hassallii
   52. Chromatophores 2–4 in each cell.................. 65. S. insignis
53. Second outer spore-wall scrobiculate................. 66. S. areolata
53. All spore-walls smooth............................ 67. S. grevilleana
   54. Spores mostly ovoid............................ 68. S. reticulata
   54. Spores mostly ellipsoid.......................... 55
55. Reticulum of median spore-wall papillate............. 69. S. inconstans
55. Reticulum of median spore-wall not papillate........... 70. S. tetrapla

1. *Spirogyra narcissiana* Transeau. Vegetative cells 12–14 $\times$ 200–400 μ, with semireplicate end walls and 1 slender chromatophore making 2–5 turns; fertile cells inflated toward the middle to 25–53 μ in diameter, rounded or quadrate in outline; aplanospores ellipsoid to ovoid, 23–30 $\times$ 50–120 μ; median wall yellow, smooth; zygotes not known. Pl. 43, figs. 451, 452.

2. *Spirogyra pratensis* Transeau. Vegetative cells 17–20 $\times$ 80–240 μ,

Fig. 458.—*Spirogyra condensata* (Vaucher) Kuetzing.

Fig. 459.—*Spirogyra lagerheimii* Wittrock.

Fig. 460.—*Spirogyra longata* (Vaucher) Kuetzing.

Fig. 461.—*Spirogyra parvula* (Transeau) Czurda.

Fig. 462.—*Spirogyra mirabilis* (Hassall) Kuetzing.

Fig. 463.—*Spirogyra juergensii* Kuetzing.

Fig. 464.—*Spirogyra varians* (Hassall) Kuetzing.

Figs. 465, 466.—*Spirogyra velata* Nordstedt; fig. 466, an enlarged diagram of zygote.

Fig. 467.—*Spirogyra borgeana* Transeau.

Fig. 468.—*Spirogyra porticalis* (Mueller) Cleve.

Fig. 469.—*Spirogyra catenaeformis* (Hassall) Kuetzing.

Fig. 470.—*Spirogyra circumlineata* Transeau.

(Figs. 458, 459, Borge; figs. 460, 463, 467, Jao; figs. 461, 462, 464, 466, 468–470, Transeau. Figs. 464, 470 $\times 150$; figs. 458, 461, 462, 468, 469 $\times 200$; fig. 465 $\times 250$; figs. 460, 463, 467 $\times 300$; fig. 466 $\times 600$.)

PLATE 44

(Figs. 458 to 470)

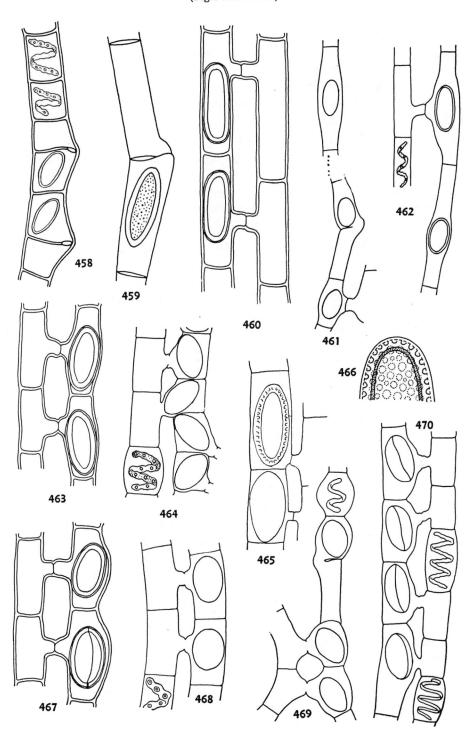

with plane end walls and 1 (rarely 2) chromatophores making 1–8 turns; conjugation scalariform and lateral, tubes formed by both gametangia; receptive gametangia inflated up to 55 μ; sterile cells cylindric, inflated or bullate, up to 90 μ in diameter; zygote polymorphic (ovoid, ellipsoid or cylindric) with pointed ends, 24–36 × 50–70 μ, with yellow, smooth median walls; aplanospores similar to zygotes. Pl. 43, fig. 457.

3. *Spirogyra condensata* (Vaucher) Kuetzing. Vegetative cells 45–60 × 45–120 μ, with plane end walls and 1 slender chromatophore making 0.5–4.0 turns in the cell; conjugation scalariform and lateral, tubes formed by both gametangia; receptive gametangia cylindric or slightly enlarged; zygote ellipsoid, 34–38 × 50–75 μ, median spore-wall yellow, smooth; sterile cells sometimes inflated. Pl. 44, fig. 458.

4. *Spirogyra communis* (Hassall) Kuetzing. Vegetative cells 18–26 × 35–90 μ, with plane end walls and 1 slender chromatophore making 1.5–4.0 turns in the cell; conjugation scalariform and lateral, tubes formed by both gametangia; fertile cells cylindric, rarely enlarged; zygote ellipsoid, 19–26 × 36–78 μ; median spore-wall yellow, smooth. Pl. 43, fig. 455.

5. *Spirogyra juergensii* Kuetzing. Vegetative cells 24–30 × 60–125 μ, with plane end walls and 1 chromatophore making 2–4 turns; conjugation scalariform and lateral, tubes formed by both gametangia; fertile cells cylindric or enlarged toward the middle to 34 μ; zygote and aplanospore ellipsoid, 28–33 × 50–75 μ, median spore-wall yellow and smooth. Pl. 44, fig. 463.

6. *Spirogyra singularis* Nordstedt. Vegetative cells 29–39 × 60–240 μ, with plane end walls; 1 chromatophore making 3–7 turns; conjugation scalariform, tubes formed by both gametangia; fertile cells cylindric, rarely enlarged; zygote ellipsoid, 27–36 × 46–70 μ, median spore-wall yellow, smooth. Pl. 43, fig. 454.

7. *Spirogyra silvicola* M. E. Britton. Vegetative cells 32–42 × 63–267 μ, with plane end walls and 1 chromatophore making 1.5–3.0 turns; conjugation scalariform, tubes formed by both gametangia; receptive gametangia cylindric or slightly enlarged; zygote ellipsoid to cylindric-ovoid, 36–43 × 56–103 μ, all walls smooth, median wall yellow or brown at maturity. Pl. 43, fig. 456.

8. *Spirogyra borgeana* Transeau. Vegetative cells 30–35 × 50–200 μ, with plane end walls and 1 chromatophore making 1.5–5.0 turns; conjugation scalariform, tubes formed by both gametangia; fertile cells inflated on the outer side, straight on the conjugating side; zygote ellipsoid, 30–40 × 54–70 μ, median spore-wall smooth, yellow. Pl. 44, fig. 467.

9. *Spirogyra gracilis* (Hassall) Kuetzing. Vegetative cells 16–24 × 50–

100 μ, with plane end walls and 1 chromatophore making 0.5–4.0 turns; conjugation scalariform, tubes formed by both gametangia; fertile cells inflated mostly on the conjugating side; zygote ellipsoid with rounded ends, 23–30 × 40–65 μ; median spore-wall yellow-brown, smooth. Pl. 43, fig. 453.

10. *Spirogyra teodoresci* Transeau. Vegetative cells 24–30 × 42–90 μ, with plane end walls; 1 chromatophore making 1–6 turns; conjugation scalariform and lateral, tubes formed by both gametangia; fertile cells strongly inflated on the conjugating side; zygote ellipsoid, 26–33 × 45–55 μ; median spore-wall smooth, yellow.

11. *Spirogyra varians* (Hassall) Kuetzing. Vegetative cells (28–) 30–40 × 30–120 μ, with plane end walls and 1 chromatophore making 1–5 turns in the cell; conjugation scalariform and lateral, tubes formed by both gametangia; fertile cells inflated, usually on the conjugating side only; sterile cells often greatly inflated; zygote 32–40 × 50–100 μ, ellipsoid (usually some ovoid and very rarely globose), with yellow, smooth median spore-wall; aplanospores similar. Pl. 44, fig. 464.

12. *Spirogyra circumlineata* Transeau. Vegetative cells (38–) 40–48 × 120–240 μ, with plane end walls and 1 slender chromatophore making 4–8 turns in the cell; conjugation scalariform, tubes formed by both gametangia; fertile cells inflated on the conjugating side only; zygote 40–50 × 70–125 μ, ellipsoid, median spore-wall smooth, yellow-brown at maturity, with outer spore-wall marked by a more or less longitudinal suture. Pl. 44, fig. 470.

13. *Spirogyra parvula* (Transeau) Czurda. Vegetative cells 20–24 × 50–105 μ, with plane end walls and 1 chromatophore making 1–6 turns; fertile cells inflated up to 37 μ; conjugation mostly lateral, sometimes scalariform, tubes formed by both gametangia; zygote 20–27 × 40–60 μ, ellipsoid, median spore-wall smooth, yellow-brown; aplanospores similar. Pl· 44, fig. 461.

14. *Spirogyra catenaeformis* (Hassall) Kuetzing. Vegetative cells 24–32 × 50–135 μ, with plane end walls and 1 broad chromatophore making 1–6 turns in the cell; conjugation scalariform and lateral, tubes formed by both gametangia; fertile cells enlarged or inflated to 38 μ; sterile cells inflated; zygote and aplanospore 27–33 × 55–90 μ, ellipsoid; median spore-wall smooth and yellow at maturity. Pl. 44, fig. 469.

15. *Spirogyra porticalis* (Mueller) Cleve. Vegetative cells 40–50 × 66–200 μ, with plane end walls; 1 chromatophore making 3–5 turns; conjugation scalariform, tubes formed by both gametangia; fertile cells cylindric

or enlarged; zygote mostly ovoid to globose-ovoid, 38–50 × 50–83 μ; median spore-wall yellow, smooth. Pl. 44, fig. 468.

16. *Spirogyra mirabilis* (Hassall) Kuetzing. Vegetative cells 23–29 × 70–200 μ, with plane end walls and 1 chromatophore making 4–7 turns in the cell; fertile cells enlarged or inflated; aplanospores (rarely zygotes) 23–29 × 50–83 μ, ovoid, less frequently varying to ellipsoid. Pl. 44, fig. 462.

17. *Spirogyra longata* (Vaucher) Kuetzing. Vegetative cells 26–38 × 45–280 μ, with plane end walls and 1 chromatophore making 2–5 turns in the cell; conjugation scalariform and lateral, tubes formed by both gametangia; fertile cells cylindric or enlarged by the spores; zygote ovoid or sometimes varying to globose, 28–38 × 50–83 μ, with smooth, yellow median spore-wall. Pl. 44, fig. 460.

18. *Spirogyra velata* Nordstedt. Vegetative cells 29–41 × 60–200 μ, with plane end walls; 1 or rarely 2 chromatophores, making 2.5–6.0 turns; conjugation scalariform, tubes formed by both gametangia; fertile cells cylindric or somewhat enlarged; zygote mostly ovoid to cylindric-ovoid, rarely ellipsoid, 37–57 × 60–100 μ; outer wall of 2 layers, of which the second is transparent and scrobiculate; the median spore-wall chitinous, yellow-brown, smooth. Pl. 44, figs. 465, 466.

19. *Spirogyra daedalea* Lagerheim. Vegetative cells 33–36 × 180–330 μ, with plane end walls; 1 chromatophore making 2.0–3.5 turns; conjugation scalariform, tubes formed by both gametangia; fertile cells cylindric or enlarged to 36–45 μ, and shortened; zygote ellipsoid, 30–40 × 50–96 μ; median spore-wall yellow-brown, very irregularly corrugate. Pl. 45, fig. 471.

20. *Spirogyra daedaleoides* Czurda. Vegetative cells 30–44 × 65–240 μ, with plane end walls and 1 chromatophore making 2–8 turns; conjugation scalariform and lateral, tubes formed by both gametangia; fertile cells en-

FIG. 471.—*Spirogyra daedalea* Lagerheim.

FIG. 472.—*Spirogyra dubia* Kuetzing.

FIGS. 473, 474.—*Spirogyra daedaleoides* Czurda; fig. 474, enlarged view of zygote to show wall ornamentation.

FIG. 475.—*Spirogyra majuscula* Kuetzing.

FIGS. 476, 477.—*Spirogyra neglecta* (Hassall) Kuetzing.

FIGS. 478, 479.—*Spirogyra maxima* (Hassall) Wittrock; fig. 478, details of wall ornamentation of zygote.

FIG. 480.—*Spirogyra setiformis* (Roth) Kuetzing.

FIGS. 481, 482.—*Spirogyra scrobiculata* (Stockmayer) Czurda; fig. 482, enlarged zygote.

FIG. 483.—*Spirogyra submaxima* Transeau.

(Figs. 471, 473, 474, 481, 482, Czurda; remainder, Transeau. Figs. 471, 475 ×*250;* figs. 472, 476, 477, 479, 480 ×*100;* figs. 473, 481 ×*300;* fig. 482 ×*700;* fig. 483 ×*150.*)

PLATE 45

(Figs. 471 to 483)

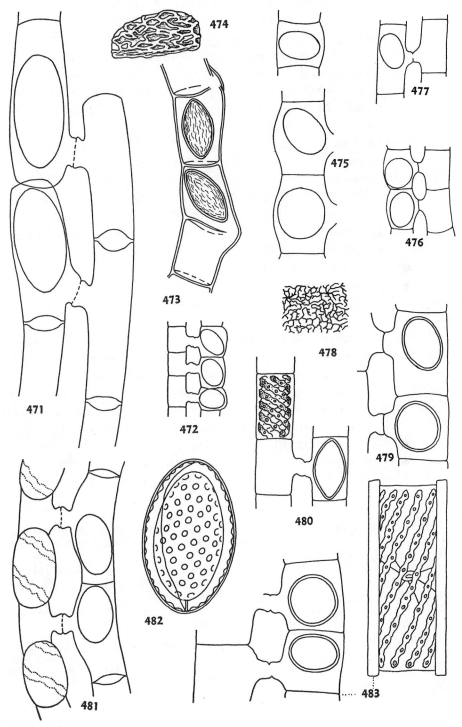

larged or slightly inflated; zygote ellipsoid, 30–46 × 46–90 μ, median spore-wall brown, with irregular reticulate ridges. Pl. 45, figs. 473, 474.

21. *Spirogyra lagerheimii* Wittrock. Vegetative cells 25–33 × 75–150 μ, with plane end walls and 1 chromatophore making 0.5–4.0 turns in the cell; conjugation scalariform and lateral, tubes formed by both cells; fertile cells cylindric or enlarged by the spore; zygote ellipsoid with more or less pointed ends, 25–38 × 50–100 μ, with yellowish-brown and finely punctate median spore-wall. Pl. 44, fig. 459.

22. *Spirogyra scrobiculata* (Stockmayer) Czurda. Vegetative cells 30–40 × 30–90 μ, with plane end walls and 1 chromatophore; conjugation scalariform, tubes formed by both gametangia; fertile cells inflated on the conjugating side; zygote ellipsoid, 34–38 × 58–68 μ, with scrobiculate, yellow to yellow-brown median spore-wall. Pl. 45, figs. 481, 482.

23. *Spirogyra crassoidea* Transeau. Vegetative cells 140–150 × 140–560 μ, with plane end walls and 3–8 chromatophores making 0.5–3.0 turns; conjugation scalariform, tubes formed by both gametangia; fertile cells cylindric; zygote compressed-ellipsoid, usually with rounded ends, 120–140 × 145–255 μ, with smooth and yellow-brown median spore-wall. Pl. 46, fig. 485.

24. *Spirogyra majuscula* Kuetzing. Vegetative cells 50–80 × 80–500 μ, with plane end walls and (3–) 5–8 chromatophores, straight or making about 0.3 turn in the cell; conjugation scalariform and lateral, tubes formed by both gametangia; fertile cells shortened, cylindric or slightly inflated; zygote compressed-spheroid (lenticular), 57–62 μ in diameter and 45–60 μ in thickness, with brown and smooth median spore-wall; aplanospores similar but smaller. Pl. 45, fig. 475.

25. *Spirogyra submaxima* Transeau. Vegetative cells 70–110 × 100–300 μ, with plane end walls and 8–9 chromatophores making 0.1–1.0 turn in

Fig. 484.—*Spirogyra ellipsospora* Transeau.

Fig. 485.—*Spirogyra crassoidea* Transeau, showing 2 views of compressed-elliptical zygote.

Fig. 486.—*Spirogyra crassa* Kuetzing.

Figs. 487, 488.—*Spirogyra nitida* (Dillwyn) Link.

Fig. 489.—*Spirogyra decimina* (Mueller) Kuetzing.

Fig. 490.—*Spirogyra irregularis* Naegeli.

Figs. 491, 492.—*Spirogyra diluta* Wood; fig. 491, details of wall ornamentation of zygote.

Fig. 493.—*Spirogyra fluviatilis* Hilse.

Fig. 494.—*Spirogyra jugalis* (Fl. Dan.) Kuetzing.

Fig. 495.—*Spirogyra formosa* (Transeau) Czurda.

(Fig. 486, Petit; figs. 487–489, Jao; remainder, Transeau. Figs. 484–486, 492, 494, 495 ×*150*; figs. 487–489 ×*300*; fig. 490 ×*100*; figs. 491, 493 ×*225*.)

PLATE 46

(Figs. 484 to 495)

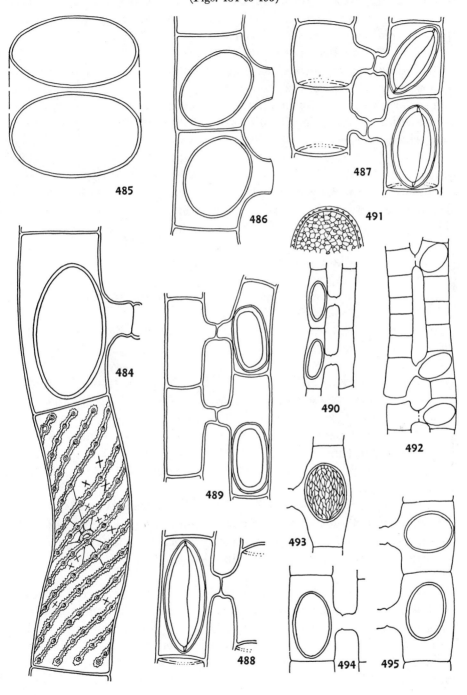

485

486

487

491

484

489

490

492

488

493

494

495

the cell; conjugation scalariform, tubes formed by both gametangia; fertile cells cylindric, enlarged, or slightly inflated; zygote compressed-spheroid (lenticular), 50–75 μ in thickness and 70–110 μ in diameter, with smooth, brown median spore-wall. Pl. **45**, fig. **483**.

26. *Spirogyra irregularis* Naegeli. Vegetative cells 32–37 × 65–250 μ, with plane end walls; 2–4 chromatophores making 0.5–1.0 turn; conjugation scalariform, tubes formed by both gametangia; fertile cells cylindric; zygote ellipsoid to cylindric-ellipsoid, 30–36 × 45–90 μ; median spore-wall yellowish-brown, smooth. Pl. **46**, fig. **490**.

27. *Spirogyra nitida* (Dillwyn) Link. Vegetative cells 70–80 × 90–300 μ, with plane end walls; 3–5 chromatophores making 0.5–1.5 turns; conjugation scalariform; tubes formed by both gametangia; fertile cells cylindric or enlarged; zygote ellipsoid, rarely somewhat ovoid, 60–76 × 90–177 μ; median spore-wall brown, smooth. Pl. **46**, figs. **487, 488**.

28. *Spirogyra setiformis* (Roth) Kuetzing. Vegetative cells 90–115 × 100–225 μ, with plane end walls and 4 chromatophores making 0.5–1.0 turn in the cell; conjugation scalariform; tubes formed by both gametangia; fertile cells cylindric; zygote ellipsoid, 85–100 × 115–160 μ, with smooth, brown median spore-wall. Pl. **45**, fig. **480**.

29. *Spirogyra ellipsospora* Transeau. Vegetative cells 125–150 × 125–500 μ, with plane end walls and 3–8 chromatophores making 0.4–5.0 turns; conjugation scalariform; tubes formed by both gametangia; fertile cells cylindric; zygote ellipsoid, more or less pointed, 100–140 × 160–255 μ, with smooth and yellow-brown median spore-wall. Pl. **46**, fig. **484**.

30. *Spirogyra distenta* Transeau. Vegetative cells 48–52 × 81–180 μ, with plane end walls; 2 chromatophores, making 1.5–2.0 turns; conjugation scalariform; tubes formed by both gametangia; fertile cells cylindric or enlarged; sterile cells inflated to 75 μ; zygote ovoid, 49–55 × 50–100 μ; median spore-wall yellow, smooth.

31. *Spirogyra triplicata* (Collins) Transeau. Vegetative cells 35–45 × 140–200 μ, with plane end walls; 3 chromatophores, making 1.5–3.0 turns; conjugation scalariform; tubes formed by both gametangia; fertile cells cylindric; zygote ovoid, 34–48 × 48–54 μ; median spore-wall yellow, smooth.

32. *Spirogyra neglecta* (Hassall) Kuetzing. Vegetative cells 55–67 × 100–300 μ, with plane end walls and 3 chromatophores making 1.0–2.5 turns in the cell; conjugation scalariform and lateral; tubes formed by both gametangia; fertile cells enlarged or inflated; zygote and aplanospore ovoid, 54–64 × 75–100 μ, with smooth and yellow median spore-wall. Pl. **45**, figs. **476, 477**.

33. *Spirogyra decimina* (Mueller) Kuetzing. Vegetative cells 32–42 ×
66–150 μ, with plane end walls; 2–3 chromatophores making 1–2 turns;
conjugation scalariform; tubes formed by both gametangia; fertile cells
cylindric or enlarged; zygote ovoid to globose, 31–40 × 31–68 μ; median
spore-wall yellow, smooth. Pl. 46, fig. 489.

34. *Spirogyra occidentalis* (Transeau) Czurda. Vegetative cells 40–50 ×
125–300 μ, with plane end walls and 1–3 chromatophores making 2–6
turns in the cell; conjugation scalariform; tubes formed by both gametangia; fertile cells cylindric or enlarged up to 66 μ in diameter; zygote ovoid
to cylindric-ovoid, 36–56 × 57–105 μ, median spore-wall smooth and
yellow-brown at maturity; outer wall of 2 layers, of which the inner is
hyaline, scrobiculate. Pl. 47, fig. 499.

35. *Spirogyra jugalis* (Fl. Dan.) Kuetzing. Vegetative cells 75–103 ×
80–300 μ, with plane end walls; 3–4 chromatophores making 1–2 turns;
conjugation scalariform; tubes formed by both gametangia; fertile cells
cylindric or enlarged; zygote ovoid, 87–108 × 120–155 μ; median spore-
wall brown, smooth. Pl. 46, fig. 494.

36. *Spirogyra dubia* Kuetzing. Vegetative cells 40–50 × 60–250 μ, with
plane end walls; 2–3 chromatophores making 2.0–8.5 turns; conjugation
scalariform; tubes formed by both gametangia; fertile cells inflated;
zygote ovoid, 42–50 × 54–67 μ; median spore-wall yellow-brown, smooth.
Pl. 45, fig. 472.

37. *Spirogyra maxima* (Hassall) Wittrock. Vegetative cells 118–150 ×
100–250 μ, with plane end walls; 6–7 chromatophores making 0.2–0.8
turn; conjugation scalariform, tubes formed by both gametangia; fertile
cells cylindric; zygote lenticular, 100–125 × 75–95 μ, median spore-wall
golden brown, reticulate. Pl. 45, figs. 478, 479.

38. *Spirogyra formosa* (Transeau) Czurda. Vegetative cells 80–95 × 80–
270 μ, with plane end walls and 6–12 chromatophores, making 0.5–1.0
turn; conjugation scalariform, tubes formed by both gametangia; fertile
cells cylindric; zygote compressed-ovoid, 88–100 × 120–150 × 70–90 μ;
median spore-wall brown and with irregular, shallow pits. Pl. 46, fig. 495.

39. *Spirogyra crassa* Kuetzing. Vegetative cells 140–165 × 126–330 μ,
with plane end walls and 6–12 chromatophores making 0.5–1.0 turn in the
cell; conjugation scalariform, tubes formed by both gametangia; fertile
cells cylindric, rarely enlarged; zygote compressed-ovoid, 120–150 × 140–
160 μ; median spore-wall brown and with irregular, shallow pits. Pl. 46,
fig. 486.

40. *Spirogyra propria* Transeau. Vegetative cells 60–68 × 80–150 μ,
with plane end walls and 3 chromatophores making 0.5–1.0 turn in the

cell; conjugation lateral; tubes formed by both gametangia; fertile cells cylindric; zygote ellipsoid, 42–60 × 80–120 μ, median spore-wall irregularly pitted, yellow-brown.

41. *Spirogyra fluviatilis* Hilse. Vegetative cells 30–45 × 70–240 μ, with plane end walls and 3–4 chromatophores making 1.5–3.5 turns in the cell; conjugation scalariform, tubes formed by both gametangia; fertile cells shortened and inflated to 70 μ; zygote ovoid, 47–85 × 68–110 μ, with median spore-wall brown, corrugate, or finely wrinkled. Pl. 46, fig. 493.

42. *Spirogyra novae-angliae* Transeau. Vegetative cells 48–60 × 150–390 μ, with plane end walls and 3–5 chromatophores making 2.5–4.5 turns in the cell; conjugation scalariform; tubes formed by both gametangia; fertile cells cylindric or enlarged; zygote ovoid, 50–65 × 70–120 μ, with median spore-wall reticulate and finely punctate, yellow. Pl. 47, fig. 503.

43. *Spirogyra diluta* Wood. Vegetative cells 70–85 × 80–160 μ, with plane end walls; 5–8 chromatophores, straight or making 1 turn; conjugation scalariform; tubes formed by both gametangia; fertile cells enlarged or inflated on the inner side; zygote ovoid, 66–90 × 90–130 μ; median spore-wall chestnut brown, verrucose-reticulate to verrucose. Pl. 46, figs. 491, 492.

44. *Spirogyra punctiformis* Transeau. Vegetative cells 27–30 × 120–390 μ, with plane end walls and 1–2 narrow chromatophores making 3–6 turns in the cell; conjugation scalariform; fertile cells inflated to 44–50 μ in diameter; receptive gametangia 100–250 μ long, male gametangia 90–140 μ long, occurring singly or in pairs, alternating with vegetative cells; conjugating tube usually produced by the male cell; zygote ovoid, 40–48 × 60–110 μ; median spore-wall punctate, yellow. Pl. 47, fig. 496.

45. *Spirogyra reflexa* Transeau. Vegetative cells 30–44 × 120–300 μ, with plane end walls and 1 chromatophore making 3–8 turns in the cell; conjugation scalariform; fertile cells in groups of 2 or 4, inflated or enlarged and strongly reflexed; conjugating tube formed by the male cell;

FIG. 496.—*Spirogyra punctiformis* Transeau.

FIG. 497.—*Spirogyra micropunctata* Transeau.

FIG. 498.—*Spirogyra rugulosa* Ivanof.

FIG. 499.—*Spirogyra occidentalis* (Transeau) Czurda.

FIG. 500.—*Spirogyra corrugata* Transeau.

FIG. 501.—*Spirogyra hydrodictya* Transeau; 3 different sets of cells.

FIG. 502.—*Spirogyra wabashensis* Tiffany.

FIG. 503.—*Spirogyra novae-angliae* Transeau.

FIGS. 504, 505.—*Spirogyra reflexa* Transeau.

(Fig. 500, Jao; fig. 502, Tiffany; remainder, Transeau. Figs. 496, 502, 503 ×200; figs. 497, 498, 501, 504, 505 ×150; figs. 499, 500 ×300.)

PLATE 47

(Figs. 496 to 505)

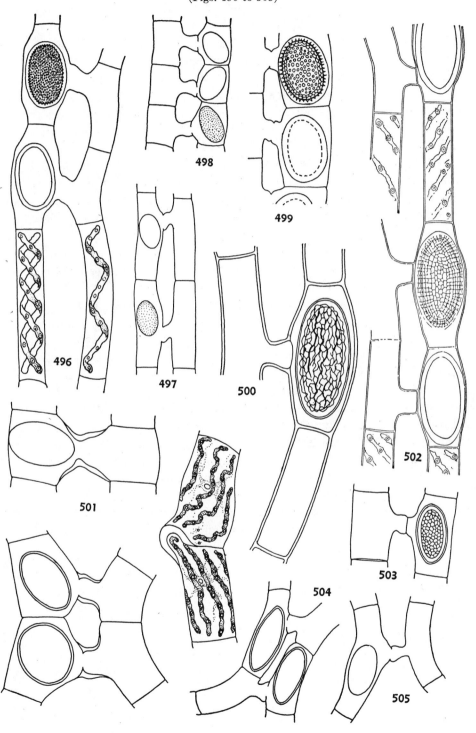

zygote and aplanospore ellipsoid, 44–64 × 90–150 μ, median spore-wall smooth, yellow-brown. Pl. 47, figs. **504, 505.**

46. *Spirogyra micropunctata* Transeau. Vegetative cells 30–36 × 120–300 μ, with plane end walls and 1 chromatophore making 3–7 turns in the cell; conjugation scalariform; fertile cells scattered in groups of 2 or 4 among the vegetative cells or continuous, inflated on the conjugating side only, up to 50 μ in diameter; conjugating tubes formed almost wholly by the male cells; zygote ellipsoid, 37–42 × 57–100 μ, median spore-wall minutely punctate, yellow. Pl. 47, fig. **497.**

47. *Spirogyra corrugata* Transeau. Vegetative cells (30–) 32–36 (–40) × 140–280 (–400) μ, with plane end walls and (1–) 2–3 chromatophores making 2–4 turns in the cell; conjugation scalariform; fertile cells solitary or in pairs (rarely series) between vegetative cells, shortened and inflated to 40–60 μ in diameter; conjugating tubes formed by the male cell, usually long and broad; zygote ovoid, 42–60 × 88–120 μ, median spore-wall of 2 layers: outer thin and coarsely and irregularly corrugate; inner finely reticulate, yellow or brownish-yellow. Pl. 47, fig. **500.**

48. *Spirogyra rugulosa* Ivanof. Vegetative cells 47–57 × 100–350 μ, with plane end walls and 1 chromatophore making 3–11 turns; conjugation scalariform; tubes formed by male gametangium; fertile cells shortened and inflated on the conjugating side; zygote ellipsoid to ovoid, 45–52 × 102–127 μ; median spore-wall yellow-brown, finely punctate. Pl. **47,** fig. **498.**

49. *Spirogyra wabashensis* Tiffany. Vegetative cells 40–50 × 120–400 μ, with plane end walls and 2–4 chromatophores making 0.5–4.5 turns in the cell; conjugation scalariform; fertile cells inflated, single or in groups of 2 alternating with vegetative cells; conjugating tube formed by the male cell; zygote ellipsoid, 56–76 × 110–150 μ, median spore-wall areolate, yellow. Pl. 47, fig. **502.**

50. *Spirogyra hydrodictya* Transeau. Vegetative cells 75–100 × 210–360 μ, with plane end walls and 7–10 chromatophores either straight or

Fig. 506.—*Spirogyra protecta* Wood.

Figs. 507, 508.—*Spirogyra inconstans* Collins; fig. 508, details of wall ornamentation of zygote.

Fig. 509.—*Spirogyra discreta* Transeau.

Figs. 510, 511.—*Spirogyra groenlandica* Rosenvinge.

Fig. 512.—*Spirogyra weberi* Kuetzing.

Fig. 513.—*Spirogyra spreeiana* Rabenhorst.

Figs. 514, 515.—*Spyrogyra quadrata* (Hassall) Petit.

Fig. 516.—*Spirogyra denticulata* Transeau.

(Fig. 512, Jao; remainder, Transeau. Figs. 506, 507, 510, 511, 513–515 ×*200;* fig. 508 ×*1000;* figs. 509, 512 ×*300;* fig. 516 ×*150.*)

PLATE 48

(Figs. 506 to 516)

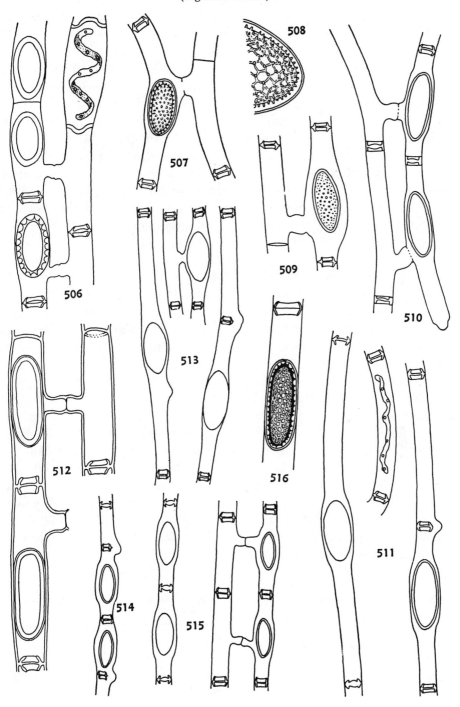

making 0.1–0.5 turn in the cell; conjugation scalariform and lateral; fertile cells shortened and enlarged or slightly inflated; conjugating tube formed by the male cell; zygote lenticular to lenticular-globose, 80–120 × 110–195 μ, median spore-wall pitted, brown. Pl. **47**, fig. **501.**

51. *Spirogyra weberi* Kuetzing. Vegetative cells 19–30 × 80–480 μ, with replicate end walls and 1 chromatophore making 3.0–6.5 turns; fertile cells usually slightly enlarged; conjugation scalariform; tubes formed by both cells; zygote ovoid to cylindric-ovoid, 21–30 × 30–96 μ; median spore-wall smooth and yellow; aplanospores similar. Pl. **48**, fig. **512.**

52. *Spirogyra latviensis* (Skuja) Czurda (*S. petitiana* Transeau). Vegetative cells 20–25 × 100–250 μ, with replicate end walls and 1 chromatophore making 3.0–5.5 turns; conjugation scalariform; tubes formed by both gametangia, receptive gametangia greatly enlarged by the spores or inflated to 30–40 μ; zygote ovoid to cylindric-ovoid, 29–39 × 75–115 μ, outer spore-wall of 2 hyaline layers: outer thin and inner thick, verrucose, with short, pointed elevations; median spore-wall smooth, yellow-brown.

53. *Spirogyra tenuissima* (Hassall) Kuetzing. Vegetative cells 8–13 × 40–250 μ, highly variable in dimensions, with replicate end walls and 1 chromatophore making 3–6 turns in the cell; conjugation lateral and scalariform; tubes formed by both cells; fertile cells enlarged or inflated toward the middle; zygotes and aplanospores ellipsoid, 25–32 × 40–70 μ; median spore-wall smooth and yellow. Pl. **49**, fig. **519.**

54. *Spirogyra inflata* (Vaucher) Rabenhorst. Vegetative cells 15–20 × 45–230 μ, with replicate end walls; 1 chromatophore, making 2.5–6.0 turns; conjugation lateral and scalariform; tubes formed by both gametangia; fertile cells inflated to 35–48 μ; zygote and aplanospore ellipsoid, 27–36 × 50–76 μ; median spore-wall yellow, smooth. Pl. **49**, fig. **518.**

55. *Spirogyra spreeiana* Rabenhorst. Vegetative cells 18–24 × 140–600 μ, with replicate end walls; 1 chromatophore making 1.5–4.0 turns; conjugation scalariform and lateral; tubes formed mostly by the male gametangia; fertile cells enlarged and inflated toward the middle to 30–42 μ; zygotes and aplanospores ellipsoid, 30–36 × 55–100 μ; median spore-wall yellow, smooth. Pl. **48**, fig. **513.**

Fig. 517.—*Spirogyra tetrapla* Transeau.

Fig. 518.—*Spirogyra inflata* (Vaucher) Rabenhorst.

Fig. 519.—*Spirogyra tenuissima* (Hassall) Kuetzing.

Fig. 520.—*Spirogyra reticulata* Nordstedt.

Figs. 521, 522.—*Spirogyra rectangularis* Transeau.

Fig. 523.—*Spirogyra hassallii* (Jenner) Petit.

(Figs. 518, 519, 523, Jao; figs. 517, 520–522, Transeau. Figs. 517, 520–522 ×*200*; figs. 518, 519, 523 ×*300*.)

PLATE 49

(Figs. 517 to 523)

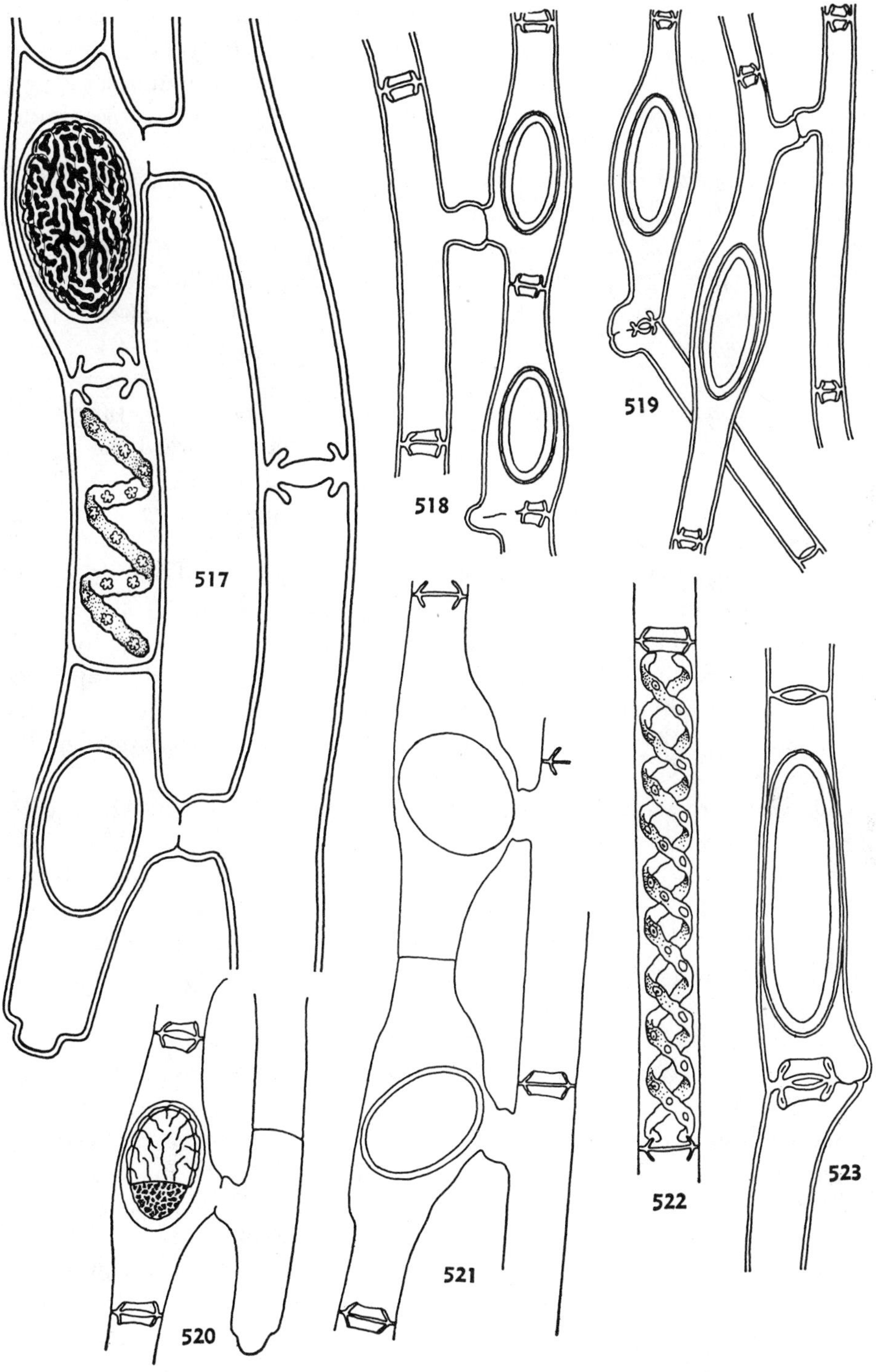

56. *Spirogyra rugosa* (Transeau) Czurda. Vegetative cells 10–13 × 50–210 μ, with replicate end walls and 1 slender chromatophore making 2–6 turns in the cell; conjugation lateral and scalariform; tubes formed by both gametangia; fertile cells greatly inflated toward the middle; zygote 28–32 × 55–66 μ, ellipsoid, with median spore-wall yellow-brown, minutely scrobiculate.

57. *Spirogyra discreta* Transeau. Vegetative cells 16–20 × 50–220 μ, with replicate end walls; 1 chromatophore making 3–6 turns in the cell; conjugation lateral and scalariform; tubes formed by both gametangia; fertile cells greatly inflated toward the middle; zygote ellipsoid, 28–36 × 50–75 μ; median spore-wall scrobiculate, yellow. Pl. 48, fig. 509.

58. *Spirogyra groenlandica* Rosenvinge. Vegetative cells 18–24 × 360–600 μ, with replicate end walls; 1 chromatophore making 3–8 turns; conjugation lateral and scalariform; tubes formed by both gametangia, receptive gametangia more or less cylindrically inflated toward the middle up to 51 μ; zygote ellipsoid to cylindric-ellipsoid, 34–48 × 100–130 μ; median spore-wall smooth, chestnut brown; aplanospores similar to zygotes, 34–44 × 60–90 μ. Pl. 48, figs. 510, 511.

59. *Spirogyra quadrata* (Hassall) Petit. Vegetative cells 24–30 × 70–300 μ, with replicate end walls and 1 chromatophore making 1.5–6.0 turns in the cell; conjugation scalariform and lateral; tubes formed by both gametangia; fertile cells cylindrically inflated toward the middle up to 60 μ; zygote ellipsoid to cylindric-ellipsoid, 33–44 × 50–82 μ; median spore-wall smooth and brown; aplanospores similar to zygotes but smaller. Pl. 48, figs. 514, 515.

60. *Spirogyra protecta* Wood. Vegetative cells 28–34 × 120–425 μ, with replicate end walls and 1 (rarely 2) chromatophore making 2–6 turns; conjugation scalariform; tubes formed by both gametangia; fertile cells cylindric or slightly enlarged; zygote ovoid, 30–38 × 66–90 μ, outer spore-wall of 2 layers: inner thick, scrobiculate and outer smooth; median spore-wall smooth and yellow; aplanospores similar to zygotes but smaller. Pl. 48, fig. 506.

61. *Spirogyra cleveana* Transeau. Vegetative cells 34–40 × 140–465 μ, with replicate end walls and 1 chromatophore (rarely 2) making 3–6 turns; conjugation scalariform; tubes formed by both gametangia; receptive gametangium cylindric or enlarged; sterile cells often greatly inflated; zygote ovoid to cylindric-ovoid, 34–50 × 70–125 μ, with median spore-wall yellow, smooth; outer spore-wall of 2 hyaline layers, the inner of which is thick and coarsely scrobiculate. Pl. 50, fig. 524.

62. *Spirogyra denticulata* Transeau. Vegetative cells 42–56 × 160–400 μ,

with replicate end walls and 1 (rarely 2) chromatophore making 3–6 turns; fertile cells cylindric or enlarged, sterile cells sometimes inflated; conjugation scalariform; tubes formed by both gametangia; zygote ovoid, 45–60 × 76–130 μ, with median spore-wall yellow, smooth; outer hyaline spore-wall of 2 layers: outer thin and smooth; inner thick and scrobiculate. Pl. 48, fig. 516.

63. *Spirogyra rectangularis* Transeau. Vegetative cells 35–40 × 150–320 μ, with replicate end walls and 2–4 chromatophores making 2–5 turns in the cell; conjugation lateral and scalariform; tubes formed by both gametangia; fertile cells cylindrically inflated toward the middle up to 48–70 μ; zygote ovoid to cylindric-ovoid, 45–65 × 75–120 μ; median spore-wall yellow-brown, smooth. Pl. 49, figs. 521, 522.

64. *Spirogyra hassallii* (Jenner) Petit. Vegetative cells 26–33 × 100–250 μ, with replicate end walls; 2 chromatophores, making 1.5–5.0 turns in the cell; conjugation lateral and scalariform; tubes formed by both gametangia; fertile cells fusiform, inflated to 50 μ; zygote ellipsoid, 39–48 × 58–136 μ; median spore-wall yellow, smooth. Pl. 49, fig. 523.

65. *Spirogyra insignis* (Hassall) Kuetzing. Vegetative cells 39–42 × 150–590 μ, with replicate end walls; 2–4 (usually 3) chromatophores, making 0.5–1.5 turns; conjugation scalariform and lateral; tubes formed by both gametangia; fertile cells shortened and inflated; zygote ellipsoid, 40–48 × 60–128 μ; median spore-wall yellow-brown, smooth. Pl. 50, fig. 525.

66. *Spirogyra areolata* Lagerheim. Vegetative cells 30–36 × 120–600 μ, with replicate end walls; 1–2 chromatophores, making 3–9 turns in the cell; conjugation scalariform; tubes formed by both gametangia; fertile cells inflated up to 67 μ; zygote ovoid to ovoid-globose, 40–57 × 60–103 μ; outer spore-wall of 2 layers, of which the inner is hyaline, scrobiculate; median spore-wall yellow-brown, smooth. Pl. 50, fig. 528.

67. *Spirogyra grevilleana* (Hassall) Kuetzing. Vegetative cells 22–33 × 60–325 μ, with replicate end walls; chromatophore 1, in some cells 2, making 4–9 turns in the cell; conjugation scalariform and lateral; tubes formed largely by the male gametangia; fertile cells fusiformly inflated to 36–43 μ; zygote ovoid, 30–37 × 60–90 μ; median spore-wall yellow, smooth. Pl. 50, figs. 526, 527.

68. *Spirogyra reticulata* Nordstedt. Vegetative cells 28–42 × 72–460 μ, usually with replicate end walls; 1–3 (usually 2) chromatophores, making 2–4 turns in the cell; conjugation scalariform and lateral; tubes formed by both gametangia; fertile cells enlarged or inflated toward the middle to 48–60 μ; zygotes mostly ovoid, 45–61 × 80–120 μ; median spore-wall yel-

low-brown, of 2 layers: outer thin and wrinkled; the inner reticulate. Pl. 49, fig. 520.

69. *Spirogyra inconstans* Collins. Vegetative cells 28–40 × 70–350 μ, with replicate end walls; (2–) 3–4 chromatophores, nearly straight or making 0.5–1.5 turns in the cell; conjugation scalariform or rarely lateral; tubes formed by both gametangia; at the time of tube formation both gametangia become reflexed and usually the conjugation between the same pair of filaments is limited to 1 or to 2 adjoining parts of cells; cross conjugation is not infrequent; receptive gametangia shortened and inflated up to 50–75 μ; zygote ellipsoid to broadly ellipsoid, 45–70 × 75–140 μ; median wall reticulate-papillate, brown. Pl. 48, figs. 507, 508.

70. *Spirogyra tetrapla* Transeau. Vegetative cells 30–40 × 100–250 μ, with replicate end walls; 1–2 chromatophores making 2–8 turns in the cell; conjugation scalariform; tubes formed by both gametangia; fertile cells inflated up to 66 μ; zygote ellipsoid, 48–58 × 68–88 μ; median spore-wall of 2 layers, of which the outer is thin and irregularly corrugate; the inner finely reticulate, yellow. Pl. 49, fig. 517.

Sirogonium Kuetzing 1843

Simple filaments with cylindrical cells, 2–6 diameters long, end walls plane, with no external pectic layer; chromatophores 2–9, straight or slightly spiral; otherwise vegetatively similar to *Spirogyra*.

Reproduction by zygotes, with median wall thick, smooth or ornamented, yellow to brown in color; conjugation direct between short genuflexed cells of different filaments, the amoeboid gamete passing through the broad opening before any tube-like structure is formed, sometimes giving the appearance of a broad conjugation tube.

KEY TO THE SPECIES

1. Zygotes with median wall smooth............................. 1. S. sticticum
1. Zygotes with median wall not smooth......................... 2. S. illinoisense

1. *Sirogonium sticticum* (English Botany) Kuetzing. Vegetative cells 38–56 × 80–300 μ, with plane end walls; chromatophores 3–5, nearly

---

FIG. 524.—*Spirogyra cleveana* Transeau.

FIG. 525.—*Spirogyra insignis* (Hassall) Kuetzing.

FIGS. 526, 527.—*Spirogyra grevilleana* (Hassall) Kuetzing.

FIG. 528.—*Spirogyra areolata* Lagerheim.

FIGS. 529, 530.—*Sirogonium illinoisense* (Transeau) G. M. Smith.

FIG. 531.—*Sirogonium sticticum* (English Botany) Kuetzing.

(Figs. 524, 531, Jao; fig. 525, Petit; figs. 526, 527, Czurda; figs. 528–530, Transeau. Figs. 524, 531 ×300; figs. 525, 528–530 ×200; figs. 526, 527 ×250.)

PLATE 50

(Figs. 524 to 531)

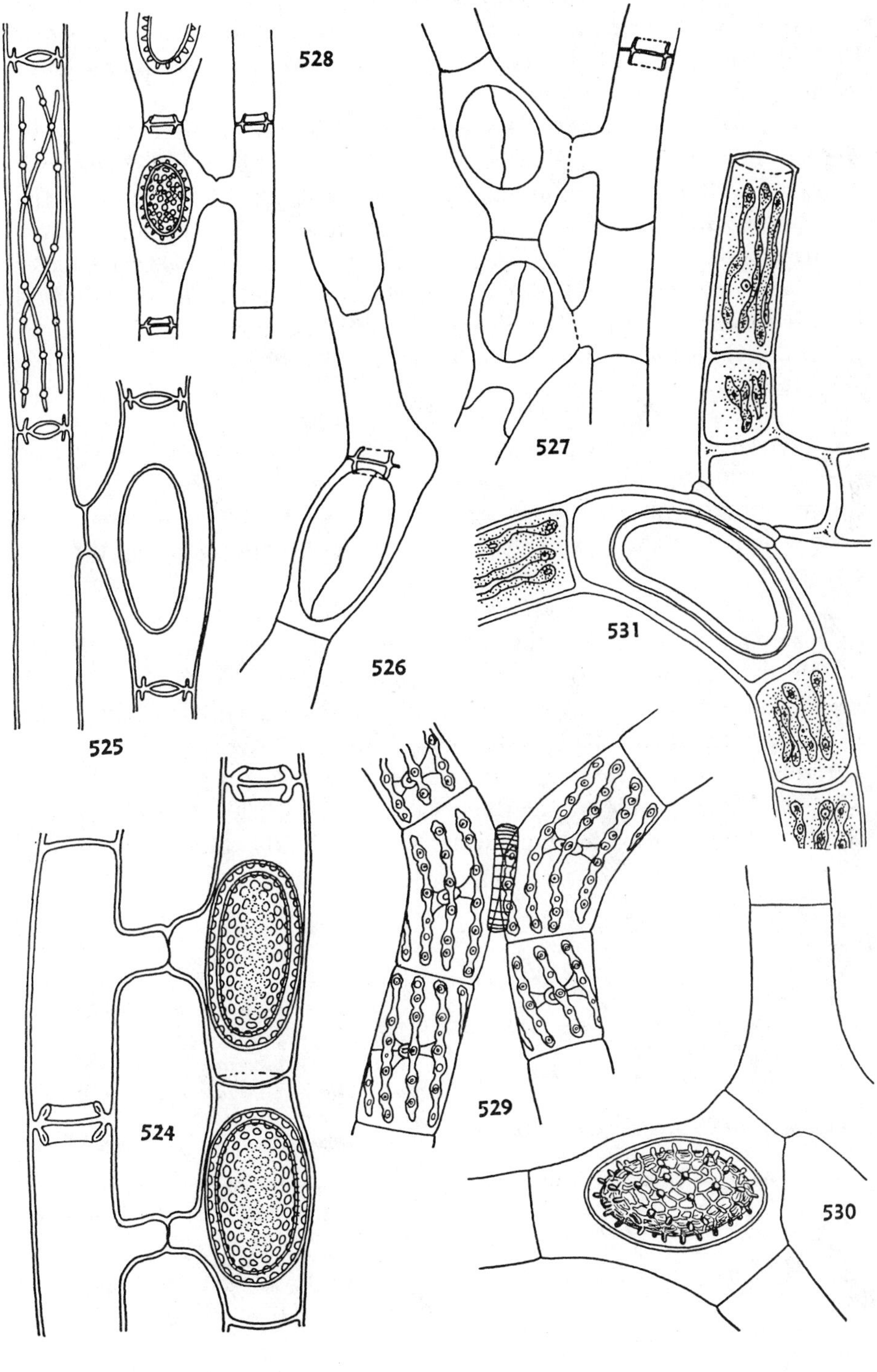

straight or making 0.5 turn; conjugation direct, gametangia usually short-ened and somewhat reflexed; receptive gametangia inflated to 71 μ; zygote ellipsoid (rarely somewhat ovoid), 41–67 $\times$ 68–127 μ, median wall smooth and yellow. Pl. **50**, fig. **531**.

2. *Sirogonium illinoisense* (Transeau) G. M. Smith. Vegetative cells 65–85 $\times$ 100–310 μ, with plane end walls; chromatophores 6–9, narrow, nearly straight and longitudinal, or spiral, making 0.1–1.0 turn in the cell; conjugating cells shortened, somewhat inflated and geniculate, the receptive one inflated; conjugating tube short and broad; male cell shorter than the female; zygote 85–115 $\times$ 140–190 μ, ellipsoid, median spore-wall thick, with scattered protuberances connected by a more or less prominent reticulum, yellow at maturity. Pl. **50**, figs. **529, 530**.

Family **Mesotaeniaceae**

Uninucleate cells of various shapes, solitary or forming simple filaments; cell-walls without pores and composed of 1 piece (saccoderm desmids); chromatophores spiral ribbons, axial plates, or stellate bodies with or without longitudinal ribs; amoeboid gametes generally fusing through conjugation tubes.

Genicularia DeBary 1858

Cells cylindric, elongate, not constricted, apices truncate, wall densely covered with minute granulations; chromatophores 2 or 3 parietal spiral bands or sometimes irregular; filamentous but dissociating sometime prior to conjugation when cells become geniculate.

Zygote between the 2 conjugating cells.

1. *Genicularia spirotaenia* DeBary. Cells 20–25 $\times$ 200–400 μ (apices 27–29 μ), 10–20 times longer than wide; apices slightly dilated; chromato-

Fig. 532.—*Genicularia spirotaenia* De-Bary.

Fig. 533.—*Roya obtusa* (Brébisson) W. and G. S. West.

Fig. 534.—*Netrium digitus* (Ehren-berg) Itsigsohn and Roth.

Fig. 535.—*Gonatozygon brebissonii* DeBary.

Fig. 536.—*Arthrodesmus convergens* Eh-renberg.

Fig. 537.—*Micrasterias americana* (Ehrenberg) Ralfs.

Fig. 538.—*Micrasterias rotata* (Greville) Ralfs.

Fig. 539.—*Micrasterias truncata* (Corda) Brébisson.

Fig. 540.—*Penium margaritaceum* (Ehrenberg) Brébisson.

Fig. 541.—*Closterium braunii* Reinsch.

Fig. 542.—*Closterium venus* Kuetzing.

Fig. 543.—*Closterium parvulum* Naegeli.

Fig. 544.—*Closterium littorale* Gay.

Fig. 545.—*Closterium strigosum* Brébis-son.

Fig. 546.—*Closterium striolatum* Ehren-berg.

(Fig. 532, W. and G. S. West; figs. 533, 540, 541, Taft; figs. 542, 545, Taylor; figs. 534–539, 543, 544, 546, Irénée-Marie. Figs. 534, 537–539, 541 $\times 165$; figs. 533, 542, 543 $\times 650$.)

PLATE 51

(Figs. 532 to 546)

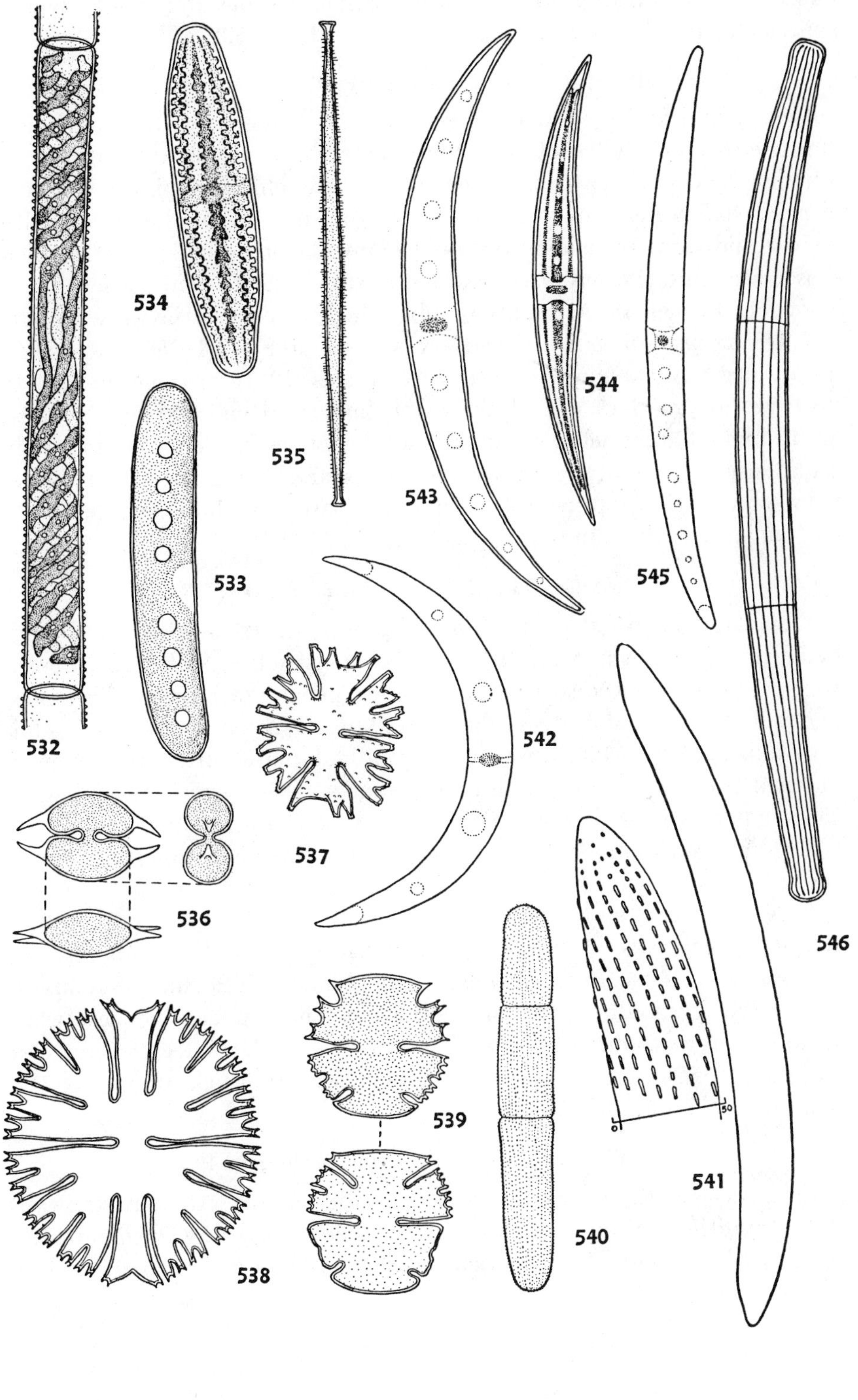
532
533
534
535
536
537
538
539
540
541
0
50
542
543
544
545
546

phores 2 or 3, making 4.5–7.5 turns, with numerous pyrenoids; zygote spherical, smooth, 48–57 μ in diameter. Pl. **51**, fig. **532.**

Gonatozygon DeBary 1856

Cells cylindric, 10–20 times longer than the diameter, without a median constriction, sides parallel except at apices which may be dilated or convergent; apices truncate and often subcapitate; chromatophores 2, rarely 1, axial, extending from pole to pole or from pole to middle of cell, with 4–16 equidistant pyrenoids; forming filaments of variable length which dissociate readily when disturbed and always prior to conjugation.

Zygote formed in conjugation tube which often gelatinizes with age.

1. *Gonatozygon brebissonii* DeBary. Cells 5–10.8 × 94–288 μ (apices 5–10 μ), larger in the middle than at the apices, 10–16 or sometimes up to 40 times longer than wide, narrowly cylindric, attenuated to narrowest width immediately below the capitate, truncate apices; cell-wall minutely and densely granulate; granules variable, scarcely visible to strongly developed, very sharp; pyrenoids 5–16 in each chromatophore; zygote spherical, smooth, 19–21 μ in diameter. Pl. **51**, fig. **535.**

Netrium Naegeli 1849; Luetkemueller 1902

Cells large, length at least 3 times diameter, straight, cylindric, oblong-cylindric or fusiform, without a median constriction; cell-wall smooth, without pores, and consisting of a homogeneous inner layer of cellulose and an outer layer of pectose; chromatophores 2 (rarely 4), 1 in each semicell, axial, with 6–12 radiating longitudinal plates often prominently notched at the edges; pyrenoids rod-like and single or several and spherical to irregular, scattered or in an axial row; poles truncate or rounded.

Zygote formed in broad conjugation tube between recently divided cells.

1. *Netrium digitus* (Ehrenberg) Itzigsohn and Roth. Cells 32–100 × 130–187 μ (apices 12.5–40.0 μ), 3–5 times longer than the diameter, size and proportions variable, not constricted, oblong-elliptic, margins convex, attenuated gradually from the middle to the truncate apices, walls smooth; chromatophore axial, with 5–8 radiating plates deeply serrate at margins; cell-wall smooth; zygote spherical, smooth, thick-walled, 73–74 μ in diameter. Pl. **51**, fig. **534.**

Roya W. and G. S. West 1896; emend. Hodgetts 1920

Cells very slightly arcuate, almost cylindric, slightly attenuated toward the extremities, apices subtruncate or obtusely rounded, wall smooth and colorless; 1 chromatophore in each cell, generally with a small excavation in the middle of the concave side, the extremities convex and extending almost to the extreme ends of the cell; pyrenoids 2–14 in a single series, lacking apical vacuoles and moving granules.

Zygote formed by union of gametes midway between gametangial protuberances.

1. *Roya obtusa* (Brébisson) W. and G. S. West. Cells 6–15 × 22–148 μ, cylindric, 1.5–8.0 times longer than the diameter, very slightly curved, apices obtusely rounded; chromatophore with an eccentric notch at the center; pyrenoids 2–8; zygote spherical, smooth. Pl. **51**, fig. **533**.

Family **Desmidiaceae**

Cells uninucleate, variously shaped, incised or ornamented, solitary or forming unbranched filaments, rarely amorphous colonies; cell-walls with pores and transversely segmented (placoderm desmids), often with 2 distinct and equal semicells separated by a constricted isthmus; chromatophores variable in appearance and number, with 1 or 2 or many pyrenoids in each semicell; aplanospores, parthenospores; amoeboid gametes uniting outside the gametangia and within a gelatinous envelope.

Closterium Nitzsch 1817

Cells elongate, usually markedly attenuate, rarely straight, in most cases curved, often strongly arcuate or lunate, without a median constriction; poles obtuse, truncate, rostrate or attenuate to fine needle-like points; cell-wall smooth, costate, or striate, colorless or yellow to brown in color, often with 1 or more transverse lines either at middle of cell or at different points along cell; chromatophore entire or with a variable number of longitudinal ridges, 1 in each semicell; pyrenoids few or many, usually in a single axial row or more rarely scattered throughout chromatophore; with a terminal vacuole between cell apex and the end of the chromatophore, containing 1 or more crystals of gypsum which exhibit a constant Brownian movement.

Conjugation between recently divided cells, or mature cells.

KEY TO THE SPECIES

1. Cells with a median girdle.. 2
1. Cells without a median girdle... 12
  2. Cell-wall smooth... 3
  2. Cell-wall striate... 6
3. Cells strongly curved, lunate........................ 1. C. dianae
3. Cells slightly curved, ventral margin almost straight...................... 4
  4. Apices broadly truncate and thickened............. 2. C. didymotocum
  4. Apices not broadly truncate or thickened............................... 5

5. Cells tapering gradually to subacute or rounded-truncate
apices... 3. C. acerosum
5. Cells tapering gradually to obtusely rounded, recurved
apices... 4. C. lunula
   6. Apices broadly truncate and thickened............ 2. C. didymotocum
   6. Apices not broadly truncate or thickened................. 7
7. Apices slightly recurved.................................. 8
7. Apices not recurved...................................... 9
   8. Striations composed of fine punctae............... 5. C. pritchardianum
   8. Striations not composed of punctae............... 6. C. turgidum
9. Cells very slightly curved, inner margin almost straight
or slightly convex .... 3. C. acerosum
9. Cells moderately curved, inner margin concave or sometimes straight........ 10
   10. 5–10 striations visible across the cell................................ 11
   10. 14–21 striations visible across the cell............ 7. C. striolatum
11. Cells more than 15 μ in width.................... 8. C. intermedium
11. Cells less than 15 μ in width..................... 9. C. juncidum var.
                                          brevior
   12. Cells moderately to strongly curved................................. 13
   12. Cells slightly curved.. 18
13. Inner margin of cells distinctly tumid............................. 14
13. Inner margin of cells only slightly or not at all tumid...................... 16
   14. Pyrenoids not in a single median series........... 10. C. ehrenbergii
   14. Pyrenoids in a single median series........................... 15
15. Apices acutely rounded, cells 17–42 × 105–250 μ...... 11. C. leibleinii
15. Apices obtusely rounded, cells 30–68 × 188–420 μ..... 12. C. moniliferum
   16. Cells more than 15 μ in width, apices obtusely rounded 1. C. dianae
   16. Cells less than 15 μ in width, apices acute or acutely rounded............ 17
17. Chromatophore with 1–2 pyrenoids.................. 13. C. venus
17. Chromatophore with 3–6 pyrenoids................. 14. C. parvulum
   18. Cell-wall smooth...................................... 19
   18. Cell-wall not smooth..................................... 25
19. Cells lanceolate, apices subacute........................... 20
19. Cells narrow and elongate, apices acute................... 23
   20. Apices recurved............................ 4. C. lunula
   20. Apices not recurved....................................... 21
21. Inner margin concave, slightly tumid in middle........ 15. C. littorale
21. Inner margin straight or slightly convex....................... 22
   22. Apices rounded-truncate....................... 3. C. acerosum
   22. Apices acutely rounded....................... 16. C. lanceolatum
23. Cells gradually curved from middle to poles........... 17. C. acutum
23. Cells straight for median ⅔ of length.............................. 24
   24. Apices acute........................... 18. C. strigosum
   24. Apices not acute............................ 19. C. gracile
25. Cell-wall costate................................ 20. C. braunii
25. Cell-wall striate... 26

26. Apices recurved... 27
26. Apices not recurved........................... 3. C. acerosum
27. Striations composed of fine punctae................. 5. C. pritchardianum
27. Striations not composed of punctae................. 6. C. turgidum

1. *Closterium dianae* Ehrenberg. Cells 16–36 × 103–380 μ (apices 4–7 μ wide), usually 10–12 times longer than wide, strongly curved, outer margin about 107–130 degrees of arc, inner margin very slightly tumid, gradually attenuated toward the obtusely rounded apices; outer margin obliquely truncate and thickened at the apex; cell-wall smooth, reddish-brown, usually without a median girdle; chromatophores obscurely ridged; pyrenoids 3–6 in a single series; terminal vacuoles with many moving granules; zygote spherical, smooth, 36–52 μ in diameter. Pl. 52, fig. 548.

2. *Closterium didymotocum* Ralfs. Cells 24–56 × 295–672 μ (apices 13–20 μ wide), 9–12 times longer than wide, slightly curved, outer margin 27–32 degrees of arc, inner margin slightly concave or almost straight, median portion with subparallel sides, gradually and slightly attenuated to the broad, rounded-truncate apices which are sometimes slightly recurved; cell-wall smooth or rarely with fine striations, reddish-brown or yellow-brown in color, generally having a median girdle, and with an annular, dark brown thickening at each apex; chromatophore with 5–10 large pyrenoids; terminal vacuoles with many moving granules; zygote unknown. Pl. 52, fig. 560.

3. *Closterium acerosum* (Schrank) Ehrenberg. Cells 19–53 × 288–530 μ (apices 4–5 μ wide), 8–16 times longer than wide, very slightly curved or almost straight, narrowly fusiform, outer margin slightly curved, about 30–38 degrees of arc, inner margin almost straight or slightly convex, gradually tapering to the narrow and often slightly thickened, rounded-truncate apices; cell-wall smooth, colorless, becoming delicately striate and yellowish-brown in color with age, with or without a median girdle; chromatophores ridged; pyrenoids 7–12 in a median series; terminal vacuoles with a number of moving granules; zygote spherical, smooth, 62–87 μ in diameter. Pl. 52, fig. 550.

a. Var. *elongatum* Brébisson. Cells 28–54 × 325–790 μ, with relatively greater length and more distinct striations; cell-wall yellowish-brown. Pl. 52, fig. 551.

4. *Closterium lunula* (Mueller) Nitzsch. Cells 71–116 × 435–680 μ (apices 18–25 μ wide), stout, 6–7 times longer than wide, almost straight, outer margin 20–50 degrees of arc, inner margin generally straight, slightly tumid in the middle, gradually narrowed to the obtusely rounded, slightly

recurved apices; cell-wall smooth, colorless, rarely with a median girdle; chromatophore with about 10–12 ridges; pyrenoids numerous, scattered; terminal vacuoles with a large cluster of moving granules; zygote spherical, smooth. Pl. **52,** fig. **561.**

5. *Closterium pritchardianum* Archer. Cells 28–55 × 350–670 μ (apices 7–12 μ wide), very slightly curved, 12–17 times longer than wide, outer margin 24–43 degrees of arc, inner margin straight or very slightly concave, gradually attenuated to the narrow, truncate, and slightly recurved apices; cell-wall finely striate, 35–40 striations visible across the cell, striations composed of fine punctae which are of irregular distribution toward apices, yellowish or becoming reddish-brown, rarely with a median girdle; chromatophore with 6–8 ridges; pyrenoids 7–8 in a median series; terminal vacuoles with many moving granules; zygote smooth, spherical to ovoid, 83–108 μ in diameter. Pl. **52,** fig. **554.**

6. *Closterium turgidum* Ehrenberg. Cells 50–75 × 616–791 μ (apices 12–15 μ wide), slightly curved, 11–12 times longer than wide, outer margin 47–55 degrees of arc, inner margin not tumid, gradually attenuated to subtruncate, recurved apices; cell-wall striate, 30–35 striations visible across the cell, yellow-brown or reddish-brown, sometimes with a median girdle; chromatophore with 7–8 ridges; pyrenoids 7–10 in a median series; terminal vacuoles with many moving granules; zygote unknown. Pl. **52,** fig. **553.**

7. *Closterium striolatum* Ehrenberg. Cells 20–53 × 135–478 μ (apices 7–14 μ wide), 8–12 times longer than wide, moderately curved, outer margin 36–69 degrees of arc, inner margin concave or sometimes medianly straight, gradually attenuated to the broad, rounded-truncate apices;

Fig. 547.—*Closterium leibleinii* Kuetzing.

Fig. 548.—*Closterium dianae* Ehrenberg.

Fig. 549.—*Closterium moniliferum* (Bory) Ehrenberg.

Fig. 550.—*Closterium acerosum* (Schrank) Ehrenberg.

Fig. 551.—*Closterium acerosum* var. *elongatum* Brébisson.

Fig. 552.—*Closterium lanceolatum* Kuetzing.

Fig. 553.—*Closterium turgidum* Ehrenberg.

Fig. 554.—*Closterium pritchardianum* Archer.

Fig. 555.—*Closterium acutum* (Lyngbye) Brébisson.

Fig. 556.—*Closterium gracile* Brébisson.

Fig. 557.—*Closterium gracile* var. *elongatum* W. and G. S. West.

Fig. 558.—*Closterium ehrenbergii* Meneghini.

Fig. 559.—*Closterium intermedium* Ralfs.

Fig. 560.—*Closterium didymotocum* Ralfs.

Fig. 561.—*Closterium lunula* (Mueller) Nitzsch.

Fig. 562.—*Closterium juncidum* Ralfs var. *brevior* Roy.

(Fig. 554, Taylor; fig. 562, W. and G. S. West; all others, Irénée-Marie. Figs. 547, 556, 562 ×*330;* fig. 555 ×*650;* all others ×*165.*)

PLATE 52

(Figs. 547 to 562)

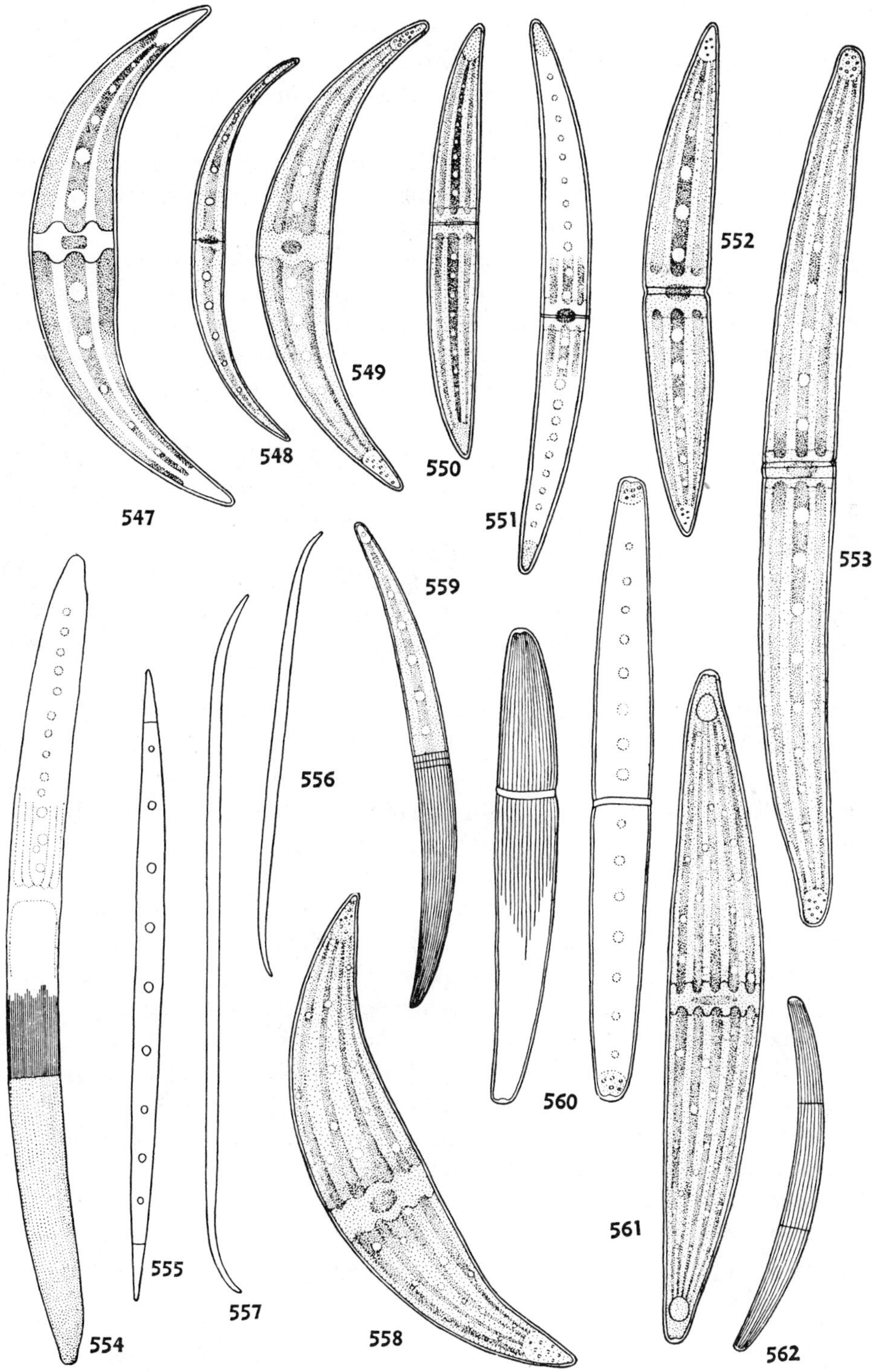

547

548

549

550

551

552

553

554

555

556

557

558

559

560

561

562

cell-wall yellowish or yellowish-brown, with a median girdle, and with 14–21 visible striations across the cell; chromatophore with 5–6 ridges; pyrenoids 5–7 in a median series; terminal vacuoles with many moving granules; zygote smooth, spherical, often enveloped in copious mucus, 65 μ in diameter. Pl. **51,** fig. **546.**

8. *Closterium intermedium* Ralfs. Cells 16–31 × 200–465 μ (apices 8–11.5 μ wide), 12–15 times longer than wide, moderately curved, outer margin 36–56 degrees of arc, inner margin slightly concave, sometimes medianly straight, gradually attenuated to the rounded-truncate apices; cell-wall yellow or yellowish-brown, strongly striate, with 8–10 visible striations across the cell, with a median girdle; chromatophore with 5–6 pyrenoids; terminal vacuole with a single large moving granule or a few smaller ones; zygote smooth, spherical, 38–54 μ in diameter. Pl. **52,** fig. **559.**

9. *Closterium juncidum* Ralfs var. *brevior* Roy. Cells 9–14 × 80–275 μ, elongate, 12–20 times longer than wide, moderately curved, inner margin slightly concave or sometimes straight in median portion, gradually attenuated toward the obtusely rounded apices; cell-wall brown or yellow, always with a median girdle, and with 8–10 frequently obscure striations; chromatophore with 4–7 pyrenoids; terminal vacuole with several moving granules; zygote spherical or slightly ellipsoid, 36–40 μ in diameter. Pl. **52,** fig. **562.**

10. *Closterium ehrenbergii* Meneghini. Cells 60–145 × 285–720 μ (apices 12–18 μ wide), stout, 4.0–5.5 times longer than wide, moderately curved, outer margin 92–140 degrees of arc, inner margin concave but inflated in the middle, gradually attenuated to the obtusely rounded apices; cell-wall smooth, colorless; chromatophores with 8–10 ridges; pyrenoids numerous, scattered; terminal vacuoles containing a cluster of small moving granules; zygote spherical, smooth, with an outer mucous envelope, 113–118 μ in diameter. Pl. **52,** fig. **558.**

11. *Closterium leibleinii* Kuetzing. Cells 17–42 × 105–250 μ (apices 5–7 μ wide), 6–8 times longer than wide, strongly curved, outer margin 124–190 degrees of arc, inner margin strongly concave, tumid in the middle, gradually attenuated to the acutely rounded apices; cell-wall smooth, colorless, rarely straw-colored, or yellowish-brown; chromatophores with about 6 ridges; pyrenoids 3–8 in a median series; terminal vacuoles large, with a number of moving granules; zygote subglobose, smooth, 40–50 μ in diameter. Pl. **52,** fig. **547.**

12. *Closterium moniliferum* (Bory) Ehrenberg. Cells 30–68 × 188–420 μ (apices 8–13 μ wide), stout, 6–8 times longer than wide, moderately

curved, outer margin 100–130 degrees of arc, inner margin inflated in the middle, uniformly narrowed to the obtusely rounded apices; cell-wall smooth, colorless; chromatophores with about 6 ridges; pyrenoids 6–7 in a median series; terminal vacuoles with numerous moving granules; zygote ellipsoid, smooth, with an outer mucous envelope. Pl. 52, fig. 549.

13. *Closterium venus* Kuetzing. Cells 7–10.5 × 50–87 μ (apices 2.0–2.5 μ wide), 8–9 times longer than wide, strongly curved, outer margin 150–180 degrees of arc, inner margin not tumid, gradually attenuated to the acute or acutely rounded apices; cell-wall smooth and colorless or rarely yellowish-brown; chromatophores ridged; pyrenoids 2 or rarely only 1; terminal vacuoles large, with a number of moving granules; zygotes 18–22 × 23.0–28.5 μ, oblong-rectangular with rounded angles, shorter sides retuse, longer sides convex, inflated in the middle; often twisted, the 2 angles at 1 end lying in a plane at right angles to those of opposite end. Pl. 51, fig. 542.

14. *Closterium parvulum* Naegeli. Cells 7.5–14.5 × 96–107 μ (apices 1.5–3.0 μ wide), 9–15 times longer than wide, strongly curved, outer margin 100–140 degrees of arc, inner margin not tumid, gradually attenuated to the acutely rounded apices; cell-wall smooth, colorless or rarely yellowish-brown; chromatophores with 4–5 ridges; pyrenoids 3–6 in a median series; terminal vacuoles with several moving granules; zygote ellipsoid or subglobose, smooth, 26–34.5 × 30–40 μ. Pl. 51, fig. 543.

15. *Closterium littorale* Gay. Cells 17.5–22.5 × 150–220 μ (apices 3.5–5.5 μ wide), 10 times longer than wide, slightly curved, outer margin 35–55 degrees of arc, inner margin a little concave and slightly but widely tumid in the middle, gradually attenuated to the acute to obtusely rounded apices; cell-wall smooth, colorless; chromatophores with 7–8 ridges; pyrenoids 4–5 in a median series; terminal vacuoles with a number of moving granules; zygote spherical, smooth, 28 μ in diameter. Pl. 51, fig. 544.

16. *Closterium lanceolatum* Kuetzing. Cells 32–72 × 234–550 μ (apices 7–8 μ wide), 5–10 times longer than wide, sublanceolate, almost straight, outer margin slightly curved, 30–55 degrees of arc, inner margin straight or slightly convex, gradually narrowed toward the acutely rounded apices; cell-wall smooth, colorless; chromatophores with 7–8 ridges; pyrenoids 6–7 in a median series; terminal vacuoles with a number of moving granules; zygote subglobose or oblong-ellipsoid, smooth, 81–104 μ in diameter. Pl. 52, fig. 552.

17. *Closterium acutum* (Lyngbye) Brébisson. Cells 3.7–11.0 × 60–180 μ (apices 2.5–3.0 μ wide), 15–33 times longer than wide, slightly curved, outer margin 30–60 degrees of arc, inner margin not tumid, gradually attenuated to the acute apices; cell-wall smooth, colorless; chromatophore

without ridges; pyrenoids 4–5 in a median series; terminal vacuoles with several small moving granules; zygote 12–27×23–49 μ, oblong-rectangular, sides concave or slightly convex, ends concave, angles produced into mammillate or conical projections. Pl. **52**, fig. **555**.

18. *Closterium strigosum* Brébisson. Cells 12.0–18.5×230–358 μ, 16–20 times longer than wide, slightly curved, median portion of cell straight, incurved toward the extremities, gradually attenuated to the acute apices; cell-wall smooth and colorless; chromatophore with a median series of 7–8 pyrenoids; terminal vacuoles with several moving granules; zygote ellipsoid, smooth. Pl. **51**, fig. **545**.

19. *Closterium gracile* Brébisson. Cells 3–6×130–206 μ (apices 1.2–2.5 μ wide), slender, linear, 28–40 times longer than wide, almost straight for about $\frac{2}{3}$ of length, margins parallel, gradually narrowed to the obtuse apices; cell-wall smooth, colorless; chromatophore with a median series of 5–7 pyrenoids; terminal vacuoles with 1 or several moving granules; zygote spherical, angular-globose, or subquadrate with rounded angles, smooth, 20.0–25.7 μ in diameter. Pl. **52**, fig. **556**.

FIG. 563.—*Cosmarium biretum* Brébisson var. *trigibberum* Nordstedt.

FIG. 564.—*Cosmarium depressum* (Naegeli) Lundell.

FIG. 565.—*Cosmarium granatum* Brébisson.

FIG. 566.—*Cosmarium holmiense* Lundell.

FIG. 567.—*Cosmarium holmiense* var. *integrum* Lundell.

FIG. 568.—*Cosmarium botrytis* Meneghini.

FIG. 569.—*Cosmarium cucumis* (Corda) Ralfs.

FIG. 570.—*Cosmarium protractum* (Naegeli) DeBary.

FIG. 571.—*Cosmarium dentatum* Wolle.

FIG. 572.—*Cosmarium nitidulum* De-Notaris.

FIG. 573.—*Cosmarium pericymatium* Nordstedt.

FIG. 574.—*Cosmarium crenatum* Ralfs.

FIG. 575.—*Cosmarium broomei* Thwaites.

FIG. 576.—*Cosmarium curtum* (Brébisson) Ralfs.

FIG. 577.—*Cosmarium moniliforme* (Turpin) Ralfs.

FIG. 578.—*Cosmarium sexangulare* Lundell.

FIG. 579.—*Cosmarium sexangulare* f. *minima* Nordstedt.

FIG. 580.—*Cosmarium quadrum* Lundell.

FIG. 581.—*Cosmarium pachydermum* Lundell var. *aethiopicum* W. and G. S. West.

FIG. 582.—*Cosmarium triplicatum* Wolle.

FIG. 583.—*Cosmarium rectangulare* Grunow.

FIG. 584.—*Cosmarium speciosum* Lundell.

FIG. 585.—*Cosmarium subcostatum* Nordstedt.

FIG. 586.—*Cosmarium reniforme* (Ralfs) Archer.

FIG. 587.—*Cosmarium porrectum* Nordstedt.

(Figs. 563, 570, 571, 577, 581–583, 586, 587, Taft; figs. 565–567, 584, 585, Taylor; figs. 564, 568, 569, Irénée-Marie; figs. 572–576, 578–580, W. and G. S. West. All $\times 330$.)

PLATE 53

(Figs. 563 to 587)

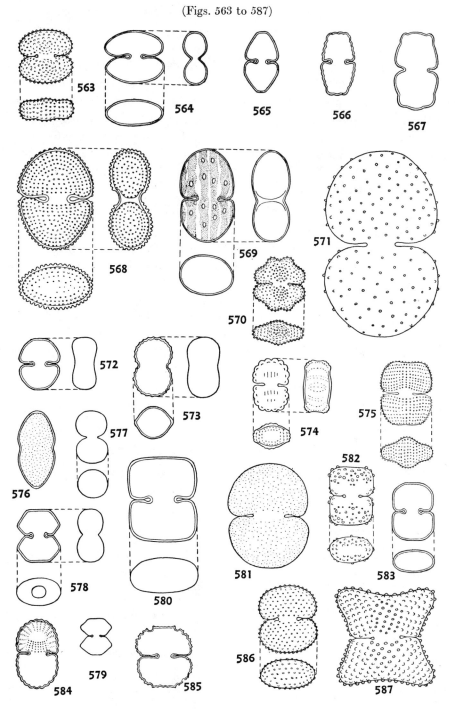

a. Var. *elongatum* W. and G. S. West. Cells 3–8 × 254–480 μ (apices 1.5–2.6 μ wide), more elongate than the type, 85–95 times longer than wide, apices obtusely rounded. Pl. **52,** fig. **557.**

20. *Closterium braunii* Reinsch. Cells 25–61 × 450–800 μ, 16–22 times longer than wide, very slightly curved, median portion cylindric, not tumid, tapering abruptly to obtusely rounded and slightly recurved apices; cell-wall yellow to brownish, with 4–6 costae consisting of double rows of punctae; wall between costae irregularly porous or with 6–10 more or less distinct striations; chromatophore with 4–5 ridges; pyrenoids 14–16 in a median series; terminal vacuoles with about 20 moving granules; zygote unknown. Pl. **51,** fig. **541.**

Penium Brébisson 1844

Cells of medium size, about 10 times longer than wide, cylindric, subcylindric, ellipsoidal, or fusiform, with or without a slight median constriction, very slightly attenuated to the broadly rounded or truncate apices; cell-wall colorless or older portions brownish, smooth to punctate or at times with longitudinal series of granules; chromatophore 1 in each semicell, axial, with longitudinal plates extending to the cell-wall; pyrenoids 1 or more in a median series.

Zygote spherical to quadrangular, usually with smooth walls; parthenospores.

1. *Penium margaritaceum* (Ehrenberg) Brébisson. Cells 12.5–26.0 × 73–170 μ, 6–12 times longer than wide, cylindric or subfusiform, very slightly

Fig. 588.—*Cosmarium subimpressulum* Borge.

Fig. 589.—*Cosmarium formosulum* Hoffman.

Fig. 590.—*Cosmarium formosulum* var. *nathorstii* (Boldt) W. and G. S. West.

Fig. 591.—*Cosmarium polygonum* (Naegeli) Archer.

Fig. 592.—*Cosmarium punctulatum* Brébisson

Fig. 593.—*Cosmarium turpinii* Brébisson.

Fig. 594.—*Cosmarium constrictum* Delponte.

Fig. 595.—*Cosmarium quinarium* Lundell.

Fig. 596.—*Cosmarium subcrenatum* Hantzsch.

Fig. 597.—*Cosmarium meneghinii* Brébisson.

Fig. 598.—*Cosmarium supraspeciosum* Wolle.

Fig. 599.—*Staurastrum margaritaceum* (Ehrenberg) Meneghini.

Fig. 600.—*Staurastrum polymorphum* Brébisson.

Fig. 601.—*Staurastrum alternans* Brébisson.

Fig. 602.—*Staurastrum dilatatum* Ehrenberg.

Fig. 603.—*Staurastrum punctulatum* Brébisson.

Fig. 604.—*Staurastrum oxyacanthum* Archer.

(Figs. 588–590, 599, 604, W. and G. S. West; figs. 591–593, 595, 601–603, Irénée-Marie; figs. 594, 598, Wolle; figs. 596, 597, 600, Taft. Figs. 589, 590, 592–595, 598 ×*330;* all others ×*650.*)

PLATE 54

(Figs. 588 to 604)

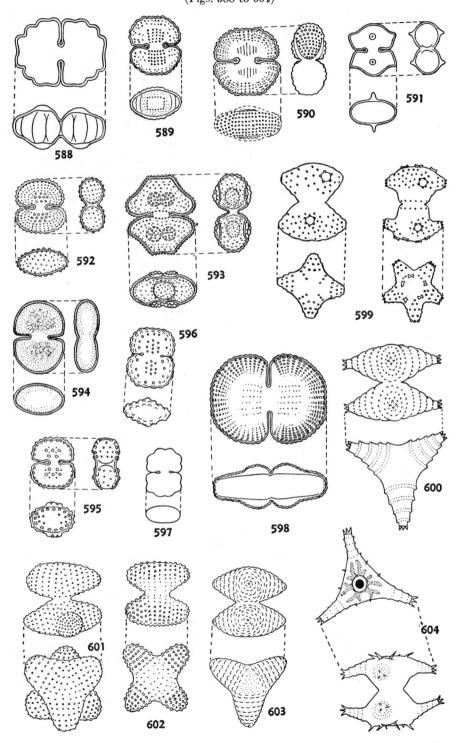

attenuated to the truncately rounded apices; cell-wall reddish-brown, with longitudinal rows of minute granules; chromatophores axial, with about 10 longitudinal ridges; pyrenoids numerous, in a median series; zygote spherical, smooth, 46 μ in diameter. Pl. **51,** fig. **540.**

Pleurotaenium Naegeli 1849

Cells usually large, length several times the width, elongate, straight, slightly constricted in the middle, with a prominent and usually projecting suture; semicells commonly inflated at the base and at times undulate above the inflation, often cylindric and slightly attenuated toward the apices, very rarely ovate; apices truncate or truncately rounded, frequently plicate and except in rare cases with a ring of mammillate to conical tubercules; cell-walls rarely smooth, commonly finely to coarsely punctate, sometimes granulose or papillate, at times of uneven thickness; chromatophores numerous, straight to undulate bands, parietal, rarely axial; pyrenoids numerous, single on small rhomboidal or lanceolate masses of fragmented chloroplasts.

Zygote spherical, smooth, rarely formed.

KEY TO THE SPECIES

1. Apices without a ring of tubercules...................... 1. P. trabecula
1. Apices with a ring of tubercules....................................... 2
  2. Strongly attenuate at poles........................... 4. P. truncatum
  2. Slightly attenuate at poles.. 3
3. Width at base of semicell 35 μ or less; cell-wall punctate...... 2. P. ehrenbergii
3. Width at base of semicell 38 μ or more; cell-wall scrobiculate.. 3. P. coronatum

1. *Pleurotaenium trabecula* (Ehrenberg) Naegeli. Cells 25–46 × 340–664 μ (apices 16–32 μ wide), 11–15 times longer than wide; semicells cylindric,

Fig. 605.—*Pleurotaenium truncata* (Brébisson) Naegeli.

Fig. 606.—*Pleurotaenium coronatum* (Brébisson) Rabenhorst.

Figs. 607, 608.—*Pleurotaenium ehrenbergii* (Brébisson) DeBary.

Fig. 609.—*Pleurotaenium trabecula* (Ehrenberg) Naegeli.

Fig. 610.—*Staurastrum cuspidatum* Brébisson.

Fig. 611.—*Staurastrum hexacerum* (Ehrenberg) Wittrock.

Fig. 612.—*Staurastrum crenatum* Bailey.

Fig. 613.—*Staurastrum gracile* Ralfs.

Figs. 614, 615.—*Cosmarium circulare* Reinsch.

Fig. 616.—*Euastrum pulchellum* Brébisson.

Fig. 617.—*Euastrum oblongum* (Greville) Ralfs.

Fig. 618.—*Euastrum johnsonii* West and West.

Fig. 619.—*Cosmocladium saxonicum* DeBary.

Fig. 620.—*Micrasterias apiculata* (Ehrenberg) Meneghini.

(Figs. 605, 606, 609–611, 613–617, 620, Irénée-Marie; fig. 607, Taylor; fig. 608, Taft; fig. 612, Wolle; fig. 618, Krieger; fig. 619, G. M. Smith. Figs. 605, 620 ×*250;* figs. 606–609, 617 ×*160;* figs. 610, 614, 615, 618 ×*600;* figs. 611–613, 616, 619 ×*330.*)

PLATE 55

(Figs. 605 to 620)

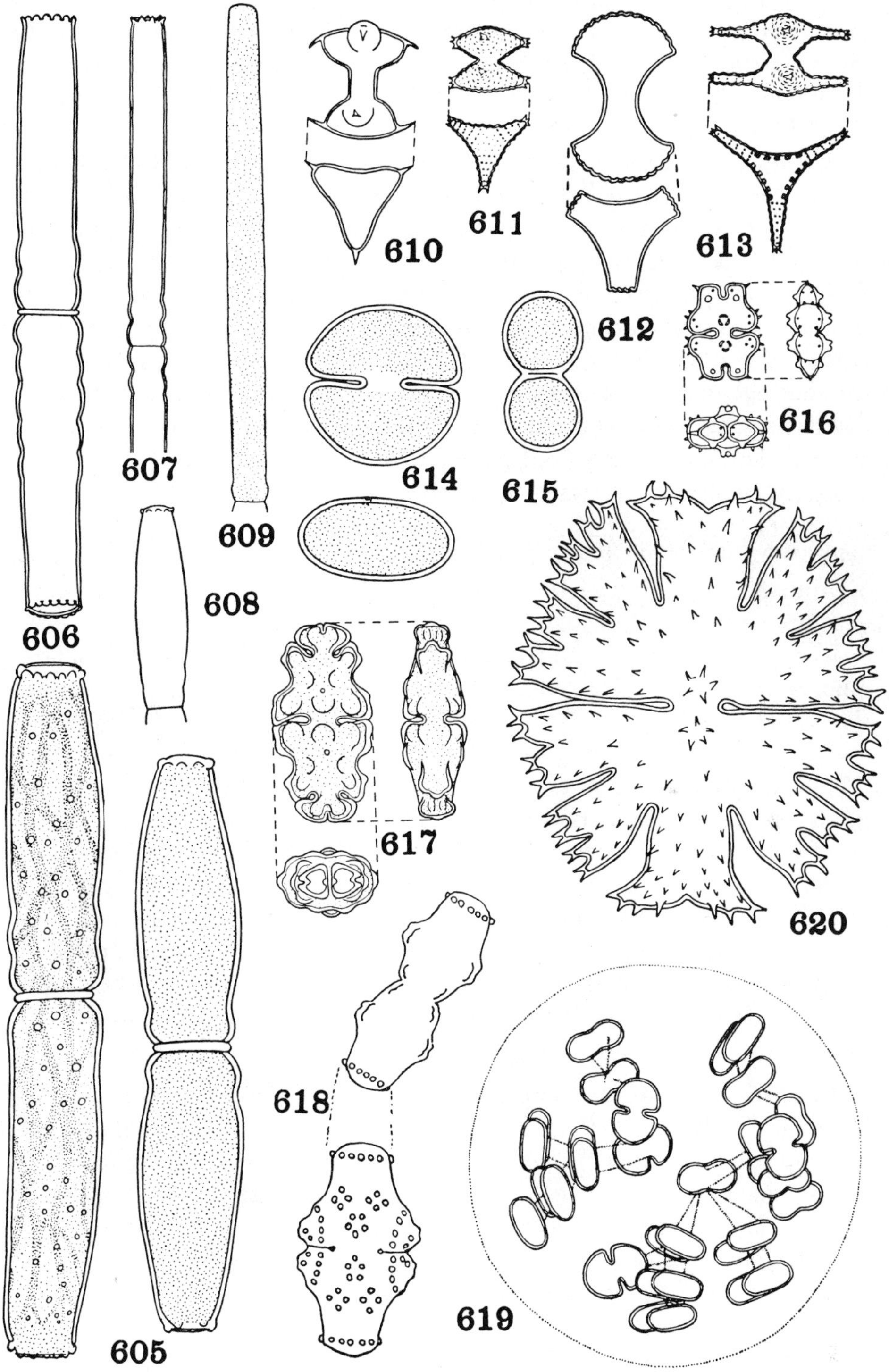

605 606 607 608 609 610 611 612 613 614 615 616 617 618 619 620

slightly and gradually attenuated toward the apices, with a single well-defined basal inflation and rarely with a single undulation above it, lateral margins straight or slightly convex; apices truncately rounded, without tubercules; cell-wall colorless, punctate; zygote ellipsoid, smooth, 48 × 70 μ. Pl. 55, fig. 609.

2. *Pleurotaenium ehrenbergii* (Brébisson) DeBary. Cells 18–35 × 240–650 μ (isthmus 23–40 μ, apices 14–33 μ wide), 15–30 times longer than wide, slightly constricted, sinus a shallow depression; semicells cylindric, somewhat variable in form, lateral margins slightly attenuated, particularly in the apical region, with a distinct basal inflation and above it 1–2 (rarely more) undulations; apices truncate with rounded margins, bearing a ring of 7–10 conical or rounded tubercules; cell-wall colorless, punctate or smooth; chromatophores numerous, parietal, undulate, longitudinal bands; several pyrenoids; zygote spherical or ellipsoid-globose, smooth, 70–90 μ in diameter. Pl. 55, figs. 607, 608.

3. *Pleurotaenium coronatum* (Brébisson) Rabenhorst. Cells 38–70 × 430–640 μ (isthmus 38–50 μ, apices 30–53 μ wide), 9–12 times longer than wide; semicells slightly and gradually attenuated from base to apex, with a prominent basal inflation and several smaller undulations, upper half of lateral margins straight; apices truncate, with a ring of 10–12 large, conical or flattened tubercules; cell-wall colorless, scrobiculate; chromatophores irregular bands; pyrenoids numerous, scattered; zygote unknown. Pl. 55, fig. 606.

4. *Pleurotaenium truncatum* (Brébisson) Naegeli. Cells 45–80 × 324–577 μ (isthmus 37–64 μ, apices 29–77 μ wide), usually 6–8 times longer than wide; semicells cylindric in lower half, somewhat medianly tumid, considerably attenuated to the apex, with a slight basal inflation; apices truncate, slightly tumid, about half the width of base of semicells, with a ring of 13–15 small flattened tubercules, about 7 being visible in front view of cell; cell-wall colorless, punctate; chromatophores numerous, parietal, slightly undulate, longitudinal bands; pyrenoids numerous; zygote unknown. (Reported from Pope County by Phinney, 1946.) Pl. 55, fig. 605.

Euastrum Ehrenberg 1832; emend. Ralfs 1844

Cells of variable size, length generally about twice the width, compressed, deeply constricted, sinus generally linear with apex inflated and outer portion open; semicells usually truncate-pyramidate, apex with a median incision of variable depth, sometimes only a shallow depression or absent, lateral margins entire, sinuate, or variously lobed; cell-wall smooth, punctate or granulate, sometimes with spines on the outer margin, 1 or more somewhat hemispherical protuberances at or near center of semicell; vertical view generally elliptic with poles rounded and 1 or more protuberances on each side; lateral view of semicells narrowly truncate-pyramidate, with rather prominent basal inflations; 1 chromatophore in each semicell, often irregularly lobed or ridged, a single central pyrenoid in small species or several scattered ones in larger species.

Zygote spherical to ellipsoid, walls smooth, mammillate, or short-spined.

KEY TO THE SPECIES

1. Polar lobe not incised.................................... 1. E. johnsonii
1. Polar lobe incised... 2
   2. Semicells distinctly 5-lobed; sinuses deep................ 2. E. oblongum
   2. Semicells obscurely 3-lobed; sinuses shallow............. 3. E. pulchellum

1. *Euastrum johnsonii* West and West. Cells 40 × 60 μ and 20 μ thick (isthmus 11 μ, apex 17 μ wide), about 1.5 times as long as wide, sinus narrowly linear; semicells almost triangular, basal lobes broadly rounded, with 2 rows of papillae; polar lobe more prominent, truncately rounded, without an incision; lateral margin convex, triundulate at the base and concave toward the apex which bears a peripheral ring of about 16 papillae; each semicell with a central protuberance to the right and left bearing 4 papillae; lateral view elliptic, with a prominent central protuberance. Pl. 55, fig. 618.

2. *Euastrum oblongum* (Greville) Ralfs. Cells 63–107 × 125–205 μ and 45–65 μ thick (isthmus 19–31 μ; polar lobe 23–30 μ wide), about twice as long as wide, deeply constricted, sinus linear, dilated at the apex and opening widely outward, isthmus narrow; semicells subrectangular, 5-lobed; polar lobe broadly cuneate with rounded angles, apex tumid, with a deep, narrow, median incision; upper lateral lobes subquadrate, smaller than the lower lateral lobes, margins somewhat retuse, angles rounded; lower lobes subquadrate, with rounded angles and concave margins; incisions between lobes deep, open and with rounded apices; cell-wall punctate, with a large protuberance just above the isthmus and a smaller one just within the margin of both the upper and lower lateral lobes, sometimes with a large scrobiculation between the smaller protuberances; lateral view narrowly elongate-pyramidate, bases at first parallel and then converging to the truncate apex; vertical view broadly elliptic, poles rounded and 4 protuberances on each side of the cell; chromatophores axial, 4-lobed plates; zygote spherical, densely covered with short mammillate protuberances, diameter without protuberances 92–148 μ. Pl. 55, fig. 617.

3. *Euastrum pulchellum* Brébisson. Cells 23–33 × 26–40 μ and 16–20 μ thick (isthmus 6.5–8.0 μ wide), deeply constricted, sinus narrowly linear,

slightly dilated at the extremity and opening slightly outward, isthmus narrow; semicells truncate-pyramidate, with a shallow sinus between the poorly defined lobes; polar lobe widely rectangular-oblong, apex truncate with a deep, broad incision, angles acute and furnished with short, widely divergent spines; lateral lobes broadly rounded, ornamented with 3–4 short sharp marginal spines; semicells with a triangle of 3 elongate verrucae just above the isthmus, a large rounded granule on each side of the apical incision and often a small granule at each angle of the apical incision; lateral view of semicells narrowly pyramidate-ovate, with apex rounded and bearing a single erect spine, base bearing a protuberance on each side; vertical view oblong-elliptic with rounded poles bearing spines, and with a protuberance on each side. Pl. **55,** fig. **616.**

Cosmarium Corda 1834

Cells variable in size, a little longer than wide, rarely twice as long as wide, a few species wider than long, generally compressed, symmetrical in 3 planes at right angles to each other; constricted in the middle to variable depths, semicells elliptic, subcircular, semicircular, subquadrate, or truncate-pyramidate, apex rounded, truncate or subtruncate, without an apical incision, center sometimes protuberant; vertical view elliptic, subelliptic, oblong, or rarely circular, often having 1 or more central protuberances on either side; chromatophores usually axial, 1 in each semicell, with 4 curved longitudinal plates and 1–2 large pyrenoids, parietal in a few species, 4–8 in each semicell, with 1 or more pyrenoids in each; cell-wall smooth, punctate, scrobiculate, granulate, verrucose, or papillate, with the markings arranged in a definite pattern.

Zygotes variable in shape, smooth or variously ornamented, sometimes bearing furcate, or rarely simple, spines; parthenospores.

KEY TO THE SPECIES

1. Cell-wall smooth, punctate, or scrobiculate.............................. 2
1. Cell-wall granulate or dentate....................................... 18
   2. Cell circular or subcircular in vertical view........................... 3
   2. Cell not circular or subcircular in vertical view........................ 4
3. Constriction deep.................................. 1. C. moniliforme
3. Constriction shallow............................... 2. C. curtum
   4. Semicell transversely elliptic, depressed............ 3. C. depressum
   4. Semicell semicircular, truncate-subsemicircular, or semielliptic............ 5
   4. Semicell pyramidate, usually truncate; basal part rectangular or not........ 10
   4. Semicell hexagonal, elliptic-hexagonal, or subhexagonal-reniform........... 14
5. Margin undulate.................................. 4. C. pericymatium
5. Margin not undulate.. 6

   6. Basal angles rectangular...................... 5. C. cucumis

   6. Basal angles not rectangular... 7

7. Cell-wall finely scrobiculate...................... 6. C. pachydermum
                                       var. aethiopicum

7. Cell-wall not scrobiculate.. 8

   8. Apex truncate............................... 7. C. nitidulum

   8. Apex not truncate.. 9

9. Semicell semielliptic.............................. 8. C. constrictum

9. Semicell semicircular.............................. 9. C. circulare

   10. Margin of semicells crenate.................................... 11

   10. Margin of semicells not crenate................................ 12

11. Semicell rectangular below......................... 10. C. subimpressulum

11. Semicell not rectangular below..................... 11. C. holmiense

   12. Apex retuse............................... 12. C. meneghinii

   12. Apex not retuse.. 13

13. Apex broad............................... 11a. C. holmiense var.
                                       integrum

13. Apex narrow............................... 13. C. granatum

   14. Semicell with a central inflation.................................. 15

   14. Semicell lacking a central inflation............................... 16

15. Margin of semicell crenate......................... 10. C. subimpressulum

15. Margin of semicell not crenate..................... 14. C. polygonum

   16. Sides of semicell parallel below.................................. 17

   16. Sides of semicell not parallel below............... 15. C. sexangulare

17. Sides retuse............................... 12. C. meneghinii

17. Sides not retuse......................... 16. C. rectangulare

   18. Semicell broadly elliptic........................ 17. C. dentatum

   18. Semicell reniform.. 19

   18. Semicell semicircular or subsemicircular, often pyramidately so.......... 21

   18. Semicell truncate-pyramidate or subpyramidate..................... 22

   18. Semicell rectangular or subrectangular............................. 32

19. Semicells with 3 prominent inflations on each side..... 18. C. biretum   var.
                                       trigibberum

19. Semicells without inflations or rarely with a slight single inflation............. 20

   20. Wall finely granulate; sinus slightly dilated........ 19. C. punctulatum

   20. Wall coarsely granulate; sinus widely dilated...... 20. C. reniforme

21. Each side of semicell about 16-crenate............... 21. C. supraspeciosum

21. Each side of semicell 3-7-crenate.................................. 22

   22. Granules in vertical series on the central inflations.................... 23

   22. Granules not in vertical series on the central inflations 22. C. subcostatum

23. Basal angles rectangular......................... 23. C. subcrenatum

23. Basal angles not rectangular..................... 24. C. formosulum

   24. Lateral margins deeply and widely incised......... 25. C. protractum

   24. Lateral margins not deeply and widely incised........................ 25

25. Margin of semicell undulate......................... 26. C. quinarium

25. Margin of semicell crenate....................................... 26

25. Margin of semicell neither undulate nor crenate........................ 29

26. Each side of semicell with about 16 crenations..... 21. C. supraspeciosum
26. Each side of semicell with 4–7 crenations............................... 27
27. Semicells lacking central inflations.................. 27. C. speciosum
27. Semicells with central inflations... 28
    28. Margins granulate.. 29
    28. Margins not granulate......................... 23. C. subcrenatum
29. Granules in vertical series on central inflation........ 24. C. formosulum
29. Granules not in vertical series on central inflation...... 22. C. subcostatum
    30. Lateral margins concave....................... 28. C. turpinii
    30. Lateral margins convex.................................. 31
31. Lateral view of semicell circular.................... 19. C. punctulatum
31. Lateral view of semicell broadly elliptic.............. 29. C. botrytis
    32. Margin of semicells crenate........................ 33
    32. Margin of semicells not crenate.................... 34
33. Lateral margins 3–4-crenate...................... 30. C. crenatum
33. Lateral margins 7-crenate...................... 27. C. speciosum
    34. Semicell with inflations............................ 35
    34. Semicell lacking inflations......................... 36
35. Semicell with a single inflation on each side........... 31. C. broomei
35. Semicell with 3 inflations on each side.............. 18. C. biretum var.
                      trigibberum
    36. Sides concave and upwardly divergent............ 32. C. porrectum
    36. Sides not concave or upwardly divergent......................... 37
37. Marginal granules few and restricted to angles........ 33. C. triplicatum
37. Marginal granules few, not restricted to angles........ 34. C. quadrum

1. *Cosmarium moniliforme* (Turpin) Ralfs. Cells 11–20 × 21.0–37.5 μ (isthmus 4–9 μ wide), about twice as long as wide, deeply constricted, sinus acute and widely open; semicells circular or subcircular in all views; cell-wall smooth; chromatophores axial, 1 in each semicell, with about 6 radiating vertical plates or lobes; pyrenoid single, central; zygotes spherical, smooth, 37 μ in diameter. Pl. 53, fig. 577.

2. *Cosmarium curtum* (Brébisson) Ralfs. Cells 10.5–32.5 × 22–60 μ (isthmus 9.5–30.0 μ wide), about 2 times as long as wide, slightly constricted, sinus shallow and open, isthmus wide; semicells attenuated, sides convex, apex rounded and sometimes slightly thickened; vertical view circular; cell-wall punctate; chromatophore axial, 1 in each semicell, consisting of a central mass with about 8 longitudinal ridges; pyrenoids several in an axial series. Pl. 53, fig. 576.

3. *Cosmarium depressum* (Naegeli) Lundell. Cells 38–53 × 37–54 μ and 17–24 μ thick (isthmus 8–14 μ wide), somewhat wider than long; deeply constricted, sinus narrowly linear, the apex dilated, opening outward; isthmus very narrow; semicells transversely elliptic, depressed, lateral margins broadly rounded, the apices convex-truncate; vertical view ellip-

tic; lateral view of semicells circular; cell-wall finely punctate, chromatophores axial; pyrenoid single, central; zygotes spherical or ellipsoid, smooth, about 35 μ in diameter. Pl. 53, fig. 564.

4. *Cosmarium pericymatium* Nordstedt. Cells 28–32 × 40–51 μ and 24–27 μ thick (isthmus 23–25 μ wide), longer than wide, moderately constricted, sinus open and the apex obtuse; semicells semielliptic, the base slightly contracted, margin with about 16 crenations; vertical view broadly elliptic, the poles slightly produced; lateral view of semicell semi-oblong-elliptic, the base slightly contracted; cell-wall somewhat thick and densely punctate. Pl. 53, fig. 573.

5. *Cosmarium cucumis* (Corda) Ralfs. Cells 34–56 × 59–102 μ and 19–38 μ thick (isthmus 15–38 μ wide), longer than wide, deeply constricted, sinus linear, the apex rounded and slightly dilated; semicells semielliptic or widely truncate-ovate, basal angles rectangular and rounded, the apex rounded or slightly truncate; vertical view broadly elliptic or elliptic-oblong; lateral view of semicell obtusely ovate; cell-wall smooth; chromatophores irregular parietal bands extending from base to apex, 6–9 in each semicell; pyrenoids several in each chromatophore. Pl. 53, fig. 569.

6. *Cosmarium pachydermum* Lundell var. *aethiopicum* W. and G. S. West. Cells 61–80 × 69–107 μ and 40–45 μ thick (isthmus 28–33 μ wide), longer than wide, broadly elliptic, deeply constricted, lower part of sides somewhat straight, basal angles broadly rounded, apices broad; vertical view elliptic; lateral view of semicell subcircular; cell-wall thin, finely scrobiculate and minutely punctate between the scrobiculations; chromatophores axial, 1 in each semicell; pyrenoids 2 in each chromatophore. Pl. 53, fig. 581.

7. *Cosmarium nitidulum* DeNotaris. Cells 23–33 × 30–41 μ and 16.0–22.5 μ thick (isthmus 8–10 μ wide), a little longer than wide, deeply constricted, sinus narrowly linear, the apex slightly dilated; semicells truncate-subsemicircular, basal angles broadly rounded, sides convex and converging upward, upper angles slightly rounded, apex small, truncate-convex, straight or slightly retuse; vertical view elliptic; lateral view of semicell subcircular; cell-wall minutely and often obscurely punctate; chromatophore axial, 1 in each semicell; pyrenoid single, central. Pl. 53, fig. 572.

8. *Cosmarium constrictum* Delponte. Cells 21–38 μ wide, broadly elliptic, longer than wide, deeply constricted, sinus acutely angled and opening outward, wall smooth; semicells semielliptic, basal angles rounded; lateral view of semicell broadly elliptic; vertical view elliptic; a single pyrenoid in each semicell. Pl. 54, fig. 594.

9. *Cosmarium circulare* Reinsch. Cells 39–90 × 47–95 μ and 22–38 μ thick (isthmus 14–28 μ wide), about as long as wide, circular in outline, deeply constricted, sinus linear, somewhat dilated at the apex, isthmus narrow; semicells semicircular, basal angles rounded; vertical view narrowly elliptic; lateral view of semicells narrowly subcircular; cell-wall minutely punctate; chromatophores axial; pyrenoids 2 in each semicell. (Reported from Pope County by Phinney, 1946.) Pl. **55**, figs. **614, 615.**

10. *Cosmarium subimpressulum* Borge. Cells 21–27 × 27–38 μ and 15.5 μ thick (isthmus 6.5–9.0 μ wide), longer than wide, constriction deep, sinus narrow and linear; semicells transversely rectangular in lower part, pyramidate-truncate above, apex prominent, sides parallel below, attenuated upward, crenate, 4 crenations on each side, in part acute and nearly forming right angles; vertical view elliptic, with a broad inflation on each side; lateral view of semicell ovate, apex truncate, tumid in the middle on both sides; cell-wall smooth. Pl. **54**, fig. **588.**

11. *Cosmarium holmiense* Lundell. Cells 26.4–40.0 × 43.2–66.0 μ and 19–28 μ thick (isthmus 14–21 μ, apex 21–29 μ wide), longer than wide, moderately constricted, sinus narrow and linear; semicells broadly pyramidate, basal and upper angles rounded, sides straight or slightly concave, faintly crenate toward the apex, the apex broadly truncate, somewhat produced and slightly biundulate; vertical view elliptic; lateral view of semicell quadrate-elliptic, apex convex-truncate; cell-wall smooth or delicately punctate; chromatophores axial; pyrenoid single, central. Pl. **53**, fig. **566.**

a. Var. *integrum* Lundell. Cells 28–40 × 45–62 μ and 24–28 μ thick (isthmus 15.6–22.0 μ wide); semicells somewhat more attenuated upward than in the species; sides almost straight; apex somewhat convex, dilated and never truncate or undulate; sinus open. Pl. **53**, fig. **567.**

12. *Cosmarium meneghinii* Brébisson. Cells 9.5–17.0 × 12.5–24.0 μ and 6.0–10.5 μ thick (isthmus 3–6 μ wide), longer than wide, deeply constricted, sinus narrow and linear; semicells transversely rectangular in lower part, pyramidate-truncate above, sides parallel below and strongly convergent upward, all sides retuse, the apex strongly so, angles rounded; vertical view elliptic; lateral view of semicell broadly elliptic or subcircular; cell-wall smooth; chromatophore axial, 1 in each semicell; pyrenoid single, central; zygote spherical, with short, acute or subacute, straight or slightly curved spines, 30–37 μ in diameter with spines, 18–26 μ without spines. Pl. **54**, fig. **597.**

13. *Cosmarium granatum* Brébisson. Cells 19–30 × 26–52 μ and 10.5–17.5 μ thick (isthmus 6.3–9.0 μ wide), longer than wide, subrhomboid-ellip-

tic, deeply constricted, sinus linear, slightly dilated at the apex; semicells truncate-pyramidate, basal angles rounded, sides straight, slightly convex, or rarely slightly concave, subparallel at the base and converging toward the apex, upper angles obtuse, apex narrowly truncate and straight; vertical view elliptic; lateral view of semicell elliptic-ovate; cell-wall finely punctate; chromatophores axial; pyrenoid single, central. Pl. **53,** fig. **565.**

14. *Cosmarium polygonum* (Naegeli) Archer. Cells 14.0–18.5 × 15.0–21.5 μ and 10.0–12.5 μ thick (isthmus 3–7 μ wide), slightly longer than wide, deeply constricted, sinus rather short and narrow; semicells broadly hexagonal, angles rounded, lateral angles slightly produced, sides faintly retuse, apex sometimes straight; vertical view subelliptic, with a prominent conical tumor at the middle of each side; lateral view of semicell depressed-circular, slightly inflated on each side; cell-wall smooth or rarely punctate; chromatophores axial; pyrenoid single, central. Pl. **54,** fig. **591.**

15. *Cosmarium sexangulare* Lundell. Cells 33–36 × 42 μ and 18.0–24.5 μ thick (isthmus 7–12 μ, apex 15–18 μ wide), slightly longer than wide, deeply constricted, sinus narrow, the apex dilated; semicells transversely elliptic-hexagonal, angles rounded, upper lateral margins slightly concave, apex truncate; lateral view of semicells subcircular; vertical view elliptic; cell-wall very finely punctate; chromatophores axial, 1 in each semicell; pyrenoid single, central. Pl. **53,** fig. **578.**

a. Forma *minima* Nordstedt. Cells 11–12 × 13.5–15.0 μ (isthmus 3 μ, apex 5–8 μ wide); semicells with the apex and upper lateral margins retuse. Pl. **53,** fig. **579.**

16. *Cosmarium rectangulare* Grunow. Cells 30–36 × 37–47 μ and 18–24 μ thick (isthmus 9–12 μ wide), longer than wide, deeply constricted, sinus narrow, the apex dilated; semicells subhexagonal-reniform, basal angles subrectangular and rounded, the sides parallel below, upper angles broadly and obliquely rounded-truncate, apex truncate; lateral view of semicells obovate-circular; vertical view subelliptic; cell-wall finely punctate. Pl. **53,** fig. **583.**

17. *Cosmarium dentatum* Wolle. Cells 88–100 × 135–169 μ (without teeth) and 66–69 μ thick (isthmus 31–33 μ wide), length about 0.5 greater than width, deeply constricted, sinus acute at the apex and opening outward; semicells broadly elliptic or nearly round, apex broadly rounded or subtruncate, without teeth, lateral margins with 10–12 subobtuse teeth, few other teeth within the margins, thickened at the center; vertical view elliptic, thickened at the middle, 3–4 teeth at the poles, irregularly arranged teeth in zones from pole to pole, center without teeth; lateral view circular or broadly elliptic; cell-wall thick, minutely scrobiculate, larger

scrobiculations in centrally thickened area, densely and minutely punctate between scrobiculations. Pl. 53, fig. 571.

18. *Cosmarium biretum* Brébisson var. *trigiberrum* Nordstedt. Cells 38–82 × 43–100 μ and 32–48 μ thick (isthmus 12–33 μ wide), about as long as wide or somewhat longer, deeply constricted, sinus narrowly linear, the apex slightly dilated; semicells variable, subrectangular-trapeziform, sometimes reniform, sides straight or usually rounded, basal angles rounded, lateral margins rarely divergent, apex convex; vertical view with 3 protuberances on each side, all slight and of about equal size or the central one larger than the other two; lateral view of semicell subcircular or ovate; cell-wall densely granulate, granules small, in vertical series or irregularly arranged; chromatophores axial; pyrenoids 2 in each semicell. Pl. 53, fig. 563.

19. *Cosmarium punctulatum* Brébisson. Cells 27–38 × 28–40 μ and 17–19 μ thick (isthmus 7.5–12.0 μ wide), length slightly greater than width; deeply constricted, sinus linear, with apex slightly dilated and outer extremity open, isthmus narrow; semicells oblong-trapeziform, somewhat reniform, or subpyramidate in outline, finely granular, basal and apical angles broadly rounded, apex truncate or slightly convex, lateral margins convex; lateral view of semicells circular; vertical view elliptic, sometimes with a very slight inflation at the middle on each side; cell-wall granulate, granules small and uniform, sometimes reduced or absent in the central area; chromatophores axial; pyrenoid single, central; zygotes spherical, with numerous long spines with broadly conical bases and deeply emarginate, or bifurcate and emarginate apices, 65–68 μ in diameter with spines, 42–45 μ without spines. Pl. 54, fig. 592.

20. *Cosmarium reniforme* (Ralfs) Archer. Cells 36–60 × 44–67 μ and 24–29 μ thick (isthmus 13–20 μ wide), length equal to width or very slightly longer, deeply constricted, sinus narrow and closed, open outward and widely dilated at the apex; isthmus narrow and somewhat elongate; semicells reniform, outline granulate; lateral view of semicells circular; vertical view elliptic; cell-wall with coarse granules arranged in obliquely decussating series and sometimes in indistinct vertical series, about 25–33 granules showing at each semicell margin; chromatophores axial; 2 pyrenoids in each semicell. Pl. 53, fig. 586.

21. *Cosmarium supraspeciosum* Wolle. Cells 65–70 × 90–95 μ, broadly ovate, longer than wide, deeply constricted, sinus narrowly linear, margins crenate; semicells pyramidate-semicircular or subpyramidate, basal angles rounded, sides convex, apex truncate, crenations usually about 16 on each side and 5–6 on the apex; wall ornamented with large undivided

granules arranged in concentric and radiating series extending from the margin nearly half way to the center; central area bearing 5–6 vertical series of smaller granules; lateral view of semicells ovate-oblong with a granulate inflation near the base; vertical view with a prominent central granulate inflation. Pl. 54, fig. 598.

22. *Cosmarium subcostatum* Nordstedt. Cells 23–43 × 24–27 μ and 14–20 μ thick (isthmus 6.4–12.0 μ wide), longer than wide, deeply constricted, sinus narrowly linear, the apex dilated; semicells subtrapeziform-reniform, subpyramidate, or subsemicircular-pyramidate in outline, basal angles rounded, sides convex and with 2 small entire crenations near the basal angles and about 4 larger emarginate or bigranulate crenations on the rest of the lateral margin, apex truncate and with 4 delicate crenulations, apical angles often slightly emarginate; lateral view of semicells ovate, with a tumor near the base at each side; vertical view narrowly elliptic, with a granulate tumor at the middle on each side; cell-wall minutely granulate within the margin, granules arranged radially and concentrically, the 2 or 3 series next to the margin binate, those nearest the center single; with a tumor in the center above the isthmus bearing about 4 granules in each of 4 or 5 subvertical series and surrounded by a small clear space; chromatophores axial, 1 in each semicell; pyrenoids 2 in each semicell. Pl. 53, fig. 585.

23. *Cosmarium subcrenatum* Hantzsch. Cells 18–32 × 23–37 μ and 12–21 μ thick (isthmus 7–16 μ wide), slightly longer than wide, deeply constricted, sinus narrowly linear; semicells subpyramidate or subsemicircular in outline, basal angles rectangular, sides with 4–6 crenations, the lower smaller than the upper, the apex truncate and with 4, or rarely 5, crenations; lateral view of semicells ovate, apex truncate, sides retuse above; vertical view elliptic, with a broad tumor on each side bearing about 5 distinct granules, poles rounded or truncate; cell-wall with minute binate granules immediately within all except the 1 or 2 basal crenations and with 1 or 2 series of minute granules arranged radially and concentrically; with a broad flattened tumor in the center above the isthmus bearing 3–6 granules in each of 5–7 vertical series; chromatophores axial, 1 in each semicell; pyrenoid single, central; zygotes spherical, with short scattered spines with conical bases and emarginate or bifurcate apices, 32–35 μ in diameter without spines; spines 8–10 μ in length. Pl. 54, fig. 596.

24. *Cosmarium formosulum* Hoffman. Cells 34–40 × 40–50 × 22–25 μ thick (isthmus 10.0–15.5 μ, apex 12–17 μ wide), slightly longer than wide, deeply constricted, sinus linear, the apex slightly dilated; semicells trapeziform-subsemicircular or subpyramidate in outline, basal angles

rounded, sides convex and 6–7-crenate, the 3 upper crenations with 2 granules, lower crenations entire, apical angles obtuse or faintly bigranulate-emarginate, apex truncate and 4- or rarely 6–7-crenate, minutely granulate within the margin, the granules in concentric and radiating series, binate except in the innermost series and near the basal angles, in the center a broad tumor with 5–7 vertical series of granules; vertical view elliptic, poles rounded and minutely crenulate, with a broad 5–7-crenate tumor at the middle on each side, in the center a small rectangular smooth area; lateral view of semicell broadly ovate, strongly granulate on the tumid margins near the base on each side; chromatophores axial; pyrenoids 2. Pl. 54, fig. 589.

a. Var. *nathorstii* (Boldt) W. and G. S. West. Cells 42–52 × 44–53 μ and 23–25 μ thick (isthmus 11–16 μ wide), with basal angles less rounded than in the species, lateral margins with 3–6 bigranulate or emarginate crenations, the granules of central tumor stronger and more pronounced. Pl. 54, fig. 590.

25. *Cosmarium protractum* (Naegeli) DeBary. Cells 33–47 × 34–45 μ and 17.5–24.0 μ thick (isthmus 8.5–12.0 μ, apex 13–20 μ wide), about as long as wide or slightly longer, very deeply constricted, sinus linear, the apex slightly dilated and outer portion somewhat open, isthmus narrow; semicells pyramidate, lateral margins deeply incised, appearing 3-lobed; apices elevated, lateral lobes broadly rounded; apical lobes truncate, the sides subparallel and apex flattened, angles of lobes somewhat rounded, cell outline granulate; vertical view elliptic, poles broadly rounded, sides with a prominent granulate protuberance at the middle; lateral view of semicell ovate, with flattened apices, with a protuberance near the base on each side; cell-wall with coarse granules more or less regularly arranged on the lateral lobes, becoming reduced in size from the margins toward the central protuberance, which bears large granules arranged in concentric rings; chromatophores axial; pyrenoids 2 in each chromatophore. Pl. 53, fig. 570.

26. *Cosmarium quinarium* Lundell. Cells 32–38 × 38–42 μ and 22–25 μ thick (isthmus 9.5–11.0 μ wide), deeply constricted, sinus linear, with the apex slightly dilated and outer margin open, isthmus narrow; semicells broadly truncate-pyramidate, outline granulate, basal angles broadly rounded, apical angles rounded, sides convex, apex truncate and with 4–5 undulations; lateral view of semicells circular, with 3 acute granules at each side; vertical view elliptic and granulate except the center, granules at the middle on each side larger and more prominent; cell-wall with 5 prominent granules in 2 rows at the center of semicell, the upper row with

3 granules and the lower with 2, with a transverse subapical row of 4 granules, and with several smaller granules near the lateral margins, and 2 or 3 punctulations between the granules at the center of the cell; chromatophores axial; 2 pyrenoids in each semicell. Pl. 54, fig. 595.

27. *Cosmarium speciosum* Lundell. Cells 37–41 × 54–64 μ and 25–28 μ thick (isthmus 20–26 μ wide), moderately constricted, sinus narrowly linear; semicells subrectangular, or subpyramidate, basal angles slightly rounded, gradually attenuated upward, apical angles rounded, apex truncate, margin with 4 apical and about 7 lateral crenations; lateral view of semicells ovate-oblong, with a broadly rounded apex; vertical view elliptic, the poles delicately crenulate and with granules arranged in curved transverse series; cell-wall granulate within the margin, the granules in regular radial and concentric series, 3–4 granules in each radial series, 6–9 vertical series of 4–5 granules each across the base just above the isthmus; chromatophore axial, 1 in each semicell; pyrenoid single, central. Pl. 53, fig. 584.

28. *Cosmarium turpinii* Brébisson. Cells 50–67 × 60–77 μ and 20–25 μ thick (isthmus 14–20 μ wide), slightly longer than wide, very deeply constricted, sinus narrowly linear with a slightly dilated apex and somewhat open outward; semicells pyramidate-trapeziform, rapidly converging from a broad base, basal angles rounded, sides concave especially above, apical angles obtuse, apex slightly retuse; lateral view of semicell ovate, with a granulate inflation on each side near the base, the apex rounded; vertical view narrowly elliptic, with a pair of adjacent granulate tumors at the middle on each side; cell-wall densely granulate, granules irregularly arranged, 36–40 visible at the margin, slightly reduced in size toward the center, with a pair of small, central tumors arising from a common base, covered with large irregularly arranged granules, and surrounded by a small ill-defined clear space; chromatophore axial, 1 in each semicell; pyrenoids 2 in each semicell. Pl. 54, fig. 593.

29. *Cosmarium botrytis* Meneghini. Cells 51–85 × 60–111 μ and 33–40 μ thick (isthmus 14–24 μ wide), length about $\frac{1}{4}$ greater than width, deeply constricted, sinus linear, with the apex slightly dilated and outer margin open, isthmus narrow; semicells truncate-pyramidate, basal angles broadly rounded, sides convex, apex narrowly truncate or subtruncate, apical angles rounded; vertical view elliptic, sides inflated in the median portion; lateral view of semicells broadly elliptic; cell-wall coarsely granulate, the granules usually not forming a definite pattern, about 30–36 visible at the margin of each semicell; chromatophores axial, 2 in each semicell, each with 4–6 radiating plates with their peripheral edges flattened against the

cell-wall; pyrenoid single, central; zygotes spherical, with numerous short processes with conical bases and trispinate apices, 51 μ in diameter, with spines 9.7 μ long. Pl. 53, fig. 568.

30. *Cosmarium crenatum* Ralfs. Cells 22–44 × 27–59 μ and 14–28 μ thick (isthmus 9–13 μ wide), longer than wide, deeply constricted, sinus linear and slightly open; semicells rectangular- or subrectangular-pyramidate, the basal angles rectangular and slightly rounded, sides 3-crenate, rarely 4-crenate, apex truncate and 4-crenate, apical and lateral crenations with 1–3 smaller subsidiary crenulations; internal crenations smooth or with 1 or 2 small granules, with 3–6 vertical costae in the center, sometimes smooth and indistinct, rarely slightly granulate; vertical view elliptic, with a broad 3–6-undulate inflation at each side, poles subtruncate and slightly granulate; lateral view of semicell rectangular, basal angles slightly tumid, sides and apex slightly retuse, apical angles minutely granulate; chromatophore axial; pyrenoid single; zygotes spherical, with many stout, slightly attenuated verrucae with 2–4-furcate apices, 38 μ in diameter, including verrucae, 29 μ excluding verrucae. Pl. 53, fig. 574.

31. *Cosmarium broomei* Thwaites. Cells 32–45 × 42–52 μ and 21–30 μ thick (isthmus 12–16 μ wide), about as long as wide, deeply constricted, sinus narrowly linear, the apex slightly dilated; semicells oblong-rectangular or rectangular-trapeziform, the angles slightly rounded, sides convex and sometimes slightly convergent upward, apex straight or slightly retuse; vertical view narrowly elliptic, with a rounded inflation at the middle on each side; lateral view of semicells subcircular-depressed; cell-wall densely covered with small granules arranged in vertical series, about 30–34 visible at the margin of each semicell; chromatophores axial; pyrenoids 2 in each semicell. Pl. 53, fig. 575.

32. *Cosmarium porrectum* Nordstedt. Cells 33–71 × 43–69 μ and 25–28 μ thick (isthmus 12–17 μ wide), about as long as wide, deeply constricted, sinus narrowly linear with a slightly dilated apex; semicells subrectangular-trapeziform, the sides concave and diverging upward, apical angles somewhat produced and rounded, basal angles slightly rounded, apex concave; vertical view oblong-elliptic; wall densely granulate, granules coarse, arranged in horizontal and vertical series, commonly with irregularities. Pl. 53, fig. 587.

33. *Cosmarium triplicatum* Wolle. Cells 40 × 50 μ, deeply constricted, sinus linear with apex slightly dilated, margins irregularly granulate; semicells subrectangular, angles rounded, lateral and apical margins slightly concave; cell-wall granulate, margins with 3 large granules at each

apical angle and 2 at each basal angle, within the margin a series of 3 granules at each apical angle, and between the angles, and a few small scattered granules at the basal angles; granules sometimes appearing in an unbroken series around the margin; vertical view quadrangular-ovate, poles truncate, with a series of large granules at the margins and a second series within the margins. Pl. 53, fig. 582.

34. *Cosmarium quadrum* Lundell. Cells 54–74 × 60–83 μ and 27–40 μ thick (isthmus 18–29 μ wide), about as long as wide or slightly longer, quadrate in outline, deeply constricted, sinus linear and slightly dilated at the apex; semicells subrectangular, basal angles rounded, apical angles broadly rounded, sides almost straight or slightly convex, apex usually slightly retuse, sometimes straight; lateral view of semicell subcircular; vertical view oblong-elliptic, the sides straight and parallel; cell-wall granulate, the granules arranged in decussating oblique series and somewhat less distinct vertical series, 34–37 showing at margin of each semicell, slightly reduced in middle of the apex; chromatophores axial; 2 pyrenoids in each semicell. Pl. 53, fig. 580.

Cosmocladium Brébisson 1856

Cells minute, constricted at the middle, sinus linear, usually compressed and symmetrical in 3 planes at right angles to each other; length somewhat greater than width; semicells subpyramidate, elliptic or subreniform, cell-wall smooth; chromatophores axial, usually 1 in each semicell, with a single central pyrenoid; cells united by bands of gelatinous material forming spherical ellipsoid, microscopic, irregularly branched, free-floating or sessile colonies that are enclosed by hyaline, homogeneous, gelatinous envelopes.

Zygotes more or less spherical, sometimes angular with short stout spines or obtuse protuberances.

1. *Cosmocladium saxonicum* DeBary. Cells 18–26 × 22–30 μ and 12–15 μ thick (isthmus 3.5–7.5 μ wide), 1.5 times as long as wide, median constriction deep, isthmus narrow, sinus deep, sublinear, acute-angled, outer margin opening widely; semicells transversely elliptic to subhemispheric, dorsal margin more rounded than the ventral, lateral angles broadly rounded; vertical view oblong-elliptic, sides subparallel; lateral view subcircular; cell-wall smooth; chromatophores axial, 4-lobed; pyrenoid central, single; cells united by 2 parallel gelatinous filaments into free-floating colonies of varying size; colonial envelope a delicate, hyaline gelatinous matrix. Pl. 55, fig. 619.

Micrasterias C. A. Agardh 1827

Cells usually solitary, rarely in filaments, of variable size, often large with the length somewhat greater than the width, deeply constricted, sinus linear to sublinear and opening outward in several species, usually much compressed; semicells semicircular to hexagonal with 2 or 4 incisions from periphery to variable depth and varying in shape from linear to cuneate; semicells divided into 1 polar and 3–4 lateral lobes; polar lobes generally widely cuneate-emarginate, or widely notched; lateral lobes usually with 1–4 series of secondary lobes with emarginate apices or spines; cell-wall usually smooth, at times with rows of spines near the incisions or marginal denticulations, rarely the entire cell covered with spines; median part of base of semicells generally without protuberances; vertical view elliptic-lanceolate or linear-lanceolate; lateral view narrowly pyramidate; chromatophore axial, lobed, 1 in each semicell; pyrenoids numerous, scattered.

Zygotes spherical, ornamented with radially disposed stout, simple to quadrifid spines; no conjugation tube formed.

KEY TO THE SPECIES

1. Polar lobe with accessory processes...................... 1. M. americana
1. Polar lobe without accessory processes.................................. 2
   2. Incisions between lateral lobes shallow................. 2. M. truncata
   2. Incisions between lateral lobes deep................................. 3
3. Cell-wall covered with short spines...................... 3. M. apiculata
3. Cell-wall without spines................................. 4. M. rotata

1. *Micrasterias americana* (Ehrenberg) Ralfs. Cells 100–145 × 120–160 μ (isthmus 17–29 μ, polar lobe 50–75 μ wide), slightly longer than wide, very deeply constricted, sinus acute and somewhat open, isthmus narrow; semicells 5-lobed, incisions between polar and lateral lobes broad with blunt apices; incisions between lateral lobes narrowly fusiform with rounded apices; polar lobe large and broad, with lateral margins parallel at base and outwardly divergent, forming a cuneate apex; apical margin widely retuse, angles produced into thick divergent processes with truncate-emarginate apices; 2 smaller, asymmetrically disposed processes, 1 on each side of the polar lobe, a rise near the base of the lateral processes; incisions on each side of polar lobe widely open; lateral lobes rather small, separated by a shallow, open incision, the 2 lobes of each side being trapezoid in form, each lobe divided into 2 lobules by a wide, shallow notch, the 2 proximate lobules being smaller than the 2 distal ones, lobules with 3 or 4 teeth at the extremity and dentate along their inner margins; semicells

with a central supraisthmal protuberance bearing a few scattered granules, with about 4 large acute granules within the apical margin of the tumid lobe, and with a number of small scattered granules on surface of polar and lateral lobes; vertical view rhomboid-fusiform with a small granulate protuberance at the middle on each side, poles produced and truncate-denticulate, polar lobe showing the asymmetrical disposition of the apical processes; lateral view narrowly pyramidate with a small granulate basal inflation, bases rounded, and apices continued in 4 short processes; chromatophore 1 in each semicell, ridged, extending into each of the lobes, and bearing 10–20 pyrenoids. Pl. **51**, fig. **537**.

2. *Micrasterias truncata* (Corda) Brébisson. Cells 60–129 × 70–138 μ (isthmus 15–27 μ, polar lobe 55–97 μ wide), almost circular in outline, somewhat longer than wide, poles widely truncate, deeply constricted, sinus narrowly linear and often slightly open outward, isthmus narrow; semicells 5-lobed, polar incision open, or rarely linear, somewhat shallow, with blunt apices; lateral incisions about half the depth of the polar incisions, acute-angled to sublinear; polar lobe widely cuneate or sometimes almost fusiform, apex convex and usually flattened or slightly retuse in the middle, lateral angles acuminate or emarginate; lateral lobes somewhat variable, typically with a very shallow, rounded incision and the lobules strongly emarginate; lateral view of semicells ovate-pyramidate; vertical view fusiform-elliptic with poles acuminate; cell-wall smooth to strongly punctate; chromatophores with 2 prominent vertical ridges and irregularly disposed accessory ridges. Pl. **51**, fig. **539**.

3. *Micrasterias apiculata* (Ehrenberg) Meneghini. Cells 120–250 × 150–294 μ (isthmus 21–56 μ, polar lobe 37–96 μ wide), length slightly greater than width, subelliptic in outline, deeply constricted, sinus linear but opening outward, isthmus narrow; semicells 5-lobed, the incisions forming lobes extending about half way from the periphery to the cell center, polar incision open and acute-angled, lateral incisions narrow, the sides slightly divergent or convergent; polar lobe exserted, the lateral margins subparallel at the base and outwardly divergent at the apex, angles with 2 diverging spines and with a large curved spine on the apical margin close to the angles, apex deeply emarginate; lateral lobes usually equal in size, with 2 series of rather wide incisions, the ultimate lobelets terminating in 1–3 marginal, outwardly curved spines; lateral view of semicells narrowly truncate-pyramidate, the apex bearing spines; vertical view rhomboid-elliptic, with acute poles; cell-wall covered with short spines irregularly arranged except near the incisions, and with 3 to 5 larger spines just above the isthmus in the middle of each semicell; chromatophores filling the

semicells, the portion in polar lobe deeply incised at the apex, with 2 prominent ridges extending from the nucleus to the apex of the polar lobe, and with secondary ridges near each incision of the lateral lobes; pyrenoids numerous in each chromatophore. (Reported from Pope County by Phinney, 1946.) Pl. 55, fig. 620.

4. *Micrasterias rotata* (Greville) Ralfs. Cells 165–305 × 205–366 μ (isthmus 28–43 μ, polar lobe 48–80 μ wide), almost circular in outline, a little longer than wide, very deeply constricted, sinus narrowly linear; semicells 5-lobed, incisions narrowly linear; polar lobe gradually widening upward, with concave sides, apex concave and emarginate at the middle, angles slightly produced and bidentate, separated from the lateral lobes by a deep incision; lateral lobes broadly cuneate and divided into 2 lobules by a deep incision; upper lateral lobes larger than the lower, subdivided into 4 equal emarginate parts by 3 incisions of which the median is deepest; lobules of lower lateral lobes divided into 2–4 bidentate or rarely tridentate parts; lateral view of semicells ovate-lanceolate, with a broadly truncate apex and an inflated base; vertical view narrowly elliptic-rhomboid, with acute poles and a small inflation in the middle of each side; cell-wall delicately punctate. Pl. 51, fig. 538.

Arthrodesmus Ehrenberg 1838

Cells mostly small, length usually equal to width, generally compressed and bilaterally symmetrical in front view, rarely triangular in vertical view and radially symmetrical; median constriction fairly deep, sinus usually widely open; semicells generally triangular in front view, rarely elliptic, subtrapeziform or subrectangular; vertical view usually elliptic, rarely triangular; lateral view subcircular; lateral angles each furnished with a single, simple, straight, or curved spine all in the same plane; cell-wall of uniform thickness, without ornamentation on body of semicells; chromatophore axial, usually 1 in each semicell; pyrenoid usually single and central.

Zygotes spherical, smooth or bearing simple spines.

1. *Arthrodesmus convergens* Ehrenberg. Cells 45–90 (23–64 without spines) × 30–54 μ (isthmus 8–20 μ wide), median constriction deep, sinus opening widely outward from the narrowly linear extremity; semicells transversely elliptic, the apex more rounded than the base, lateral margins broadly rounded and furnished with a single stout tapering spine, spines strongly convergent, the extremities of opposite pairs frequently apposed; vertical view narrowly elliptic, with a short spine at each pole; chromatophore axial, with a single pyrenoid; zygote spherical, smooth, 39–48 μ in diameter. Pl. 51, fig. 536.

Staurastrum Meyen 1829

Cells variable in size, usually longer than wide excluding processes or other appendages, usually with a radial symmetry, median constriction variable but usually deep, sinus generally acute and isthmus narrow; semi-cells extremely variable in outline, spherical, cylindric, ellipsoid, triangular, hexagonal, campanulate, etc., with the angles frequently produced into hollow processes of variable length that almost always bear some sort of ornamentation and usually terminate in a truncate end with short divergent spines or at times with bifurcate ends resembling spines; cell-wall smooth, punctate, scrobiculate, granulate or bearing spines or simple to emarginate verrucae, or combinations of these ornamentations; vertical view predominantly triangular, but 4–8-radiate species are common, and there may be as many as 11 angles in 1 whorl; chromatophore generally an axial mass with 1 pyrenoid and with deeply incised lobes radiating into the angles or processes, or in some species parietal, with several pyrenoids; cells sometimes enclosed in a spherical gelatinous envelope.

Zygotes spherical or angular, rarely winged or bearing blunt warts, commonly clothed with mammillate or obtusely conical protuberances that are continued in long spines with simple or furcate apices; 1–4 vegetative cells formed from germinating zygote.

KEY TO THE SPECIES

1. Angles of cells continued in hollow processes.............................. 6
1. Angles of cells not continued in hollow processes......................... 2
   2. Cell-walls with small granules.. 4
   2. Cell-walls not with granules... 3
3. Cells bearing a single spine at each angle............. 1. S. cuspidatum
3. Cells not bearing spines at the angles.................. 2. S. crenatum
   4. Semicells oblong-elliptic, apex flattened or slightly convex.............. 5
   4. Semicells angularly elliptic, apex distinctly convex.... 3. S. punctulatum
5. Sinus acute-angled and open......................... 4. S. alternans
5. Sinus acuminate and widely open..................... 5. S. dilatatum
   6. Cells with prominent accessory spines............... 6. S. oxyacanthum
   6. Cells without prominent accessory spines............................ 7
7. Processes as long or longer than width of cell........... 7. S. gracile
7. Processes not as long as width of cell................................ 8
   8. Dorsal and ventral margins of semicell almost equally
     convex .... 8. S. hexacerum
   8. Dorsal margin of semicell less convex than the ventral.................... 9
9. Processes bearing 3 or 4 small terminal spines.......... 9. S. polymorphum
9. Processes not bearing terminal spines................. 10. S. margaritaceum

1. *Staurastrum cuspidatum* Brébisson. Cells 16–28 × 20–31 μ (isthmus 5–8 μ wide, spines 5–20 μ long), about as long as wide or a little longer not

including the spines, deeply constricted, sinus opening widely and with
apex broadly rectangular, isthmus narrow, rectangular, greatly elongated;
semicells fusiform, ventral margin slightly convex, the dorsal convex or
slightly concave, lateral angles acute and terminating in a straight, acute
spine; spines parallel, convergent or divergent; vertical view usually triangular, rarely quadrangular, sides concave, each with a straight spine;
cell-wall smooth; chromatophores triangular, with 2 parallel lobes extending to each angle of the semicell; pyrenoid single, central; zygotes spherical, with stout straight spines swollen at the base, 25 μ in diameter without
spines, 55 μ with spines. Pl. 55, fig. 610.

2. *Staurastrum crenatum* Bailey. Cells about twice as long as wide, sides
deeply concave, walls smooth; semicells cuneate or fan-shaped, apical
margin crenate; vertical view triangular, sides concave, angles rounded-
truncate and crenate. Pl. 55, fig. 612.

3. *Staurastrum punctulatum* Brébisson. Cells 23.0–36.5 $\times$ 26.0–40.5 μ
(isthmus 8–16 μ wide), some longer than wide, deeply constricted, sinus
acute and widely open; semicells angularly elliptic or rhomboidal with dorsal
and ventral margins equally convex, angles acutely rounded; vertical view
triangular or rarely 4- or 5-angular, the sides usually concave, the angles
acutely rounded; cell-wall with flattened granules arranged in regular series around the angles; zygote spherical, bearing short spines with broadly
mammillate bases and doubly furcate apices, 42–58 μ in diameter with
spines, 29–38 μ without spines. Pl. 54, fig. 603.

4. *Staurastrum alternans* Brébisson. Cells 21–37 $\times$ 21–35 μ (isthmus 7–
13 μ wide), length about equal to the width, twisted at the isthmus
through 60°, deeply constricted, sinus open and acute-angled, isthmus
narrow; semicells transversely oblong-elliptic, the dorsal margin more flattened than the ventral, lateral angles rounded, apex flattened in the
middle; vertical view triangular, angles of 1 semicell alternating with those
of the other, sides concave, angles rounded; cell-wall finely granulate,
granules in concentric rings around the angles, scattered and somewhat
reduced in the middle of the apex; zygote spherical, furnished with bifurcate spines. Pl. 54, fig. 601.

5. *Staurastrum dilatatum* Ehrenberg. Cells 17–48 $\times$ 19–46 μ (isthmus
6–13 μ wide), about as long as wide, deeply constricted but less so in the
quadrangular than the triangular form, sinus acuminate at the apex and
opening widely; semicells elliptic-subfusiform, dorsal margin flattened,
slightly convex, ventral margin much inflated in the median part, lateral
angles rounded or slightly truncate; vertical view 3–5-angular, usually
quadrangular, angles of 1 semicell often alternating with those of the

other, sides deeply concave, angles rounded or slightly truncate; cell-wall with granules in concentric rings around the angles and scattered on the apex, except the extreme part which may be smooth or punctate. Pl. **54,** fig. **602.**

6. *Staurastrum oxyacanthum* Archer. Cells 36–40 (including processes) × 26–29 μ (isthmus 10 μ wide), wider than long, including the processes, deeply constricted, sinus almost rectangular, acute; semicells subfusiform or subcuneate, dorsal margin slightly convex, ventral margin tumid, angles produced to long, slender, slightly convergent processes terminating with about 3 minute spines and 3–4 concentric series of minute teeth; apex with a pair of fairly long spreading spines at the origin of the processes; vertical view 2–4- but usually 3-angled, sides straight and smooth, a pair of stout spines projecting from within each margin, angles produced to denticulate processes; chromatophore axial, with a pair of plates extending into each angle; pyrenoid single, central. Pl. **54,** fig. **604.**

7. *Staurastrum gracile* Ralfs. Cells 44–118 × 27–107 μ (isthmus 5.5–13.0 μ wide), length often greater than the width, excluding the processes, deeply constricted, sinus with an acute apex and opening widely, isthmus narrow; semicells broadly triangular to cup-shaped, dorsal margin slightly concave to convex with a row of small emarginate verrucae, below which there is sometimes a short row of granules; angles continued in processes of variable length which are slightly alternated, horizontal or sometimes slightly converging; vertical view triangular, the sides slightly concave and angles continued in straight processes; cell-wall with an intramarginal row of pairs of granules and sometimes with short rows of granules at right angles to the sides of the cell, the center without ornamentation, processes with transverse rings of granules and terminating in 3 or 4 small spines; chromatophore axial, with 2 laminate blades extending to each angle or a short distance into the processes; pyrenoid single, central; zygote spherical, with numerous spines broad at the base and terminating in widely bifurcate apices, 60 μ in diameter with spines, 32 μ without spines. Pl. **55,** fig. **613.**

8. *Staurastrum hexacerum* (Ehrenberg) Wittrock. Cells 20–34 × 18–25 μ (isthmus 4.5–8.0 μ wide), slightly wider than long, deeply constricted, sinus open and acute at the apex; semicells fusiform, margins convex, tapering to the angles which are continued to very short processes terminating in 3 small spines; cell-wall covered with small granules arranged in concentric series around the angles, reduced in size and number on the apex and center of the cell face; vertical view usually triangular, lateral margins concave; chromatophore axial; pyrenoid single, central; zygote spherical,

with numerous long, stout spines, broad at the base and bifurcate at the apex, 30 μ in diameter without spines; length of spines about 16 μ. Pl. 55, fig. 611.

9. *Staurastrum polymorphum* Brébisson. Cells 21–43 $\times$ 20–30 μ (isthmus 5.5–10.0 μ wide), wider than long, including the processes, constriction deep, sinus widely open, almost rectangular, acute at the apex; semicells variable, elliptic, fusiform, cuniform, the ventral margin more convex than the dorsal, angles attenuated to short, stout, horizontal or convergent processes, which terminate in 3–4 small spines, and with 3–4 series of minute teeth; cell-wall with granules arranged in concentric series around the angles, center of the apex smooth; vertical view 3–7-angular, the 2 semicells often differing in the number of processes, lateral margins slightly concave; chromatophore axial, with a pair of lobes extending into each angle; pyrenoid single, central; zygote spherical or somewhat angular, with stout processes, branched at the apex, 55 μ in diameter with processes, 30 μ without processes. Pl. 54, fig. 600.

10. *Staurastrum margaritaceum* (Ehrenberg) Meneghini. Cells 16–48 $\times$ 24–35 μ (isthmus 6–13 μ wide), about as long as wide or sometimes longer, constriction shallow, sinus open; semicells variable, cup-shaped, subspherical or subfusiform, upper angles produced to short, obtuse, horizontal or sometimes convergent processes; cell-wall with minute granules arranged in concentric series around the angles, sometimes with a circle of granules around the base of the semicell; vertical view 3–9-angled, usually 4–6-angled, sides concave, center of apex smooth, angles produced to short, truncate, spineless but often emarginate processes; zygote spherical, with numerous appendages twice dichotomous at the apices, 30 μ in diameter without processes, 50 μ with processes. Pl. 54, fig. 599.

Onychonema Wallich 1860

Cells small, width usually greater than the length, forming simple filaments, compressed, deeply constricted, sinus narrow and usually closed; semicells elliptic or reniform, lateral angles smooth or with a single long convergent spine and bearing 2 capitate processes on the apices, lateral view usually circular; cell-wall smooth, or with transverse rows of granules or pores or sometimes finely punctate; vertical view fusiform-elliptic, poles rounded or bearing a single straight spine, the apical processes arranged alternately; chromatophore axial, 1 in each semicell; pyrenoid single, central; filaments long and twisted and usually embedded in a broad gelatinous sheath.

Zygotes spherical, bearing many simple, short spines; parthenospores.

KEY TO THE SPECIES

1. Lateral angles with spines............................. 1. O. laeve var. latum
1. Lateral angles without spines.......................... 2. O. filiforme

1. *Onychonema laeve* Nordstedt var. *latum* W. and G. S. West. Cells
23.0–36.5 (including spines) × 20–29 μ (including processes), 18.0–28.5
(excluding spines) × 15–20 μ (excluding processes); isthmus 3.5 × 6.0 μ,
wider than long, deeply constricted, sinus open, the apex acute or slightly
inflated, isthmus narrow; cells united in filaments usually with a gelatinous sheath; semicells transversely elliptic, apical margin with a median,
truncate elevation, those of adjacent cells in the filament in contact; apex
bearing 2 divergent spine-like processes; lateral angles bearing a single incurved spine. Pl. **56,** fig. **624.**

2. *Onychonema filiforme* (Ehrenberg) Roy and Bissett. Cells 8.5–17.0 ×
8.5–13.5 μ, without processes; isthmus 3.0–5.6 μ wide, width slightly
greater than length, deeply constricted, sinus sublinear with the apex
acute and outer margin widely open, isthmus narrow; semicells broadly
elliptic or subreniform, dorsal margin broadly rounded, ventral margin
almost straight, lateral angles broadly rounded, without spines; apical
processes long, divergent, with a slight swelling at the ends, asymmetrical,
overlapping the adjacent cell; lateral view of semicells subcircular; cells
united into long twisting filaments, adjacent cells not in contact except by
the processes; cell-wall with 2 transverse rows of pores; chromatophores
axial; pyrenoids single. (Reported from Pope County by Phinney, 1946.)
Pl. **56,** figs. **621–623.**

Spondylosium Brébisson 1844

Cells of small or medium size, flattened, moderately to deeply constricted, sinus linear to open, the apex acute or rounded; cells united in
long, sometimes twisted filaments with or without a gelatinous sheath;
semicells usually compressed, rarely radially symmetrical, elliptic to
oblong or triangular, often with concave or broadly truncate apices; cell-
wall smooth or punctate, rarely granulate; chromatophores axial;
pyrenoids usually single.

Zygotes usually spherical, smooth or bearing simple spines; aplanospores.

KEY TO THE SPECIES

1. Cells 9.5–22.0 × 9.5–18.0 μ.................................... 1. S. planum
1. Cells 5–8 × 5–8 μ... 2. S. pygmaeum

1. *Spondylosium planum* (Wolle) W. and G. S. West. Cells 9.5–22.0 ×
9.5–18.0 μ and 5.5–11.0 μ thick (isthmus 5–12 μ wide), slightly wider than

long, compressed, deeply constricted, sinus widely open with the apex broadly rounded, isthmus narrow, united in filaments without a gelatinous sheath, not twisted; semicells oblong-elliptic, ventral margin more rounded than the dorsal, lateral margins broadly rounded, apices flat, region of contact between adjacent cells very broad; vertical view oblong-elliptic; lateral view subcircular; cell-wall smooth; chromatophore axial; pyrenoid single. Pl. **56,** fig. **625.**

2. *Spondylosium pygmaeum* (Cooke) W. West. Cells 5–8 × 5–8 μ (isthmus 2.5–3.2 μ wide), about as long as wide or slightly wider, deeply constricted, sinus acute, almost linear for part of its length; semicells elliptic, united by a relatively small surface of their apices into long filaments frequently embedded in a gelatinous sheath; vertical view subelliptic; cell-wall smooth. Pl. **56,** fig. **626.**

Hyalotheca Ehrenberg 1841

Cells united into long filaments, usually with a thick gelatinous sheath, sometimes twisted; cells subcylindric, shorter or longer than wide, very slightly constricted; semicells trapezoidal, subquadrate or oblong, lateral margin straight or slightly convex; vertical view circular; cell-wall without ornamentation except for transverse ridges or rows of granules beneath the apices; chromatophore axial, 1 in each semicell, and with several vertical lobes extending to the cell-walls, usually with a central pyrenoid.

Zygote spherical and smooth, some species also forming aplanospores, formed in conjugation tube or in the female gametangium; conjugation scalariform or lateral.

FIGS. 621–623.—*Onychonema filiforme* (Ehrenberg) Roy and Bissett.

FIG. 624.—*Onychonema laeve* Nordstedt var. *latum* W. and G. S. West.

FIG. 625.—*Spondylosium planum* (Wolle) W. and G. S. West.

FIG. 626.—*Spondylosium pygmaeum* (Cooke) W. West.

FIG. 627.—*Desmidium aptogonum* Brébisson.

FIG. 628.—*Desmidium scwartzii* C. A. Agardh.

FIG. 629.—*Desmidium grevillei* DeBary.

FIG. 630.—*Hyalotheca mucosa* (Mertens) Ehrenberg.

FIG. 631.—*Hyalotheca dissiliens* (J. E. Smith) Brébisson.

FIG. 632.—*Ophiocytium parvulum* (Perty) A. Braun.

FIG. 633.—*Ophiocytium cochleare* (Eichwald) A. Braun.

FIG. 634.—*Ophiocytium capitatum* Wolle.

FIG. 635.—*Ophiocytium arbusculum* (A. Braun) Rabenhorst.

FIGS. 636, 637.—*Ophiocytium majus* Naegeli.

FIGS. 638, 639.—*Ophiocytium gracilipes* Rabenhorst.

(Figs. 621–623, Irénée-Marie; figs. 624, 628, 629, G. M. Smith; figs. 625–627, 630, 631, W. and G. S. West; figs. 632–635, Tiffany; figs. 636–639, Pascher. Figs. 621–623, 632–634, 636–639 ×*1000;* figs. 624, 625, 627–631 ×*330;* figs. 626, 635 ×*600*.)

PLATE 56

(Figs. 621 to 639)

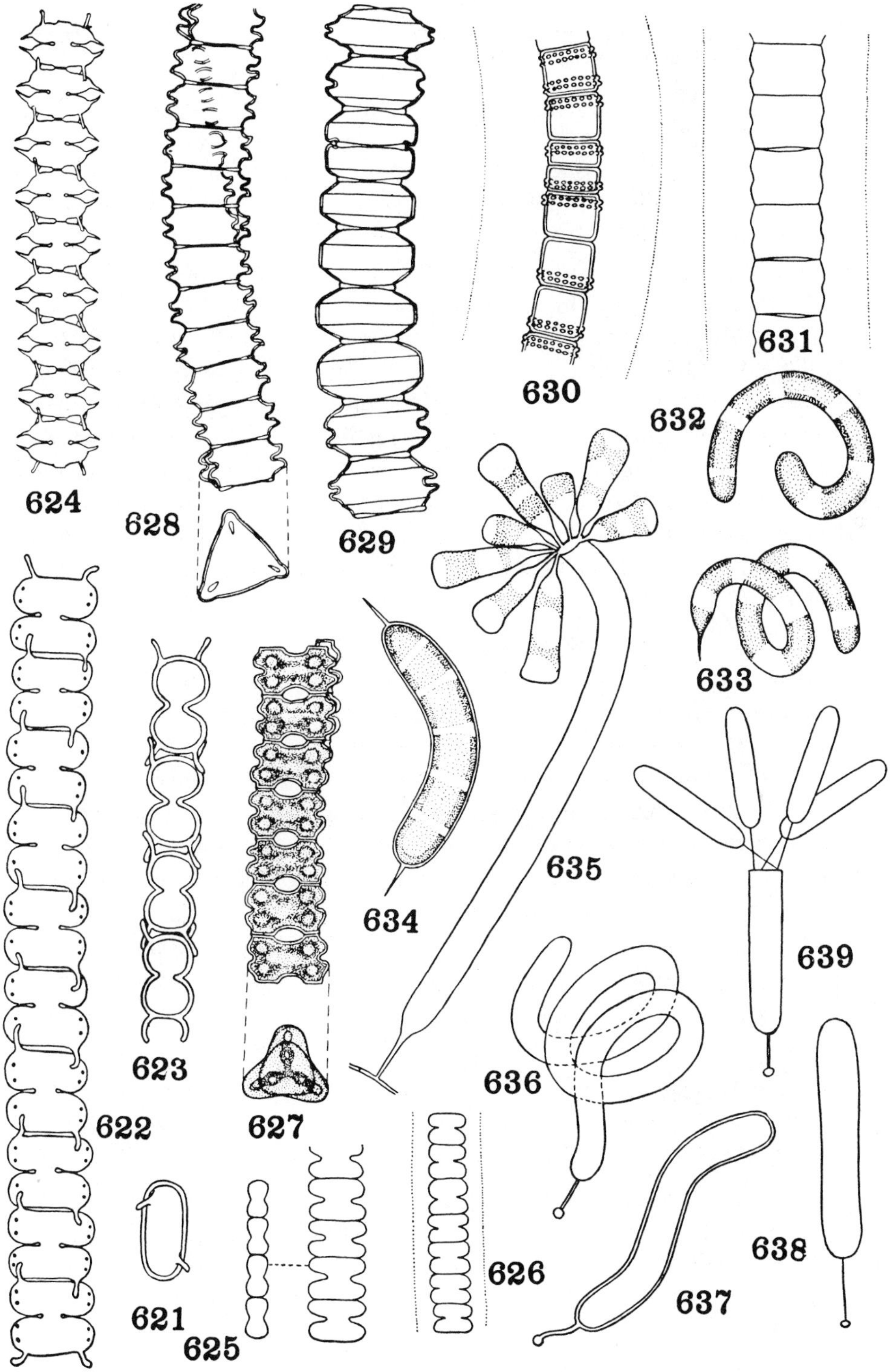

624

628

629

630

632

631

633

622

623

627

634

635

636

639

621

625

626

637

638

KEY TO THE SPECIES

1. Cells with 2 transverse, subapical rows of granules................ 1. H. mucosa
1. Cells without transverse rows of granules........................ 2. H. dissiliens

1. *Hyalotheca mucosa* (Mertens) Ehrenberg. Cells 16–22 × 14–26 μ, quadrangular, about as long as wide or slightly longer, cylindric, usually without a constriction; semicell with 2 subapical, parallel rows of small granules; vertical view circular; chromatophore axial, 1 in each semicell, with several radiating ridges and a central pyrenoid; filament enclosed in a thick gelatinous sheath; zygote spherical or oblong with rounded ends, 27–30 μ in diameter. Pl. 56, fig. 630.

2. *Hyalotheca dissiliens* (J. E. Smith) Brébisson. Cells 10–39 × 10–33 μ, width greater than length, very faintly constricted, sinus a very slight concavity in the middle of the lateral margins; cells cylindric-discoidal, united by their truncate apices into long filaments constricted at the joints, lateral margins slightly convex; vertical view circular, sometimes with 2 opposite or 3 equidistant papillae; chromatophore axial, 1 in each semicell, with a number of radiating ridges; pyrenoid single, central; filaments usually embedded in a conspicuous gelatinous sheath; zygote spherical or rounded-oblong, smooth, 15–25 μ in diameter. Pl. 56, fig. 631.

Desmidium C. A. Agardh 1825

Cells united in long, twisting filamentous colonies, usually embedded in a broad, tough gelatinous sheath; cells about twice as wide as long, with a distinct but usually shallow median constriction; vertical view of semicells elliptic, usually with mammillate poles or 3–4-angled; front view trapezoidal, the apices plane or depressed in the median portion and forming an elliptic open space between cells; lateral view trapezoidal, or subrectangular to octagonal; cell-wall usually smooth; chromatophore axial, 1 in each semicell; 1 or several pyrenoids.

Zygote spherical or ellipsoid, smooth or with short, flattened conical papillae, formed within female gametangium, or in the conjugation tube; parthenospores.

KEY TO THE SPECIES

1. Filaments cylindric...................................... 1. D. grevillei
1. Filaments not cylindric.. 2
　　2. Cell apices with broad depressions...................... 2. D. aptogonum
　　2. Cell apices plane.. 3. D. swartzii

1. *Desmidium grevillei* DeBary. Filaments spirally twisted, with a thickened protruding rim between each pair of cells, usually embedded in broad, firm, gelatinous sheath; cells 41–63 × 22–46 μ (isthmus 25–42 μ

wide), 2.0–2.5 times wider than long, slightly constricted, sinus linear or a small semicircular depression, isthmus broad; semicells short, pyramidate-truncate, broad angles acutely rounded, apical angles obtuse; apices flat, without open spaces between adjacent cells; cells in vertical view elliptic with a rounded nodule at each pole; lateral view octagonal; chromatophore axial, 1 in each semicell, usually having 4 radiating lobes each bearing a single pyrenoid; cell-wall smooth except for faint vertical striations just above the isthmus; zygote spherical, subspherical, smooth, formed within one of the conjugating cells after dissociation of the filament, 26–40 μ in diameter, or larger. Pl. 56, fig. 629.

2. *Desmidium aptogonum* Brébisson. Cells united in spirally twisted filaments, usually without a gelatinous sheath, cells 21–43 × 12–20 μ (isthmus 14–35 μ wide), about twice as wide as long, moderately constricted, sinus with sides subparallel and apex rounded, outer portion widely open; semicells narrowly oblong, lateral angles broadly rounded, apex broad and concave in the middle, with connecting processes at the angles that form elliptic to subrectangular open spaces between adjacent cells; vertical view triangular or sometimes quadrangular, sides slightly concave, angles very broadly rounded; cell-wall smooth; chromatophore axial, 1 in each semicell with a lobe bearing 1 pyrenoid extending into each angle; zygote smooth, subspherical, 18–26 μ in diameter. Pl. 56, fig. 627.

3. *Desmidium swartzii* C. A. Agardh. Cells united in spirally twisted filaments, with or without a gelatinous sheath, 35–50 × 12–20 μ (isthmus 21–40 μ wide), 2.0–2.5 times wider than long, moderately constricted, sinus linear toward the apex, opening widely outward; semicells narrowly oblong, lateral margins usually obliquely truncate with the upper angle protruded toward the apex, the lower angle more rounded; apex of semicell plane, without a depression that forms spaces between adjacent cells; vertical view triangular, sides slightly concave, angles acutely rounded; cell-wall smooth; chromatophore axial, 1 in each semicell with lobes extending to the angles of the cell; pyrenoids in each lobe and at times in the central mass; zygote smooth, subspherical to ellipsoid, 20–28 × 28–36 μ. Pl. 56, fig. 628.

Phylum CHRYSOPHYTA

Class *XANTHOPHYCEAE*

VEGETATIVE cells uninucleate or multinucleate and siphonaceous, sometimes branched, unicellular or multicellular, motile by means of flagella or immobile. All motile cells, vegetative or reproductive, have a pair of anteriorly placed flagella of unequal length. The cell-walls consist of pectic materials sometimes impregnated with silica, with varying amounts of cellulose in a few genera. The walls of certain genera are composed of a series of overlapping pieces that appear H-shaped, each protoplast enclosed by one-half of each of 2 successive H-pieces. Chromatophores are usually discoid, numerous, yellow-green, and without pyrenoids. Pigments include chlorophylls *a* and *e*, an abundance of beta-carotene and a xanthophyll. Accumulated food occurs as oil and leucosin, and starch is never present.

Asexual reproduction by vegetative cell division, fragmentation, zoospores, aplanospores, akinetes, hypnospores, and statospores (cysts). Sexual reproduction by fusion of isogamous gametes is known for only a few genera; oogamy occurs only in *Vaucheria*.

The Xanthophyceae occur mainly in freshwater habitats and most are aquatics. Some species occur on diverse moist aerial and terrestrial substrates.

KEY TO THE GENERA OF XANTHOPHYCEAE

1. Plants not filamentous. 2
1. Plants filamentous. 5
  2. Cells solitary. 3
  2. Cells colonial. 4
3. Cells cylindric, aquatic. . . . . Ophiocytium (p. 207)
3. Cells balloon-shaped, terrestrial. . . . . Botrydium (p. 211)
  4. Colony dendroid in shape. . . . . Ophiocytium (p. 207)
  4. Colony irregular, cells in groups. Botryococcus (p. 207)
5. Vegetative filament unicellular; coenocytic. . . . . Vaucheria (p. 211)
5. Vegetative filament multicellular. . . . . Tribonema (p. 210)

Order HETEROCOCCALES

Vegetative cells uninucleate or multinucleate, solitary or forming colonies within a gelatinous matrix, immobile, free-floating, or epiphytic; cell-wall frequently of 2 overlapping H-pieces; chromatophores and food reserves as in other Xanthophyceae; vegetative cell division, zoospores, aplanospores and thick-walled cysts (hypnospores).

Family **Botryococcaceae**

Vegetative cells uninucleate, small, solitary or forming gelatinous colonies; reproduction usually by autospores; never producing zoospores; fragmentation; sometimes referred to Chlorococcales.

Botryococcus Kuetzing 1849

Colonies free-floating, indefinite in shape, with cells closely appressed and enclosed in a gelatinous or tough membrane; cells usually in several aggregates connected by broad or delicate strands of the colonial membrane; cells spherical, ovoid or cuneate; chromatophore single, parietal, laminate or disciform, yellowish-green to nearly green; affinities uncertain because of reported presence of starch in cells and of pyrenoids in chloroplasts.

Vegetative division of the cells; autospores.

KEY TO THE SPECIES

1. Colonial envelope tough, irregular............................ 1. B. braunii
1. Colonial envelope thin, gelatinous............................ 2. B. sudeticus

1. *Botryococcus braunii* Kuetzing. Cells 3.5–5.5 × 6–11 μ, ovoid or ellipsoid, forming a single layer around a central cavity, held together by an irregular, tough membrane; sometimes brick red in color, due to a reddish oil. Pl. **57**, figs. **642, 643**.

2. *Botryococcus sudeticus* Lemmermann. Cells 6–13 μ in diameter, spherical or subspherical, 16–32 cells (or more) in a group and arranged around a common center, groups in hyaline gelatinous envelopes. Pl. **57**, fig. **644**.

Family **Chlorotheciaceae**

Vegetative cells multinucleate, solitary or forming dendroid colonies; free-floating or epiphytic; reproduction by zoospores or aplanospores; incapable of vegetative cell division.

Ophiocytium Naegeli 1849

Cells epiphytic or free-floating, solitary or colonial, straight, curved or spiral cylinders with round or capitate extremities that may or may not be apiculate or attenuate; chromatophores pale yellowish-green, H-shaped in optical cross-section, without pyrenoids; coenocytic cells with a homogeneous cap at one end and with the remainder of the wall laminate.

Formation of aplanospores and zoospores with 2 flagella of unequal length.

KEY TO THE SPECIES

1. Cells forming dendroid colonies.. 2
1. Cells not forming dendroid colonies.. 3
    2. Stipe usually less than 7 μ long........................ 1. O. arbusculum
    2. Stipe usually more than 10 μ long...................... 2. O. gracilipes
3. Cells with polar spines.. 4
3. Cells without polar spines.................................... 3. O. parvulum
    4. Spine at 1 pole only.. 5
    4. Spine at each pole.. 4. O. capitatum
5. Spine apically knobbed....................................... 5. O. majus
5. Spine apically attenuate..................................... 6. O. cochleare

1. *Ophiocytium arbusculum* (A. Braun) Rabenhorst. Cells 3–7 μ in diameter, straight or curved, forming umbellate colonies; lowest cell (without stipe) up to 150 μ long; stipe about as long as diameter of cell; on filamentous algae. Pl. **56**, fig. **635**.

2. *Ophiocytium gracilipes* Rabenhorst. Cells 5–7 μ in diameter, usually straight and forming 2-tiered colonies; lowest cell (without stipe) up to 100 μ long; stipe about twice the diameter of the cell. Pl. **56**, figs. **638, 639**.

3. *Ophiocytium parvulum* (Perty) A. Braun. Cells 3–15 (usually 4–5) μ broad, without polar spines, curved or bent, often very long and much intertwined. Pl. **56**, fig. **632**.

4. *Ophiocytium capitatum* Wolle. Cell 5–10 (–15) μ in diameter, often very long, solitary, curved, with a spine at each pole 5–7 μ long. Pl. **56**, fig. **634**.

5. *Ophiocytium majus* Naegeli. Cell 8–25 μ in diameter, scarcely bent, sometimes coiled, solitary, with a single knobbed polar spine. Pl. **56**, figs. **636, 637**.

6. *Ophiocytium cochleare* (Eichwald) A. Braun. Cell 5–8 μ broad, curved or coiled, with a single attenuate spine. Pl. **56**, fig. **633**.

Figs. 642, 643.—*Botryococcus braunii* Kuetzing; fig. 642 showing external view of compound colonies.

Fig. 644.—*Botryococcus sudeticus* Lemmermann.

Fig. 645.—*Botrydium granulatum* (Linnaeus) Greville.

Fig. 646.—*Botrydium walrothii* (Kuetzing) Mueller.

Fig. 647.—*Tribonema utriculosum* (Kuetzing) Hazen.

Fig. 648.—*Tribonema bombycinum* (Agardh) Derbes and Solier, indicating a single H-piece.

Fig. 649.—*Tribonema bombycinum* var. *tenue* (Hazen) Tiffany.

Fig. 650.—*Tribonema minus* (Wille) Hazen.

(Figs. 642–644, 647–650, Tiffany; figs. 645, 646, Smith. Fig. 642 ×250; figs. 643, 644 ×500; figs. 645, 646 ×25; figs. 647–650 ×1000.)

PLATE 57

(Figs. 642 to 650)

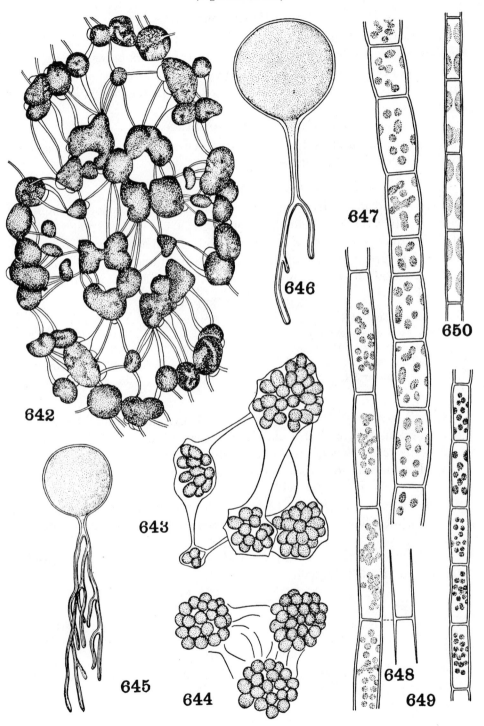

642

646

647

650

645

643

644

648

649

Order HETEROTRICHALES

Vegetative cells uninucleate, united end to end in branched or un-branched filaments; chromatophores and food reserves as in other Xanthophyceae; asexual reproduction by fragmentation, zoospores, aplanospores, and akinetes; sexual reproduction isogamous, known only in 1 genus.

Family **Tribonemataceae**

Filaments unbranched; thickness of cell-wall and articulation of H-pieces differing in the 2 genera.

Tribonema Derbes and Solier 1856

Cells cylindric or barrel-shaped, forming unbranched, simple filaments; cell-wall often thick and lamellose, pulling apart at definite places forming H-shaped pieces at times of fragmentation; chromatophores 2 to numerous, yellow-green, disc-shaped, parietal, with oil and without starch.

Fragmentation; aplanospores, akinetes, zoospores; isogamous gametes.

KEY TO THE SPECIES

1. Chromatophores 2–4 .... 1. T. minus
1. Chromatophores numerous 2
   2. Cell diameter 11–17 μ .... 2. T. utriculosum
   2. Cell diameter 6–11 μ .... 3. T. bombycinum
   2. Cell diameter 3–6 μ .... 3a. T. bombycinum
                                    var. tenue

1. *Tribonema minus* (Wille) Hazen. Cells cylindric or slightly inflated, 5–6 μ in diameter, with 2–4 chromatophores. Pl. **57**, fig. **650**.

2. *Tribonema utriculosum* (Kuetzing) Hazen. Cells usually barrel-shaped, sometimes cylindric, 11–17 μ in diameter, chromatophores large and numerous. Pl. **57**, fig. **647**.

3. *Tribonema bombycinum* (Agardh) D́erbes and Solier. Cells cylindric or somewhat inflated, 6–11 μ in diameter, with numerous chromatophores. Pl. **57**, fig. **648**.

   a. Var. *tenue* (Hazen) Tiffany. Cells 3–6 μ in diameter; otherwise like the species. Pl. **57**, fig. **649**.

Order HETEROSIPHONALES

Vegetative cells multinucleate, siphonaceous, aquatic or terrestrial.

Family **Botrydiaceae**

Vegetative cell terrestrial, with inflated pigmented aerial and colorless rhizoidal portions.

Botrydium Wallroth 1815

Cells single, multinucleate, terrestrial: epiterranean portion vesicular, pear-shaped to spherical or dichotomously branched, with many discoid chromatophores; rhizoidal portion penetrating soil, little or much branched, colorless; starch absent.

No vegetative division; zoospores, aplanospores, hypnospores; isogamous gametes.

KEY TO THE SPECIES

1. Cell-wall thin.. 1. B. granulatum
1. Cell-wall thick, stratified................................. 2. B. wallrothii

1. *Botrydium granulatum* (Linnaeus) Greville. Aerial portion of cell pear-shaped to nearly spherical, often with much-branched rhizoids, reaching diameters up to 2 mm.; cell-wall thin, often encrusted with lime. Pl. 57, fig. **645.**

2. *Botrydium wallrothii* (Kuetzing) Mueller. Aerial portion spherical, abruptly narrowing into a somewhat branched rhizoidal system, often very dark green, 1.0–1.5 mm. in diameter, cell-wall thick, stratified. Pl. **57,** fig. **646.**

Family **Vaucheriaceae**

Tubular coenocytic filaments, sparingly branched, multinucleate, aquatic or terrestrial; food reserve oil; aplanospores, hypnospores, microaplanospores and multiflagellate multinucleate zoospores; oogamy.

Vaucheria DeCandolle 1803

Filaments coenocytic, sparsely or numerously branched, multinucleate, aquatic or terrestrial, often attached by rhizoids, sometimes forming densely tufted, velvety masses; chromatophores numerous, small, discoid and rather peripherally located in the protoplasm, each with a pyrenoid, or pyrenoids absent; nuclei minute.

Multiflagellate "compound" zoospores; aplanospores, microaplanospores; eggs and sperms in oogonia and antheridia (homothallic).

KEY TO THE SPECIES

1. Antheridium sessile, straight or nearly so................................... 2
1. Antheridium stalked, hooked or spirally coiled........................... 3
   2. Antheridium 20–25 μ in diameter.................... 1. V. ornithocephala
   2. Antheridium 30–40 μ in diameter.................... 2. V. aversa
3. Oogonium sessile or shortly stipitate... 4
3. Oogonium at end of evident branch or long pedicel........................... 6
   4. Oogonia and antheridia single on lateral branches........................ 5
   4. Oogonia and antheridia on same lateral branch........ 3. V. geminata

5. Filament 15–33 μ in diameter........................ 4. V. polysperma
5. Filament 33–50 μ in diameter........................ 5. V. repens
5. Filament 50–130 μ in diameter....................... 6. V. sessilis
  6. Oogonia and antheridia borne singly on radiating pedicels 7. V. gardneri
  6. Oogonia and antheridia at ends of one main branch..................... 7
7. Pedicels supporting sex organs less than 100 μ long......................... 8
7. Pedicels supporting sex organs more than 100 μ long...... 8. V. longipes
  8. Oogonial pedicel much shorter than antheridial........ 9. V. terrestris
  8. Oogonial pedicel nearly equal in length to antheridial... 10. V. hamata

1. *Vaucheria ornithocephala* C. A. Agardh. Filaments 24–75 μ in diameter; oogonia 2–6-seriate, unilateral, obliquely ovoid, 80–150 × 85–225 μ, opening through a broad beak, sessile or very short-pedicelled and in form not unlike a bird's beak, oospore nearly globose, about as wide as the oogonium, but not filling it longitudinally, reddish when ripe, with triple membrane; antheridia 1–2 at one end of a series of oogonia, cylindric to subclavate, 20–25 μ in diameter, about 4 diameters long, bent nearly horizontally; zoospores 80–100 × 90–115 μ, in cylindric or very slightly clavate sporangia, with flagella much more closely set at the forward end. Pl. 36, fig. 379.

2. *Vaucheria aversa* Hassall. Filaments 50–131 μ in diameter, oogonia obliquely ovoid, sessile or shortly stipitate, 2, rarely more in a series, the beaks usually in opposite directions, mostly erect, 125–250 μ in diameter; oospore globose or ovoid, with triple membrane, 75–100 μ in diameter, not filling the oogonium; antheridium cylindric or subclavate, 30–40 μ in diameter, erect, more or less incurved, on each side of the series of oogonia. Pl. 37, fig. 381.

3. *Vaucheria geminata* (Vaucher) DeCandolle. Filaments 29–130 μ in diameter; oogonia 1–6, 52–225 × 64–190 μ, ellipsoid-hemispheric to convex-concave, shortly stipitate near the end of a short branch; antheridium cylindric, hooked or circinate, usually on a stipe longer than that of the oogonium; mature oospore brown-spotted with triple membrane, filling oogonium; aplanospores 120–200 × 120–190 μ, in ovoid sporangia usually terminating short lateral branches; thick-walled cells ("akinetes"). Pl. 37, fig. 385.

4. *Vaucheria polysperma* Hassall. Filaments 15–33 μ in diameter; oogonia 3–5-seriate, unilateral, obliquely ovoid, 60–65 μ in diameter, and more nearly erect than in other closely allied species; oospore globose, 44–61 μ in diameter; zoospores 66–88 × 82–94 μ; antheridium always single. Pl. 37, fig. 382.

5. *Vaucheria repens* Hassall. Filaments 33–50 μ in diameter; oogonium single, rarely 2, sessile, obliquely ovoid, 55–80 × 70–80 μ, ending in a

short beak, usually horizontal to main filament; oospore quite filling the oogonium, grayish, coarse-grained, with triple membrane and 1 or more brown spots; antheridium close to the oogonium, circinate on a straight or curved pedicel; zoospores 75–120 × 80–130 μ, formed in nearly cylindric sporangia with flagella uniformly distributed. Pl. 37, fig. 383.

6. *Vaucheria sessilis* (Vaucher) DeCandolle. Filaments 50–130 μ in diameter; oogonia usually 2, sometimes single, sessile or on very short stalks, ovoid or oblong-ovoid, 70–85 × 75–100 μ, more or less oblique, with short beak; antheridium between the 2 oogonia or beside the single oogonium, on a short pedicel, straight, hooked or circinate; mature oospore dark-spotted, with triple membrane, filling oogonium; zoosporangium ovoid-clavate, terminal, producing a single zoospore, 77–154 × 82–176 μ. Pl. 36, fig. 378.

7. *Vaucheria gardneri* Collins. Filaments 50–70 μ in diameter, sparingly branched, branches mostly at right angles; antheridia and oogonia borne on pedicels of about the same size, 15–20 × 60–100 μ, arising from the same point on the filament; antheridium solitary, terminal on the central, vertical pedicel, less commonly 2–3 on independent pedicels, hooked or circinate, tapering to 10 μ in diameter; oogonia 2–4, occasionally more, 60–70 × 85–95 μ, quite oblique, often concave on the inner side, on opposite sides of the antheridium or encircling it, each pedicel at about a 45-degree angle to the filament, usually surpassing antheridia. Pl. 37, fig. 384.

8. *Vaucheria longipes* Collins. Filaments 80–90 μ in diameter; oogonia 35–40 × 70–85 μ, ovoid, slightly oblique, 2–4 on pedicels 20–30 × 100–150 μ, arising a little above antheridium and usually surpassing it; antheridium terminal, cylindric or slightly tapering, hooked or circinate; both sex organs borne at end of a branch, 30–40 × 1,000–3,000 μ. Pl. 37, fig. 386.

9. *Vaucheria terrestris* (Vaucher) DeCandolle. Filaments 43–100 μ in diameter; oogonium usually solitary, 85–125 × 60–100 μ, lateral on a short branch containing at its summit a curved or circinate antheridium 18–24 μ in diameter; oospore globose to plano-convex, with 4 membranes and numerous brown spots. Pl. 37, fig. 387.

10. *Vaucheria hamata* (Vaucher) DeCandolle. Filaments 38–80 μ in diameter; oogonium solitary or 2, 75–90 × 60–75 μ, ovoid to convex-concave, borne on the shorter division of the apparently forking branch, the longer division recurved, bearing the hooked or circinate antheridium; if 2 oogonia, the antheridium between them; oospore with 4 membranes, filling oogonium, with a dark-brown or blackish central spot. Pl. 37, fig. 380.

Class *BACILLARIOPHYCEAE*

Vegetative cells of the diatoms are uninucleate, without flagella, unicellular or forming simple colonies, and have a silicified cell-wall (frustule) of two distinguishable "halves," one of which overlaps the other. The cell-wall is composed of pectic compounds and is usually heavily impregnated with silica; cellulose has been reported, but it is not a regular constituent of the wall. The longer "half" of the wall, the epivalve (epitheca), and the shorter "half," the hypovalve (hypotheca), each consists of a somewhat flattened valve attached at the margins to a connecting band or cingulum. The cingulum extends almost completely around the periphery of the valve, but there is always a gap between the two ends. A cell lying with the valve side up is seen in the valve view and with the cingulum uppermost, in the girdle view. In addition to the cingulum some genera exhibit one or more additional intercalary bands. The valves are variously ornamented with coarse or very fine striae, punctae, or areolae that are radially disposed about a central point in centric genera or bilaterally with respect to an axial field in pennate genera. The axial field may be symmetric or asymmetric with respect to the longitudinal axis and may be perforated by a complicated longitudinal slot or raphe. In the absence of a raphe the axial field is referred to as a pseudoraphe. Ornamentations are usually thin places in the silicified wall, although small pores may perforate the walls within the areolae of centric diatoms, and larger median or polar perforations characterize a few pennate species. The raphe usually has thickenings in the walls at each end and at the center, the central and polar nodules.

Chromatophores are rarely absent, usually numerous, and discoid or irregular in the Centrales, and single, lobed and perforate, or two and laminate in the Pennales. The color is usually golden brown but in some cases is bright green. Pyrenoids without starch sheaths may be present or absent. Beta- and epsilon-carotene and 5 xanthophylls usually obscure the chlorophylla *a* and *c*. Reserve foods include fats in the form of oil droplets, and volutin or leucosin, but never starch.

Many of the Pennales exhibit motility involving forward and backward progression in the direction of the long axis of the cell. Movement is confined to those species with raphes and is ascribed to the streaming of cytoplasm between the polar and central nodules through fissures on the outer wall faces.

Reproduction is by cell division, statospores (cysts or endospores),

auxospores formed without any sexual union or by fusion either of amoeboid gametes or of autogamous nuclei, and uni- or biflagellate microspores
variously interpreted as zoospores or gametes. Vegetative cells are diploid
in all species so far investigated.

Widely distributed in fresh and salt waters, sessile or free-floating, they
are often very abundant, particularly in cold water of spring and autumn
seasons. Although mostly aquatic, many species occur within the soil and
on wet surfaces of terrestrial substrates. Those species in flowing waters
often form copious gelatinous masses on rock surfaces.

KEY TO THE GENERA OF BACILLARIOPHYCEAE

1. Valve with ornamentation radial about a central point 2
1. Valve with transverse ornamentation (sometimes longitudinal also) 6
    2. Cells united into long filaments . . . . Melosira (p. 221)
    2. Cells not united into long filaments (sometimes in short chains) 3
3. Each valve with a single long spine . . . . Rhizosolenia (p. 226)
3. Each valve with several short marginal spines 4
3. Each valve without spines 5
    4. Protuberances or ocelli near valve margin . . . . Actinocyclus (p. 224)
    4. Protuberances or ocelli absent . . . . Stephanodiscus (p. 222)
5. Valve face quite bent and saddle-shaped . . . . Campylodiscus (p. 289)
5. Valve face flat . . . . Cyclotella (p. 217)
    6. Valve longitudinally symmetric 7
    6. Valve longitudinally asymmetric 39
7. Valve transversely asymmetric 8
7. Valve transversely symmetric 11
    8. Valves joined into fan-shaped or spiral colonies . . . . Meridion (p. 228)
    8. Valves not so joined 9
9. Valves with transverse costae . . . . Surirella (p. 290)
9. Valves without such costae 10
    10. Valve margin adjoined by longitudinal line . . . . Gomphoneis (p. 274)
    10. Valve margin not so adjoined . . . . Gomphonema (p. 270)
11. Girdle view asymmetric 12
11. Girdle view symmetric 14
    12. Girdle view wedge-shaped . . . . Rhoicosphenia (p. 242)
    12. Girdle view not wedge-shaped 13
13. Girdles longitudinally bent or bowed . . . . Achnanthes (p. 241)
13. Girdles transversely bent or bowed . . . . Cocconeis (p. 240)
    14. Colony formation frequent 15
    14. Colony formation rare or absent 24
15. Cells united into filaments, chains or stellate colonies 16
15. Cells radiating from a common center 21
15. Cells within a gelatinous matrix 22
    16. Central nodule extending across valve . . . . Stauroneis (p. 264)
    16. Central nodule not extending across valve 17

17. Valves inflated both medianly and apically . . . . Tabellaria (p. 227)
17. Valves not so inflated 18
    18. Valves with transverse costae 19
    18. Valves without transverse costae 20
19. Girdle view apically truncate . . . . Denticula (p. 288)
19. Girdle view rectangular . . . . Diatoma (p. 230)
    20. Ends of a valve of same size . . . . Fragilaria (p. 231)
    20. Ends of a valve not of same size . . . . Asterionella (p. 231)
21. Cells linear to fusiform . . . . Fragilaria (p. 231)
21. Cells narrow and greatly elongated . . . . Synedra (p. 234)
    22. Nodules connected by two parallel ribs . . . . Frustulia (p. 244)
    22. Nodules not so connected 23
23. Cells medianly constricted in girdle view . . . . Amphiprora (p. 245)
23. Cells rectangular in girdle view . . . . Mastogloia (p. 249)
    24. Valve view sigmoid 25
    24. Valve view otherwise 26
25. Striae in two series . . . . Gyrosigma (p. 268)
25. Striae in three series . . . . Pleurosigma (p. 269)
    26. Central or polar nodule elongate 27
    26. Central or polar nodule not elongate 28
27. Central nodule greatly elongate . . . . Amphipleura (p. 244)
27. Central nodules shortly elongate . . . . Frustulia (p. 244)
    28. Central nodule extending across valve . . . . Stauroneis (p. 264)
    28. Central nodule not extending across valve 29
29. Valves with pseudoraphes . . . . Synedra (p. 234)
29. Valves with true raphes 30
    30. Girdle view with hour-glass appearance . . . . Amphiprora (p. 245)
    30. Girdle view otherwise 31
31. Raphe in a marginal keel (sometimes difficulty visible) 32
31. Raphe not in a marginal keel 34
    32. Face of valve transversely undulate . . . . Cymatopleura (p. 289)
    32. Face of valve not undulate 33
33. Keel in each lateral margin of valve . . . . Surirella (p. 290)
33. Keel in only one lateral margin of valve . . . . Denticula (p. 288)
    34. Longitudinal lines or smooth areas crossing striae 35
    34. Longitudinal lines or smooth areas absent 38
35. Central nodule prolonged into horns . . . . Diploneis (p. 249)
35. Central nodule not so prolonged 36
    36. Longitudinal lines or pores parallel to valve margins 37
    36. Longitudinal spaces zigzag . . . . Anomoeoneis (p. 245)
37. Valves with transverse striae . . . . Caloneis (p. 246)
37. Valves with transverse rows of punctae . . . . Neidium (p. 262)
    38. Valves with transverse costae . . . . Pinnularia (p. 256)
    38. Valves with transverse striae or rows of punctae . . Navicula (p. 250)
39. Convex margin of valve often undulate . . . . Eunotia (p. 237)
39. Convex margin of valve smooth 40

40. Raphe within a marginal keel 41
40. Raphe not within a marginal keel. 42
41. Cells rectangular in cross-section. . . . . Hantzschia (p. 288)
41. Cells rhombic in cross-section. . . . . Nitzschia (p. 282)
   42. Valves with transverse costae. 43
   42. Valves without transverse costae. 44
43. Girdle view rectangular. . . . . Epithemia (p. 280)
43. Girdle view medianly inflated. . . . . Rhopalodia (p. 281)
   44. Cells with parallel sides in girdle view. . . . . Cymbella (p. 275)
   44. Cells broadly elliptic in girdle view. . . . . Amphora (p. 274)

Order Centrales

Cells solitary or united variously into filamentous, dendroid or zigzag colonies, free-floating or sessile; cell-shape disc-like, cylindric or irregular, with valves round, elliptic, polygonal or irregular, and with radial or concentric ornamentation about a central point; raphe or pseudoraphe none; cells immobile, often with spine-like, mammillate or long horn-like projections; chromatophores small and discoid or not infrequently irregular and laminate, with or without pyrenoids; cell division, statospores; microspores; auxospores often formed by the rejuvenescence of cells without sexual reproduction; some genera known to have diploid vegetative cells and autogamous sexual reproduction; largely marine, some freshwater.

Suborder COSCINODISCINEAE

Cells disc-like or cylindric, sometimes with small marginal spines but not long horn-like projections, solitary or filamentous, with valves directly adjoining or with cells separated by gelatinous material; chromatophores small and fairly numerous; auxospores; microspores.

Family Coscinodiscaceae

Cells discoid, often longer than broad; ornamentation of valve radial, not sectorial; without mammillate projections or ocelli; girdles with or without ornamentation.

Cyclotella Kuetzing 1834

Cells solitary or filamentous or colonial within a gelatinous envelope, discoid, drum-shaped; valve view circular or sometimes elliptic; ornamentation of valve in two concentric regions: outer zone radially striate or punctate, inner zone smooth or irregularly and finely punctate; girdle view straight or undulate; chromatophores numerous, small and discoid.

Auxospores formed singly within the cell; some species known to be autogamous.

KEY TO THE SPECIES

1. Cells single, or rarely in temporary chains. 2
1. Cells forming chains or colonies. 8
   2. Ornamentation absent between peripheral radial striae. 3
   2. Ornamentation present between peripheral radial striae. 5
3. Striae about 8–9 in 10 μ. . . . .   1. C. meneghiniana
3. Striae about 15–18 in 10 μ. 4
   4. Central zone smooth or with a few fine punctae. . . . .   2. C. kuetzingiana
   4. Central zone usually with 3 large circular dots. . . . .   3. C. ocellata
   4. Central zone with irregularly placed beads. . . . .   4. C. michiganiana
5. Central zone with a ring of triangular depressions. . . . .   5. C. antiqua
5. Central zone punctate. 6
5. Central zone smooth. . . . .   6. C. operculata
   6. Punctae scattered. . . . .   6. C. operculata
   6. Punctae in radial lines. 7
7. Radial lines few, short. . . . .   7. C. comta
7. Radial lines numerous, prominent. . . . .   8. C. bodanica
   8. Chains loose, with spaces between cells. . . . .   9. C. glomerata
   8. Chains compact, cells joined as in *Melosira*. . . . .   10. C. melosiroides

1. *Cyclotella meneghiniana* Kuetzing. Cells 10–30 μ in diameter or up to 48 μ in cells newly formed from auxospores; outer zone broad, striae 8–9 in 10 μ; central zone smooth or finely radially punctate, often with a large isolated puncta. Pl. **58,** fig. **660.**

2. *Cyclotella kuetzingiana* Thwaites. Cells 10–45 μ in diameter; outer zone with striae about 15–17 in 10 μ; inner zone smooth or with fine, scattered punctae. Pl. **58,** fig. **657.**

FIG. 651.—*Cyclotella antiqua* Wm. Smith.

FIG. 652.—*Cyclotella comta* (Ehrenberg) Kuetzing.

FIG. 653.—*Cyclotella bodanica* Eulenstein.

FIG. 654.—*Cyclotella bodanica* var. *michiganensis* Skvortzow, valve view and edge view of single valve.

FIG. 655.—*Cyclotella bodanica* var. *stellata* Skvortzow, valve view and edge view of single valve.

FIG. 656.—*Cyclotella glomerata* Bachmann, part of a colony and valve views.

FIG. 657.—*Cyclotella kuetzingiana* Thwaites.

FIG. 658.—*Cyclotella melosiroides* (Kirchner) Lemmermann, part of a colony and a single cell in valve view.

FIG. 659.—*Cyclotella comta* var. *glabriuscula* Grunow.

FIG. 660.—*Cyclotella meneghiniana* Kuetzing, valve and girdle views.

FIG. 661.—*Cyclotella operculata* (Agardh) Kuetzing.

FIG. 662.—*Cyclotella ocellata* Pantocsek.

FIGS. 663–665.—*Cyclotella michiganiana* Skvortzow, valve view and edge view of single valve.

FIG. 666.—*Actinocyclus niagarae* H. L. Smith.

(Figs. 651–653, 656–658, 660–662, Hustedt; fig. 659, Van Heurck; figs. 654, 655, 663–665, Skvortzow; fig. 666, H. L. Smith. Fig. 659 ×*2000;* all others ×*1000.*)

PLATE 58
(Figs. 651 to 666)

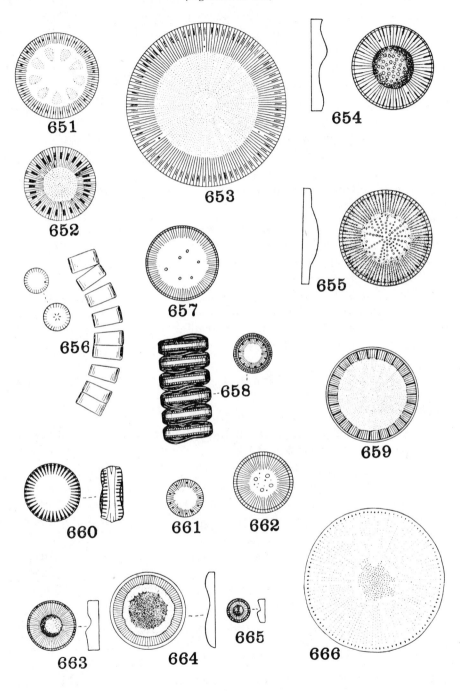

3. *Cyclotella ocellata* Pantocsek. Cells 6–20 μ in diameter; outer zone with pronounced striae about 15 in 10 μ; inner zone with several (often 3 or 4) circular dots, each about 1 μ in diameter. Pl. **58**, fig. **662**.

4. *Cyclotella michiganiana* Skvortzow. Cells 5–20 μ in diameter, depressed and undulate in the middle; valve circular, separated into two areas: marginal area with one or two zones of radiating striae, 15–18 in 10 μ, and with a pronounced rim, and the central area, about half the diameter of the valve, covered at one side with large beads irregularly disposed. Pl. **58**, figs. **663–665**.

5. *Cyclotella antiqua* Wm. Smith. Cells 10–30 μ in diameter; outer concentric zone 2–3 μ wide, striae about 16 in 10 μ and dots about 6 in 10 μ; central zone smooth with 6–15 triangular depressions forming a marginal ring. Pl. **58**, fig. **651**.

6. *Cyclotella operculata* (Agardh) Kuetzing. Cells 6–30 μ in diameter, more or less tangentially undulate; outer zone with striae, about 13–15 in 10 μ; inner zone smooth or very finely and weakly punctate, punctae scattered. Pl. **58**, fig. **661**.

7. *Cyclotella comta* (Ehrenberg) Kuetzing. Cells 10–50 μ in diameter; outer zone with prominent striae, 13–15 in 10 μ (in the inner half a ring of short lines, 4–5 in 10 μ), dots between radial striae; inner zone with scattered centrally placed punctae, surrounded by an area radially punctate. Pl. **58**, fig. **652**.

a. Var. *glabriuscula* Grunow. Central zone densely and regularly punctate. Pl. **58**, fig. **659**.

8. *Cyclotella bodanica* Eulenstein. Cells 20–80 μ in diameter; outer zone broad with prominent striae, about 13 in 10 μ, with sometimes a marginal ring of short lines about 5 in 10 μ; inner zone with irregularly punctate central area surrounded by punctae in radiating lines. Pl. **58**, fig. **653**.

a. Var. *michiganensis* Skvortzow. Cells 18–20 μ in diameter; marginal striae about 12 in 10 μ; central area punctate and densely covered with distinct granular subequal beads; two distinct isolated punctae among marginal radiating striae. Pl. **58**, fig. **654**.

b. Var. *stellata* Skvortzow. Cells 23–25 μ in diameter, with striae about 15 in 10 μ; central area covered with rows of beads in stellate pattern and surrounded by a single row of punctae. Pl. **58**, fig. **655**.

9. *Cyclotella glomerata* Bachmann. Cells 4–10 μ in diameter, forming colonies of coiled and intertwining chains, cells not touching each other; outer zone with radial striae, about 13–15 in 10 μ; inner zone smooth or with a ring of short striae in the central part. Pl. **58**, fig. **656**.

10. *Cyclotella melosiroides* (Kirchner) Lemmermann. Cells 4–13 μ in di-

ameter, tangentially undulate, forming *Melosira*-like chains; outer zone with 16–18 delicate striae in 10 μ; inner zone smooth. Pl. **58**, fig. **658**.

Melosira C. A. Agardh 1824

Cells cylindrical, closely united into long filaments; valve view circular, valves with or without marginal teeth, flat or convex with ornamentations in two distinct concentric areas; girdles with or without sulcus: if sulcus is absent, entire girdle ornamented; if present, part of girdle below sulcus is smooth; chromatophores numerous, small, discoid, often crowded.

Auxospore formation asexual or autogamous; biflagellate gametes reported.

KEY TO THE SPECIES

1. Girdles very weakly punctate, appearing smooth.............. 1. M. varians
1. Girdles evidently punctate.. 2
  2. Sulcus absent.. 2. M. juergensii
  2. Sulcus present.. 3
3. Striations 7–9 in 10 μ........................... 3. M. granulata
3. Striations 12–18 in 10 μ.. 4
  4. Valves with long marginal teeth................... 4. M. italica
  4. Valves with short marginal teeth........................ 5
  4. Valves with no marginal teeth................... 5. M. distans
5. Teeth evident and always present................ 6. M. crenulata
5. Teeth often indistinct............................... 5. M. distans

1. *Melosira varians* C. A. Agardh. Cells 8–35 × 9–13 μ; sulcus absent; valves somewhat convex, finely punctate, and interspersed with coarser dots; girdles very finely punctate, appearing nearly smooth. Pl. **59**, fig. **673**.

2. *Melosira juergensii* C. A. Agardh. Cells 6–38 × 13–22 μ; sulcus absent; valves marginally smooth; girdles uniformly punctate, striations about 28 in 10 μ. Pl. **59**, fig. **672**.

3. *Melosira granulata* (Ehrenberg) Ralfs. Cells 5–21 × 5–18 μ; sulcus shallow but acute; valves with short marginal teeth and large scattered indistinct punctae; girdles coarsely punctate, striations parallel and straight, about 7–9 in 10 μ. Pl. **59**, fig. **667**.

4. *Melosira italica* (Ehrenberg) Kuetzing. Cells 5–28 × 8–21 μ; sulcus shallow; valves with prominent and long teeth and very finely punctate; girdles finely punctate, striations spiral, sometimes wavy and intersecting, 12–20 in 10 μ. Pl. **59**, fig. **668**.

  a. Var. *tenuissima* (Grunow) Mueller. Cells 3–5 μ in diameter. Pl. **59**, fig. **669**.

5. *Melosira distans* (Ehrenberg) Kuetzing. Cells 4–20 × 4–9 μ; sulcus

evident and angular; valves with short or no marginal teeth and with large scattered pores, mostly in tangential series; girdles finely punctate, striations slightly spiral, about 12–15 in 10 μ. Pl. **59,** fig. **671.**

6. *Melosira crenulata* (Ehrenberg) Kuetzing. Cells 3–20 × 12–17 μ; indistinct sulcus near end of cell; valves with fine punctae scattered at center, radiate at circumference, and marginal teeth; girdles finely punctate, striations usually somewhat oblique, about 18 in 10 μ. [This species also appears as *M. italica* f. *crenulata* (Ehrenberg) Mueller]. Pl. **59,** fig. **670.**

Stephanodiscus Ehrenberg 1845

Cells discoid, drum-shaped or cylindric, single and free-floating, rarely in short chains; valves circular, radially punctate and marginally short-spined; outer areas of punctae in multiseriate rows, each row gradually or abruptly becoming uniseriate toward the middle, small central areas usually irregularly punctate; girdles generally somewhat undulate, with smooth surfaces, without intercalary bands; chromatophores several small discs or one or two large irregular flat plates.

Auxospores spherical or ellipsoid, asexually formed, one to a cell.

KEY TO THE SPECIES

1. Valves very finely punctate, appearing smooth . . . . 1. S. hantzschii
1. Valves prominently punctate 2
   2. Radially punctate almost to center . . . . 2. S. astraea
   2. Large central area irregularly punctate . . . . 3. S. niagarae

1. *Stephanodiscus hantzschii* Grunow. Cells 8–20 μ in diameter, disc- to drum-shaped, single or in short chains, with long floating hairs; valves indistinctly punctate, outer punctae in double rows, striations about 8–10 in 10 μ; spines stout, alternating with striations; chromatophores numerous small bodies; auxospore rounded. Pl. **60,** fig. **679.**

2. *Stephanodiscus astraea* (Ehrenberg) Grunow. Cells 30–70 μ in diame-

Fig. 667.—*Melosira granulata* (Ehrenberg) Ralfs.

Fig. 668.—*Melosira italica* (Ehrenberg) Kuetzing.

Fig. 669.—*Melosira italica* var. *tenuissima* (Grunow) Mueller.

Fig. 670.—*Melosira crenulata* (Ehrenberg) Kuetzing.

Fig. 671.—*Melosira distans* (Ehrenberg) Kuetzing, part of filament and valve view of a single cell.

Fig. 672.—*Melosira juergensii* C. A. Agardh, part of filament with auxospore.

Fig. 673.—*Melosira varians* C. A. Agardh, part of filament and auxospore.

Fig. 674.—*Rhizosolenia eriensis* H. L. Smith.

Fig. 675.—*Rhizosolenia longiseta* Zachary.

(Figs. 667, 668, 671–673, 675, Hustedt; fig. 669, Meister; fig. 670, Schmidt; fig. 674, G. M. Smith. Figs. 674, 675 ×*500;* all others ×*1000.*)

PLATE 59

(Figs. 667 to 675)

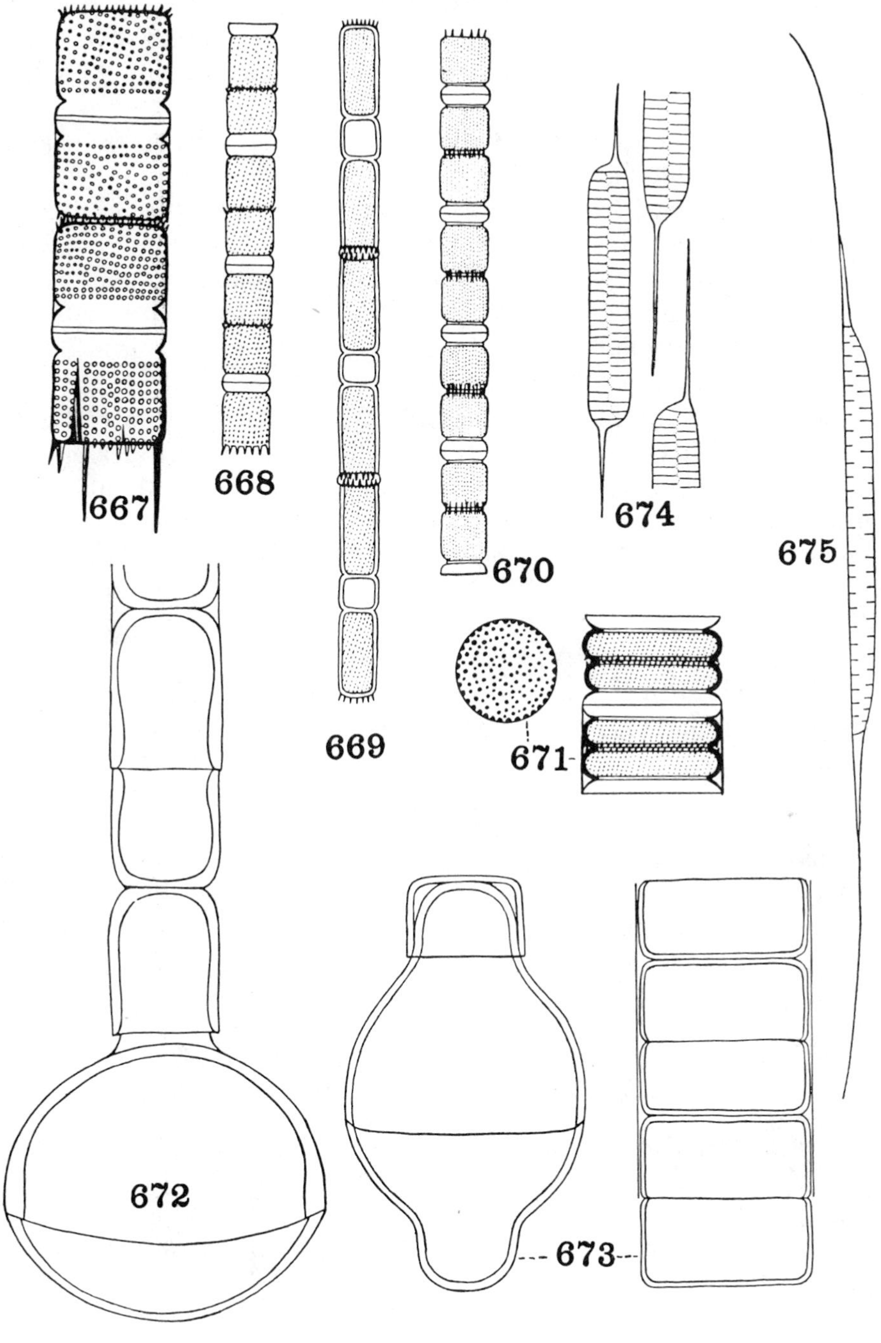

667

668

670

674

675

669

671

672

673

ter, discoid, single or rarely in short chains; valves prominently punctate, striations about 9 in 10 μ, outer punctae in double to quadruple rows with about 12 punctae in 10 μ, irregular punctation in center; spines stout; chromatophores numerous small plates; auxospore ellipsoid. Pl. **60,** fig. **676.**

a. Var. *intermedia* Fricke. Cells 20–25 μ in diameter, outer striations in 3–5 rows. Pl. **60,** fig. **677.**

b. Var. *minutula* (Kuetzing) Grunow. Smaller, 8–30 μ in diameter, walls weakly silicified. Pl. **60,** fig. **678.**

3. *Stephanodiscus niagarae* Ehrenberg. Cells 25–65 μ in diameter, discoid; valves distinctly punctate, striations about 16 in 10 μ, extending nearly to the irregularly punctate center; outer punctae in 3–5 rows; spines about 4 in 10 μ. Pl. **60,** fig. **680.**

a. Var. *magnifica* Fricke. Cells 72–80 μ in diameter; valves with a large isolated marking in otherwise undifferentiated central area; with marginal rib about 2 μ broad; beaded rows of two different shapes: one filiform and double-beaded, the other 3–5-beaded in its lower part and diminishing in width toward the center; rows about 4 in 10 μ; beads about 2 in 10 μ. Pl. **60,** figs. **681, 682.**

Family **Eupodiscaceae**

Cells discoid with circular, elliptic or polygonal valves having marginal mammillate protuberances or small ocelli; ornamentation of valves radiate, sometimes in two concentric zones; auxospores.

Actinocyclus Ehrenberg 1837

Cells discoid, single; valves usually circular, sometimes elliptic to nearly rhomboidal, radially punctate or areolate, peripherally smooth or finely striate, marginally minutely toothed; near margin of valves mammillate protuberances or unsculptured areas (ocelli); numerous discoid chromatophores.

FIG. 676.—*Stephanodiscus astraea* (Ehrenberg) Grunow.

FIG. 677.—*Stephanodiscus astraea* var. *intermedia* Fricke, valve view and edge view of 1 valve.

FIG. 678.—*Stephanodiscus astraea* var. *minutula* (Kuetzing) Grunow.

FIG. 679.—*Stephanodiscus hantzschii* Grunow.

FIG. 680.—*Stephanodiscus niagarae* Ehrenberg.

FIGS. 681, 682.—*Stephanodiscus niagarae* var. *magnifica* Fricke, valve view with cell-wall detail and edge view of 1 valve.

(Figs. 676, 678, 679, Hustedt; figs. 677, 681, 682, Schmidt; fig. 680, G. M. Smith. Figs. 681, 682 ×*500;* all others ×*1000.*)

PLATE 60

(Figs. 676 to 682)

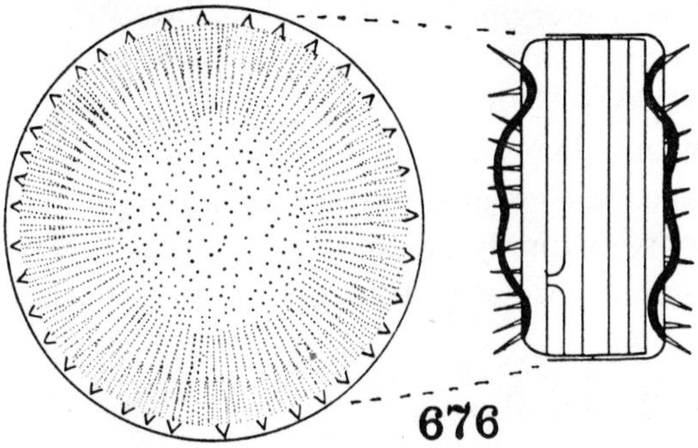

676

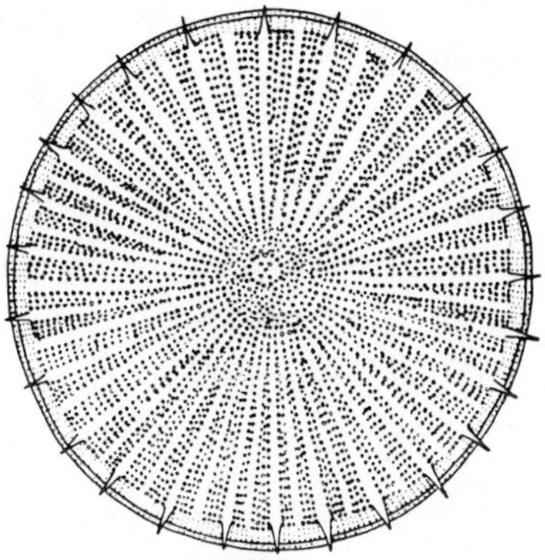

680

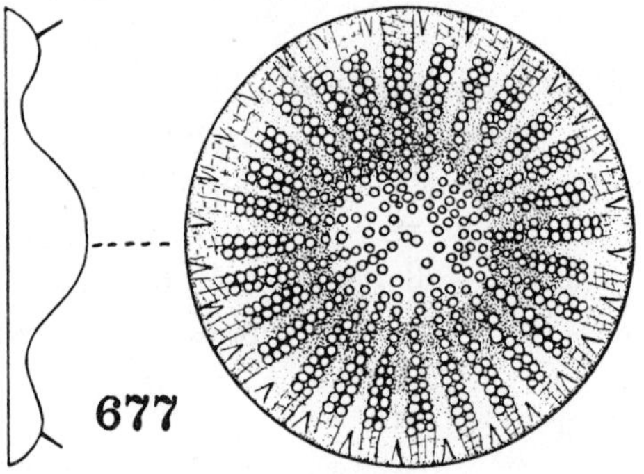

677

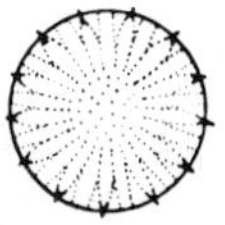

678 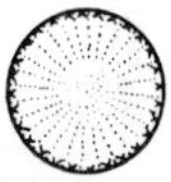   679

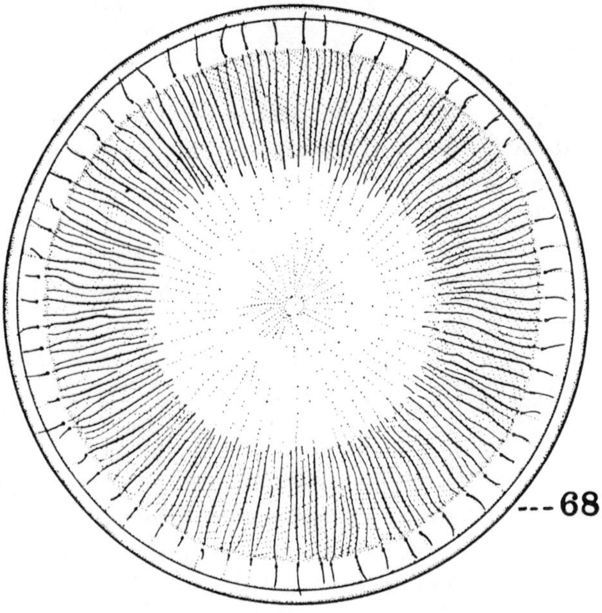

681 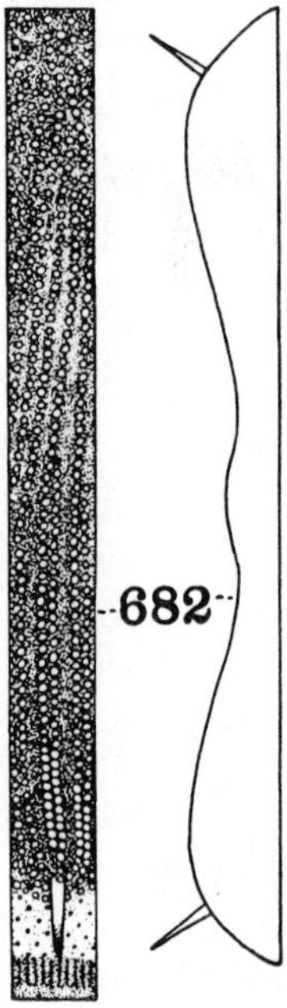   682

1. *Actinocyclus niagarae* H. L. Smith. Cells 60–110 μ in diameter, discoid; valves minutely punctate, with marginal teeth and ocellus. Pl. **58,** fig. **666.**

Suborder *RHIZOSOLENINEAE*

Cells elongate, cylindric, with circular or ovate valves separated by numerous intercalary bands between the girdles, solitary or in temporary chains, free-floating, often with long, medianly or excentrically placed terminal spines; chromatophores small, discoid; statospores, auxospores; freshwater or marine.

Family **Rhizosoleniaceae**

Planktonic diatoms, marine and freshwater; with characteristics of the Suborder.

Rhizosolenia Ehrenberg 1843; emend. Brightwell 1858

Cells elongate cylinders, with many intercalary bands, and circular or elliptical in cross-section, free-floating, solitary or in straight to spirally twisted chains; valve naviculoid or calyptrate to conical, apically terminating in a long centric or excentric spine; walls very finely punctate or without markings; silicification slight; chromatophores small, discoid, and scattered.

Auxospores, statospores, and microspores.

KEY TO THE SPECIES

1. Seta shorter than the cell, imbrication evident.................... 1. R. eriensis
1. Seta longer than the cell, imbrication not evident................. 2. R. longiseta

1. *Rhizosolenia eriensis* H. L. Smith. Cells 5–15 $\times$ 40–150 μ, flatly rod-shaped; intercalary bands scale-like and imbricated, about 2–4 in 10 μ; valve asymmetrically calyptra-like, terminating in a single seta shorter than the cell length. Pl. **59,** fig. **674.**

2. *Rhizosolenia longiseta* Zachary. Cells 4–10 $\times$ 70–200 μ, spindle-shaped; intercalary bands in two rows, one dorsal and one ventral, bands in the two rows alternating with each other, imbrication not clear; valve calyptra-like, terminating in a single seta longer than the cell length; chromatophores two round plates in the middle of the cell. Pl. **59,** fig. **675.**

Order PENNALES

Cells solitary or variously united into ribbon-like, stellate, zigzag, dendroid, radiate or irregular colonies, free-floating or attached by gelatinous stalks or by other mucous secretions; valves elongate, rarely nearly round, bilaterally symmetric or asymmetric to a median longitudinal line; ornamentation bilateral with respect to a median longitudinal line, not radiating from a central point; pseudoraphe or raphe present; cells with raphe mobile; valves without marginal spines or other projections, rarely winged; chromatophores variable: small and discoid or larger laminate structures with pyrenoids; one or two auxospores (zygotes) formed in the conjugation of two cells, or a single auxospore formed autogamously by union of two sister nuclei within a single cell, either with or without cytoplasmic division; vegetative cells diploid; abundant in freshwater, also marine; terrestrial forms sometimes saprophytic.

Suborder *FRAGILARINEAE*

Cells solitary, or in band-like and zigzag chains or stellate colonies, freefloating or sessile; chromatophores usually numerous, small and discoid, sometimes few and large; cells generally elongate, with pseudoraphe or a primitive type of raphe in the valves.

Family **Tabellariaceae**

Cells united in straight or zigzag chains or solitary, free-floating or attached; numerous, small, discoid chromatophores; valves narrowly linear, symmetric longitudinally and transversely, with pseudoraphe and median inflation; girdle view tabular; cells with 2 to many intercalary bands; longitudinal septa present.

Tabellaria Ehrenberg 1839

Cells tabular in girdle view, united usually into zigzag chains, sometimes into stellate colonies, with 4 to numerous intercalary bands per cell; between girdles and intercalary bands are longitudinal septa penetrating nearly to cell center; valves elongate, bilaterally symmetric, generally inflated both at the poles and in the middle; narrow pseudoraphe with laterally placed transverse finely punctate striae; chromatophores numerous small discs.

Auxospores from solitary cells.

KEY TO THE SPECIES

1. Cell with four longitudinal septa. . . . . 1. T. fenestrata
1. Cell with numerous longitudinal septa. . . . . 2. T. flocculosa

1. *Tabellaria fenestrata* (Lyngbye) Kuetzing. Cells 3–9 × 30–140 μ, with 4 intercalary bands, and 4 septa (2 abutting each pole), forming zigzag chains; valves elongate, with finely punctate striations, 18–20 in 10 μ, inflated in the middle and at the poles; pseudoraphe narrow. Pl. **61**, figs. **692, 693.**

2. *Tabellaria flocculosa* (Roth) Kuetzing. Cells 5–16 × 12–50 μ, with numerous intercalary bands and septa, forming zigzag chains; valves

short-elongate, with finely punctate striations, about 18 in 10 μ, inflated markedly in the middle and slightly or not at all at the poles; pseudoraphe narrow; cells sometimes asymmetric in valve view. Pl. **61,** fig. **694.**

Family **Meridionaceae**

Cells joined valve to valve into fan-shaped colonies, stalked or free-floating, cuneate in both valve and girdle view; chromatophores numerous, small and discoid; cells with one or two intercalary bands; pseudoraphe rarely inflated at the poles; transverse septa present.

Meridion C. A. Agardh 1824

Cells wedge-shaped, joined valve to valve into free-floating, fan-shaped or flat spiral colonies, with one or two intercalary bands; transverse septa rudimentary, appearing often as costae on valves and girdles; valves wedge-shaped, club-shaped or obovate, with fine transverse striations between the costae; pseudoraphe indistinct; chromatophores small, numerous, discoid, each often with a pyrenoid.

Auxospores formed singly from the cells.

KEY TO THE SPECIES

1. Valves with straight sides.............................. 1. M. circulare
1. Valves constricted at broader ends.................... 1a. M. c. var. constricta

1. *Meridion circulare* (Greville) C. A. Agardh. Cells 4–8 × 12–80 μ; valves wedge-shaped, costae 3–5 in 10 μ and finely punctate striations about 15 in 10 μ. Pl. **61,** figs. **689, 690.**

a. Var. *constricta* (Ralfs) Hustedt. Valve constricted at broader end, larger pole broadly capitate. Pl. **61,** fig. **691.**

Family **Diatomaceae**

Cells forming zigzag or flat chains or solitary, free-floating or sessile; valves bilaterally symmetric longitudinally and transversely; in girdle view both axes symmetric or symmetric only longitudinally; chromato-

---

Fig. 683.—*Diatoma anceps* (Ehrenberg) Kirchner.

Fig. 684.—*Diatoma hiemale* (Lyngbye) Heiberg.

Fig. 685.—*Diatoma hiemale* var. *mesodon* (Ehrenberg) Grunow.

Figs. 686, 687.—*Diatoma vulgare* Bory, colony.

Fig. 688.—*Diatoma elongatum* Agardh var. *tenuis* (Agardh) Van Heurck.

Figs. 689, 690.—*Meridion circulare* (Greville) C. A. Agardh.

Fig. 691.—*Meridion circulare* var. *constricta* (Ralfs) Hustedt.

Figs. 692, 693.—*Tabellaria fenestrata* (Lyngbye) Kuetzing.

Fig. 694.—*Tabellaria flocculosa* (Roth) Kuetzing.

(Figs. 683–691, 694, Hustedt. Figs. 687, 692 ×500; all others ×1000.)

PLATE 61

(Figs. 683 to 694)

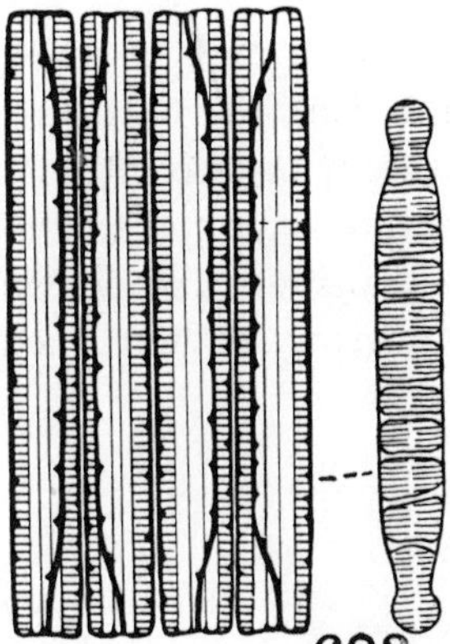

683

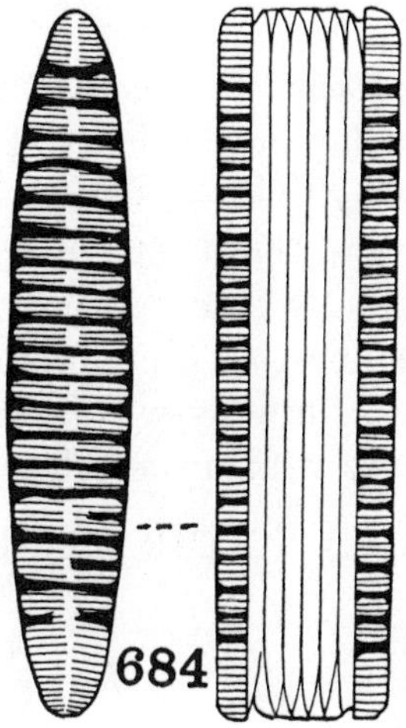

684

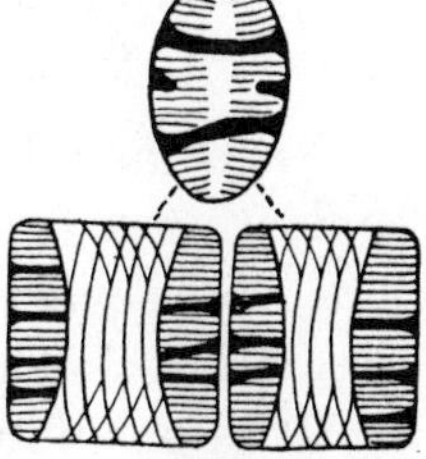

685

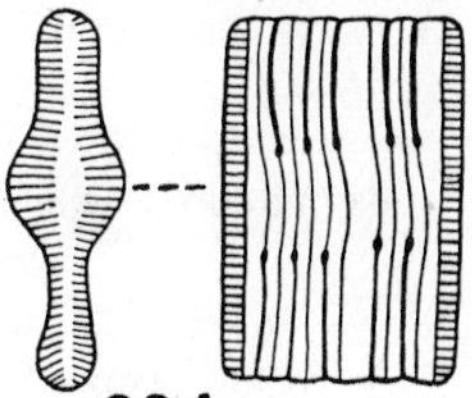

694

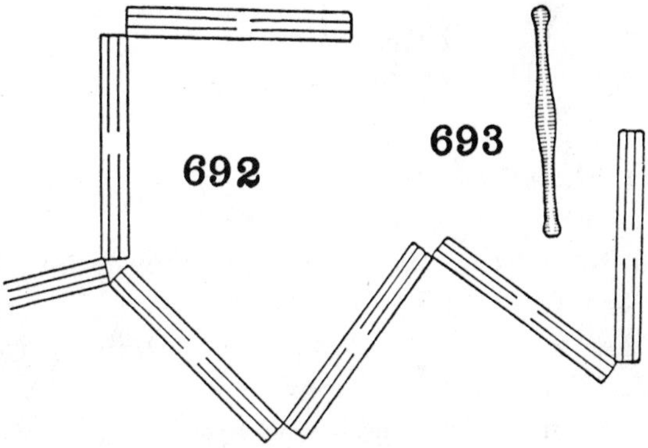

692

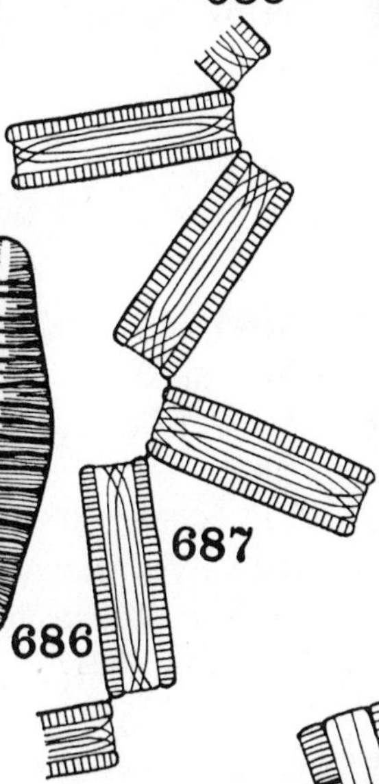

693

686

687

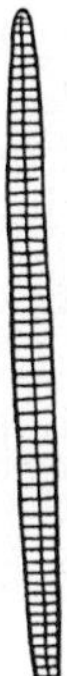

688

691

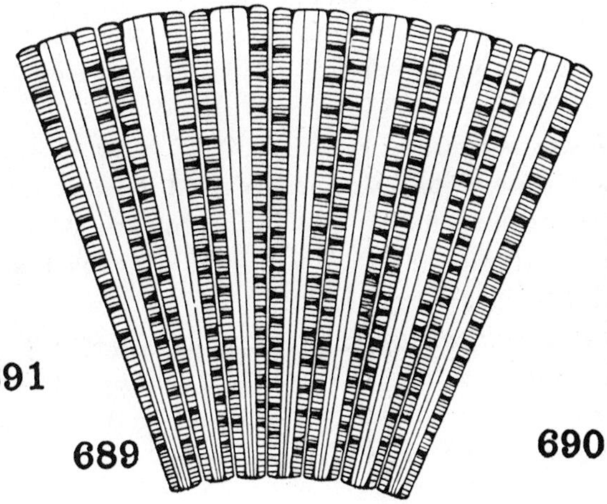

689

690

phores usually numerous, small and discoid; pseudoraphe distinct or not; transverse septa present.

Diatoma DeCandolle 1805

Cells rectangularly tabular in girdle view, united at the corners into free-floating or sessile, zigzag to linear chains, with one or two intercalary bands, with several transverse septa appearing as transverse costae; valves lanceolate to linear, bilaterally symmetric, with transverse, finely punctate striations between the costae; pseudoraphe narrow, without median expansion; chromatophores numerous, ellipsoid.

Auxospores formed singly within the cells.

KEY TO THE SPECIES

1. Cells united into linear bands.. 2
1. Cells united into zigzag chains.. 4
    2. Valves capitate, narrowly linear................. 1. D. anceps
    2. Valves not capitate, linear... 3
3. Cells 100–300 μ long............................. 2. D. hiemale
3. Cells 12–40 μ long.............................. 2a. D. h. var. mesodon
    4. Cells 10–13 μ broad............................ 3. D. vulgare
    4. Cells about 2 μ broad........................... 4. D. elongatum var.
                                                 tenuis

1. *Diatoma anceps* (Ehrenberg) Kirchner. Cells 4–8 × 15–100 μ, united into nearly closed chains, with few or no intercalary bands; valves linear, capitate at the poles, with narrow pseudoraphe; costae delicate, 3–6 in 10 μ; transverse striations 18–20 in 10 μ. Pl. **61**, fig. **683**.

2. *Diatoma hiemale* (Lyngbye) Heiberg. Cells 7–13 × 30–100 μ, united into closed chains, with numerous intercalary bands; valves linear-lanceolate, only slightly narrowed toward the rounded poles; costae prominent, 2–4 in 10 μ; transverse striations 18–20 in 10 μ. Pl. **61**, fig. **684**.

    a. Var. *mesodon* (Ehrenberg) Grunow. Cells 6–15 × 12–40 μ, broadly elliptical in valve view; ribbon-like chains frequently becoming zigzag. Pl. **61**, fig. **685**.

3. *Diatoma vulgare* Bory. Cells 10–13 × 30–60 μ, united into zigzag colonies, with rounded corners and several delicate intercalary bands; valves elliptic-lanceolate, narrowed slightly toward the rounded poles, with very narrow pseudoraphe; costae 6–8 in 10 μ; transverse striations about 16 in 10 μ. Pl. **61**, figs. **686, 687**.

4. *Diatoma elongatum* C. A. Agardh var. *tenuis* (Agardh) Van Heurck. Cells 2 × 20–50 μ, united into zigzag colonies, without evident intercalary bands; valves lanceolate, costae about 6–10 in 10 μ and transverse striations about 17 in 10 μ. Pl. **61**, fig. **688**.

Family **Fragilariaceae**

Cells forming stellate, band-like or zigzag colonies or solitary, free-floating or sessile, often stalked; valves generally symmetric in both axes, with pseudoraphe distinct or not; intercalary bands present or absent; no internal septation; chromatophores small, numerous and discoid, or two and laminate.

Asterionella Hassall 1850

Cells united into stellate colonies; intercalary bands, septa and costae absent; valves linear, with inflated ends, finely transversely striated; valve and girdle views symmetric; pseudoraphe indistinct; chromatophores two to several somewhat lobed plates.

KEY TO THE SPECIES

1. Contact ends of cells much broader than free ends. . . . . 1. A. formosa
1. Contact ends of cells scarcely broader than free ends. . . . . 2. A. gracillima

1. *Asterionella formosa* Hassall. Cells 1–2 × 40–130 μ, linear, with inflated ends, united into stellate colonies; free end of cell less inflated than the one joined to other cells; transverse striae very fine, 25–28 in 10 μ. Pl. 63, fig. 709.

2. *Asterionella gracillima* (Hantzsch) Heiberg. Cells 1–2 × 42–100 μ, united into stellate colonies, linear with slightly inflated ends—basal end scarcely larger than free end; transverse striae fine, 15–17 in 10 μ. Pl. 62, figs. 707, 708.

Fragilaria Lyngbye 1819; Rabenhorst 1864

Cells rectangular in girdle view, with one or two (sometimes none) intercalary bands, without septa and costae, united into free-floating or sessile colonies: mostly zigzag chains, sometimes flat, stellate colonies; valves linear to fusiform, bilaterally symmetric, usually attenuated at the poles, sometimes capitate, often medianly inflated (rarely constricted); transverse striae usually fine, sometimes coarse; pseudoraphe narrow and indistinct or broad and prominent; chromatophores numerous small discoid bodies or one to four laminate plates with pyrenoids.

Auxospores formed singly within the cells.

KEY TO THE SPECIES

1. Cells united in middle portion only. . . . . 1. F. crotonensis
1. Cells united through entire length. 2
   2. Valves medianly constricted. 3
   2. Valves medianly inflated. 4
   2. Valves neither medianly inflated nor medianly constricted. 5

3. Valves under 6 μ broad.............................. 6a. F. capucina var.
                      mesolepta
3. Valves over 6 μ broad................................. 2. F. constricta
 4. Radial striations 6–8 in 10 μ........................ 3. F. harrisonii
 4. Radial striations 14–17 in 10 μ..................... 4. F. construens
5. Striations 10–12 in 10 μ.............................. 5. F. pinnata
5. Striations 12–19 in 10 μ.. 6
 6. Ornamentation absent in center of valve.............. 6. F. capucina
 6. Ornamentation present in center of valve............. 7. F. virescens

1. *Fragilaria crotonensis* Kitton. Cells 1–3 × 40–150 μ, united medianly into ribbon-like bands, ends often touching; valves narrowly linear, somewhat widened medianly and slightly enlarged at the poles; transverse striations fine, about 15–18 in 10 μ; pseudoraphe narrow with a rectangular central area. Pl. **62**, fig. **703.**

 a. Var. *prolongata* Grunow. Larger and with narrowly prolonged poles. Pl. **62**, fig. **704.**

2. *Fragilaria constricta* Ehrenberg. Cells 7–15 × 20–70 μ, united into bands or zigzag colonies; valves broadly linear, more or less deeply concave in the middle, with somewhat rostrate, abruptly rounded poles; striations 13–18 in 10 μ; pseudoraphe narrow, linear; central area absent. Pl. **62**, fig. **695.**

3. *Fragilaria harrisonii* (Wm. Smith) Grunow. Cells 10–16 × 15–30 μ, united into short, closed chains; valves cruciform with lance-like pseudoraphe; transverse striations very prominent, 6–8 in 10 μ, crossed by fine lines, 25–30 in 10 μ. Pl. **62**, fig. **705.**

 a. Var. *rhomboides* Grunow. Cells rhomboid in valve view, with broader poles than in the species. Pl. **62**, fig. **706.**

4. *Fragilaria construens* (Ehrenberg) Grunow. Cells 5–12 × 7–25 μ,

Fɪɢ. 695.—*Fragilaria constricta* Ehrenberg.

Fɪɢ. 696.—*Fragilaria construens* (Ehrenberg) Grunow.

Fɪɢ. 697.—*Fragilaria construens* var. *venter* (Ehrenberg) Grunow.

Fɪɢ. 698.—*Fragilaria capucina* Desmazieres.

Fɪɢ. 699.—*Fragilaria capucina* var. *mesolepta* Rabenhorst.

Fɪɢ. 700.—*Fragilaria pinnata* Ehrenberg.

Fɪɢ. 701.—*Fragilaria pinnata* var. *lancettula* (Schumann) Hustedt.

Fɪɢ. 702.—*Fragilaria virescens* Ralfs.

Fɪɢ. 703.—*Fragilaria crotonensis* Kitton.

Fɪɢ. 704.—*Fragilaria crotonensis* var. *prolongata* Grunow.

Fɪɢ. 705.—*Fragilaria harrisonii* (Wm. Smith) Grunow.

Fɪɢ. 706.—*Fragilaria harrisonii* var. *rhomboides* Grunow.

Fɪɢs. 707, 708.—*Asterionella gracillima* (Hantzsch) Heiberg.

(Fig. 695, Wm. Smith; figs. 696–703, 705–708, Hustedt; fig. 704, G. M. Smith. All ×1000.)

PLATE 62

(Figs. 695 to 708)

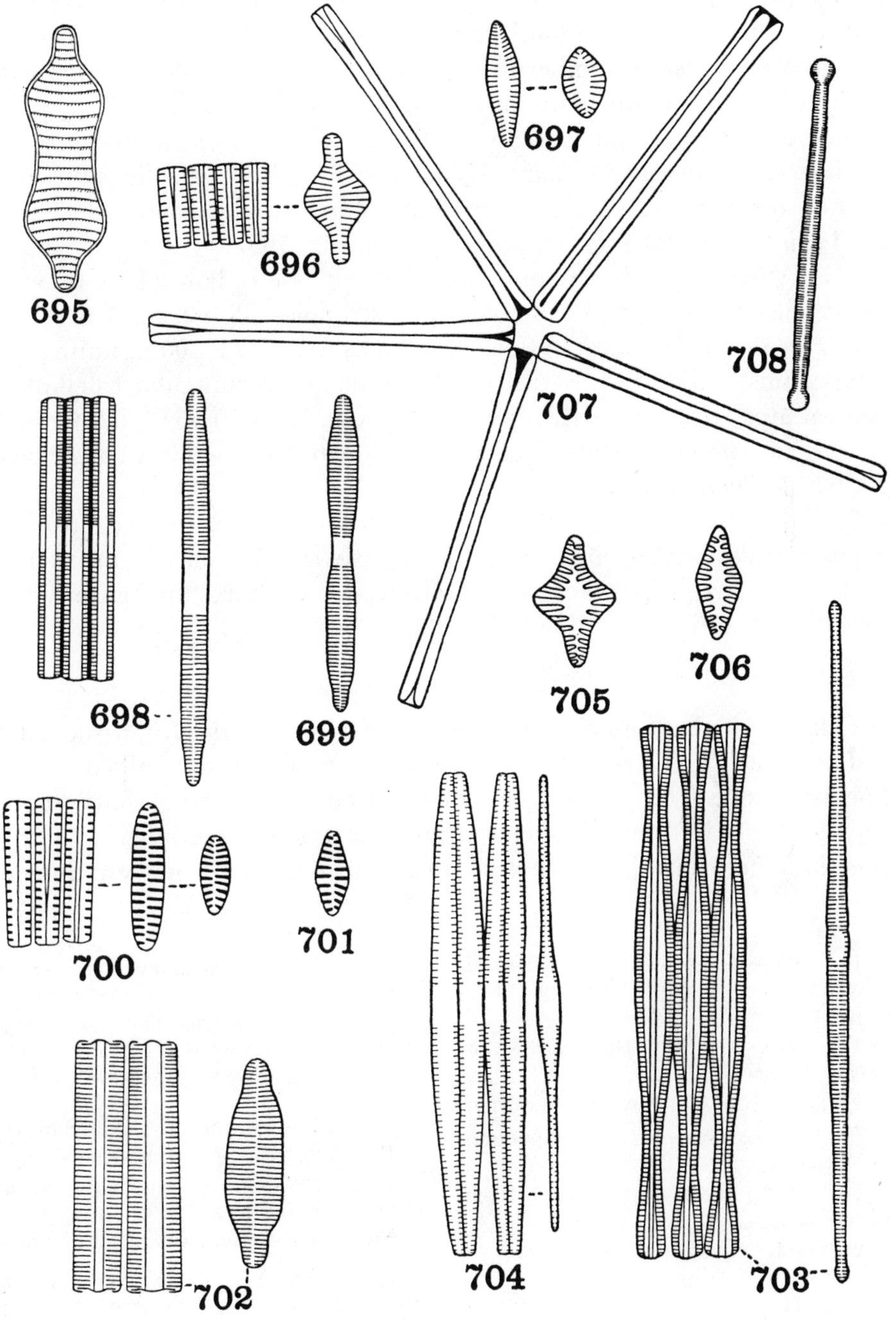

695

696

697

698

699

700

701

702

703

704

705

706

707

708

united into rather long compact chains; valves greatly expanded medianly, almost cruciform, with lance-like pseudoraphe; transverse striations 14–17 in 10 μ, slightly radial. Pl. **62**, fig. **696**.

a. Var. *venter* (Ehrenberg) Grunow. Cells broadly elliptical to naviculoid, often with distorted poles, in valve view. Pl. **62**, fig. **697**.

5. *Fragilaria pinnata* Ehrenberg. Cells 2–6 × 3–30 μ, united into flat chains; valves broadly to narrowly elliptical, with evident linear pseudoraphe; transverse striations prominent, almost rib-like, sometimes radial, 10–12 in 10 μ, with finer cross lines. Pl. **62**, fig. **700**.

a. Var. *lancettula* (Schumann) Hustedt. Cells lanceolate in valve view, with more or less beaked and pointed poles. Pl. **62**, fig. **701**.

6. *Fragilaria capucina* Desmazieres. Cells 2–5 × 25–100 μ, united into long chains; valves linear with pseudoraphe and rectangular to elliptical central area; transverse striations fine, about 15 in 10 μ. Pl. **62**, fig. **698**.

a. Var. *mesolepta* Rabenhorst. Cells more or less medianly constricted. Pl. **62**, fig. **699**.

7. *Fragilaria virescens* Ralfs. Cells 5–10 × 12–120 μ, united into long chains; valves linear, with straight to slightly convex sides, rounded poles and very narrow pseudoraphe; transverse striations moderately fine, parallel, 12–19 in 10 μ. Pl. **62**, fig. **702**.

Synedra Ehrenberg 1830

Cells narrow and much elongated, solitary or in tufted, fan-shaped or radiating colonies, free-floating or epiphytic, sessile or stalked; valves linear to lanceolate, straight or sometimes curved, with poles attenuated or not, often capitate; transverse striation lateral to a conspicuous narrow pseudoraphe; central smooth area present or not; in girdle view elongate

Fig. 709.—*Asterionella formosa* Hassall, colony with cells in girdle view and a single cell in valve view.

Fig. 710.—*Synedra parasitica* (Wm. Smith) Hustedt.

Fig. 711.—*Synedra rumpens* Kuetzing.

Fig. 712.—*Synedra dorsiventralis* Mueller.

Fig. 713.—*Synedra ulna* (Nitzsch) Ehrenberg.

Fig. 714.—*Synedra ulna* var. *aequalis* (Kuetzing) Hustedt.

Fig. 715.—*Synedra ulna* var. *danica* (Kuetzing) Grunow.

Fig. 716.—*Synedra ulna* var. *spathulifera* Grunow.

Fig. 717.—*Synedra ulna* var. *biceps* (Kuetzing) Schoenfeld.

Fig. 718.—*Synedra pulchella* (Ralfs) Kuetzing.

Fig. 719.—*Synedra tenera* Wm. Smith.

Fig. 720.—*Synedra acus* Kuetzing.

Fig. 721.—*Synedra acus* var. *radians* (Kuetzing) Hustedt.

Fig. 722.—*Synedra capitata* Ehrenberg.

(Figs. 709–711, 713–722, Hustedt; fig. 712, Schmidt. Figs. 709–712, 718, 719 ×*1000;* all others ×*500.*)

PLATE 63

(Figs. 709 to 722)

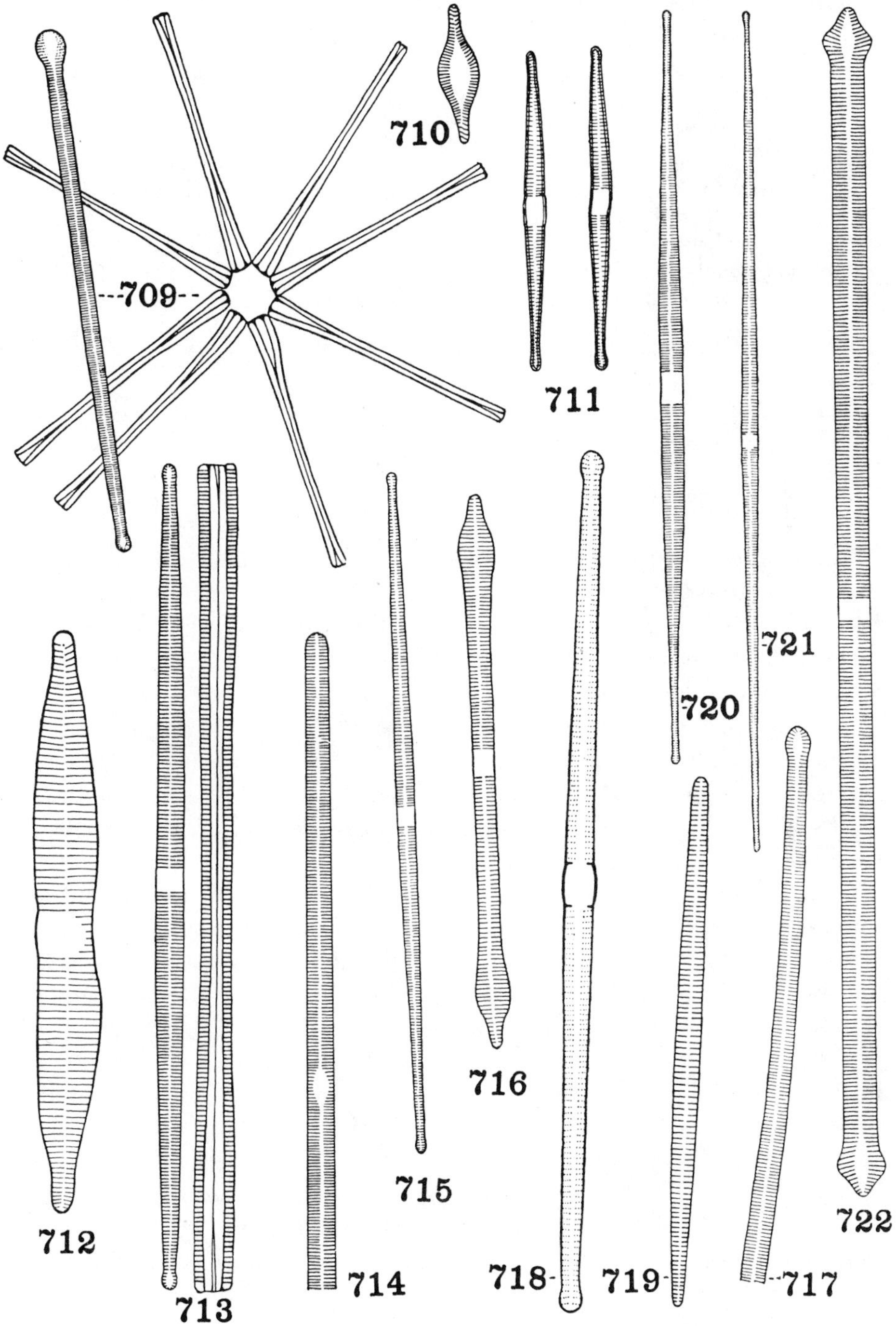

709
710
711
712
713
714
715
716
717
718
719
720
721
722

with truncate ends and striated; chromatophores two large plates, each usually with three or more pyrenoids.

1–2 auxospores in a single cell, without conjugation.

KEY TO THE SPECIES

1. Cells 10–25 μ long, epiphytic............................ 1. S. parasitica
1. Cells 27–600 μ long.. 2
   2. Central area excentric............................... 2. S. dorsiventralis
   2. Central area medianly placed......................... 3
3. Central pseudonodule present........................... 3. S. pulchella
3. Central pseudonodule absent............................. 4
   4. Valves with parallel sides and angularly capitate ends.... 4. S. capitata
   4. Valves not as above................................. 5
5. Transverse striae more than 20 in 10 μ.................. 5. S. tenera
5. Transverse striae less than 20 in 10 μ.................. 6
   6. Cells 27–70 μ long................................. 6. S. rumpens
   6. Cells 50–350 μ long................................ 7
7. Diameter of valve at poles less than 3 μ................ 7. S. acus
7. Diameter of valve at poles more than 3 μ............... 8. S. ulna

1. *Synedra parasitica* (Wm. Smith) Hustedt. Cells 3–5 × 10–25 μ, solitary and epiphytic, rectangular in girdle view; valves lanceolate to rhombo-lanceolate becoming slenderly beaked toward the slightly capitate poles; transverse striations fine, somewhat radial, 16–19 in 10 μ; no central area; pseudoraphe lanceolate. Pl. **63**, fig. **710**.

2. *Synedra dorsiventralis* Mueller. Cells 10–16 × 100–200 μ, solitary; valves irregularly elliptic with narrowed but broadly obtuse ends (sometimes nearly rostrate); transverse striations coarse, rarely somewhat radial, 13–17 in 10 μ; pseudoraphe narrow, linear; central area conspicuous, usually excentric. Pl. **63**, fig. **712**.

3. *Synedra pulchella* (Ralfs) Kuetzing. Cells 5–8 × 33–150 μ, solitary, linear-lanceolate in girdle view; valves lanceolate with rounded or slightly capitate ends and with central pseudonodule; transverse striations 12–15 (sometimes 20) in 10 μ; conspicuous central area, rectangular to quadrate in shape; pseudoraphe narrow and linear. Pl. **63**, fig. **718**.

4. *Synedra capitata* Ehrenberg. Cells 7–10 × 125–500 μ, solitary, broadly linear in girdle view; valve conspicuously linear with nearly parallel edges and cuneate ends; transverse striations evident, 8–11 in 10 μ, pseudoraphe narrowly linear, central area usually not evident. Pl. **63**, fig. **722**.

5. *Synedra tenera* Wm. Smith. Cells 2–4 × 30–120 μ, solitary; valves narrowly lanceolate, scarcely capitate; transverse striations 19–20 in 10 μ;

pseudoraphe very narrow, linear, with central area generally absent. Pl. 63, fig. 719.

6. *Synedra rumpens* Kuetzing. Cells 2–3 × 27–70 μ, solitary, narrowly linear; valves narrowly lanceolate, scarcely capitate; transverse striations 19–20 in 10 μ; pseudoraphe narrow and linear with central area variable or wanting. Pl. 63, fig. 711.

7. *Synedra acus* Kuetzing. Cells 5–6 × 100–300 μ, solitary; valves linear-lanceolate, becoming needle-like toward the scarcely rounded poles (about 1.5 μ in diameter); transverse striations 12–14 in 10 μ; pseudoraphe narrow, linear, with central area usually present, rectangular. Pl. 63, fig. 720.

    a. Var. *radians* (Kuetzing) Hustedt. Cells 2–4 × 40–200 μ, central area small and elliptic, often absent. Pl. 63, fig. 721.

8. *Synedra ulna* (Nitzsch) Ehrenberg. Cells 5–9 × 50–350 μ, linear in girdle view, with widened extremities, solitary; valves linear to linear-lanceolate, gradually narrowed toward the ends, with broadly rounded poles; transverse striations 8–12 (mostly 10) in 10 μ, finely but plainly punctate; pseudoraphe narrowly linear, with central area varying, often absent. Pl. 63, fig. 713.

    a. Var. *aequalis* (Kuetzing) Hustedt. Cells with straight sides in valve view, scarcely narrowed toward the rounded ends. Pl. 63, fig. 714.

    b. Var. *biceps* (Kuetzing) Schoenfeldt. Cells up to 600 μ long, straight or frequently bent, poles rounded and spoon-shaped. Pl. 63, fig. 717.

    c. Var. *danica* (Kuetzing) Grunow. Cells about 5 μ in diameter, scarcely attenuate toward the slightly capitate ends. Pl. 63, fig. 715.

    d. Var. *spathulifera* Grunow. Cells linear in valve view, with widened, oval ends terminating in a rather evident beak. Pl. 63, fig. 716.

Family **Eunotiaceae**

Cells in filaments or clusters, or solitary, free-floating or sessile; valves curved or arcuate, with dissimilar sides and with excentric pseudoraphe or raphe lying toward concave side; girdle view rectangular or cuneate, usually with two laminate chromatophores.

Eunotia Ehrenberg 1837

Cells rectangular to linear to tabular in girdle view, both girdles and valves strongly ornamented, usually with intercalary bands, free-floating or epiphytic, solitary or united valve to valve into chains; valves arcuate, with similar poles but dissimilar margins: concave side regular, convex side inflated only at the poles or regular or undulate, sometimes nearly straight; raphe very short, extending from the fairly evident polar nodule diagonally to the concave margin, no central nodule; neither costae nor septa present; intercalary bands usually present; transverse striations or punctations present; two somewhat laminate chromatophores, without pyrenoids.

Auxospores single from the conjugation of two cells.

KEY TO THE SPECIES

1. Valves nearly straight or slightly curved.................................... 2
1. Valves broadly curved.. 3
    2. Valves 2–5 μ in diameter.............................. 1. E. flexuosa
    2. Valves 7–13 μ in diameter............................. 2. E. formica
3. Cells 3–4 × 20–150 μ................................... 3. E. lunaris
3. Cells 5–10 × 10–50 μ.................................. 4. E. pectinalis
                                                            var. minor
3. Cells 11–15 × 100–190 μ............................. 5. E. monodon
                                                            var. major

1. *Eunotia flexuosa* (Brébisson) Kuetzing. Cells 2–5 × 130–300 μ, linear in girdle view; valves very slender with parallel margins, straight or slightly curved or rarely undulate, poles broadly rounded; transverse striations 14–18 in 10 μ; raphe a short line extending inward from the polar nodule parallel to the linear axis of the valve. Pl. **64**, fig. **728**.

2. *Eunotia formica* Ehrenberg. Cells 7–13 × 40–160 μ, rectangular in girdle view; valves slightly curved or straight, with parallel sides and cuneate ends; transverse striations 8–11 in 10 μ, irregular. Pl. **64**, fig. **731**.

3. *Eunotia lunaris* (Ehrenberg) Grunow. Cells 3–4 × 2–150 μ, linear in girdle view; valve curved, forming wide arc, with more or less parallel

Fig. 723.—*Achnanthes exilis* Kuetzing.

Fig. 724.—*Achnanthes lanceolata* (Brébisson) Grunow.

Fig. 725.—*Achnanthes lanceolata* var. *rostrata* Hustedt.

Fig. 726.—*Achnanthes microcephala* (Kuetzing) Cleve.

Fig. 727.—*Achnanthes minutissima* (Kuetzing) Cleve.

Fig. 728.—*Eunotia flexuosa* (Brébisson) Kuetzing.

Fig. 729.—*Eunotia pectinalis* (Kuetzing) Rabenhorst var. *minor* (Kuetzing) Rabenhorst.

Fig. 730.—*Eunotia lunaris* (Ehrenberg) Grunow.

Fig. 731.—*Eunotia formica* Ehrenberg.

Fig. 732.—*Eunotia monodon* Ehrenberg var. *major* (Wm. Smith) Hustedt.

Fig. 733.—*Cocconeis pediculus* Ehrenberg.

Figs. 734, 735.—*Cocconeis placentula* Ehrenberg.

Fig. 736.—*Cocconeis placentula* var. *lineata* (Ehrenberg) Cleve.

Fig. 737.—*Cocconeis flexella* (Kuetzing) Cleve.

(Figs. 723–727, 729–737, Hustedt; fig. 728, Van Heurck. Figs. 723–727, 737 ×*1500*; figs. 728–731, 733–736 ×*1000*; fig. 732 ×*500*.)

PLATE 64

(Figs. 723 to 737)

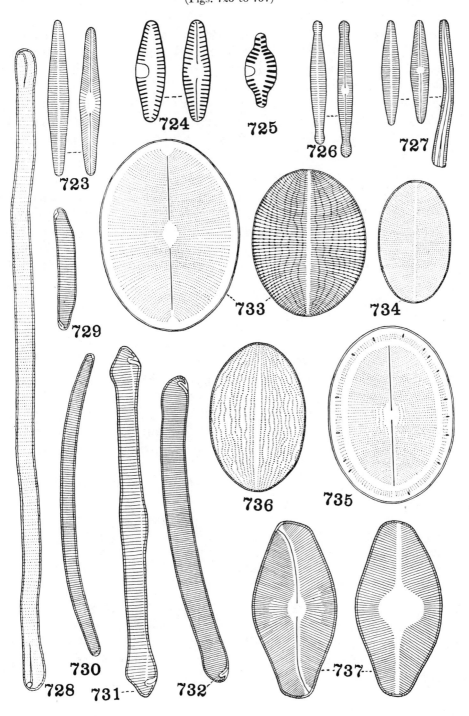

723

724

725

726

727

729

733

734

728

730

731

732

736

735

737

sides and slightly thinner poles; polar nodules small; raphe slightly developed; transverse striations 14–17 in 10 μ. Pl. **64,** fig. **730.**

4. *Eunotia pectinalis* (Kuetzing) Rabenhorst var. *minor* (Kuetzing) Rabenhorst. Cells 5–10 $\times$ 10–50 μ, rectangular in girdle view; valve linear, slightly to broadly curved, with nearly parallel sides and rounded poles; transverse striations about 12 in 10 μ. Pl. **64,** fig. **729.**

5. *Eunotia monodon* Ehrenberg var. *major* (Wm. Smith) Hustedt. Cells 11–15 $\times$ 100–190 μ, rectangular in girdle view; valves broadly curved, with nearly parallel sides and slightly cuneate poles with rounded ends; transverse striations 7–8 in 10 μ. Pl. **64,** fig. **732.**

Suborder *ACHNANTHINEAE*

Cells solitary or in aggregates, generally sessile and stalked or flattened against the substrate; dissimilar valves: convex epivalve with a pseudoraphe and usually concave hypovalve with a true raphe; valve view symmetric in both axes, girdle view asymmetric longitudinally or transversely; chromatophores one or two, laminate and lobed, or numerous and discoid.

Family **Achnanthaceae**

With characteristics of the Suborder.

Cocconeis Ehrenberg 1835; Grunow 1868

Cells transversely curved in girdle view, solitary, epiphytic upon submerged aquatics, especially upon slow-growing filamentous algae; septa incomplete, intercalary bands absent; valves elliptic, epivalve with axial pseudoraphe, hypovalve with median raphe, straight or sigmoid, with central and polar nodules, with transverse striae or punctate rows; chromatophore single, laminate, usually with one or two pyrenoids, and adjoining the epivalve.

Auxospores single from two conjugated cells, or formed parthenogenetically from a single gamete.

KEY TO THE SPECIES

1. Raphe sigmoid.. 1. C. flexella
1. Raphe straight... 2
    2. Hyaline intramarginal ring in hypovalve.................. 2. C. placentula
    2. No hyaline intramarginal ring in hypovalve............... 3. C. pediculus

1. *Cocconeis flexella* (Kuetzing) Cleve. Cells 10–26 $\times$ 20–80 μ, irregularly rectangular in girdle view; valves elliptic-lanceolate with blunt ends; striae strictly transverse to somewhat radial, 22–30 in 10 μ; raphe sigmoid, central nodule widened into a small circular area; pseudoraphe narrow, with large rectangular central area. Pl. **64,** fig. **737.**

2. *Cocconeis placentula* Ehrenberg. Cells 8–40 × 11–70 μ, flat or slightly curved; valves elliptic, transverse striae sometimes radial, 23–25 in 10 μ; hypovalve with filamentous, straight raphe and intramarginal hyaline ring, central area round, small; epivalve with narrow linear pseudoraphe. Pl. **64**, figs. **734, 735.**

    a. Var. *lineata* (Ehrenberg) Cleve. Striae in both transverse and longitudinal series, with isolated punctae and hyaline areas appearing toward margin; auxospores parthenogenetic. Pl. **64**, fig. **736.**

3. *Cocconeis pediculus* Ehrenberg. Cells 10–37 × 15–56 μ, curved; valves broadly elliptic; hypovalve with radially arranged transverse striae, 16–18 in 10 μ, with round punctae 18–20 in 10 μ, raphe thread-like, straight with small rounded central area; epivalve with striations 15–17 in 10 μ crossed by irregularly longitudinal rows of larger punctae, with narrow linear pseudoraphe scarcely medianly widened. Pl. **64**, fig. **733.**

Achnanthes Bory 1822

Cells somewhat rectangular and longitudinally bent or curved in girdle view, generally attached by gelatinous stalks, or sessile and united into bundles at the valves, rarely into filaments, sometimes free-floating, solitary; valves generally linear-lanceolate or somewhat elliptic; hypovalve usually concave, with raphe, a distinct central nodule, rather inconspicuous polar nodules, central area sometimes transversely widened into a stauros; epivalve generally convex, with a pseudoraphe; transverse striations, often somewhat radiate, and in some species prominent costae; chromatophores one, two, or numerous and discoid.

Two auxospores formed from two cells by the conjugation of two pairs of gametes.

KEY TO THE SPECIES

1. Striations pronounced, 13–17 in 10 μ . . . . 1. A. lanceolata
1. Striations fine, 20–36 in 10 μ 2
   2. Central area widened transversely, small 3
   2. Central area not widened transversely . . . . 2. A. exilis
   3. Valves constricted toward capitate poles . . . . 3. A. microcephala
   3. Valves gradually tapering toward poles . . . . 4. A. minutissima

    1. *Achnanthes lanceolata* (Brébisson) Grunow. Cells 4–10 × 8–40 μ; valves elliptic-lanceolate, with transverse striations 13–17 in 10 μ; hypovalve with pronounced thread-like raphe, with central area broad, somewhat rectangular; hypovalve with slender pseudoraphe, and with a U-shaped spot on one side. Pl. **64**, fig. **724.**

    a. Var. *rostrata* Hustedt. Valves broadly elliptic, abruptly narrowed toward the poles. Pl. **64**, fig. **725.**

2. *Achnanthes exilis* Kuetzing. Cells 4–6 × 13–30 μ; valves linear-lanceolate gradually narrowed to rounded poles; transverse striations about 20–22 in 10 μ (up to 27 at the poles); hypovalve with thread-like raphe, with wide central area, and transverse striations somewhat radial; epivalve with linear pseudoraphe and striations only slightly radial. Pl. 64, fig. 723.

3. *Achnanthes microcephala* (Kuetzing) Cleve. Cells 2–3 × 8–26 μ; valves linear-lanceolate, constricted toward the rounded, capitate poles, with transverse striations 26–36 in 10 μ; hypovalve with very slender raphe, central area small; epivalve with very slender pseudoraphe and scarcely evident central area. Pl. 64, fig. 726.

4. *Achnanthes minutissima* (Kuetzing) Cleve. Cells 2–4 × 5–40 μ; valves linear-elliptic, slightly narrowed to rounded poles; transverse striations 33–35 in 10 μ; hypovalve with delicate thread-like raphe, central area small; epivalve with very narrow pseudoraphe, central area absent. Pl. 64, fig. 727.

Rhoicosphenia Grunow 1860

Cells curved and cuneate in girdle view, sessile and attached at the smaller ends to submerged plants by a branching system of gelatinous stalks or by gelatinous pads; hypovalve concave, with median raphe, with central and polar nodules; epivalve convex, with median pseudoraphe; both valves oblanceolate in outline, with transverse striations; girdles striate, intercalary bands smooth, longitudinal septa two; chromatophore single, often extending across the cell.

FIG. 738.—*Anomoeoneis serians* (Brébisson) Cleve.

FIG. 739.—*Anomoeoneis exilis* (Kuetzing) Cleve.

FIG. 740.—*Anomoeoneis follis* (Ehrenberg) Cleve.

FIG. 741.—*Caloneis alpestris* (Grunow) Cleve.

FIG. 742.—*Caloneis bacillaris* (Gregory) Cleve.

FIG. 743.—*Caloneis silicula* (Ehrenberg) Cleve.

FIG. 744.—*Caloneis silicula* var. *inflata* (Grunow) Cleve.

FIG. 745.—*Caloneis silicula* var. *undulata* (Grunow) Cleve.

FIG. 746.—*Caloneis silicula* var. *gibberula* (Kuetzing) Cleve.

FIG. 747.—*Caloneis silicula* var. *alpina* Cleve.

FIG. 748.—*Caloneis bacillum* (Grunow) Mereschkowsky.

FIG. 749.—*Amphipleura pellucida* Kuetzing.

FIG. 750.—*Amphiprora ornata* Bailey.

FIG. 751.—*Diploneis puella* (Schumann) Cleve.

FIG. 752.—*Diploneis elliptica* (Kuetzing) Cleve.

FIG. 753.—*Rhoicosphenia curvata* (Kuetzing) Grunow.

(Figs. 738–741, 743, 746–751, Hustedt; figs. 742, 744, 745, Van Heurck; figs. 752, 753, G. M. Smith. All ×*1000*.)

PLATE 65

(Figs. 738 to 753)

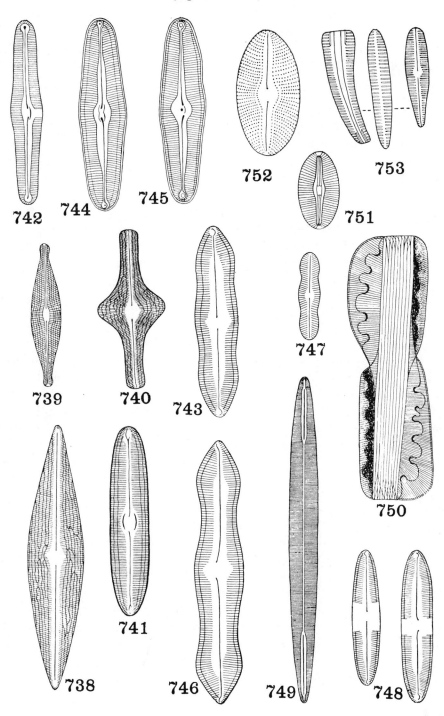

742 744 745 752 751 753

739 740 743 747 750

738 741 746 749 748

A single auxospore formed by conjugation of sister cells.

1. *Rhoicosphenia curvata* (Kuetzing) Grunow. Cells 4–8 × 12–75 μ, curved and cuneate in girdle view; valves clavate, transversely striate, with 12–15 striae in 10 μ; hypovalve concave, with filamentous raphe and small central area; epivalve convex, with linear pseudoraphe; frequently on filamentous algae. Pl. **65**, fig. **753**.

Suborder *NAVICULINEAE*

Cells solitary and free-floating, or occasionally with gelatinous stalks or within gelatinous tubes; generally symmetric in both axes, or asymmetric in one axis only; true raphe in each valve; no intercalary bands; chromatophores usually two and laminate.

Family **Naviculaceae**

Cells generally solitary and free-floating, or sometimes aggregated or in branched gelatinous tubes; valves similar, symmetric in both axes, variously elliptic, lanceolate or naviculoid, with raphe having distinct though variable central and polar nodules; girdle view usually symmetric in both axes and generally rectangular, with or without intercalary bands; two laminate chromatophores.

Amphipleura Kuetzing 1844

Cells linear-lanceolate to fusiform in valve view, solitary, free-floating; valve with greatly elongated central nodule terminating at each end in two parallel prongs which unite at each pole with the polar nodule, with short straight raphe within each pair of prongs, with very minute transverse striations; chromatophores two, adjacent to the girdle side of cell.

Auxospores formed sexually in pairs between two cells.

1. *Amphipleura pellucida* Kuetzing. Cells 7–9 × 80–140 μ, fusiform, with sharply rounded ends; valves with very fine striations, 37–40 in 10 μ, terminal forks 18–20 μ long. Pl. **65**, fig. **749**.

Frustulia C. A. Agardh 1824; Grunow 1865

Cells solitary and free-floating or sessile and enclosed in a gelatinous envelope, sometimes in a gelatinous tube; in valve view linear-elliptic to rhombo-lanceolate, in girdle view rectangular, without intercalary bands; central nodule longitudinally elongated, prolonged toward each pole into two parallel ribs apically united with the polar nodule; transverse striations, often medianly radial and crossed by fine undulate longitudinal lines; two chromatophores, sometimes longitudinally incised, on opposite sides of the girdle and connected by a cytoplasmic bridge.

Auxospores formed in pairs from two cells.

KEY TO THE SPECIES

1. Striae somewhat radially arranged.........................1. F. vulgaris
1. Striae rather rigidly transverse..2
   2. Valves elliptic-lanceolate...............................2. F. viridula
   2. Valves rhomboidly lanceolate...........................3. F. rhomboides

1. *Frustulia vulgaris* (Thwaites) DeToni. Cells 10–13 × 40–80 μ, in un-branched tubes, with elliptic- to linear-lanceolate valves having obtuse to rostrate extremities; striae somewhat radial, about 24 in 10 μ in the middle and about 34 in 10 μ at the poles. Pl. **66,** fig. **756.**

2. *Frustulia viridula* (Brébisson) DeToni. Cells 13–20 × 100–110 μ, in gelatinous tubes; valves elliptic-lanceolate, with transverse striations 28–30 in 10 μ. Pl. **66,** fig. **755.**

3. *Frustulia rhomboides* (Ehrenberg) DeToni. Cells 15–30 × 70–160 μ, with rhombo-lanceolate valves, transverse striations 23–30 in 10 μ and longitudinal lines 20–30 in 10 μ. Pl. **66,** fig. **754.**

Amphiprora Ehrenberg 1843; emend. Cleve 1891

Cells solitary, free-floating, or sessile and adhering to objects by a gelatinous envelope, naviculoid in valve view, hour-glass shape in girdle view with a sigmoid girdle; sigmoid raphe in outer margin of keel with small central and polar nodules; transverse striations on both valve face and keel; several intercalary bands, straight or sigmoid, with both bands and girdles usually striate in parallel rows; cells broader in girdle view than in valve view; chromatophore one, sometimes two, irregularly marginally incised.

1. *Amphiprora ornata* Bailey. Cells 34–50 × 45–80 μ, with thin-walled valves; deeply constricted in the middle in girdle view; keel undulate; striations 20–22 in 10 μ. Pl. **65,** fig. **750.**

Anomoeoneis Pfitzer 1871

Cells generally solitary, lanceolate to rhombic and elliptic in valve view, rectangular in girdle view; valves regularly with convex sides, sometimes abruptly medianly inflated, with acute, rounded or capitate poles; axial area with a median circular expansion, small, sometimes lyrate; raphe straight; transverse striations interrupted by hyaline space longitudinally zigzag on valve face; intercalary bands absent; a single, longitudinally incised, laminate chromatophore.

Formation of two auxospores from the union of gametes in pairs from two sister cells enclosed in a gelatinous envelope.

KEY TO THE SPECIES

1. Valves abruptly and strikingly medianly inflated................ 1. A. follis
1. Valves regularly lanceolate to rhombo-lanceolate............................. 2
   2. Cells 4–6 × 15–35 μ..................................... 2. A. exilis
   2. Cells 9–18 × 40–90 μ.................................... 3. A. serians

1. *Anomoeoneis follis* (Ehrenberg) Cleve. Cells 14–17 × 27–40 μ; valves rhombic, with marked median inflation; raphe straight, filiform, central area small, circular; transverse striations radial, 24–26 in 10 μ, crossed by longitudinal, undulate striations, sometimes hyaline spaces. Pl. **65**, fig. **740**.

2. *Anomoeoneis exilis* (Kuetzing) Cleve. Cells 4–6 × 15–35 μ; valves narrowly lanceolate, with subcapitate poles; raphe straight, filiform; central area small, circular; transverse striations radial, 30 or more in 10 μ, crossed by undulate longitudinal striations. Pl. **65**, fig. **739**.

3. *Anomoeoneis serians* (Brébisson) Cleve. Cells 9–18 × 40–90 μ; valves rhombo-lanceolate, gradually attenuated toward acute poles; raphe straight, filiform; central area circular or somewhat angular; transverse striations, lightly radial, 21–24 in 10 μ, crossed by hyaline, undulate, longitudinal lines, about 12 in 10 μ. Pl. **65**, fig. **738**.

Caloneis Cleve 1891

Cells solitary, free-floating, linear or lanceolate, generally with evidently convex sides, sometimes with marginal inflations in valve view, rectangular in girdle view; raphe straight with rounded central and polar nodules; transverse striations crossed by one or more longitudinal lines or hyaline areas parallel to the valve margin; intercalary bands absent; usually two irregular chromatophores, each commonly with two pyrenoids.

Fig. 754.—*Frustulia rhomboides* (Ehrenberg) DeToni.

Fig. 755.—*Frustulia viridula* (Brébisson) DeToni.

Fig. 756.—*Frustulia vulgaris* (Thwaites) DeToni.

Fig. 757.—*Gyrosigma wormleyi* (Sullivant) Boyer.

Fig. 758.—*Gyrosigma attenuatum* (Kuetzing) Cleve.

Fig. 759.—*Gyrosigma acuminatum* (Kuetzing) Cleve.

Fig. 760.—*Gyrosigma eximium* (Thwaites) Boyer.

Fig. 761.—*Gyrosigma kuetzingii* (Grunow) Cleve.

Fig. 762.—*Gyrosigma scalproides* (Rabenhorst) Cleve.

Fig. 763.—*Gyrosigma spencerii* (Quekett) Cleve.

(Fig. 754, G. M. Smith; figs. 755, 756, 760, Van Heurck; fig. 757, Boyer; figs. 758, 759, 761–763, Hustedt. Fig. 758 ×750; all others ×1000.)

PLATE 66

(Figs. 754 to 763)

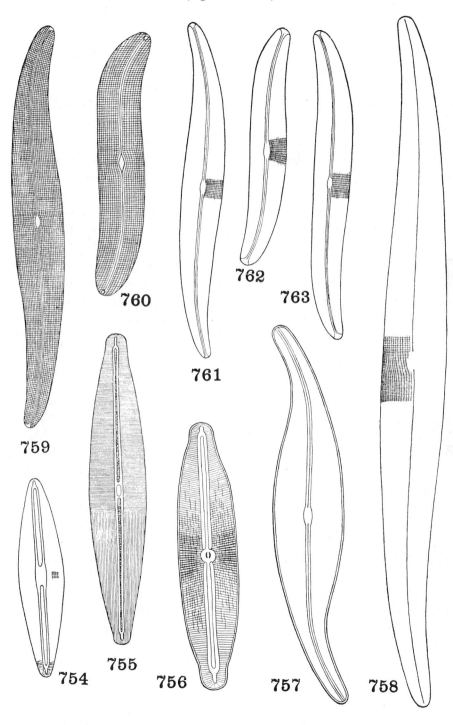

759

760

762

763

761

754

755

756

757

758

KEY TO THE SPECIES

1. Valves with straight to convex sides.. 2
1. Valves with undulate margins.. 4
  2. Smooth central area broad and band-like.................... 1. C. bacillum
  2. Smooth central area not broad and band-like............................. 3
3. Central area widened on one side only........................ 2. C. bacillaris
3. Central area regularly widened.............................. 3. C. alpestris
  4. Margins with three pronounced inflations*................. 4. C. trinodis
  4. Margins with three moderate inflations*.................... 5. C. silicula

1. *Caloneis bacillum* (Grunow) Mereschkowsky. [*C. fasciata* (Lagerstedt) Cleve]. Cells 4–9 × 15–45 μ; valves linear to linear-lanceolate, with straight or slightly convex sides and broadly rounded ends; transverse striations 22–28 in 10 μ, crossed by a fine longitudinal line near each valve margin; central area band-like; raphe straight. Pl. **65**, fig. **748.**

2. *Caloneis bacillaris* (Gregory) Cleve. Cells 5–6 × 25–50 μ; valves linear with straight sides, rounded ends, and with transverse striations 23–30 in 10 μ; central area mostly on one side; raphe straight; longitudinal lines, near margin, distinct. Pl. **65**, fig. **742.**

3. *Caloneis alpestris* (Grunow) Cleve. Cells 6–15 × 45–92 μ; valves linear-elliptic, with slightly convex sides and rounded ends, transverse striations somewhat radial, 20–24 in 10 μ; central area small, roundish, central nodule with crescent structures; raphe straight; longitudinal lines distinct. Pl. **65**, fig. **741.**

4. *Caloneis trinodis* (Lewis) Boyer. Cells 7–15 × 22–57 μ; valves linear with three nodal marginal inflations and usually with cuneate ends; axial area narrow; central area elliptic with a lunate marking on each side; transverse striations radiate in the middle, parallel elsewhere, 18–20 in 10 μ; marginal longitudinal lines indistinct. Pl. **79**, fig. **919.**

5. *Caloneis silicula* (Ehrenberg) Cleve. (*C. silicula* var. *genuina* Cleve). Cells 6–20 × 25–120 μ; valves linear to linear-lanceolate, with three gently rounded marginal inflations on each side; transverse striations somewhat radial, 16–20 in 10 μ, crossed near the margin by an evident, though fine, longitudinal line; raphe straight; central area a median expansion of the relatively wide axial area. Pl. **65**, fig. **743.**

  a. Var. *alpina* Cleve. Small form with cells 20–30 (–40) μ long, valves prominently trinodal, axial area very narrow. Pl. **65**, fig. **747.**

  b. Var. *gibberula* (Kuetzing) Cleve. Cells with three rounded inflations in valve view, poles cuneate. Pl. **65**, fig. **746.**

---

* Varieties of *C. silicula* may be sought here.

c. Var. *inflata* (Grunow) Cleve. Valves long-elliptic, with rounded median inflation. Pl. **65,** fig. **744.**

d. Var. *undulata* (Grunow) Cleve. Valves elliptic, margins undulate, central area broadly rounded. Pl. **65,** fig. **745.**

Diploneis Ehrenberg 1844

Cells solitary, rectangular in girdle view; valves usually elliptic, sometimes linear or with a median constriction; central nodule transversely quadrate, prolonged toward the poles into horns which enclose the straight raphe; a longitudinal furrow on each side of the horns and central nodule; transverse costae or rows of punctae, sometimes somewhat radial, often crossed by longitudinal costae or rows of punctae; chromatophores two, longitudinally incised or not.

KEY TO THE SPECIES

1. Transverse costae 9–13 in 10 μ; longitudinal costae evident..........1. D. elliptica
1. Transverse costae 14–18 in 10 μ; longitudinal costae faint............2. D. puella

1. *Diploneis elliptica* (Kuetzing) Cleve. Cells 10–30 $\times$ 20–65 μ; valves broadly elliptic, with large roundly quadrate central nodule with distinct horns, furrow slender, medianly somewhat widened; transverse costae somewhat radial, 9–13 in 10 μ, crossed by numerous irregular longitudinal costae, forming areolae 9–14 in 10 μ. Pl. **65,** fig. **752.**

2. *Diploneis puella* (Schumann) Cleve. Cells 6–14 $\times$ 13–27 μ; valves elliptic, central area large and four-sided, horns evident, furrow very narrow; transverse costae delicate, somewhat radial, 14–18 in 10 μ, with intermediate spaces very finely punctate; longitudinal costae indistinct. Pl. **65,** fig. **751.**

Mastogloia Thwaites 1856

Cells solitary or in gelatinous tubes, often in formless gelatinous envelopes, rectangular in girdle view, internal septation fusiform and chambered; valves lanceolate, elliptic or rhombic, poles broadly rounded, acute or rostrate; with two internal septa, each with a central oval chamber and several linear perforations; narrow axial field with small central and polar nodules and straight raphe, transversely striated; chromatophores two, with extensive lateral projections.

Auxospores formed in pairs by the conjugation of two cells.

KEY TO THE SPECIES

1. Valves slightly or not rostrate.. 2
1. Valves evidently rostrate............................. 1a. M. smithii var. amphicephala

2. Striations 18–20 in 10 μ............................. 1. M. smithii
2. Striations 15–18 in 10 μ............................. 1b. M. smithii var. lacustris

1. *Mastogloia smithii* Thwaites. Cells 8–16 × 20–65 μ; valves elliptic-lanceolate, with transverse striations fine, 18–20 in 10 μ, slightly radial, axial area narrow and linear, raphe straight; rectangular to quadrate chambers of internal septa 6–8 in 10 μ. Pl. **68**, fig. **792**.

a. Var. *amphicephala* Grunow. Valves elliptic with pronounced rostrate ends. Pl. **68**, fig. **793**.

b. Var. *lacustris* Grunow. Valves linear to elliptic-lanceolate, with slightly rostrate ends; striations 15–18 in 10 μ; central area large, not symmetric. Pl. **68**, fig. **794**.

Navicula Bory 1822; emend. Cleve 1894

Cells generally solitary and free-floating, sometimes aggregated into irregularly radiating clusters, rectangular in girdle view, with smooth girdles and without intercalary bands; valves elongate, usually attenuated toward capitate, rounded or rostrate poles; axial field narrow with distinct, straight raphe and polar and central expansions, nodules small; transverse striations, sometimes somewhat medianly radial; two laminate chromatophores, rarely four to eight, infrequently with one or more pyrenoids.

Auxospores formed in pairs by the fusion of two gametes from each of two approximated cells.

FIG. 764.—*Navicula anglica* Ralfs.

FIG. 765.—*Navicula bacillum* Ehrenberg.

FIG. 766.—*Navicula confervacea* (Kuetzing) Grunow.

FIG. 767.—*Navicula cryptocephala* Kuetzing.

FIG. 768.—*Navicula dicephala* (Ehrenberg) Wm. Smith.

FIG. 769.—*Navicula dicephala* var. *elginensis* (Gregory) Cleve.

FIG. 770.—*Navicula exigua* (Gregory) Mueller.

FIG. 771.—*Navicula reinhardtii* (Grunow) Van Heurck.

FIG. 772.—*Navicula gracilis* Ehrenberg.

FIG. 773.—*Navicula mutica* Kuetzing.

FIG. 774.—*Navicula platystoma* Ehrenberg.

FIG. 775.—*Navicula protracta* (Grunow) Cleve.

FIG. 776.—*Navicula pupula* Kuetzing.

FIG. 777.—*Navicula seminulum* Grunow.

FIG. 778.—*Navicula scutelloides* Wm. Smith.

FIG. 779.—*Navicula tuscula* (Ehrenberg) Grunow.

FIG. 780.—*Navicula radiosa* Kuetzing.

FIG. 781.—*Navicula radiosa* var. *tenella* (Brébisson) Grunow.

FIG. 782.—*Navicula rhyncocephala* Kuetzing.

FIG. 783.—*Navicula salinarum* Grunow.

FIG. 784.—*Navicula salinarum* var. *intermedia* (Grunow) Cleve.

FIG. 785.—*Navicula viridula* Kuetzing.

FIG. 786.—*Navicula gastrum* Ehrenberg.

FIG. 787.—*Navicula oblonga* Kuetzing.

FIG. 788.—*Navicula oblonga* var. *subcapitata* Pantocsek.

(Figs. 764–768, 770–780, 782, 783, 785, 787, 788, Hustedt; fig. 769, Gregory; figs. 781, 784, Meister; fig. 786, Van Heurck. Figs. 787, 788 ×*500;* all others ×*1000*.)

PLATE 67

(Figs. 764 to 788)

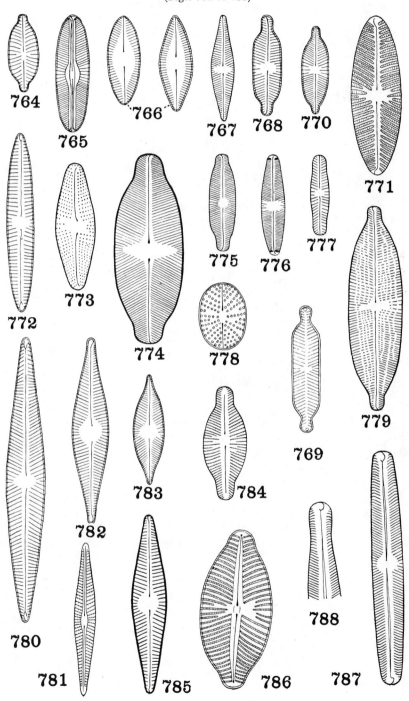

764
765
766
767
768
770
771
772
773
774
775
776
777
778
769
779
780
782
781
783
784
785
786
788
787

KEY TO THE SPECIES

1. Transverse striae punctate... 2
1. Transverse striae cross-lined... 10
   2. Longitudinal striations parallel to middle line of valve................... 3
   2. Longitudinal striations more or less undulate........................... 4
3. Valves gradually attenuated, poles rounded............ 1. N. cuspidata
3. Valves with rostrate or nearly capitate ends............. 1a. N. c. var. am-
                                            bigua
   4. Transverse striations evidently punctate............ 2. N. scutelloides
   4. Transverse striations faintly punctate.................................. 5
5. Polar nodules with strongly widened pattern........................... 6
5. Polar nodules not of striking pattern................................... 7
   6. Valves 10–20 μ wide, linear...................... 3. N. bacillum
   6. Valves 7–10 μ wide, lanceolate.................... 4. N. pupula
7. Valves with broadly rostrate ends.................... 5. N. protracta
7. Valves not rostrate.. 8
   8. Axial area narrow.. 9
   8. Axial area broad, somewhat lanceolate.............. 6. N. confervacea
9. Central area with a single isolated puncta.............. 7. N. mutica
9. Central area without an isolated puncta............... 8. N. seminulum
   10. Transverse striations interrupted by longitudinal hya-
       line lines....................................... 9. N. tuscula
   10. Transverse striations without such lines............................ 11
11. Striations bent in polar area....................... 10. N. oblonga
11. Striations not bent.. 12
   12. Striations at valve end convergent or parallel........................ 13
   12. Striations at valve end radial....................................... 18
13. Median striations alternately long and short........... 11. N. salinarum
13. Median striations not alternately long and short...................... 14
   14. Central area circular... 15
   14. Central area not circular.. 16
15. Valves with blunt and broad ends................... 12. N. viridula
15. Valves with slender, somewhat capitate ends........... 13. N. rhyncocephala
   16. Valves with slender, capitate ends................ 14. N. cryptocephala
   16. Valves not thus attenuated.. 17
17. Valves with gradually attenuated sides............... 15. N. radiosa
17. Valves with nearly parallel sides.................... 16. N. gracilis

FIG. 789.—*Navicula cuspidata* Kuetzing.
FIG. 790.—*Navicula cuspidata* var. *am-bigua* (Ehrenberg) Cleve.
FIG. 791.—*Pleurosigma angulatum* (Quekett) Wm. Smith.
FIG. 792.—*Mastogloia smithii* Thwaites.
FIG. 793.—*Mastogloia smithii* var. *amphicephala* Grunow.

FIG. 794.—*Mastogloia smithii* var. *lacustris* Grunow.
FIG. 795.—*Pinnularia major* (Kuetzing) Wm. Smith.

(All from Hustedt. Figs. 789–790, 795 ×800; figs. 792–794 ×1500.)

PLATE 68

(Figs. 789 to 795)

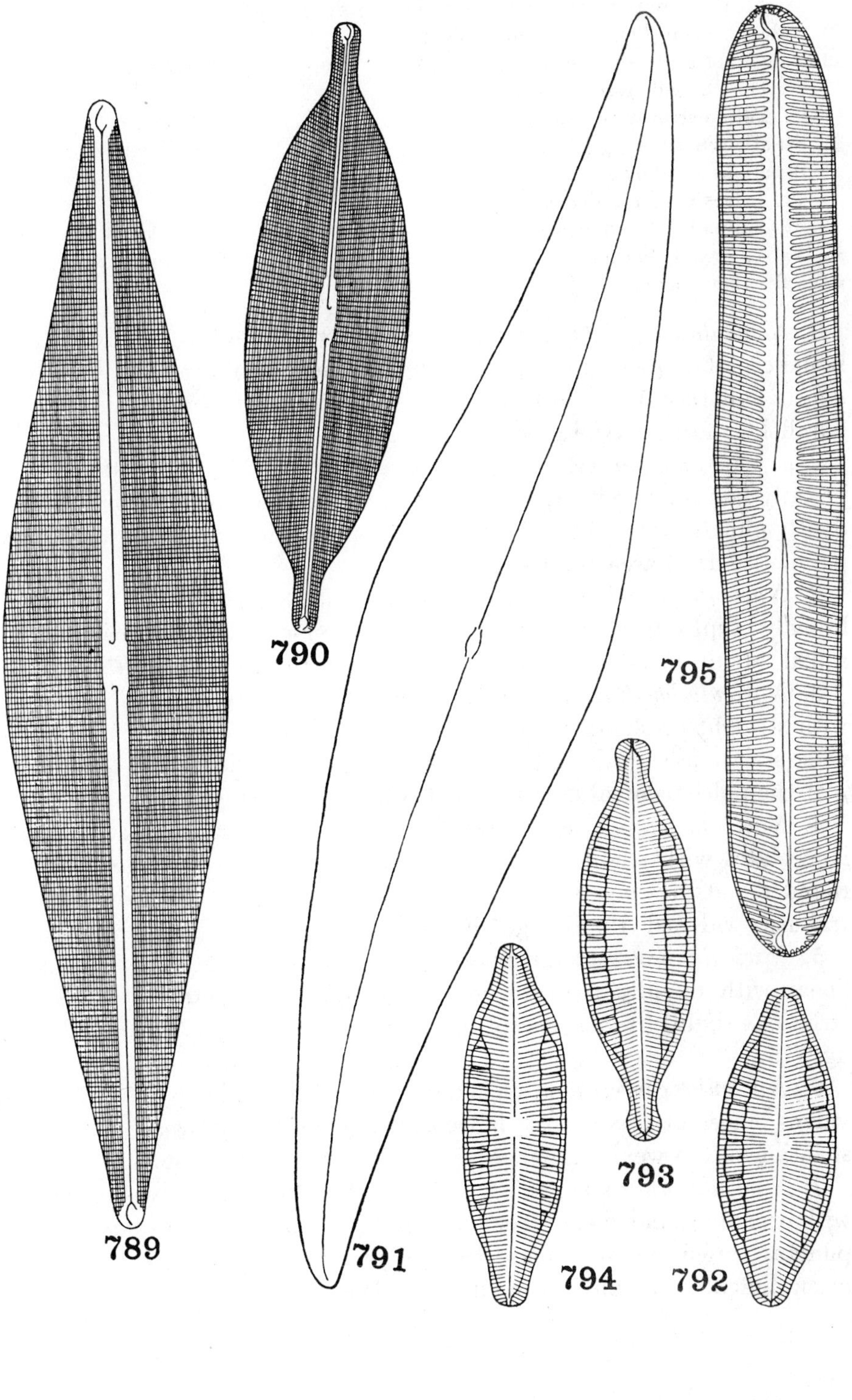

789

790

791

792

793

794

795

18. Median striations alternately long and short......................... 19
18. Median striations not alternately long and short..................... 22
19. Valves evidently rostrate at the ends................................. 20
19. Valves not evidently rostrate at the ends............. 17. N. reinhardtii
20. Poles broadly rostrate... 21
20. Poles narrowly rostrate......................... 18. N. exigua
21. Striations 8–10 in 10 μ........................... 19. N. gastrum
21. Striations about 17 in 10 μ......................... 20. N. platystoma
22. Valves 8–14 μ in diameter.. 23
22. Valves 15–20 μ in diameter...................... 20. N. platystoma
23. Valves broadly linear............................ 21. N. dicephala
23. Valves lanceolate................................ 22. N. anglica

1. *Navicula cuspidata* Kuetzing. Cells 17–37 × 50–170 μ; valves rhombo-lanceolate, tapering sharply to rounded ends, transverse striations, evidently punctate, 11–19 in 10 μ; longitudinal striations about 25 in 10 μ and parallel to narrow axial area. Pl. **68,** fig. **789.**

a. Var. *ambigua* (Ehrenberg) Cleve. Cells 15–33 × 45–100 μ; valves broadly lanceolate with rostrate-capitate ends; transverse striations, evidently punctate, 17–19 in 10 μ; longitudinal striations about 24 in 10 μ and parallel to axial area. Pl. **68,** fig. **790.**

2. *Navicula scutelloides* Wm. Smith. Cells 8–20 × 10–30 μ; valves broadly elliptic to nearly round, with transverse striations conspicuously radial, about 10 in 10 μ, and punctae about 10 in 10 μ. Pl. **67,** fig. **778.**

3. *Navicula bacillum* Ehrenberg. Cells 10–20 × 30–80 μ; valves linear, with straight or slightly convex sides and broadly rounded ends; transverse striations slightly radial, 12–14 in 10 μ at the middle and 18–20 in 10 μ at the poles; central area rounded. Pl. **67,** fig. **765.**

4. *Navicula pupula* Kuetzing. Cells 7–10 × 20–40 μ; valves linear-lanceolate, with slight median expansion and gradually attenuated to rounded ends; transverse striations radial, 22–26 in 10 μ, rectangular central area widened. Pl. **67,** fig. **776.**

5. *Navicula protracta* (Grunow) Cleve. Cells 7–10 × 20–35 μ; valves linear with broadly rostrate ends, axial area very narrow; transverse striations slightly radial except at the extremities, 18–22 in 10 μ. Pl. **67,** fig. **775.**

6. *Navicula confervacea* (Kuetzing) Grunow. Cells 6–8 × 17–25 μ; valves lanceolate, axial area lanceolate and medianly broad; transverse striations often weak, radial, 20–22 in 10 μ. Pl. **67,** fig. **766.**

7. *Navicula mutica* Kuetzing. Cells 7–12 × 10–40 μ; valves lanceolate with broadly rounded ends, central area rectangular, with a single isolated puncta; transverse striations strongly punctate, radial, 15–20 in 10 μ, often difficultly visible in the middle of the valve. Pl. **67,** fig. **773.**

8. *Navicula seminulum* Grunow. Cells 4–5 × 11–16 μ; valves linear-elliptic, with slight median expansion and broadly rounded poles; transverse striations radial, 18–20 in 10 μ. Pl. **67,** fig. **777.**

9. *Navicula tuscula* (Ehrenberg) Grunow. Cells 7–22 × 12–70 μ; valves elliptic, with more or less rostrate-capitate ends, linear and narrow axial area; transverse striations radial, interrupted by longitudinal hyaline lines, 10–14 in 10 μ. Pl. **67,** fig. **779.**

10. *Navicula oblonga* Kuetzing. Cells 13–24 × 70–220 μ; valves linear-lanceolate with broadly rounded ends; transverse striations in polar and subpolar area bent, generally radial, 6–8 in 10 μ; central area large, round. Pl. **67,** fig. **787.**

a. Var. *subcapitata* Pantocsek. Valves with evidently capitate ends. Pl. **67,** fig. **788.**

11. *Navicula salinarum* Grunow. Cells 8–12 × 23–41 μ; valves lanceolate with more or less rostrate, often lightly capitate ends, central area round; transverse striations, medianly alternately long and short, radial, 14–16 in 10 μ. Pl. **67,** fig. **783.**

a. Var. *intermedia* (Grunow) Cleve. Valves lanceolate with broadly rostrate ends, weakly capitate, 7–8 × 35–40 μ; transverse striations 14–18 in 10 μ, alternating long and short and strongly radial in the middle. Pl. **67,** fig. **784.**

12. *Navicula viridula* Kuetzing. Cells 10–15 × 40–80 μ; valves linear-lanceolate with bluntly and broadly rounded ends, central area round; transverse striations, radial in the middle, lightly convergent at the poles, about 10 in 10 μ. Pl. **67,** fig. **785.**

13. *Navicula rhyncocephala* Kuetzing. Cells 10–13 × 35–60 μ; valves lanceolate with slender, slightly capitate ends; central area round; transverse striations, medianly radial, polarly convergent, 10–12 in 10 μ. Pl. **67,** fig. **782.**

14. *Navicula cryptocephala* Kuetzing. Cells 5–7 × 20–40 μ; valves lanceolate with slender, somewhat capitate ends, central area elongated transversely; striations, medianly radial and polarly convergent, 16–18 in 10 μ, lines fine. Pl. **67,** fig. **767.**

15. *Navicula radiosa* Kuetzing. Cells 10–19 × 40–120 μ; valves lanceolate, gradually tapering to more or less pointed ends; transverse striations radial, except at the ends, 10–12 in 10 μ. Pl. **67,** fig. **780.**

a. Var. *tenella* (Brébisson) Grunow. Smaller and narrower, cells 5–6 × 25–65 μ; striations 15–18 in 10 μ. Pl. **67,** fig. **781.**

16. *Navicula gracilis* Ehrenberg. Cells 6–10 × 36–60 μ; valves linear with nearly parallel sides and cuneately rounded ends, central area rec-

tangular; transverse striations, only slightly radial in the middle, 11–12 in 10 μ. Pl. **67,** fig. **772.**

17. *Navicula reinhardtii* (Grunow) Van Heurck. Cells 14–20 × 35–70 μ; valves elliptic to elliptic-lanceolate gradually tapering to blunt ends, axial area linear and sharply defined, central area broad and irregularly defined; transverse striations radial, alternately long and short in the middle of the valve, 7–9 in 10 μ, noticeably lined. Pl. **67,** fig. **771.**

18. *Navicula exigua* (Gregory) Mueller. Cells 7–15 × 16–35 μ; valves elliptic-lanceolate with rostrate, sometimes slightly capitate, ends; central area transversely widened, irregular; transverse striations radial, 12–14 in 10 μ, medianly alternately long and short. Pl. **67,** fig. **770.**

19. *Navicula gastrum* Ehrenberg. Cells 12–20 × 25–60 μ; valves broadly elliptic with short rostrate and broadly rounded ends; central area widened, irregular; transverse striations radial, 8–10 in 10 μ, medianly alternately long and short. Pl. **67,** fig. **786.**

20. *Navicula platystoma* Ehrenberg. Cells 15–20 × 37–50 μ; valves elliptic-lanceolate with broadly and bluntly rostrate ends; central area widened, rhombo-elliptic; transverse striations radial, 16–18 in 10 μ at the center, about 25 in 10 μ at the ends. Pl. **67,** fig. **774.**

21. *Navicula dicephala* (Ehrenberg) Wm. Smith. Cells 8–13 × 20–40 μ; valves broadly linear to linear-lanceolate with ends abruptly rostrate and somewhat capitate; transverse striations radial, 9–11 in 10 μ; central area rectangular. Pl 67, fig. **768.**

a. Var. *elginensis* (Gregory) Cleve. Cells up to 50 μ long; valves with nearly parallel sides; transverse striations slightly radial or inclined, 10–12 in 10 μ; central area compressed-elliptic. Pl. **67,** fig. **769.**

22. *Navicula anglica* Ralfs. Cells 8–14 × 20–40 μ; valves elliptic with short rostrate and slightly capitate ends; transverse striations radial, 9–12 in 10 μ, shortened on either side of the rounded central area. Pl. **67,** fig. **764.**

Pinnularia Ehrenberg 1840

Cells solitary and free-floating, rarely in short filaments, symmetric, rectangular in girdle view, girdles smooth, intercalary bands absent; valves usually with straight sides, sometimes medianly inflated or undulate, generally with broadly rounded poles; axial field usually broad, expanded both polarly and medianly, with complicated straight or sigmoid raphe; costae, with internal openings, smooth, radial or transverse (convergent at the poles), with two longitudinal lines visible in the costate part of the valve; chromatophores two, laminate, usually with pyrenoids.

KEY TO THE SPECIES

1. Axial area linear-elliptic, wide.. 2
1. Axial area linear-lanceolate, narrow or moderately wide.................... 4
   2. Valves capitate at poles........................ 1. P. parva
   2. Valves not capitate at the poles............................ 3
3. Valves with broadly rounded poles................. 2. P. brevicostata var.
                                        leptostauron
3. Valves with cuneate poles......................... 3. P. hemiptera
   4. Raphe usually filiform, longitudinal lines faint......................... 5
   4. Raphe usually wider, longitudinal lines evident....................... 14
5. Valves usually constricted, with capitate poles........................ 6
5. Valves usually not constricted, without capitate poles.................... 11
   6. Valves with three marginal inflations............. 4. P. mesolepta
   6. Valves not undulate.. 7
7. Valves lanceolate... 8
7. Valves linear... 10
   8. Valves 4–6 × 18–36 μ......................... 5. P. appendiculata
   8. Valves 8–12 × 30–60 μ... 9
9. Transverse striae about 11–12 in 10 μ................ 6. P. braunii
9. Transverse striae about 15–16 in 10 μ................ 7. P. globiceps
   10. Valves with straight sides..................... 8. P. interrupta f. bi-
                                            capitata
   10. Valves with somewhat concave sides............ 9. P. termes
11. Valves linear... 12
11. Valves elliptic-lanceolate to linear-elliptic............................ 13
   12. Valves 7–13 × 50–140 μ........................ 10. P. gibba
   12. Valves 15–20 × 100–200 μ..................... 11. P. tabellaria
13. Valves 10–11 × 40–60 μ........................ 12. P. brebissonii
13. Valves 13–20 × 50–140 μ....................... 13. P. divergens
   14. Raphe simple, longitudinal band narrow........ 14. P. major
   14. Raphe complex, longitudinal band wide................. 15
15. Transverse striations usually 6 or more in 10 μ....... 15. P. viridis
15. Transverse striations usually 5 or less in 10 μ........................ 16
   16. Valves not medianly widened................. 16. P. cardinalis
   16. Valves medianly widened..................... 17. P. nobilis

1. *Pinnularia parva* Gregory. Cells 7–13 × 40–100 μ; valves linear, gradually tapering to obtuse, somewhat capitate ends; axial area broad; central area band-like, often extending to the margin; transverse striations, slightly radiate in the middle, convergent at the poles, sometimes bilaterally interrupted in the middle, 8–12 in 10 μ. Pl. **70**, fig. **813.**

2. *Pinnularia brevicostata* Cleve var. *leptostauron* Cleve. Cells 15–16 × 100–120 μ; valves linear, with parallel sides, broadly rounded ends, and wide lanceolate axial area; transverse striations parallel, 8–9 in 10 μ, absent in the middle of the valve. Pl. **69**, fig. **805.**

3. *Pinnularia hemiptera* (Kuetzing) Wm. Smith. Cells 11–15 × 40–80 μ; valves linear-elliptic, with lightly concave or straight sides, cuneate ends, and wide and linear (somewhat polarly lanceolate) axial area not widened in the center; raphe filiform, with central pore sometimes one-sided; transverse striations parallel, 8–10 in 10 μ. Pl. **69,** fig. **800.**

4. *Pinnularia mesolepta* (Ehrenberg) Wm. Smith. Cells 9–11 × 30–65 μ; valves linear, marginally trinodal, with constricted capitate ends; axial area lightly linear, with circular central area; transverse striations, radial in the center, convergent at the poles, 10–14 in 10 μ. Pl. **69,** fig. **799.**

5. *Pinnularia appendiculata* (Agardh) Cleve. Cells 4–6 × 18–36 μ; valves linear-lanceolate, with nearly straight sides scarcely tapering to broadly rounded ends; axial area narrow, slightly lanceolate in the middle, with transversely banded central area; transverse striations, somewhat radial in the middle and convergent at the poles, 16–18 in 10 μ. Pl. **69,** fig. **796.**

6. *Pinnularia braunnii* (Grunow) Cleve. Cells 8–12 × 30–60 μ; valves elliptic-lanceolate, constricted toward the capitate poles; axial area widely lanceolate, with a broadly banded central area; transverse striations short, medianly radial and polarly convergent, 11–12 in 10 μ. Pl. **69,** fig. **797.**

7. *Pinnularia globiceps* Gregory. Cells 8–10 × 30–40 μ; valves elliptic-lanceolate, with convex sides and broadly capitate poles; axial area narrow, with a wide-banded central area; transverse striations, medianly radial and polarly convergent, 15–18 in 10 μ. Pl. **69,** fig. **798.**

8. *Pinnularia interrupta* Wm. Smith forma *bicapitata* (Lagerstedt) Fritsch. Cells 8–12 × 20–60 μ; valves linear with straight sides and rostrate, capitate ends; axial area linear, with rhombic central area;

Fig. 796.—*Pinnularia appendiculata* (Agardh) Cleve.

Fig. 797.—*Pinnularia braunii* (Grunow) Cleve.

Fig. 798.—*Pinnularia globiceps* Gregory.

Fig. 799.—*Pinnularia mesolepta* (Ehrenberg) Wm. Smith.

Fig. 800.—*Pinnularia hemiptera* (Kuetzing) Wm. Smith.

Fig. 801.—*Pinnularia gibba* (Van Heurck) Boyer.

Fig. 802.—*Pinnularia brebissonii* (Kuetzing) Rabenhorst.

Fig. 803.—*Pinnularia interrupta* Wm. Smith f. *bicapitata* (Lagerstedt) Fritsch.

Fig. 804.—*Pinnularia divergens* Wm. Smith.

Fig. 805.—*Pinnularia brevicostata* Cleve var. *leptostauron* Cleve.

Fig. 806.—*Pinnularia nobilis* Ehrenberg.

Fig. 807.—*Pinnularia major* (Kuetzing) Wm. Smith var. *transversa* (A. Schmidt) Cleve.

Fig. 808.—*Pinnularia cardinalis* (Ehrenberg) Wm. Smith.

(Figs. 796–801, 804, 806, 808, Hustedt; figs. 802, 803, Van Heurck; fig. 805, Meister; fig. 807, Schmidt. Figs. 796–805 ×*1000;* figs. 806–808 ×*500.*)

PLATE 69

(Figs. 796 to 808)

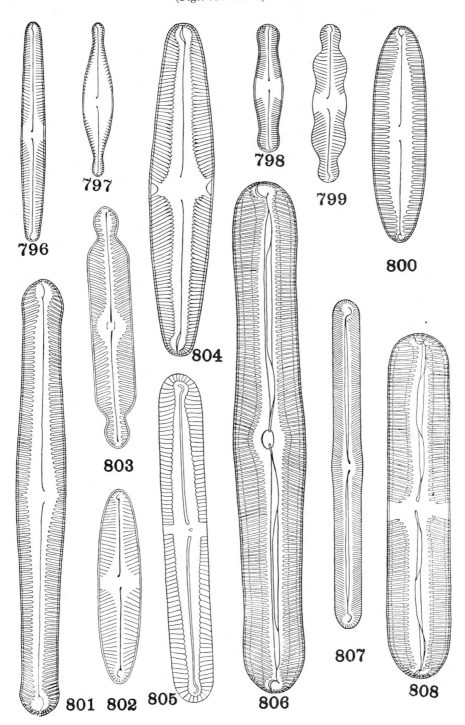

796 797 798 799 800 801 802 803 804 805 806 807 808

transverse striations, medianly radial and convergent toward the poles, 9–10 in 10 μ. Pl. **69,** fig. **803.**

9. *Pinnularia termes* Ehrenberg. Cells 12–13 $\times$ 17–76 μ; valves linear, with concave or nearly straight margins and rostrate-capitate ends; axial area narrow, central area band-like, subquadrate; striations medianly radiate and polarly convergent, 9–15 in 10 μ. Pl. **70,** fig. **812.**

10. *Pinnularia gibba* (Van Heurck) Boyer. Cells 7–13 $\times$ 50–140 μ; valves linear-lanceolate with lightly convex sides diminishing toward broad capitate to cuneate poles, with varyingly wide axial area and an elliptically banded central area; transverse striations radial in the middle, parallel toward the poles and convergent at the poles, 9–11 in 10 μ; a variable species. Pl. **69,** fig. **801.**

11. *Pinnularia tabellaria* Ehrenberg. Cells 15–20 $\times$ 100–200 μ; valves linear, broadest medianly and polarly, with broad and capitate ends; axial area narrow, central area rounded; striations medianly radial and polarly convergent, 12–15 in 10 μ. Pl. **70,** fig. **811.**

12. *Pinnularia brebissonii* (Kuetzing) Rabenhorst. Cells 10–11 $\times$ 40–60 μ; valves linear-elliptic with rounded ends; axial area narrow, central area a broad subquadrate band; striations medianly radiate, polarly convergent, 10–13 in 10 μ. Pl. **69,** fig. **802.**

13. *Pinnularia divergens* Wm. Smith. Cells 13–20 $\times$ 50–140 μ; valves elliptic-lanceolate, with convex sides and broadly rounded ends; axial area wide, central area extending to the margins and with a conical thickening at each extension; raphe somewhat undulate; transverse striations medianly radial and polarly convergent, 10–12 in 10 μ. Pl. **69,** fig. **804.**

14. *Pinnularia major* (Kuetzing) Wm. Smith. Cells 25–40 $\times$ 140–180 μ; valves with nearly straight sides, tapering apically to rounded poles; axial area about a third the diameter of the cell, widened in the middle; raphe broad, with a one-sided central pore; transverse striations medianly radial,

Fig. 809.—*Pinnularia viridis* (Nitzsch) Ehrenberg.

Fig. 810.—*Pinnularia viridis* var. *elliptica* Meister.

Fig. 811.—*Pinnularia tabellaria* Ehrenberg.

Fig. 812.—*Pinnularia termes* Ehrenberg.

Fig. 813.—*Pinnularia parva* Gregory.

Fig. 814.—*Neidium amphirhyncus* (Ehrenberg) Pfitzer.

Fig. 815.—*Neidium dubium* (Ehrenberg) Pfitzer.

Fig. 816.—*Neidium iridis* (Ehrenberg) Pfitzer.

Fig. 817.—*Neidium iridis* var. *firma* (Kuetzing) Van Heurck.

Fig. 818.—*Neidium amphigomphus* (Ehrenberg) Pfitzer.

(Figs. 810, 811, 813, Meister; fig. 812, Boyer; fig. 814, Van Heurck; figs. 815, 816, Hustedt; fig. 817, Dippel. Fig. 811 $\times 750$; all others $\times 1000$.)

PLATE 70

(Figs. 809 to 818)

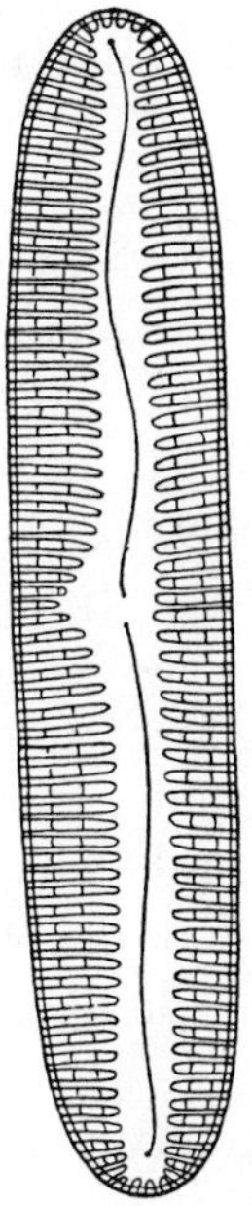

809

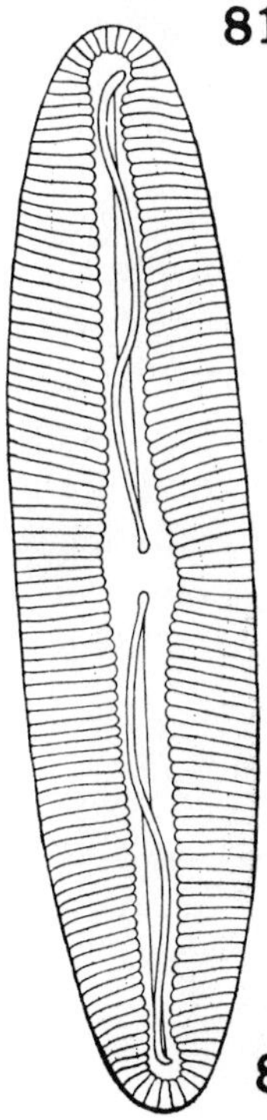

810

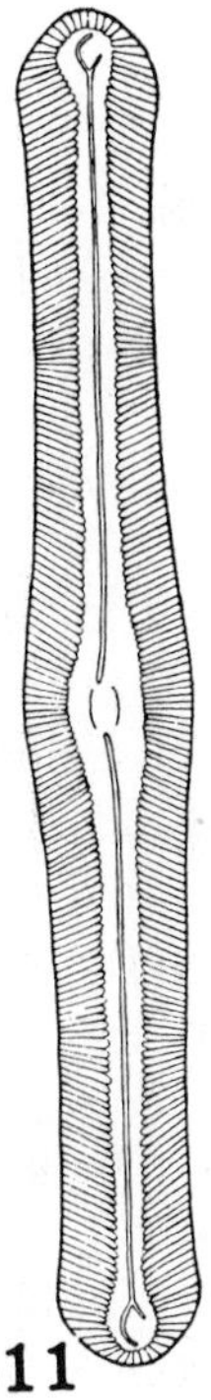

811

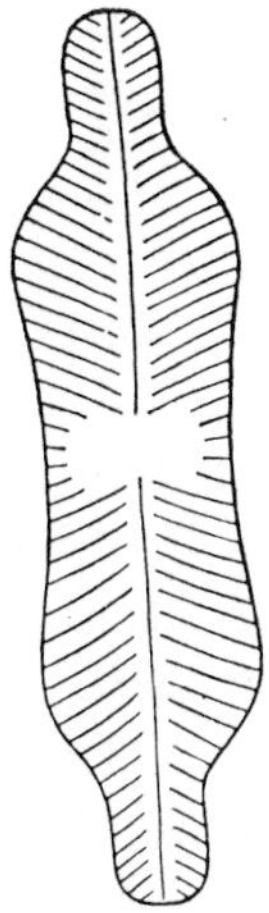

812

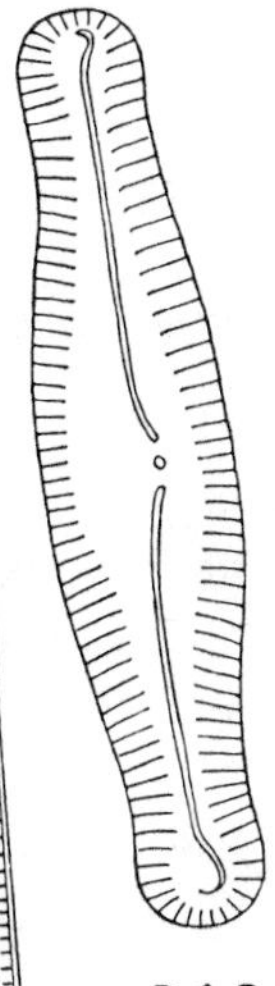

813

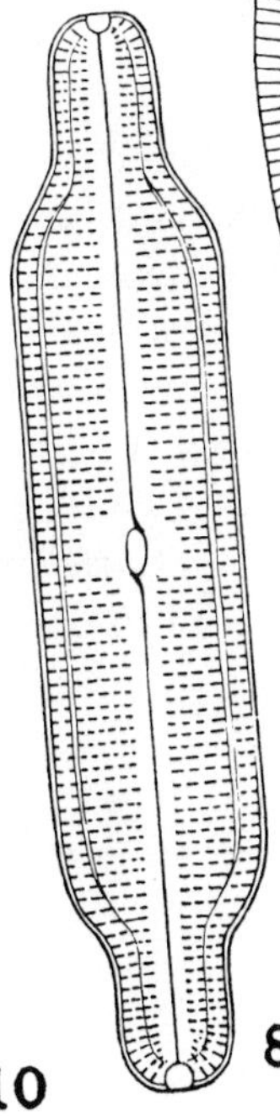

814

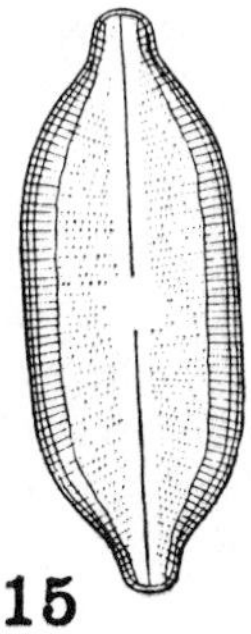

815

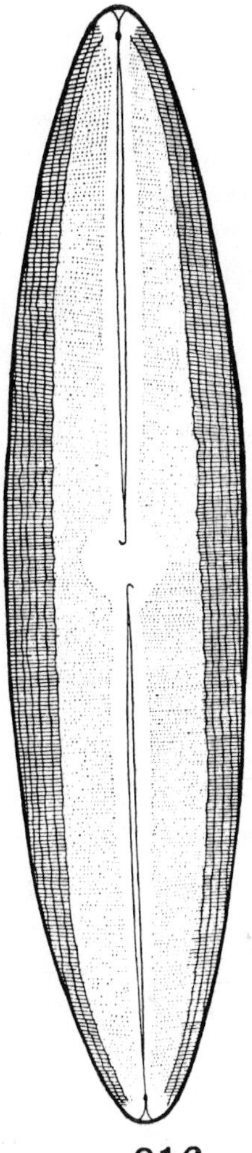

816

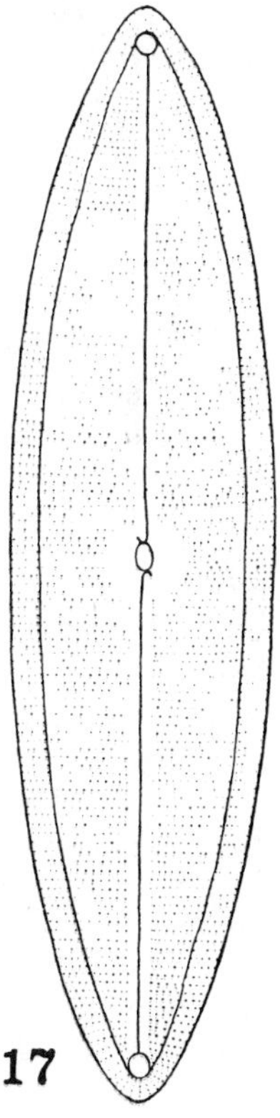

817

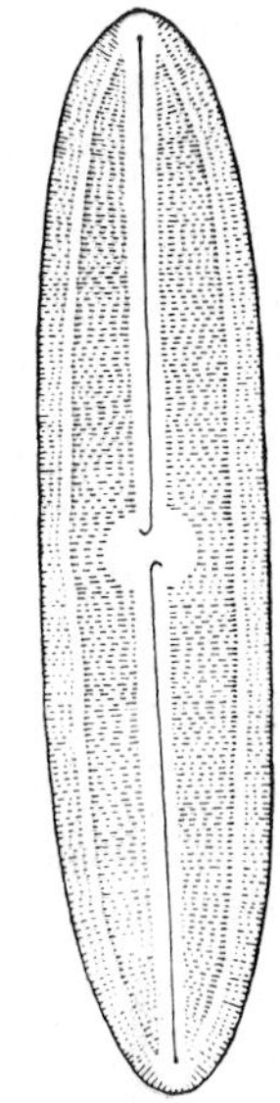

818

polarly convergent, 5–7 in 10 μ, crossed by a narrow longitudinal band. Pl. **68,** fig. **795.**

a. Var. *transversa* (Schmidt) Cleve. Valves slender, raphe oblique, striations 8–9 in 10 μ. Pl. **69,** fig. **807.**

15. *Pinnularia viridis* (Nitzsch) Ehrenberg. Cells 10–30 $\times$ 50–130 μ; valves linear to elliptic-linear with lightly convex sides and broadly rounded ends; axial area usually less than a fourth the cell diameter, widened centrally; raphe complex, somewhat undulate, and with a one-sided central pore; transverse striations medianly lightly radial, polarly convergent, 6–9 in 10 μ, crossed by a wide longitudinal band. Pl. **70,** fig. **809.**

a. Var. *elliptica* Meister. Valves elliptic, 17–22 $\times$ 70–130 μ; transverse striations 8–9 in 10 μ. Pl. **70,** fig. **810.**

16. *Pinnularia cardinalis* (Ehrenberg) Wm. Smith. Cells 30–45 $\times$ 150–320 μ; valves with nearly parallel sides and broadly rounded ends; axial area wide, central area transversely widened to the margins; raphe complex, with undulate outer groove; transverse striations, radial in the middle, convergent at the ends, about 5 in 10 μ, crossed by a wide longitudinal band. Pl. **69,** fig. **808.**

17. *Pinnularia nobilis* Ehrenberg. Cells 34–50 $\times$ 200–350 μ; valves linear, a little wider at the rounded poles; axial area about a third of the cell diameter, with rounded central area; raphe complex, undulate; transverse striations, medianly radial, polarly convergent, 4–5 in 10 μ, crossed by a wide longitudinal band. Pl. **69,** fig. **806.**

Neidium Pfitzer 1871

Cells usually solitary and free-floating, rectangular in girdle view and without girdle bands; valve-view linear, somewhat lanceolate, elliptic, or irregularly undulate with poles acute, rounded, nearly capitate or rostrate; axial field usually narrow, with a rounded or oval central area; raphe straight, usually bifurcated at the poles, with central ends facing in opposite directions; transverse rows of punctae crossed near the valve margin by narrow longitudinal clear spaces or furrows; two longitudinally incised chromatophores (often appearing as four), each with a pyrenoid.

Two auxospores formed by the conjugation of two approximated cells.

KEY TO THE SPECIES

1. Valves with regularly convex sides...................... 1. N. iridis
1. Valves with polar constrictions or with undulations.......................... 2
    2. Valves with triundulate margins.................... 2. N. hitchcockii
    2. Valves without triundulate margins....................................... 3
3. Cells usually under 45 μ long.......................... 3. N. dubium
3. Cells usually over 45 μ long.. 4

4. Poles of valves wedge-shaped...................... 4. N. amphigomphus
4. Poles of valves rostrate-capitate....................................... 5
5. Valves linear....................................... 5. N. amphirhyncus
5. Valves linear-elliptic............................... 6. N. productum

1. *Neidium iridis* (Ehrenberg) Pfitzer. Cells 15–30 × 45–200 μ; valves linear-lanceolate to linear-elliptic, with regularly convex sides terminating in round poles; axial area narrow, widened between the poles and the center; central area somewhat elliptic; striations evidently punctate, crossed near the margins by parallel or sometimes irregular longitudinal furrows, 22–29 in 10 μ. Pl. **70**, fig. **816**.

a. Var. *firma* (Kuetzing) Van Heurck. Valves broadly linear-elliptic, with gradually reduced, sharply rounded ends, 23–24 × 60–100 μ. Pl. **70**, fig. **817**.

2. *Neidium hitchcockii* (Ehrenberg) Cleve. Cells 25–30 × 50–100 μ; valves linear, with triundulate margins and cuneate subacute ends; axial area narrow; central area small, rounded; striations varyingly oblique, about 20 in 10 μ. Pl. **71**, fig. **819**.

3. *Neidium dubium* (Ehrenberg) Pfitzer. Cells 10–16 × 30–46 μ; valves linear with slightly convex sides and cuneate, somewhat pointed ends; raphe straight; axial area narrow and nearly linear; central area small, rounded or roundly quadrate; striations somewhat radial, finely punctate, 18–24 in 10 μ, crossed by a longitudinal furrow. Pl. **70**, fig. **815**.

4. *Neidium amphigomphus* (Ehrenberg) Pfitzer. Cells 12–40 × 90–150 μ; valves broadly linear, with cuneate rounded ends; axial area narrow; central area small, quadrately oval; striations parallel, evidently punctate, 15–18 in 10 μ, crossed by longitudinal furrows near the margins. Pl. **70**, fig. **818**.

5. *Neidium amphirhyncus* (Ehrenberg) Pfitzer. Cells 5–20 × 50–100 μ; valves linear, with parallel sides and protracted rostrate-capitate ends; axial area narrow; central area quadrately elliptic; striations evidently punctate, 22–29 in 10 μ, with punctae often in evident longitudinal rows, and crossed by longitudinal furrow near margin. Pl. **70**, fig. **814**.

6. *Neidium productum* (Wm. Smith) Pfitzer. Cells 18–36 × 40–100 μ, valves broadly linear-elliptic with narrowed rostrate-capitate poles with rounded ends; raphe straight; axial area narrow, usually linear; central area elliptic, widened laterally; striations parallel, sometimes irregular at the center, evidently punctate, 16–18 in 10 μ, crossed by more or less parallel longitudinal furrows at varying distances from the margin. Pl. **71**, fig. **820**.

Stauroneis Ehrenberg 1843

Cells solitary or united valve to valve in short filaments, of the general shape of *Navicula*, sometimes with intercalary bands and longitudinal septa visible at the poles; valves with straight raphe having small polar nodules and a central nodule thickened and extended laterally to the margins (stauros); axial area narrow but conspicuous; striations slightly radiate and parallel, finely punctate, with more or less irregularly undulate longitudinal lines; two chromatophores, each with two to four pyrenoids. Auxospores formed in pairs between two conjugating cells.

KEY TO THE SPECIES

1. Cells joined into short filaments.......................... 1. S. acuta
1. Cells solitary... 2
    2. Valves with rounded or obtuse ends........................ 3
    2. Valves with rostrate to capitate ends..................... 4
3. Valves 6–8 μ wide.................................. 2. S. gracilis
3. Valves 16–53 μ wide.............................. 3. S. phoenicentron
    4. Raphe usually narrow..................................... 5
    4. Raphe usually wide.............................. 4. S. phyllodes
5. Striae coarsely punctate......................... 5. S. producta
5. Striae finely punctate............................ 6. S. anceps

1. *Stauroneis acuta* Wm. Smith. Cells 15–40 × 80–166 μ, joined at their valves into short filaments; valves rhombo-lanceolate, sometimes with a slight median inflation, rounded poles; raphe straight, moderately wide; axial area linear, broad stauros wider at the margins; polar septum extending inward a considerable distance; transverse striations radial, 12–16 in 10 μ, evidently punctate. Pl. **72**, fig. **829**.

2. *Stauroneis gracilis* Ehrenberg. Cells 6–8 × 70–100 μ, solitary, without polar septum; valves lanceolate, with obtuse ends; axial area narrow, distinct; stauros not extending to the margin; transverse striations about 27 in 10 μ. Pl. **71**, fig. **828**.

Fig. 819.—*Neidium hitchcockii* (Ehrenberg) Cleve.

Fig. 820.—*Neidium productum* (Wm. Smith) Pfitzer.

Fig. 821.—*Stauroneis phyllodes* Ehrenberg.

Fig. 822.—*Stauroneis anceps* Ehrenberg.

Fig. 823.—*Stauroneis anceps* var. *birostris* (Ehrenberg) Cleve.

Fig. 824.—*Stauroneis anceps* var. *linearis* (Grunow) Van Heurck.

Fig. 825.—*Stauroneis phoenicentron* (Nitzsch) Ehrenberg.

Fig. 826.—*Stauroneis phoenicentron* var. *amphilepta* (Ehrenberg) Cleve.

Fig. 827.—*Stauroneis producta* Grunow.

Fig. 828.—*Stauroneis gracilis* Ehrenberg.

(Figs. 819, 821, Schmidt; figs. 820, 822–825, Hustedt; fig. 826, Meister; fig. 827, Van Heurck; fig. 828, Boyer. All ×*1000*.)

PLATE 71

(Figs. 819 to 828)

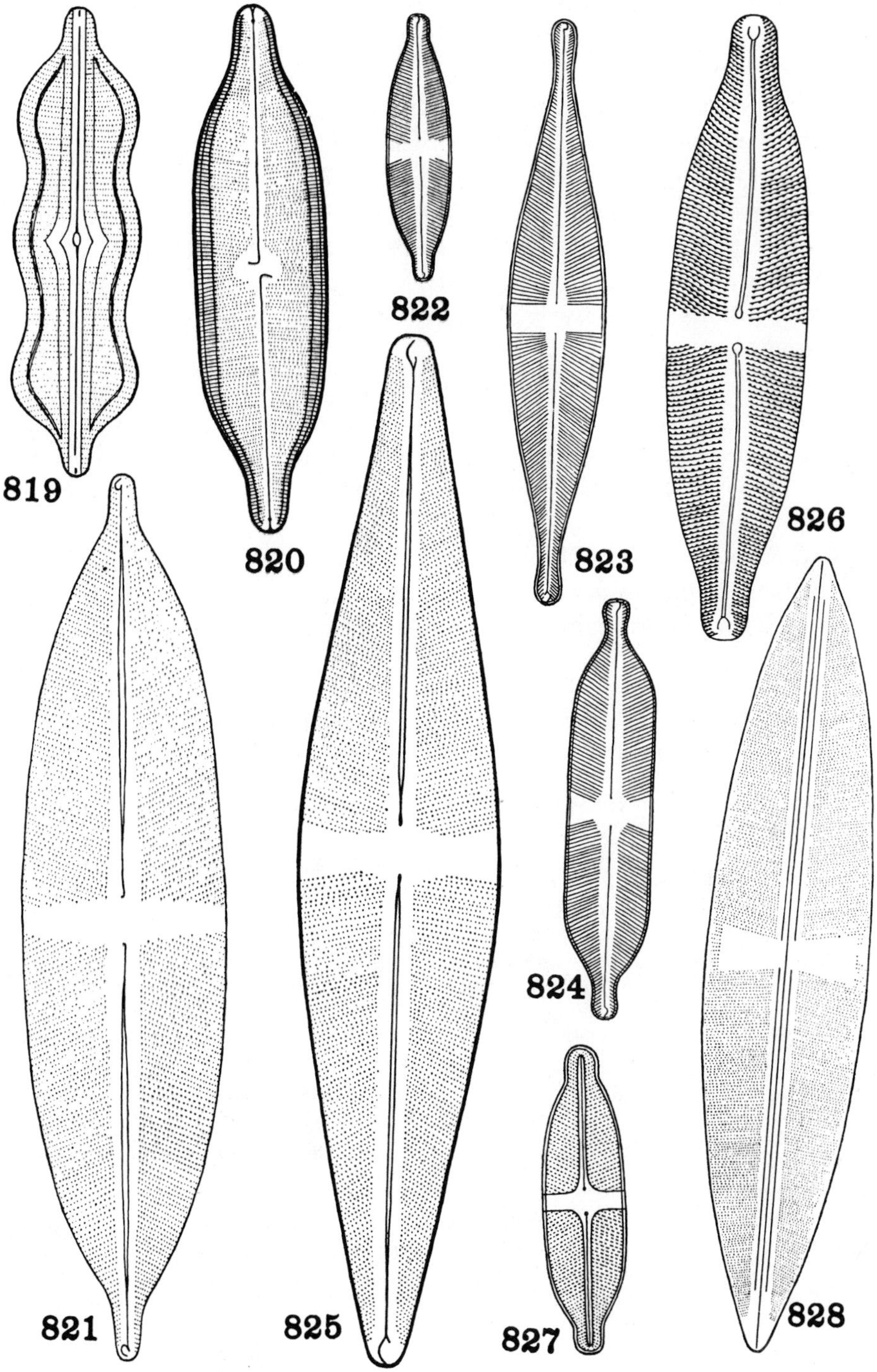

819

820

822

823

826

821

825

824

827

828

3. *Stauroneis phoenicentron* (Nitzsch) Ehrenberg. Cells 16–53 × 70–325 μ, solitary, without polar septum; valves lanceolate, with regularly attenuated rounded poles; raphe straight, wide; axial area broad, linear; stauros generally a linear band; transverse striations radial throughout, 12–20 in 10 μ, evidently punctate. Pl. **71**, fig. **825.**

a. Var. *amphilepta* (Ehrenberg) Cleve. Cells 15–20 × 70–100 μ; striations finely punctate, about 18 in 10 μ. Pl. **71**, fig. **826.**

4. *Stauroneis phyllodes* Ehrenberg. Cells 25–50 × 100–250 μ, solitary; valves broadly lanceolate, with rostrate ends; raphe straight, wide; axial area linear, broad; stauros generally an elliptically elongate band; transverse striations radial throughout, 10–14 in 10 μ, evidently punctate. Pl. **71**, fig. **821.**

5. *Stauroneis producta* Grunow. Cells 15–24 × 60–75 μ, solitary; valves elliptic to broadly lanceolate, with broadly rostrate to slightly capitate ends; raphe straight, narrow; axial area linear, broad; stauros a linear band; transverse striations radial, 10–13 in 10 μ, with elongate punctae. Pl. **71**, fig. **827.**

6. *Stauroneis anceps* Ehrenberg. Cells 6–18 × 25–130 μ, solitary, without polar septum; valves elliptic to linear-lanceolate, with rostrate to capitate ends; raphe straight, usually narrow; axial area narrow; stauros a

Fig. 829.—*Stauroneis acuta* Wm. Smith.

Fig. 830.—*Gomphonema acuminatum* Ehrenberg.

Fig. 831.—*Gomphonema acuminatum* var. *trigonocephalum* (Ehrenberg) Cleve.

Fig. 832.—*Gomphonema acuminatum* var. *laticeps* (Ehrenberg) A. Schmidt.

Fig. 833.—*Gomphonema acuminatum* var. *coronatum* (Ehrenberg) Rabenhorst.

Fig. 834.—*Gomphonema acuminatum* var. *elongatum* (Wm. Smith) Van Heurck.

Fig. 835.—*Gomphonema acuminatum* var. *turris* (Ehrenberg) Cleve.

Fig. 836.—*Gomphonema intricatum* Kuetzing.

Fig. 837.—*Gomphonema intricatum* var. *vibrio* (Ehrenberg) Cleve.

Fig. 838.—*Gomphonema parvulum* (Kuetzing) Grunow.

Fig. 839.—*Gomphonema constrictum* Ehrenberg.

Fig. 840.—*Gomphonema constrictum* var. *capitatum* (Ehrenberg) Grunow.

Fig. 841.—*Gomphonema constrictum* var. *capitatum* f. *turgidum* (Ehrenberg) A. Mayer.

Fig. 842.—*Gomphonema angustatum* (Kuetzing) Grunow.

Fig. 843.—*Gomphonema angustatum* var. *obtusatum* (Kuetzing) Van Heurck.

Figs. 844, 845.—*Gomphonema olivaceum* (Lyngbye) Kuetzing.

Fig. 846.—*Gomphonema olivaceum* var. *calcarea* Cleve.

Fig. 847.—*Gomphonema sphaerophorum* Ehrenberg.

Fig. 848.—*Gomphonema gracile* Ehrenberg var. *dichotoma* (Kuetzing) Grunow.

Fig. 849.—*Gomphonema semiapertum* Grunow.

(Figs. 829–831, 833, 835–840, 842, 844–847, Hustedt; fig. 832, Dippel; figs. 834, 841, Van Heurck; figs. 843, 848, Meister. Fig. 843 ×*1500;* all others ×*1000.*)

PLATE 72

(Figs. 829 to 849)

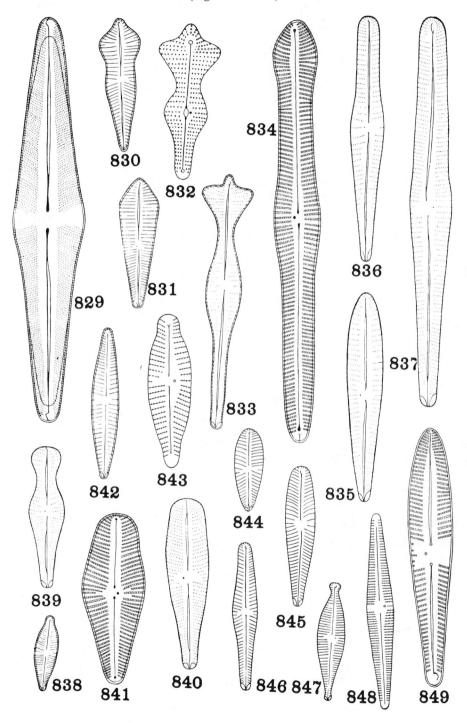

band, wider at the margins; transverse striations all radial, finely punctate, 20–30 in 10 μ. Pl. **71**, fig. **822**.

a. Var. *birostris* (Ehrenberg) Cleve. Valves lanceolate, with narrowly elongate, capitate poles. Pl. **71**, fig. **823**.

b. Var. *linearis* (Grunow) Van Heurck. Valves linear, with nearly parallel sides and rostrate-capitate ends, 8–12 $\times$ 45–50 μ. Pl. **71**, fig. **824**.

Gyrosigma Hassall 1845; emend. Cleve 1894

Cells solitary and free-floating, sometimes in gelatinous tubes, ellipticlanceolate in girdle view, intercalary bands and septa absent; valves sigmoid, usually gradually attenuate—sometimes narrowly so, rarely with nearly straight sides—to broadly rounded poles; raphe sigmoid, with small central and polar nodules; axial area narrow with small, usually rounded central area; transverse striations crossing longitudinal striations at right angles; two chromatophores, regularly or irregularly shaped plates, generally with several pyrenoids.

KEY TO THE SPECIES

1. Spacing of transverse and longitudinal striae equal............................ 2
1. Spacing of transverse striae finer than that of longitudinal
   striae... 1. G. attenuatum
1. Spacing of transverse striae coarser than that of longitudinal striae............ 3
   2. Valves 75–86 μ long... 2. G. wormleyi
   2. Valves 100–200 μ long... 3. G. acuminatum
3. Valves linear, with parallel sides.. 4. G. eximium
3. Valves lanceolate, evidently sigmoid.. 4
   4. Valves 5–10 μ in diameter... 5. G. scalproides
   4. Valves 12–25 μ in diameter.. 5
5. Valves only slightly attenuated.. 6. G. spencerii
5. Valves evidently attenuated... 7. G. kuetzingii

1. *Gyrosigma attenuatum* (Kuetzing) Cleve. Cells 23–26 $\times$ 150–240 μ; valves slightly sigmoid, lanceolate, gradually tapering to rounded poles; tranvserse striations perpendicular to the middle line, 14–16 in 10 μ; longitudinal striations with larger spacings, 10–12 in 10 μ. Pl. **66**, fig. **758**.

2. *Gyrosigma wormleyi* (Sullivant) Boyer. Cells 28–30 $\times$ 75–86 μ; valves lanceolate, strongly sigmoid, abruptly narrowed to produced, subacute ends; raphe sometimes excentric, usually sigmoid; transverse and longitudinal striations 21–23 in 10 μ. Pl. **66**, fig. **757**.

3. *Gyrosigma acuminatum* (Kuetzing) Cleve. Cells 15–20 $\times$ 100–200 μ; valves sigmoid, lanceolate, gradually attenuated to rounded poles; transverse and longitudinal striations about 18 in 10 μ, the former perpendicular to the middle line of the valve. Pl. **66**, fig. **759**.

4. *Gyrosigma eximium* (Thwaites) Boyer. Cells, in gelatinous tubes, 18–20 × 60–80 μ; valves linear, with obliquely rounded ends; raphe straight, slightly sigmoid at the poles; central area rounded; transverse striations 23–25 in 10 μ; longitudinal striations 27–28 in 10 μ. Pl. **66**, fig. **760.**

5. *Gyrosigma scalproides* (Rabenhorst) Cleve. Cells 5–10 × 25–70 μ; valves lanceolate, sigmoid, gradually attenuated to rounded poles; transverse striations, usually perpendicular to the middle line, sometimes medianly radial, 22–24 in 10 μ; longitudinal striations about 28–30 in 10 μ. Pl. **66**, fig. **762.**

6. *Gyrosigma spencerii* (Quekett) Cleve. Cells 12–25 × 70–220 μ; valves sigmoid, with narrowly rounded ends; transverse striations, parallel to the middle line, 17–22 in 10 μ; longitudinal striations 22–24 in 10 μ. Pl. **66**, fig. **763.**

7. *Gyrosigma kuetzingii* (Grunow) Cleve. Cells 12–15 × 80–120 μ; valves sigmoid, lanceolate, tapering to narrowly rounded ends; transverse striations, radial in the middle, perpendicular to the middle line elsewhere, 20–23 in 10 μ; longitudinal striations 24–26 in 10 μ. Pl. **66**, fig. **761.**

Pleurosigma Wm. Smith 1852; emend. Cleve 1894

Cells solitary, elliptic-lanceolate in girdle view, intercalary bands and septa usually absent; valves sigmoid, gradually tapering to rounded or subacute ends; raphe sigmoid, with small central and polar nodules; axial area narrow; central area usually round; striations in three series: one perpendicular to the middle line of the valve, the other two oblique to the middle line; chromatophores two, four, or many regular or irregular plates.

Two auxospores formed from the conjugation of two cells.

1. *Pleurosigma angulatum* (Quekett) Wm. Smith. Cells 36–50 × 150–360 μ; valves sigmoid, rhombo-lanceolate, medianly angular and polarly sharply rounded; central area small, rhombic; striations 18–22 in 10 μ; oblique striations at an angle of about 60° with the transverse. Pl. **68**, fig. **791.**

Family **Gomphonemataceae**

Cells usually epiphytic on the ends of branched gelatinous stalks or sessile, rarely solitary, longitudinally symmetric and transversely asymmetric; girdle view usually cuneate; valves straight, lanceolate or club-shaped, with one pole broader than the other or capitate; a single chromatophore; valves with true raphe.

Gomphonema C. A. Agardh 1824

Cells usually epiphytic on the ends of dichotomously branched gelatinous stalks, sometimes sessile, sometimes solitary and free-floating, transversely asymmetric in both girdle and valve views, cuneate in girdle view, girdles smooth without intercalary bands or septa; valves cuneate, clavate, lanceolate, or nearly straight, with one pole capitate or broader than the other; axial field narrow, straight, with a straight raphe and conspicuous central and polar nodules; striations strictly transverse or somewhat radial; central area, sometimes extending to the margins, with an asymmetrically placed dot (sometimes several dots); chromatophore a single, lobed plate, usually with a single pyrenoid.

Auxospores formed in pairs between two conjugating cells.

KEY TO THE SPECIES

1. Central area with a single dot... 2
1. Central area with two to four dots in a row............. 1. G. geminatum
1. Central area without such dots........................ 2. G. olivaceum
   2. Median striations alternately long and short.......... 3. G. constrictum
   2. Median striations frequently lacking.. 3
   2. Median striations otherwise... 5
3. One valvar pole always acute........................ 4. G. gracile var. dichotoma
3. Both valvar poles obtuse... 4
   4. Length of cell less than 70 μ...................... 5. G. intricatum
   4. Length of cell more than 70 μ.................... 6. G. semiapterum
5. Valves lanceolate-rostrate... 6
5. Valves not lanceolate-rostrate... 7
   6. Striations 9–14 in 10 μ........................... 7. G. angustatum
   6. Striations 14–16 in 10 μ.......................... 8. G. parvulum
7. Valves cuneate... 9. G. acuminatum
7. Valves clavate to subclavate... 8
   8. Valves apically capitate............................ 10. G. sphaerophorum
   8. Valves not apically capitate........................ 11. G. montanum var. subclavatum

1. *Gomphonema geminatum* (Lyngbye) C. A. Agardh. Cells 25–43 × 60–135 μ; valves biconstricted, with broad rounded subtruncate poles, the apex considerably larger than the base; axial area linear; central area rounded, with 2 to 4 dots in a longitudinal row; raphe terminally with dorsal hooks; transverse striations, 9–10 in 10 μ, generally radiate, medially alternately long and short, coarsely punctate. Pl. **73**, fig. **850.**

2. *Gomphonema olivaceum* (Lyngbye) Kuetzing. Cells 5–10 × 15–40 μ; valves ovoid-clavate, with broadly rounded apex and acutely rounded

base; axial area narrow, linear; central area widened transversely without dots; raphe straight; transverse striations 10–14 in 10 μ, radial and indistinctly punctate. Pl. **72**, figs. **844, 845.**

a. Var. *calcarea* Cleve. Valves more slender, with evident median expansion, about 70 μ long. Pl. **72**, fig. **846.**

3. *Gomphonema constrictum* Ehrenberg. Cells 8–14 $\times$ 25–65 μ; valves clavate, constricted below the broad rounded apical pole, with attenuated basal pole; axial area narrow; central area broad and irregularly defined, with a dot on one side; transverse striations 10–12 in 10 μ, radial, evidently punctate, alternately long and short in the middle of the valve. Pl. **72**, fig. **839.**

a. Var. *capitatum* (Ehrenberg) Grunow. Valves typically clavate, without transverse constriction, 15–65 μ long. Pl. **72**, fig. **840.**

(1). Forma *turgidum* (Ehrenberg) A. Mayer. Valves turgid. Pl. **72**, fig. **841.**

4. *Gomphonema gracile* Ehrenberg var. *dichotoma* (Kuetzing) Grunow. Cells 4–9 $\times$ 30–75 μ; valves linear-lanceolate, poles slightly cuneate and bluntly rounded, nearly symmetric; axial area wide, linear; central area small, quadrately rounded, with a dot on one side; transverse striations only slightly radial, indistinctly punctate, 9–17 in 10 μ; gelatinous stalks long and largely dichotomously branched. Pl. **72**, fig. **848.**

5. *Gomphonema intricatum* Kuetzing. Cells 5–9 $\times$ 25–70 μ; valves linear-clavate, expanded medially, with broadly rounded apex and attenuated base; axial area wide; central area broad, one-sided, with isolated dot and median striations short, often lacking; transverse striations somewhat radial, evidently punctate, about 8–11 in 10 μ. Pl. **72**, fig. **836.**

a. Var. *vibrio* (Ehrenberg) Cleve. Valves up to 110 μ long, transverse striations mostly 10 in 10 μ. Pl. **72**, fig. **837.**

6. *Gomphonema semiapterum* Grunow. Cells up to 105 μ in length; valves clavate-lanceolate, with obtuse apex and broad base; axial area widened between central and median nodules; central area broad, one-sided, with several short median striae and evident dot; transverse striations scarcely radiate, punctate, about 10 in 10 μ. Pl. **72**, fig. **849.**

7. *Gomphonema angustatum* (Kuetzing) Grunow. Cells 5–9 $\times$ 12–45 μ; valves slender, clavate-lanceolate, nearly symmetric, with slightly constricted and abruptly rounded poles; axial area narrow but evident; central area broad, one-sided, with isolated dot; transverse striations radial, indistinctly punctate, 9–14 in 10 μ. Pl. **72**, fig. **842.**

a. Var. *obtusatum* (Kuetzing) Van Heurck. Valves clavate, with obtuse poles. Pl. **72**, fig. **843.**

8. *Gomphonema parvulum* (Kuetzing) Grunow. Cells 4–7 $\times$ 12–30 μ; valves clavate-lanceolate, with shortly constricted poles; axial area very narrow; central area small, one-sided, with isolated dot; transverse striations radial, indistinctly punctate, 14–16 in 10 μ. Pl. **72**, fig. **838**.

9. *Gomphonema acuminatum* Ehrenberg. Cells 5–11 $\times$ 20–70 μ; valves generally cuneate, expanded near the apex and less so medianly, with cuneate and acute apex and with evidently attenuated base; axial area linear, narrow; central area large, often indefinitely limited, with an isolated dot; transverse striations somewhat radial, evidently punctate, 10–13 in 10 μ. Pl. **72**, fig. **830**.

a. Var. *coronatum* (Ehrenberg) Rabenhorst. Valves up to 100 μ long, with a broad flat apex medianly acutely topped and with a deep subapical constriction. Pl. **72**, fig. **833**.

b. Var. *elongatum* (Wm. Smith) Van Heurck. Valves elongate, gibbous in the middle and at the subcuneate apex. Pl. **72**, fig. **834**.

c. Var. *laticeps* (Ehrenberg) A. Schmidt. Cells smaller and valves terminally broader than the species. Pl. **72**, fig. **832**.

d. Var. *trigonocephalum* (Ehrenberg) Cleve. Valves cuneate, without evident constriction, apex roundly cuneate. Pl. **72**, fig. **831**.

e. Var. *turris* (Ehrenberg) Cleve. Valves scarcely constricted, slightly attenuate toward the somewhat cuneate apex, gradually attenuate toward the base. Pl. **72**, fig. **835**.

10. *Gomphonema sphaerophorum* Ehrenberg. Cells 7–10 $\times$ 30–47 μ; valves elliptic-clavate, sharply narrowing toward a rounded and slightly capitate basal pole and with a much wider knob-like apical pole; axial area narrow, linear; central area small, with a dot at one side; transverse striations 11–16 in 10 μ, more or less clearly punctate, slightly radial. Pl. **72**, fig. **847**.

11. *Gomphonema montanum* Schumann var. *subclavatum* Grunow. Cells 6–10 $\times$ 40–80 μ; valves slightly clavate, poles rounded; axial area narrow;

Fig. 850.—*Gomphonema geminatum* (Lyngbye) C. A. Agardh.

Fig. 851.—*Gomphonema montanum* Schumann var. *subclavatum* Grunow.

Fig. 852.—*Gomphoneis herculeana* (Ehrenberg) Cleve.

Fig. 853.—*Gomphoneis herculeana* var. *robusta* (Grunow) Cleve.

Fig. 854.—*Amphora normani* Rabenhorst.

Fig. 855.—*Amphora ovalis* Kuetzing.

Fig. 856.—*Cymbella affinis* Kuetzing.

Fig. 857.—*Cymbella triangulum* (Ehrenberg) Cleve.

Fig. 858.—*Cymbella aspera* (Ehrenberg) Cleve.

(Fig. 850, Meister; fig. 851, Van Heurck; fig. 852, G. M. Smith; fig. 853, Schmidt; figs. 854–856, 858, Hustedt; fig. 857, Wolle. Figs. 850, 858 $\times 750$; figs. 851–857 $\times 1000$.)

PLATE 73

(Figs. 850 to 858)

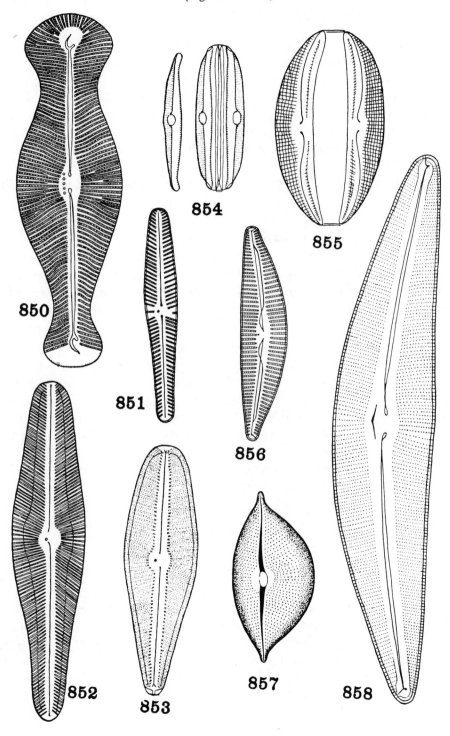

850

851

852

853

854

855

856

857

858

central area evident, sometimes one-sided, with isolated dot; transverse striations slightly radial, 9–10 in 10 μ. Pl. **73**, fig. **851**.

Gomphoneis Cleve 1894

Cells as in *Gomphonema*, except in the presence of a longitudinal line more or less parallel to each of the valvar margins.

1. *Gomphoneis herculeana* (Ehrenberg) Cleve. Cells 12–22 × 38–136 μ; valves clavate, with broad apex and somewhat acute base; axial area very narrow; central area rounded with a single dot; transverse striations, alternating with a double row of punctae, 9–12 in 10 μ, radial; longitudinal lines indistinct; a short septum at the apex. Pl. **73**, fig. **852**.

a. Var. *robusta* (Grunow) Cleve. Larger dimensions of cells. Pl. **73**, fig. **853**.

Family Cymbellaceae

Cells solitary or free-floating, or attached at the ends of gelatinous stalks, sessile or within gelatinous tubes; valves longitudinally asymmetric, one side convex and the other variously convex, straight or concave, with true raphe; girdle view symmetric but variable in shape; one large chromatophore or less often two that are symmetrically placed; transverse costae present or not.

Amphora Ehrenberg 1840

Cells usually sessile with concave faces attached in girdle view, broadly elliptic in outline, with truncate ends, girdles usually separated by several punctate or striate intercalary bands; valves lunate, longitudinally asymmetric, transversely striate; axial field strongly excentric, nearer the concave side of the valve; raphe gibbous, with its central nodule close to the concave margin; chromatophores single, or 2–4.

Auxospores formed in pairs between two conjugating cells or formed singly by the union of gametes in a single cell.

KEY TO THE SPECIES

1. Cells without intercalary bands, in girdle view 17–63 μ broad........1. A. ovalis
1. Cells with intercalary bands, in girdle view 10–14 μ broad...........2. A. normani

1. *Amphora ovalis* Kuetzing. Cells in girdle view broadly elliptic with truncate ends, 17–63 × 20–140 μ; valve lunate, with rather blunt poles, ventrally concave, dorsally convex; raphe gibbous; axial area narrow, central area developed only on the ventral side; transverse striations 10–13 in 10 μ, convergent ventrally at the poles, radial elsewhere. Pl. **73**, fig. **855**.

2. *Amphora normani* Rabenhorst. Cells in girdle view long-elliptic with broadly rounded ends, 10–14 × 16–40 μ; intercalary bands numerous,

about 12 in 10 μ on the dorsal side, finely cross-lined; valves lunate with constrictions below the capitate poles and dorsally slightly undulate; axial area narrow, central area absent; central nodule large; transverse striations somewhat radial, 16–18 in 10 μ; ventral side of valve without ornamentation except at the margin. Pl. 73, fig. **854.**

Cymbella C. A. Agardh 1830

Cells solitary and free-floating or attached at the ends of gelatinous stalks or confined within little branched gelatinous tubes, with parallel sides in girdle view and smooth girdles, without intercalary bands; valves asymmetric (sometimes only slightly so), lunate or nearly elliptic or rhombic or naviculoid, dorsally convex, ventrally concave, straight or somewhat convex; axial field wide or narrow, nearer the ventral margin, with central area with or without dots; raphe curved, with well-defined nodules; transverse striations radiate, sometimes cross-lined; chromatophore a single expanded plate.

Auxospores formed in pairs between conjugating cells.

KEY TO THE SPECIES

1. Valves only slightly asymmetric or curved 2
1. Valves strongly asymmetric and curved 8
   2. Valves gradually attenuate to broad poles 3
   2. Valves generally constricted below narrowed poles 4
3. Transverse striations cross-lined . . . . 1. C. lacustris
3. Transverse striations not cross-lined . . . . 2. C. aequalis
   4. Valves more than 14 μ in diameter 5
   4. Valves less than 14 μ in diameter 6
5. Striations 7–9 in 10 μ . . . . 3. C. ehrenbergii
5. Striations 9–14 in 10 μ . . . . 4. C. cuspidata
   6. Poles rostrate-capitate 7
   6. Poles not rostrate-capitate . . . . 5. C. leptoceros
7. Central area large, rhombic . . . . 6. C. amphicephala
7. Central area small, round . . . . 7. C. naviculiformis
   8. With dots in central area 9
   8. Without dots in central area 12
9. Dots single 10
9. Dots two or more (sometimes lacking) . . . . 8. C. cistula
   10. Dot isolated, on ventral side . . . . 9. C. tumida
   10. Dot ending a median striation 11
11. Striations with about 20 cross-lines in 10 μ . . . . 10. C. cymbiformis
11. Striations with 24–30 cross-lines in 10 μ . . . . 11. C. affinis
   12. Raphe straight (except at nodules) 13
   12. Raphe curved ventrally 16
13. Transverse striations strongly cross-lined 14
13. Transverse striations indistinctly cross-lined 15

14. Raphe evidently excentric...................... 12. C. turgida

14. Raphe nearly median......................... 13. C. prostrata

15. Ventral margin of valve straight, except near poles...... 14. C. gracilis

15. Ventral margin slightly convex..................... 15. C. ventricosa

16. Transverse striations strongly crossed-lined......... 16. C. parva

16. Transverse striations indistinctly or not cross-lined.................... 17

17. Axial area very wide.............................. 17. C. aspera

17. Axial area narrow................................ 18

18. Valve ventrally concave........................ 18. C. lanceolata

18. Valve ventrally convex, or straight................................. 19

19. Valves with acute ends........................... 19. C. triangulum

19. Valves with broad ends........................... 20. C. laevis

1. *Cymbella lacustris* (Agardh) Cleve. Cells 7–12 × 25–60 μ; valves linear-lanceolate, scarcely asymmetric, with broadly rounded poles; axial area linear, more or less medianly expanded; raphe only slightly excentric and curved; transverse striations 9–12 in 10 μ, cross-lined, somewhat radiate in the center, convergent toward the ends, and scattered at the poles. Pl. 74, fig. 867.

2. *Cymbella aequalis* Wm. Smith. Cells 4–12 × 15–54 μ; valves linear-elliptic to linear-lanceolate, somewhat asymmetric, with convex sides, slightly attenuated to rounded poles; axial area narrow; central area not well developed, angular to round; raphe slightly excentric, outwardly cleft; transverse striations radiate, 11–16 in 10 μ, finely punctate. Pl. 74, fig. 866.

3. *Cymbella ehrenbergii* Kuetzing. Cells 19–50 × 50–220 μ; valves broadly elliptic to nearly rhombo-elliptic, slightly constricted below abruptly rounded poles, only slightly asymmetric; raphe straight; axial area wide,

FIG. 859.—*Cymbella prostrata* (Berkeley) Cleve.

FIG. 860.—*Cymbella tumida* (Brébisson) Van Heurck.

FIG. 861.—*Cymbella cistula* (Hemprich) Grunow.

FIG. 862.—*Cymbella turgida* Gregory.

FIG. 863.—*Cymbella cuspidata* Kuetzing.

FIG. 864.—*Cymbella naviculiformis* Auerswald.

FIG. 865.—*Cymbella gracilis* (Rabenhorst) Cleve.

FIG. 866.—*Cymbella aequalis* Wm. Smith.

Fig. 867.—*Cymbella lacustris* (Agardh) Cleve.

FIG. 868.—*Cymbella leptoceros* (Ehrenberg) Grunow.

FIG. 869.—*Cymbella laevis* Naegeli.

FIG. 870.—*Cymbella amphicephala* Naegeli.

FIG. 871.—*Cymbella ventricosa* Kuetzing.

FIG. 872.—*Cymbella lanceolata* (Ehrenberg) Van Heurck.

FIG. 873.—*Cymbella cymbiformis* (Kuetzing) Brébisson.

FIG. 874.—*Cymbella parva* (Wm. Smith) Cleve.

FIG. 875.—*Cymbella ehrenbergii* Kuetzing.

(All figs., Hustedt; ×*1000*.)

PLATE 74

(Figs. 859 to 875)

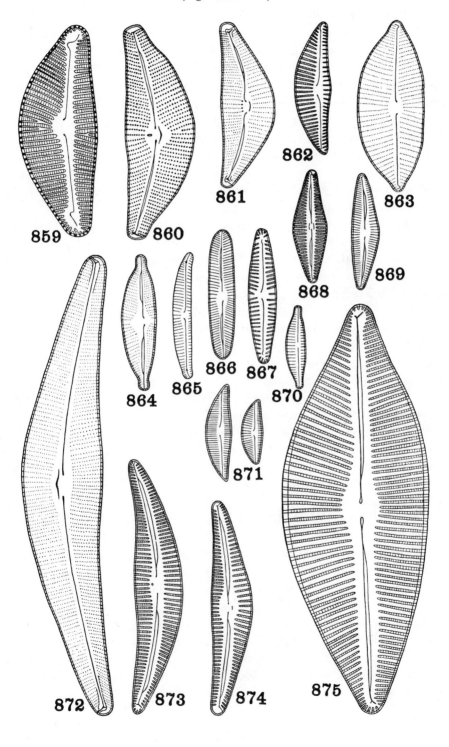

centrally expanded; striations somewhat radiate, 7–9 in 10 μ, with cross-lines 13–16 in 10 μ. Pl. **74,** fig. **875.**

4. *Cymbella cuspidata* Kuetzing. Cells 14–28 × 40–100 μ; valves broad, somewhat asymmetrically linear-lanceolate, with slight constriction below the somewhat capitate poles; raphe excentric, nearly straight; axial area narrow; central area large and circular; transverse striations radiate, 9–14 in 10 μ, indistinctly cross-lined. Pl. **74,** fig. **863.**

5. *Cymbella leptoceros* (Ehrenberg) Grunow. Cells 7–13 × 17–60 μ; valves lanceolate, with somewhat asymmetric and evidently convex sides, poles sharply rounded; raphe slightly excentric, a little curved; central nodule prominent; axial area narrow, sharply limited; central area not evident; transverse striations very pronounced, 9–12 in 10 μ, with evident cross lines, 22–25 in 10 μ. Pl. **74,** fig. **868.**

6. *Cymbella amphicephala* Naegeli. Cells 9–10 × 25–40 μ; valves lanceolate, somewhat asymmetric, with convex sides and evident constrictions below the rostrate-capitate poles; raphe straight, slightly excentric; axial area narrow, not enlarged medianly; transverse striations radiate, 12–16 in 10 μ. Pl. **74,** fig. **870.**

7. *Cymbella naviculiformis* Auerswald. Cells 9–16 × 30–50 μ; valves naviculoid, somewhat asymmetric, with evident constrictions below the rostrate-capitate poles; raphe slightly curved and excentric; axial area narrow; central area large, circular; transverse striations radiate, 12–14 in 10 μ in the middle, becoming finer toward the poles. Pl. **74,** fig. **864.**

8. *Cymbella cistula* (Hemprich) Grunow. Cells 15–36 × 35–180 μ; valves strongly asymmetric, naviculoid in shape with dorsal sides convex, ventral sides concave with a median expansion; raphe excentric, broad, dorsally convex; axial area narrow, somewhat widened at the middle; transverse striations radiate, 6–9 in 10 μ, with punctae about 18–22 in 10 μ; median ventral striations ending in two or more dots (sometimes lacking). Pl. **74,** fig. **861.**

9. *Cymbella tumida* (Brébisson) Van Heurck. Cells 15–23 × 40–105 μ; valves asymmetric and curved, broadly naviculoid, with rostrate poles, convex dorsal sides and straight or slightly convex ventral sides having a median expansion; raphe excentric; axial area narrow; central area large, round, with a ventrally placed prominent isolated dot; transverse striations 8–10 in 10 μ, radiate, punctate. Pl. **74,** fig. **860.**

10. *Cymbella cymbiformis* (Kuetzing) Brébisson. Cells 9–14 × 30–100 μ; valves naviculoid, strongly curved, dorsally convex, ventrally nearly straight, with slight median expansion; raphe excentric, broad; axial area narrow, somewhat medianly widened; transverse striations radiate, 8–10 in 10 μ, with cross-lines about 20 in 10 μ. Pl. **74,** fig. **873.**

11. *Cymbella affinis* Kuetzing. Cells 7–16 × 20–70 μ; valves quite asymmetric, semilanceolate to semielliptic, convex dorsally, concave to straight ventrally, with rostrate, rounded poles; raphe excentric, undulate toward the central nodule; axial area narrow, slightly medianly widened, with ventral median stria ending in an isolated dot; transverse striations 9–12 in 10 μ, radiate with cross-lines 24–30 in 10 μ. Pl. **73,** fig. **856.**

12. *Cymbella turgida* Gregory. Cells 9–25 × 30–100 μ; valves lunate, very convex dorsally and nearly straight ventrally, with acutely rounded poles; raphe excentric, with polar nodules at the dorsal margin; axial area narrow and linear, slightly widened centrally, without dots; transverse striations 7–9 in 10 μ, slightly convergent ventrally and polarly, otherwise radiate. Pl. **74,** fig. **862.**

13. *Cymbella prostrata* (Berkeley) Cleve. Cells 10–30 × 20–100 μ; valves quite asymmetric, semielliptic, dorsally convex, ventrally straight with median expansion, poles broadly rounded; raphe straight with polar deviations; axial area narrow; central area small, round, without isolated dots; transverse striations 7–10 in 10 μ, radiate to parallel, with cross-lines about 20 in 10 μ. Pl. **74,** fig. **859.**

14. *Cymbella gracilis* (Rabenhorst) Cleve. Cells 7–10 × 30–60 μ; valves asymmetric, narrowly lanceolate, dorsally convex, straight ventrally, with bent, usually rounded ends; raphe excentric, straight except at nodules; axial area narrow with slight median expansion, without isolated dots; transverse striations 10–13 in 10 μ, finely punctate and nearly parallel except at the poles. Pl. **74,** fig. **865.**

15. *Cymbella ventricosa* Kuetzing. Cells 5–12 × 10–40 μ; valves somewhat semielliptic, dorsally convex, ventrally straight to slightly convex, with sharply rounded poles; raphe straight, closer to the ventral side except at the poles; axial area narrow, slightly expanded medianly, without isolated dots; transverse striations 12–18 in 10 μ, generally radiate, punctate, with punctae about 35 in 10 μ. Pl. **74,** fig. **871.**

16. *Cymbella parva* (Wm. Smith) Cleve. Cells 8–12 × 25–70 μ; valves semilanceolate, generally convex dorsally and straight or slightly concave ventrally, gradually attenuated to round poles; raphe excentric; axial area narrow, more or less centrally expanded, without isolated dots; transverse striations radiate, 9–13 in 10 μ, strongly cross-lined. Pl. **74,** fig. **874.**

17. *Cymbella aspera* (Ehrenberg) Cleve. Cells 20–48 × 70–265 μ; valves asymmetric, semilanceolate, dorsally convex and ventrally straight with a slight median expansion, poles broadly rounded; raphe excentric, somewhat curved and widened between the central nodule and the polar nodules; axial area very broad, sharply defined, with little central expansion,

without isolated dots; transverse striations nearly perpendicular to the long axis, 7–9 in 10 μ, punctae 12–15 in 10 μ. Pl. **73**, fig. **858**.

18. *Cymbella lanceolata* (Ehrenberg) Van Heurck. Cells 24–34 × 70–210 μ; valves quite asymmetric, naviculoid, dorsally convex, ventrally concave with a median expansion; raphe excentric, narrow, and medianly curved; axial area narrow, with slight median expansion, no isolated dots; transverse striations perpendicular to the median line, except near the poles, 9–16 in 10 μ, with punctae 15–18 in 10 μ. Pl. **74**, fig. **872**.

19. *Cymbella triangulum* (Ehrenberg) Cleve. Cells 29–32 × 40–50 μ; valves asymmetric, semielliptic, with acute ends, dorsally convex, ventrally straight or slightly convex; transverse striations 9–11 in 10 μ, coarsely punctate. Pl. **73**, fig. **857**.

20. *Cymbella laevis* Naegeli. Cells 6–10 × 20–35 μ; valves asymmetric, semilanceolate, convex dorsally and lightly so ventrally, with sharply rounded ends; raphe excentric, curved; axial area narrow, slightly medianly expanded, without isolated dots; transverse striations 12–16 (–20) in 10 μ, radiate, with punctae about 35 in 10 μ. Pl. **74**, fig. **869**.

Epithemia Brébisson 1838

Cells solitary, usually epiphytic upon submerged aquatics, attached at the girdle, rectangular in girdle view, smooth girdles, intercalary bands; valves slightly to strongly curved dorsally convex, ventrally straight to concave, with broadly rounded to capitate and sometimes recurved poles; axial field near ventral side except for V-shaped median extension toward dorsal side; raphe with polar and central nodules, with the inner fissure containing circular pores; transverse septa appearing as costae and alternating with two or more rows of punctae; a single chromatophore with irregular projections.

Auxospores formed in pairs between two cells, elongating perpendicularly to the long axes of the cells.

KEY TO THE SPECIES

1. Valves with constricted ends... 2
1. Valves not constricted... 4
   2. Valves prominently ventrally concave..................... 1. E. sorex
   2. Valves ventrally straight or slightly concave............................ 3
3. Costae alternating with 2 (–3) rows of punctae............. 2. E. turgida
3. Costae alternating with 3–8 rows of punctae.................. 3. E. argus
   4. Valves strongly curved................................. 4. E. ocellata
   4. Valves slightly curved.. 5
5. Valves linear, costae 1–2 in 10 μ............................ 5. E. muelleri
5. Valves lanceolate, costae 2–4 in 10 μ........................ 6. E. zebra

1. *Ephithemia sorex* Kuetzing. Cells 8–15 × 20–65 μ; valves ventrally concave, dorsally convex, constricted below the recurved capitate poles; costae 5–7 in 10 μ, with two rows of striations between each two costae, 12–15 rows of striae in 10 μ. Pl. **75**, fig. **881**.

2. *Epithemia turgida* (Ehrenberg) Kuetzing. Cells 15–18 × 60–220 μ; valves ventrally straight to slightly concave, dorsally convex, slightly constricted below the recurved, somewhat capitate poles; costae radial, 3–5 in 10 μ, alternating with 2–3 rows of striations, 7–9 in 10 μ. Pl. **75**, fig. **876**.

   a. Var. *westermanii* (Ehrenberg) Grunow. Valves smaller, ends not capitate. Pl. **75**, fig. **877**.

3. *Epithemia argus* (Ehrenberg) Kuetzing. Cells 6–15 × 30–130 μ; valves ventrally straight to slightly concave, dorsally quite convex, with recurved, broadly rounded ends; costae somewhat radial, 1–2 in 10 μ, alternating with 6–8 rows of striations, 10–12 in 10 μ. Pl. **75**, fig. **878**.

   a. Var. *alpestris* (Wm. Smith) Grunow. Valves gradually attenuated to rounded ends, not capitate. Pl. **75**, fig. **879**.

4. *Epithemia ocellata* (Ehrenberg) Kuetzing. Cells 5–6 × 25–45 μ; valves uniformly curved to rounded ends; costae 3–4 in 10 μ, alternating with more than two rows of striations. Pl. **75**, fig. **883**.

5. *Epithemia muelleri* Fricke. Cells 12–18 × 40–100 μ; valves slightly curved, nearly linear; costae about 1.5 in 10 μ, alternating with several rows of striations, 10–12 in 10 μ. Pl. **75**, fig. **880**.

6. *Epithemia zebra* (Ehrenberg) Kuetzing. Cells 7–14 × 30–150 μ; valves lanceolate, gently curved with nearly parallel sides, gradually attenuated to rounded poles; costae radial, 2–4 in 10 μ, alternating with 4–8 rows of striations, 12–14 in 10 μ. Pl. **75**, fig. **882**.

Rhopalodia Mueller 1895

Cells usually solitary and free-floating, girdle faces broader than valve faces, girdles linear, nearly elliptic, clavate, medianly inflated, with broadly rounded to nearly flat poles; valves lunate to sickle-shaped, convex margin often inflated, with acute ends, sometimes elongate; axial field adjacent to convex margin, with raphe bearing central and polar nodules; transversely costate with alternating delicate striations; with or without intercalary bands; a single laminate chromatophore with irregular margins.

Auxospores formed in pairs between two generally differently sized cells; elongation of auxospore as in *Epithemia*.

KEY TO THE SPECIES

1. Margins subparallel in girdle view...................................... 1. R. ventricosa
1. Margins converging toward subcapitate poles.................... 2. R. gibba

1. *Rhopalodia ventricosa* (Kuetzing) Mueller. Cells in girdle view elliptic, 19–22 × 37–100 μ, medianly inflated; valves medianly inflated on the dorsal side, ventrally straight, with reflexed ends; costae 6–7 in 10 μ, striations granular, 12–16 in 10 μ. Pl. 75, fig. 885.

2. *Rhopalodia gibba* (Kuetzing) Mueller. Cells in girdle view broadly linear with median inflation and broadly rounded poles, 18–30 × 35–300 μ; valves very broadly lunate with almost straight ventral sides and recurved acute poles; costae 6–8 in 10 μ, alternating with 2–3 rows of striations, 12–14 in 10 μ. Pl. 75, fig. 884.

Suborder SURIRELLINEAE

Cells solitary and free-floating, or less often epiphytic and within gelatinous tubes; similar valves with raphe somewhat hidden in a keel at one or both sides, usually flat or sometimes curved, undulate; cells symmetric in both axes or only transversely.

Family Nitzschiaceae

Cells generally solitary and free-floating, sometimes band-like, epiphytic and within gelatinous tubes, elongate, rhombic or rectangular in transverse section; valves straight or sigmoid, transversely symmetric and longitudinally asymmetric; raphe on one lateral margin in each valve, concealed within an excentric keel; two laminate chromatophores separated at the girdle.

Nitzschia Hassall 1845

Cells solitary and free-floating or densely clustered in simple or unbranched gelatinous tubes, elongate-rectangular, or sigmoid in girdle view, with somewhat attenuated poles, rhombic in cross-section; valves longitudinally asymmetric, very variable in shape: straight, sigmoid, linear, el-

Fig. 876.—*Epithemia turgida* (Ehrenberg) Kuetzing.

Fig. 877.—*Epithemia turgida* var. *westermanii* (Ehrenberg) Grunow.

Fig. 878.—*Epithemia argus* (Ehrenberg) Kuetzing.

Fig. 879.—*Epithemia argus* var. *alpestris* (Wm. Smith) Grunow.

Fig. 880.—*Epithemia muelleri* Fricke.

Fig. 881.—*Epithemia sorex* Kuetzing.

Fig. 882.—*Epithemia zebra* (Ehrenberg) Kuetzing.

Fig. 883.—*Epithemia ocellata* (Ehrenberg) Kuetzing.

Fig. 884.—*Rhopalodia gibba* (Kuetzing) Mueller.

Fig. 885.—*Rhopalodia ventricosa* (Kuetzing) Mueller.

Fig. 886.—*Hantzschia amphioxys* (Ehrenberg) Grunow.

Fig. 887.—*Hantzschia amphioxys* f. *capitata* Mueller.

Fig. 888.—*Denticula tenuis* Kuetzing.

(Figs. 876, 878–882, 884, 886–888, Hustedt; fig. 877, Meister; figs. 883, 885, Schmidt. All ×1000.)

PLATE 75

(Figs. 876 to 888)

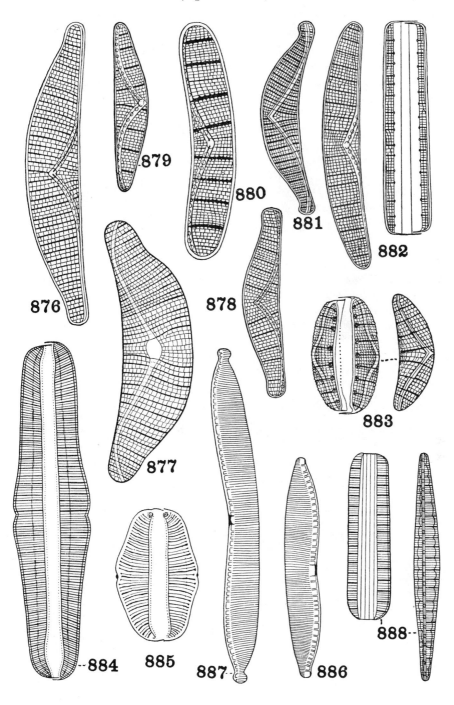

liptic, somewhat undulate, medianly constricted or not, poles acute or rostrate or capitate, often much attenuate; near one margin is a keel with a raphe having small nodules and a row of circular pores ("carinal dots") opening toward the interior of the cell; transversely striate or punctate; two chromatophores on the same girdle face.

Two auxospores formed by the conjugation of two cells in a somewhat crossed apposition.

KEY TO THE SPECIES

1. Cells with very long rostrate ends.. 2
1. Cells otherwise.. 3
   2. Cells generally quite straight...................... 1. N. acicularis
   2. Cells strongly curved............................. 2. N. closterium
3. Cells with evident sigmoid curves.................................... 4
3. Cells without evident sigmoid curves............................... 5
   4. Valves 3–5 µ broad.............................. 3. N. clausii
   4. Valves 5–7 µ broad.............................. 4. N. vermicularis
   4. Valves 8–14 µ broad............................. 5. N. sigmoidea
5. Valve margins undulate.............................. 6. N. sinuata
5. Valve margins otherwise.. 6
   6. Keel punctations elongate....................... 7. N. denticula
   6. Keel punctations not elongate................................... 7
7. Keel very excentric... 8
7. Keel slightly excentric or central................................. 10
   8. Valves with longitudinal folds.................. 8. N. hungarica
   8. Valves without longitudinal folds............................. 9
9. Valves medianly constricted....................... 9. N. commutata
9. Valves not medianly constricted................... 10. N. palea
   10. Valves spindle-shaped, 15–70 µ long............ 11. N. dissipata
   10. Valves linear, 70–180 µ long................... 12. N. linearis

Fig. 889.—*Hantzschia amphioxys* var. *vivax* (Hantzsch) Grunow.

Fig. 890.—*Nitzschia vermicularis* (Kuetzing) Hantzsch.

Fig. 891.—*Nitzschia linearis* (Agardh) Wm. Smith.

Fig. 892.—*Nitzschia linearis* var. *tenuis* (Wm. Smith) Grunow.

Fig. 893.—*Nitzschia clausii* Hantzsch.

Fig. 894.—*Nitzschia closterium* (Ehrenberg) Wm. Smith.

Fig. 895.—*Nitzschia sigmoidea* (Nitzsch) Wm. Smith.

Fig. 896.—*Nitzschia sinuata* (Wm. Smith) Grunow.

Fig. 897.—*Nitzschia sinuata* var. *tabellaria* Grunow.

Fig. 898.—*Nitzschia dissipata* (Kuetzing) Grunow.

Fig. 899.—*Nitzschia hungarica* Grunow.

Fig. 900.—*Nitzschia palea* (Kuetzing) Wm. Smith.

Fig. 901.—*Nitzschia palea* var. *tenuirostris* Grunow.

(Figs. 889–891, 893–900, Hustedt; figs. 892, 901, Van Heurck. Figs. 889, 891–894, 896, 897, 899–901 ×*1000*; figs. 890, 895, 898 ×*500*.)

PLATE 76
(Figs. 889 to 901)

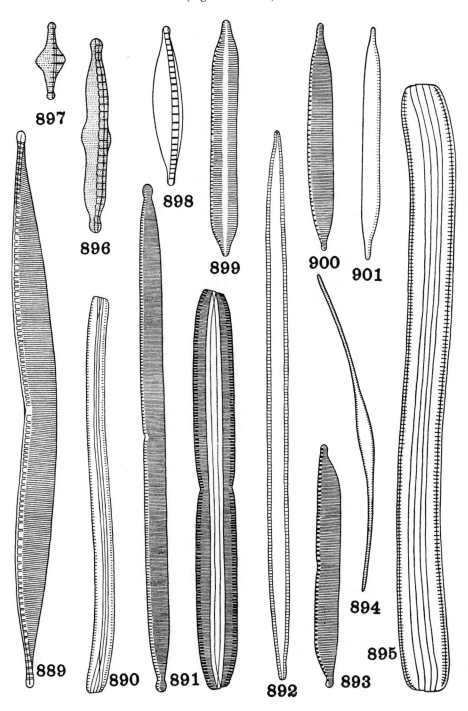

897

896

898

889

890

891

899

892

893

894

895

900

901

1. *Nitzschia acicularis* (Kuetzing) Wm. Smith. Cells 3–4 × 50–150 μ; medianly spindle-shaped with long attenuate poles, weakly silicified; striations very fine, scarcely visible, keel punctae 17–20 in 10 μ. Pl. **77**, fig. **904**.

2. *Nitzschia closterium* (Ehrenberg) Wm. Smith. Cells 2–6 × 32–260 μ, sickle-shaped; valves spindle-like and strongly curved with very long attenuate poles; striations fine, not clear; keel punctae 12–16 in 10 μ. Pl. **76**, fig. **894**.

3. *Nitzschia clausii* Hantzsch. Cells 3–5 × 20–55 μ; valves linear, slightly sigmoid, with shortly constricted, capitate poles; striations 32–38 in 10 μ, keel punctae 12–14 in 10 μ. Pl. **76**, fig. **893**.

4. *Nitzschia vermicularis* (Kuetzing) Hantzsch. Cells 5–7 × 90–250 μ, slightly sigmoid with parallel sides in girdle view; valves slender, somewhat naviculoid with capitate poles; striations 30–36 in 10 μ, keel punctae 8–12 in 10 μ. Pl. **76**, fig. **890**.

5. *Nitzschia sigmoidea* (Nitzsch) Wm. Smith. Cells 8–14 × 160–500 μ, somewhat sigmoid in girdle view, almost linear with parallel sides; valves naviculoid, with cuneate, acute, somewhat recurved poles; keel slightly excentric, with punctae 5–7 in 10 μ; striations 23–26 in 10 μ. Pl. **76**, fig. **895**.

6. *Nitzschia sinuata* (Wm. Smith) Grunow. Cells 5–8 × 20–50 μ, rectangular in girdle view; valves lanceolate with undulate margins and rostrate-capitate poles; striations about 18 in 10 μ, keel punctae 5–6 in 10 μ. Pl. **76**, fig. **896**.

a. Var. *tabellaria* Grunow. Cells mostly 15–30 μ long, with pronounced median expansion. Pl. **76**, fig. **897**.

7. *Nitzschia denticula* Grunow. Cells 3–8 × 10–100 μ, rectangular in girdle view, with straight or slightly convex sides and rounded poles; valves long-lanceolate, with acutely rounded poles; transverse striations 14–20 in 10 μ, keel punctae appearing costate, 5–8 in 10 μ. Pl. **77**, fig. **902**.

8. *Nitzschia hungarica* Grunow. Cells 6–9 × 20–110 μ; valves narrowly

FIG. 902.—*Nitzschia denticula* Grunow.
FIG. 903.—*Nitzschia commutata* Grunow.
FIG. 904.—*Nitzschia acicularis* (Kuetzing) Wm. Smith.
FIG. 905.—*Cymatopleura solea* (Brébisson) Wm. Smith.
FIG. 906.—*Cymatopleura solea* var. *subconstricta* Mueller.
FIG. 907.—*Cymatopleura solea* var. *vulgaris* Meister.

FIG. 908.—*Cymatopleura solea* var. *apiculata* (Wm. Smith) Ralfs.
FIG. 909.—*Cymatopleura elliptica* (Brébisson) Wm. Smith.
FIG. 910.—*Cymatopleura elliptica* f. *spiralis* (Chase) Boyer.

(Figs. 902–905, 908, 909, Hustedt; figs. 906, 907, Meister; fig. 910, Boyer. Figs. 902–904 ×*1000*; figs. 905–910 ×*750*.)

PLATE 77
(Figs. 902 to 910)

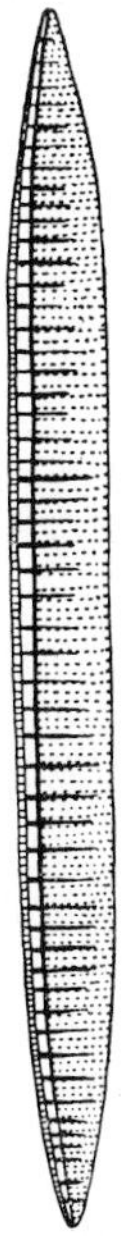

902 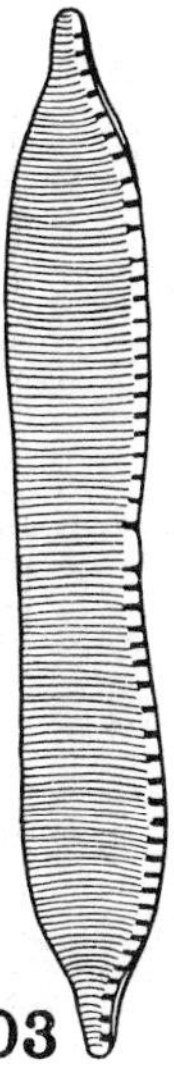
903 
904 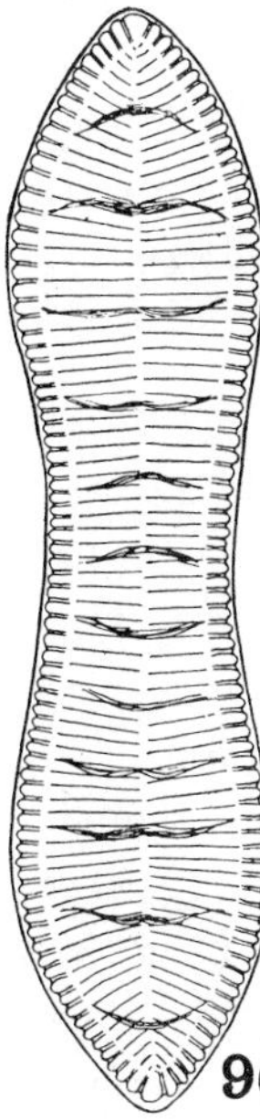
905 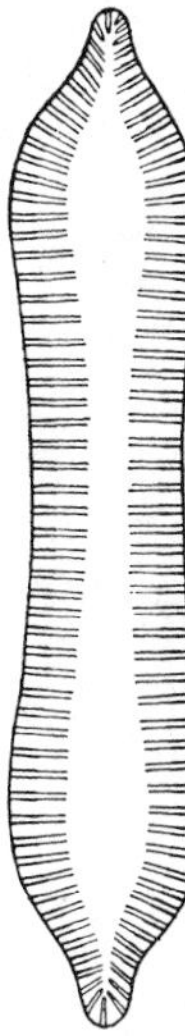
906 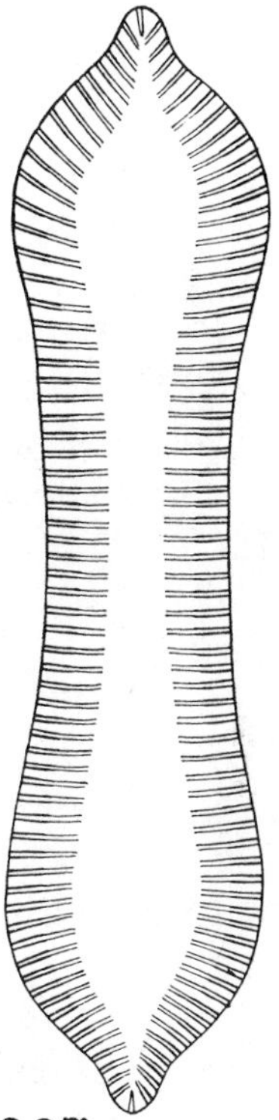
907 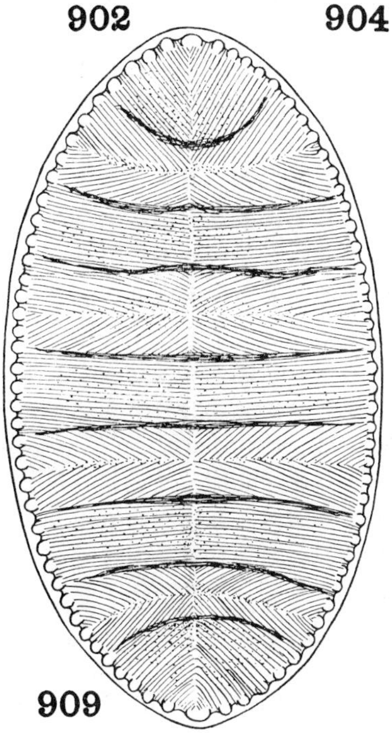
908
909 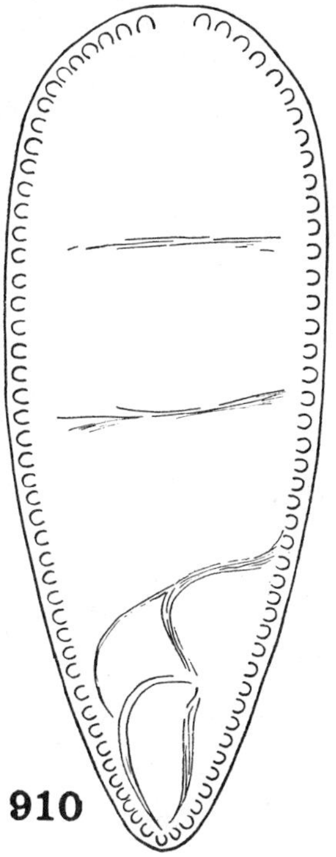
910

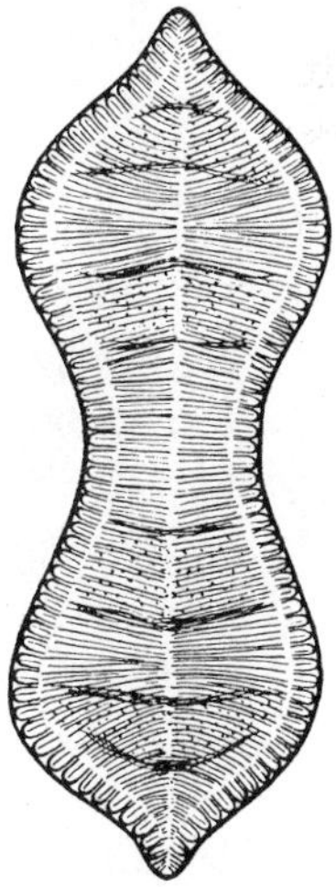

linear, with parallel or somewhat concave sides and slightly rostrate poles; striations 16–20 in 10 μ, interrupted by a fairly wide fold; keel punctae 7–9 in 10 μ. Pl. **76**, fig. **899**.

9. *Nitzschia commutata* Grunow. Cells 7–12 × 50–80 μ, in girdle view broadly linear, somewhat constricted, with rounded poles; valves linear with concave (sometimes parallel) sides and cuneate, acute ends; striations 20–24 in 10 μ, faintly punctate; keel punctae 7–10 in 10 μ. Pl. **77**, fig. **903**.

10. *Nitzschia palea* (Kuetzing) Wm. Smith. Cells 2.5–5.0 × 20–65 μ; valves linear to linear-lanceolate with cuneate poles; striations 35–40 in 10 μ; keel punctae 10–15 in 10 μ. Pl. **76**, fig. **900**.

a. Var. *tenuirostris* Grunow. Valves longer, with more acute ends. Pl. **76**, fig. **901**.

11. *Nitzschia dissipata* (Kuetzing) Grunow. Cells 4–7 × 15–70 μ, linear-lanceolate in girdle view, with narrower blunt ends; valves spindle-shaped with acutely rounded, somewhat capitate poles; striations scarcely visible; keel punctae 6–8 in 10 μ. Pl. **76**, fig. **898**.

12. *Nitzschia linearis* (Agardh) Wm. Smith. Cells 5–6 × 70–180 μ, rectangular-linear in girdle view, with median constriction; valves linear and generally with parallel sides and smaller, capitate poles; striations 28–30 in 10 μ; keel punctae 8–13 in 10 μ. Pl. **76**, fig. **891**.

a. Var. *tenuis* (Wm. Smith) Grunow. Valves more slender, about 85 μ long; striations more than 30 in 10 μ; keel punctae about 11 in 10 μ. Pl. **76**, fig. **892**.

Denticula Kuetzing 1844; emend. Grunow 1880

Cells solitary and free-floating, or joined valve to valve into short filaments, with somewhat convex sides and truncate poles in girdle view, with several intercalary bands, usually elongate; valves linear, lanceolate or elliptic, with scarcely visible keel next to one margin containing raphe with small nodules; internal face of fissure with indistinct circular pores; transverse septa, appearing as costae, alternating with several striations or rows of punctae; two longitudinal septa, each with a single perforation between successive transverse costae, the latter capitate and reaching to the girdle.

1. *Denticula tenuis* Kuetzing. Cells 3–7 × 6–60 μ; valves lanceolate, gradually attenuate to acutely rounded, somewhat rostrate poles; costae 5–7 in 10 μ, alternating with striations 25–30 in 10 μ. Pl. **75**, fig. **888**.

Hantzschia Grunow 1880

Cells rectangular in cross-section, with keeled margins opposite each other; otherwise as in the genus *Nitzschia*.

1. Poles rostrate...1. H. amphioxys
1. Poles capitate...................................... 1a. H. a. forma capitata
1. Poles elongate...................................... 1b. H. a. var. vivax

1. *Hantzschia amphioxys* (Ehrenberg) Grunow. Cells 5–10 × 20–100 μ; valves concave on one side and convex on the other, with rostrate, somewhat recurved poles; rectangular in girdle view; transverse striations 13–20 in 10 μ, keel punctae 5–8 in 10 μ. Pl. 75, fig. **886.**

   a. Forma *capitata* Mueller. Valves with capitate poles. Pl. 75, fig. **887.**

   b. Var. *vivax* (Hantzsch) Grunow. Valves slender with elongate poles. Pl. 76, fig. **889.**

Family **Surirellaceae**

Cells solitary and free-floating; valves symmetric in both axes or only longitudinally so, with flat, undulate or curved faces, having transverse costation especially prominent at the margins of the valves; raphe concealed in keel at each margin of the valve; girdle view rectangular, sinuate or irregular; chromatophore single, laminate or appearing as two expanded lobes.

Campylodiscus Ehrenberg 1840

Cells solitary and free-floating, circular or nearly so in outline, saddle-shaped, bent in valve face, girdle view various; valves peripherally costate, costae converging toward a hyaline punctate or striate center; raphe marginal; pseudoraphe more or less distinct through the center of the valve, and the one in each valve perpendicular to that in the other; a single broad laminate chromatophore.

1. *Campylodiscus noricus* Ehrenberg. Cells with circular valves, 60–150 μ in diameter; costae radial, somewhat parallel, 2–3 in 10 μ with punctate striations; valve face ornamentation appearing in four equal sectors. Pl. 80, fig. **934.**

Cymatopleura Wm. Smith 1851

Cells generally solitary and free-floating, linear in girdle view with undulate margins; valves linear, naviculoid, or elliptic, sometimes medially concave, transversely undulate on the face, with a marginal keel containing a raphe; broadly costate at the periphery, sometimes very short; transverse striations interrupted by longitudinal pseudoraphe, sometimes obscure; chromatophore single, appearing as two expanded lobes, one next each valve, connected by a cytoplasmic bridge.

A single auxospore formed by the juncture of two cells; or a single auxospore from each of the cells without conjugation.

KEY TO THE SPECIES

1. Valves with broad median constriction.......................... 1. C. solea
1. Valves without constriction.................................... 2. C. elliptica

1. *Cymatopleura solea* (Brébisson) Wm. Smith. Cells 12–40 × 30–300 μ; valves broadly linear with very wide median constriction and somewhat cuneate ends; costae 6–9 in 10 μ, with transverse striations perpendicular to the margin. Pl. **77,** fig. **905.**

a. Var. *apiculata* (Wm. Smith) Ralfs. Cells with apiculate poles and deeper concave margin in valve view. Pl. **77,** fig. **908.**

b. Var. *subconstricta* Mueller. Constriction evident, but only about 1–4 μ in extent; valves 13–27 μ in the middle, 14–30 μ at the broadest point and 70–145 μ long. Pl. **77,** fig. **906.**

c. Var. *vulgaris* Meister. Valves 15–20 μ in the middle, 20–30 μ at the widest point and 80–150 μ long, the extent of the constriction 4–9 μ; striations 6–7 in 10 μ. Pl. **77,** fig. **907.**

2. *Cymatopleura elliptica* (Brébisson) Wm. Smith. Cells 40–90 × 50–220 μ; valves broadly elliptic with rounded poles; costae 2–5 in 10 μ and striations, irregularly interrupted, 15–20 in 10 μ. Pl. **77,** fig. **909.**

a. Var. *hibernica* (Wm. Smith) Hustedt. Valves rhombo-elliptic, sometimes slightly rounded at the apiculate poles. Pl. **78,** fig. **911.**

b. Forma *spiralis* (Chase) Boyer. Valves ovate, inflated into curved ridges at one end, with a contraction of the valve. Pl. **77,** fig. **910.**

Surirella Turpin 1828

Cells generally solitary and free-floating, rectangular, naviculoid, cuneate or sigmoid in girdle view, girdles smooth; valves linear, elliptic or ovate, sometimes spirally twisted; valve-faces transversely folded, the folds appearing as costae; along each valve-margin is a keel, containing a raphe; transverse costae parallel, either long or short, and delicate striations across the valve face, interrupted by a median longitudinal pseudoraphe; chromatophore single, appearing as two laminate plates.

A single auxospore formed from the end-to-end conjugation of two cells.

Fig. 911.—*Cymatopleura elliptica* var. *hibernica* (Wm. Smith) Hustedt.

Fig. 912.—*Surirella minuta* Brébisson.

Fig. 913.—*Surirella apiculata* Wm. Smith.

Fig. 914.—*Surirella elegans* Ehrenberg.

Fig. 915.—*Surirella elegans* var. *norvegica* (Eulenstein) Brunnthaler.

Figs. 916, 917.—*Surirella biseriata* Brébisson.

Fig. 918.—*Surirella biseriata* var. *bifrons* (Ehrenberg) Hustedt.

(Figs. 911, 914, 916–918, Hustedt; figs. 912, 913, Wolle; fig. 915, Schmidt. Fig. 911 ×*750;* figs. 912, 913 ×*1000;* figs. 914–918 ×*500.*)

PLATE 78

(Figs. 911 to 918)

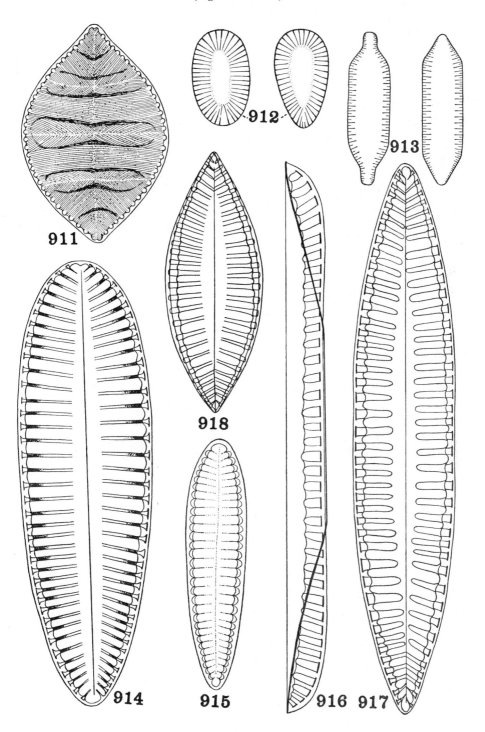

KEY TO THE SPECIES

1. Cells spirally twisted.................................... 1. S. spiralis
1. Cells not spirally twisted.. 2
   2. Cells normally isopolar.. 3
   2. Cells not isopolar... 6
3. Valves with broad, flat poles, medianly concave......... 2. S. didyma
3. Valves otherwise... 4
   4. Cells 9–25 μ broad... 5
   4. Cells 30–80 μ broad....................... 3. S. biseriata
   4. Cells 90–110 μ broad........................... 4. S. oregonica
5. Costae 2–5 in 10 μ................................. 5. S. linearis
5. Costae 6–8 in 10 μ.................................. 6. S. angusta
5. Costae 9–10 in 10 μ............................... 7. S. apiculata
   6. Costae 0.7–3.0 in 10 μ.. 7
   6. Costae 4–7 in 10 μ... 12
7. Pseudoraphe indistinct................... 8. S. guatemalensis
7. Pseudoraphe distinct, sometimes narrow.............................. 8
   8. Valves 19–30 μ broad....................... 9. S. patella
   8. Valves 40–150 μ broad... 9
9. Pseudoraphe narrow... 10
9. Pseudoraphe broad.. 11
   10. Costae usually less than 2 in 10 μ............. 10. S. splendida
   10. Costae usually more than 2 in 10 μ............ 11. S. saxonica
11. Spaces between costae very narrow.................... 12. S. elegans
11. Spaces between costae broad...................... 13. S. robusta
   12. Pseudoraphe lanceolate........................... 14. S. minuta
   12. Pseudoraphe linear, narrow...................................... 13
13. Transverse striations 14–16 in 10 μ................. 15. S. ovalis
13. Transverse striations 16–20 in 10 μ................. 16. S. ovata

1. *Surirella spiralis* Kuetzing. Cells spirally twisted around the longitudinal axis resembling the figure 8, especially in girdle view, 40–50 × 50–200 μ; valves elliptic-lanceolate with somewhat cuneate poles; costae 1.5–3.0 in 10 μ. Pl. **80**, fig. **930**.

2. *Surirella didyma* Kuetzing. Cells isopolar, 17–19 × 65–90 μ, rectan-

Fig. 919.—*Caloneis trinodis* (Lewis) Boyer.

Fig. 920.—*Surirella linearis* Wm. Smith.

Fig. 921.—*Surirella linearis* var. *constricta* (Ehrenberg) Grunow.

Fig. 922.—*Surirella ovalis* Brébisson.

Fig. 923.—*Surirella ovalis* var. *pinnata* Wm. Smith.

Fig. 924.—*Surirella splendida* (Ehrenberg) Kuetzing.

Fig. 925.—*Surirella patella* Kuetzing.

Fig. 926.—*Surirella ovata* Kuetzing.

Fig. 927.—*Surirella oregonica* Ehrenberg.

Fig. 928.—*Surirella angusta* Kuetzing.

Fig. 929.—*Surirella didyma* Kuetzing.

(Figs. 920–923, 925, 926, 927, 929, Hustedt; fig. 924, Van Heurck; fig. 928, Schmidt. Figs. 919, 922–924, 926, 929 ×*500;* all others ×*1000.*)

PLATE 79

(Figs. 919 to 929)

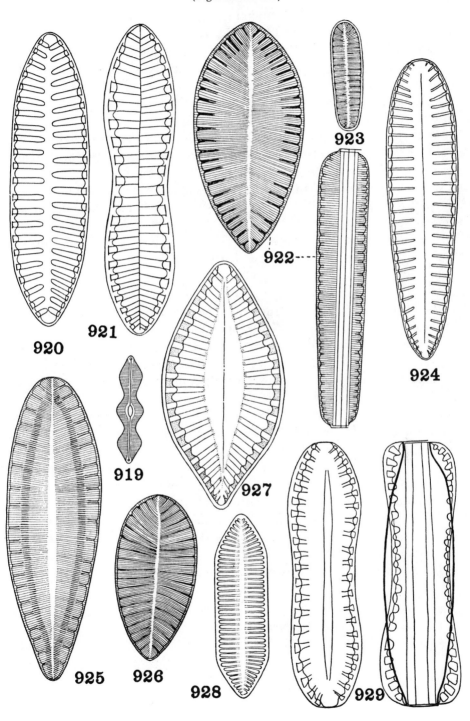

920

921

923

922

924

919

925

926

927

928

929

gular with slight median constriction in girdle view, broadly linear with concave sides and broadly rounded poles in valve view; costae 2.8–3.5 in 10 μ; valve surface sunken. Pl. **79**, fig. **929.**

3. *Surirella biseriata* Brébisson. Cells isopolar, 30–80 × 80–350 μ; valves elliptic-lanceolate, with parallel or slightly convex sides and somewhat cuneate poles; costae 1–2 in 10 μ, radial at the poles. Pl. **78**, figs. **916, 917.**

a. Var. *bifrons* (Ehrenberg) Hustedt. Valves broadly elliptic-lanceolate with very convex sides. Pl. **78**, fig. **918.**

4. *Surirella oregonica* Ehrenberg. Cells isopolar, 90–110 × 180–220 μ; valves rhombic, about twice as long as wide, with rounded poles; axial area fusiform; costae radiate, 0.8–1.5 in 10 μ. Pl. **79**, fig. **927.**

5. *Surirella linearis* Wm. Smith. Cells isopolar, 9–25 × 20–125 μ; valves linear with parallel or slightly convex sides and bluntly rounded nearly cuneate poles; costae 2–5 in 10 μ. Pl. **79**, fig. **920.**

a. Var. *constricta* (Ehrenberg) Grunow. Valves with broad median constriction; pseudoraphe often indistinct. Pl. **79**, fig. **921.**

6. *Surirella angusta* Kuetzing. Cells isopolar, 6–15 × 18–70 μ, rectangular in girdle view, with nearly flat ends; valves linear with parallel sides and cuneate, sometimes rostrate ends; costae 6.0–7.5 in 10 μ; transverse striations fine but distinct. Pl. **79**, fig. **928.**

7. *Surirella apiculata* Wm. Smith. Cells isopolar, 15–18 × 50–70 μ; valves rectangular with broadly cuneate to rectangularly narrowed poles; costae alternately long and short, mostly radiate, 9–10 in 10 μ; an imperfectly known species. Pl. **78**, fig. **913.**

8. *Surirella guatemalensis* Ehrenberg. Cells not isopolar, valves ovate, 35–40 × 100–120 μ; costae 2.0–2.5 in 10 μ; pseudoraphe very narrow, indistinct. Pl. **80**, fig. **933.**

9. *Surirella patella* Kuetzing. Cells not isopolar, somewhat cuneate in girdle view, 19–30 × 40–90 μ; valves elongate-ovate, with costae 2.4–3.0 in 10 μ and transverse striations about 14–16 in 10 μ. Pl. **79**, fig. **925.**

10. *Surirella splendida* (Ehrenberg) Kuetzing. Cells not isopolar, with ovate valves, 40–60 × 75–250 μ; costae 1–2 in 10 μ; pseudoraphe linear, narrow. Pl. **79**, fig. **924.**

11. *Surirella saxonica* Auerswald. Cells not isopolar, with ovate valves,

---

Fig. 930.—*Surirella spiralis* Kuetzing.
Fig. 931.—*Surirella robusta* Ehrenberg.
Fig. 932.—*Surirella saxonica* Auerswald.
Fig. 933.—*Surirella guatemalensis* Ehrenberg.

Fig. 934.—*Campylodiscus noricus* Ehrenberg.

(Figs. 930–932, 934, Hustedt; fig. 933, Boyer. All ×500.)

PLATE 80

(Figs. 930 to 934)

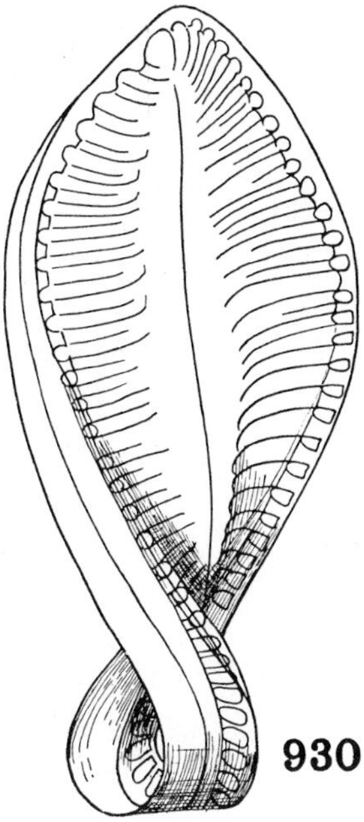

930

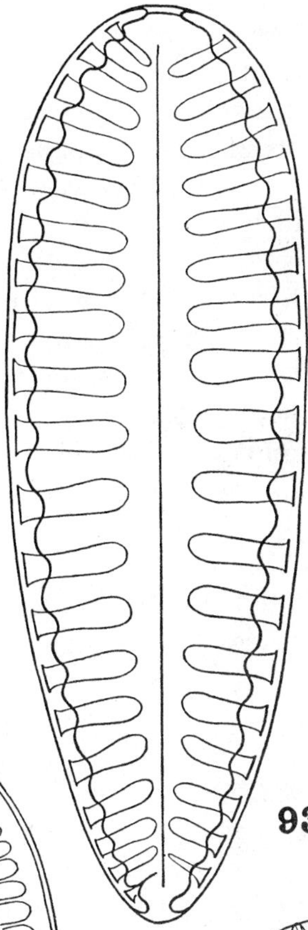

931

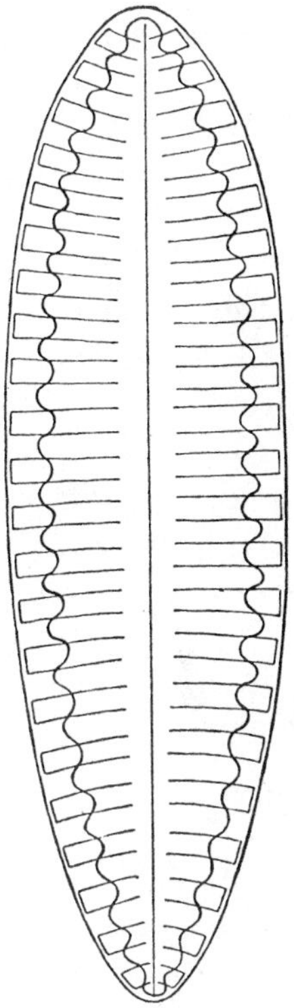

932

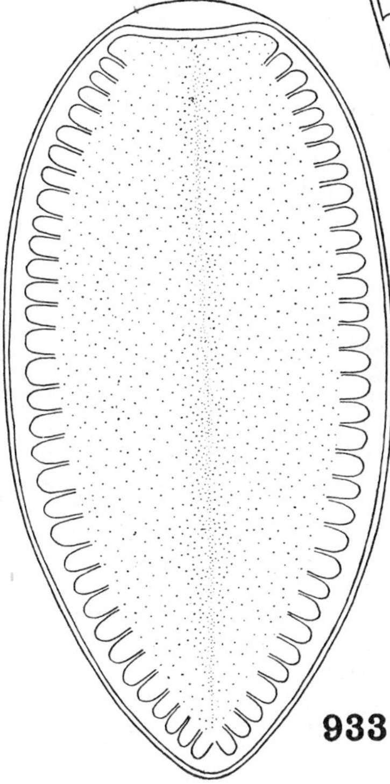

933

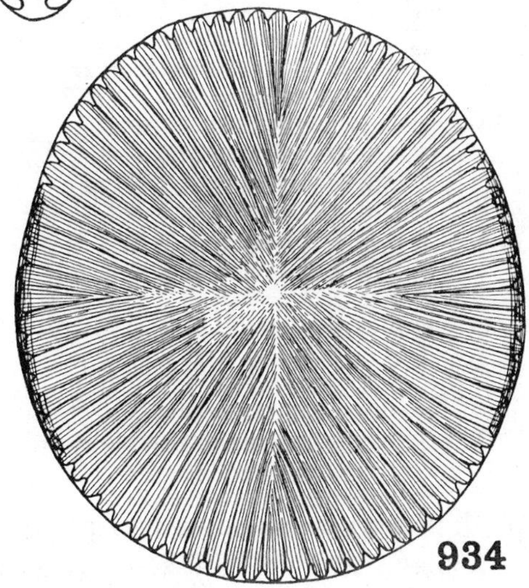

934

50–70 × 120–200 μ; girdle view rectangular, ends somewhat rounded; costae about 2 in 10 μ; striations fine, sometimes indistinct. Pl. **80,** fig. **932.**

12. *Surirella elegans* Ehrenberg. Cells not isopolar, 40–90 × 130–435 μ; valves usually ovate, sometimes nearly linear, with both poles broadly rounded; costae 1.2–2.0 in 10 μ, with spaces between the costae slender; wall transversely finely striate; pseudoraphe broad. Pl. **78,** fig. **914.**

a. Var. *norvegica* (Eulenstein) Brunnthaler. Cells 80–90 × 290–350 μ; striations 1.25 in 10 μ, finely cross-lined; girdle view long-cuneate; wings of the valves scarcely visible. Pl. **78,** fig. **915.**

13. *Surirella robusta* Ehrenberg. Cells not isopolar, 50–150 × 150–400 μ, with ovate to elliptic valves having broadly rounded poles; costae 0.7–1.5 in 10 μ, with broad alternating spaces; wall transversely punctate-striate; pseudoraphe broad. Pl. **80,** fig. **931.**

14. *Surirella minuta* Brébisson. Cells not isopolar, 8–10 × 12–25 μ, with ovate-elliptic valves; costae radiate, 5–7 in 10 μ; pseudoraphe lanceolate. Pl. **78,** fig. **912.**

15. *Surirella ovalis* Brébisson. Cells not isopolar, sometimes twisted, 10–40 × 20–100 μ, with ovate-lanceolate valves having somewhat cuneate poles; costae 4–5 in 10 μ; transverse striations 14–16 in 10 μ. Pl. **79,** fig. **922.**

a. Var. *pinnata* Wm. Smith. Cells smaller, long-oval with broadly rounded ends; valves sometimes with slight median constriction; costae 6–8 in 10 μ. Pl. **79,** fig. **923.**

16. *Surirella ovata* Kuetzing. Cells not isopolar, 8–23 × 15–70 μ, often cuneate in girdle view; valves ovate, with rounded poles; costae 4–7 in 10 μ; transverse striations 16–20 in 10 μ. Pl. **79,** fig. **926.**

Class *CHRYSOPHYCEAE*

Vegetative cells of the Chrysophyceae are uninucleate, solitary or forming colonies of definite shape, naked or enclosed within a wall, and amoeboid, motile by means of flagella, or immobile. The flagella are anterior in position and may be single or 2 that are equal or unequal in length or rarely 3. Flagellate protoplasts are usually naked but some have sheaths of pectic compounds that may contain siliceous scales. A loose, rigid envelope or lorica, open at one end, encloses the protoplast in certain genera. Other genera, including filamentous forms, have firm, tightly fitting walls.

The chromatophores are golden brown, usually occur 1–2 in each cell, and in some cases contain pyrenoid-like bodies. The pigments are chlorophyll *a*, beta-carotene and xanthophylls: lutein and fucoxanthin. Nutrition is autotrophic or in some genera partly heterotrophic. Accumulated foods include fats, leucosin, and volutin. The presence of glycogen in cysts has been reported. There is never a formation of starch. A complex neuro-motor apparatus is known for one genus and many of the motile genera have contractile vacuoles.

Asexual reproduction is by vegetative cell division, fragmentation, zoospores, and statospores. Sexual reproduction has been reported.

The Chrysophyceae occur in lakes and small pools mainly during the spring months. They are predominately cold-water organisms and disintegrate rapidly after collection. Certain genera form gelatinous masses on rocks in springs and mountain streams.

KEY TO THE GENERA OF CHRYSOPHYCEAE

1. Cell surrounded by a lorica........................ Dinobryon (p. 302)
1. Cell not surrounded by a lorica... 2
   2. Cells without flagella, amoeboid................. Rhizochrysis (p. 305)
   2. Cells with flagella.. 3
3. Cells solitary..................................... Mallomonas (p. 298)
3. Cells in colonies... 4
   4. Cell with 1 flagellum......................... Chrysosphaerella (p. 297)
   4. Cell with 2 flagella.. 5
5. Colony enclosed in a sheath...................... Syncrypta (p. 300)
5. Colony not enclosed in a sheath.................. Synura (p. 300)

Order CHRYSOMONADALES

Vegetative cells motile, solitary or in colonies of definite shape; protoplast naked, completely or incompletely surrounded by a close fitting envelope with or without siliceous plates, or surrounded by a lorica open at the anterior end; flagella 1 or 2 that may be equal or unequal in length; chromatophores golden-brown, rarely lacking, usually without pyrenoids; asexual reproduction by division of motile cells, zoospores, amoeboid protoplasts, and statospores (endogenous cysts); sometimes forming palmelloid stages; isogamous gametes reported for one genus.

Family **Mallomonadaceae**

Vegetative cells solitary or in colonies, free-swimming, with a single long flagellum; anterior vacuolar system with both contractile and non-contractile vacuoles; envelope firm, slightly elastic, ornamented with siliceous plates and spines; reproduction by vegetative division of motile cells, zoospores, cysts; at times forming palmelloid stages.

Chrysosphaerella Lauterborn 1896

Cells ellipsoid to pyriform, in spherical colonies partially embedded in hyaline, gelatinous envelopes containing numerous, tangentially placed, minute plates of silica; with 2 short, vase-shaped anterior projections, each bearing a long, straight siliceous seta; a single anterior flagellum; 2 elongate, laterally placed golden-brown chromatophores, a single eyespot, and several vacuoles in each cell.

Vegetative cell division.

1. *Chrysosphaerella longispina* Lauterborn. Cells about 9 × 15 μ; colonies 50–250 μ in diameter. Pl. **81**, figs. **941, 942.**

Mallomonas Perty 1852

Cells solitary, motile with 1 flagellum, ovoid to ellipsoid or variously shaped; periplast with numerous small circular or angular silicified imbricating scales; scales regularly or irregularly arranged, bearing siliceous spines, occasionally toothed; chromatophores golden-brown, 2, lateral and parietal; with contractile vacuoles; nucleus ellipsoid, often large and distinct.

Longitudinal division of the cells, the amoeboid products giving rise to palmelloid stages; cysts.

KEY TO THE SPECIES

1. Setae basally placed on cell. . . . . 1. M. producta
1. Setae covering practically entire cell. 2
    2. Cells 7–12 × 20–26 μ. . . . . 2. M. acaroides
    2. Cells 12–30 × 40–85 μ. . . . . 3. M. caudata

1. *Mallomonas producta* Ivanof. Cells 9–13 × 40–70 μ, cylindric, with rounded and tapering apices, straight or convex sides; scales diamond-shaped or transversely elongate, in regular transverse to diagonal series; setae straight or curved, on basal part of cell; chromatophores 2, golden-brown, laminate, parietal. Pl. **81**, fig. **936.**

2. *Mallomonas acaroides* Perty. Cells 7–12 × 20–26 μ, ovoid to ellipsoid, rounded posteriorly, somewhat bluntly pointed anteriorly; scales oval to elliptic, more or less in spiral rows; setae generally somewhat bent, covering entire cell; chromatophores 2, parietal. Pl. **81,** fig. **937.**

3. *Mallomonas caudata* Ivanof. Cells 12–30 × 40–85 μ, broadly ovoid, posteriorly somewhat narrowed; scales oval, in transverse series; setae about as long as the cell, generally straight, covering the entire surface and

Fig. 935.—*Mallomonas caudata* Ivanof.
Fig. 936.—*Mallomonas producta* Ivanof.
Fig. 937.—*Mallomonas acaroides* Perty.
Fig. 938.—*Syncrypta volvox* Ehrenberg.
Figs. 939, 940.—*Synura uvella* Ehrenberg; fig. 940, a single cell.

Figs. 941, 942.—*Chrysosphaerella longispina* Lauterborn; fig. 942, a single cell.

(All figs., G. M. Smith. Figs. 935–939, 941 ×*500;* figs. 940, 942 ×*1000.*)

PLATE 81

(Figs. 935 to 942)

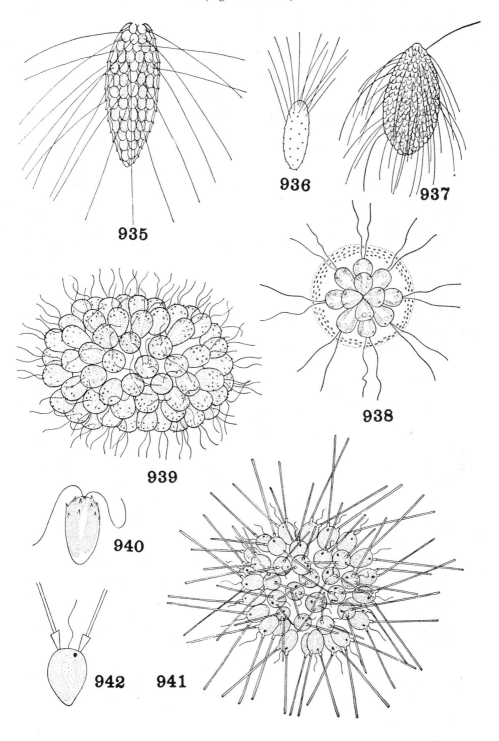

935

936

937

938

939

940

942   941

often having minute teeth-like projections at the distal end; chromato-phores 2, elongate, parietal, laminate. Pl. 81, fig. 935.

Family Syncryptaceae

Cells free-swimming or attached to substrate, envelope without siliceous scales; reproduction by vegetative cell division, zoospores, and cysts.

Syncrypta Ehrenberg 1833

Cells ovoid to pyriform, united radially into spherical, free-swimming colonies, embedded in a colorless gelatinous envelope containing numerous granules; 2 flagella of equal length emerging from the rounded anterior end of each cell; chromatophores 2, laterally disposed, golden-brown, lami-nate; contractile vacuoles 2; no definite eyespot.

Longitudinal division.

1. *Syncrypta volvox* Ehrenberg. Cells 7–12 × 8–14 μ; colonies 20–70 μ in diameter. Pl. 81, fig. 938.

Family Synuraceae

Vegetative cells motile, solitary or in colonies, with 2 flagella of equal length; protoplast naked; envelope firm and covered with siliceous scales; reproduction by division of vegetative cells, zoospores, amoeboid proto-plasts, statospores; at times forming palmelloid stages.

Synura Ehrenberg 1838

Colonies more or less spherical and compact, composed of broadly pyri-form to elongate biflagellate cells; envelope with siliceous scales and short small spines or reticulations; chromatophores 2, lateral and parietal; with-out eyespot.

Longitudinal division of cells and liberation of contents as amoeboid cells or as zoospores; cysts.

1. *Synura uvella* Ehrenberg. Cells 8–17 × 20–35 μ, with fine spines, broadly pyriform. Pl. 81, figs. 939, 940.

Family Ochromonadaceae

Cells free-swimming, sessile or epiphytic, protoplast naked or surround-ed by a lorica; envelope undifferentiated; reproduction by vegetative cell

FIGS. 943–946.—*Dinobryon divergens* Imhof.

FIGS. 947–950.—*Dinobryon pediforme* (Lemmermann) Steinecke.

FIGS. 951–954.—*Dinobryon sertularia* Ehrenberg.

FIGS. 955, 956.—*Dinobryon cylindricum* Imhof.

(All figs., Ahlstrom; ×650.)

PLATE 82

(Figs. 943 to 956)

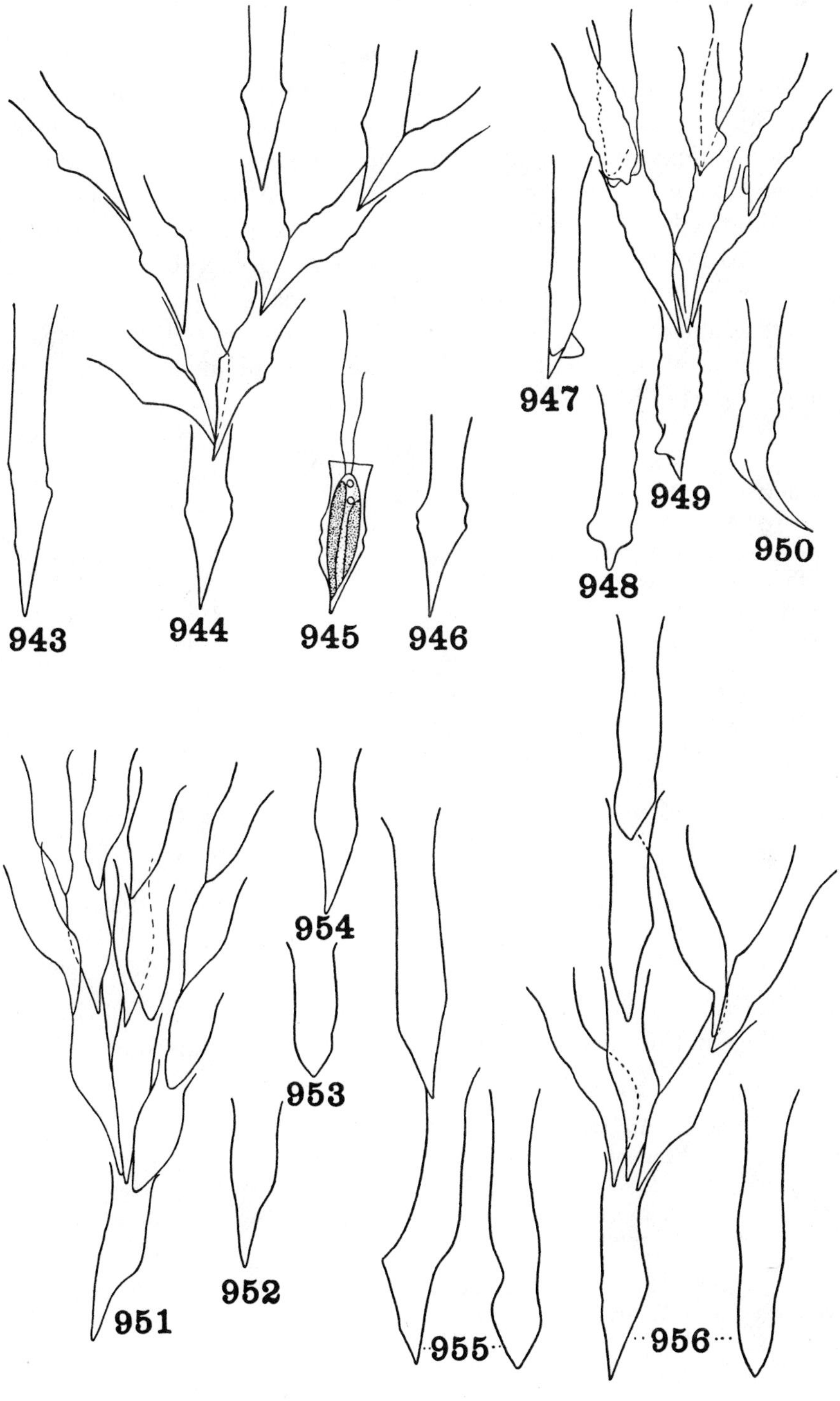

943   944   945   946   947   948   949   950

951   952   953   954   955   956

division, zoospores, amoeboid protoplasts, binucleate statospores; isogamous gametes reported for 1 species.

Dinobryon Ehrenberg 1835

Cells free-floating, sessile or epiphytic, solitary or in colonies, enclosed in conical, campanulate or cylindric, smooth or undulate cellulose receptacles (loricas) with pointed bases and open at the top; colonies arbuscular, divergent or rather compact; protoplast spindle-shaped, conical or ovoid, attached to the base or side of the receptacle; 2 flagella of unequal length; cells with 1–2, elongate, parietal, golden-brown chromatophores, several contractile vacuoles, and 1 apical eyespot.

Longitudinal division of cell contents, the daughter cells migrating only to the mouths of the receptacle or becoming free; palmelloid stages; cysts; isogamy reported in *D. sertularia*.

KEY TO THE SPECIES

1. Colony with cells divergent. 2
1. Colony more or less compact. 4
   2. Sides of receptacle straight. . . . . 1. D. cylindricum
   2. Sides of receptacle undulate. 3
3. Receptacle swollen basally. . . . . 2. D. pediforme
3. Receptable not swollen basally. . . . . 3. D. divergens
   4. Receptacle more or less conical. 4. D. sociale
   4. Receptacle cylindric in upper portion. 5
   4. Receptacle bell-shaped. . . . . 5. D. sertularia
5. Receptacle undulate. . . . . 6. D. bavaricum
5. Receptacle not undulate. 6
   6. Receptacle acutely pointed at base. . . . . 4a. D. sociale var.
                                                               americanum
   6. Receptacle bluntly pointed at base. 7
7. Basal part of receptacle rather symmetric. . . . . 5. D. sertularia
7. Basal part of receptacle irregular. . . . . 5a. D. sertularia var.
                                                                protuberans

1. *Dinobryon cylindricum* Imhof. Receptacles 30–77 μ in length, 8–13 μ in diameter at the mouth, colonial with divergent (sometimes compact)

Figs. 957–960.—*Dinobryon sertularia* var. *protuberans* (Lemmermann) Krieger.

Figs. 961–964.—*Dinobryon bavaricum* Imhof.

Figs. 965–968.—*Dinobryon sociale* Ehrenberg.

Figs. 969, 970.—*Dinobryon sociale* var. *americanum* (Brunnthaler) Bachmann.

Fig. 971.—*Rhizochrysis limnetica* G. M. Smith.

(Figs. 957–970, Ahlstrom; fig. 971, G. M. Smith. Figs. 957–970 ×650; fig. 971 ×500.)

PLATE 83

(Figs. 957 to 971)

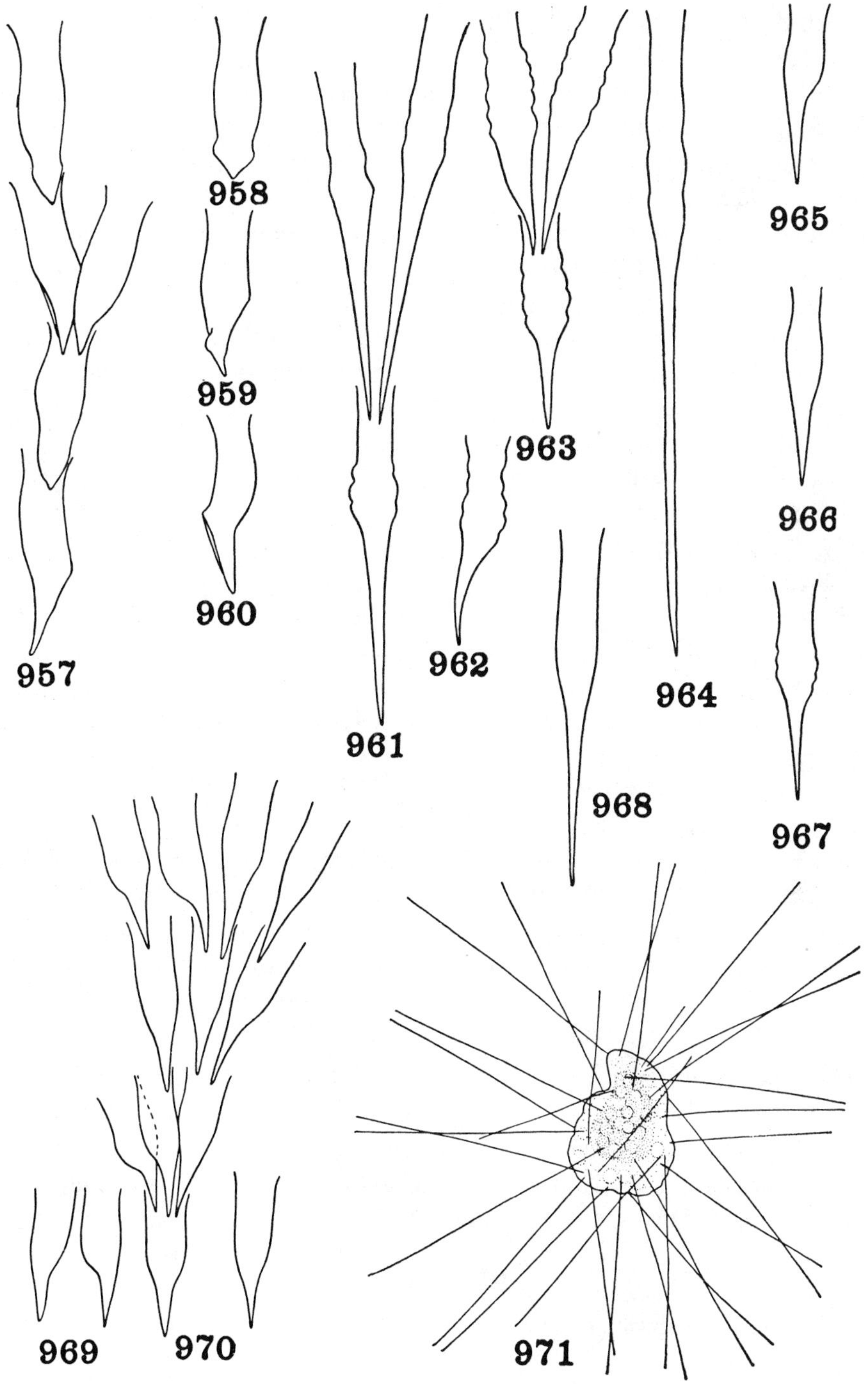

957 958 959 960 961 962 963 964 965 966 967 968 969 970 971

branching, roughly cylindric, tapering to a blunt (rarely acute) point; mouth flaring, often with swelling above base; cysts 11–15 μ. Pl. **82**, figs. **955, 956**.

2. *Dinobryon pediforme* (Lemmermann) Steinecke. Receptacles 7–10 × 24–48 μ, colonial with divergent branching, with undulate sides and conspicuous swellings on basal portions; basal portion often reduced. Pl. **82**, figs. **947–950**.

3. *Dinobryon divergens* Imhof. Receptacles 7–8 × 28–68 μ, with divergent branching and slightly flaring mouth, usually with 2–3 undulations on a side. Pl. **82**, figs. **943–946**.

4. *Dinobryon sociale* Ehrenberg. Receptacles 7–8 × 28–76 μ, with rather compact branching, roughly conical with flaring mouth, undulations usually absent (often present on basal receptacle), gradually tapering from the swollen anterior part. Pl. **83**, figs. **965–968**.

a. Var. *americanum* (Brunnthaler) Bachmann. Receptacle proportionately wider and plumper compared to length (21–40 μ) with moderately flaring mouth, anterior portion quite cylindric, often asymmetric. Pl. **83**, figs. **969, 970**.

5. *Dinobryon sertularia* Ehrenberg. Receptacles 8–12 × 23–43 μ, short and plump, with flaring mouth and bluntly pointed base, cylindric to campanulate with swollen central portion; dense branching and often large colonies; terminal receptacle often longer than the others. Pl. **82**, figs. **951–954**.

a. Var. *protuberans* (Lemmermann) Krieger. Receptacles with irregular basal swellings; colonies smaller. Pl. **83**, figs. **957–960**.

6. *Dinobryon bavaricum* Imhof. Receptacles 6–10 × 38–119 μ, forming compact colonies, with a cylindric, undulate upper portion and a tapering, somewhat conical basal region; undulations weak or missing near mouth; cysts 9–12 μ wide, encased in a gelatinous envelope. Pl. **83**, figs. **961–964**.

Order RHIZOCHRYSIDALES

Cells amoeboid, solitary or united in amorphous colonies, at times forming temporary flagellate stages; protoplast naked, or partially or completely surrounded by a lorica; golden-brown chromatophores; partly autotrophic and partly heterotrophic; reproduction by cell division in the amoeboid state, fragmentation and cysts (statospores).

Family **Rhizochrysidaceae**

With characteristics of the Order.

Rhizochrysis Pascher 1913

Cells free-floating, solitary or in colonies either with or without sheath, amoeboid with delicate acicular pseudopodia; no flagellate stages known; 1 or 2 golden-brown chromatophores, and 1 to numerous vacuoles, or none.

Vegetative cell division; cysts(?).

1. *Rhizochrysis limnetica* G. M. Smith. Cells 35–45 μ (without processes) in diameter, nearly spherical, solitary, free-floating, with numerous spicule-like pseudopodia extending outward in all directions; golden-brown chromatophores and numerous vacuoles. Pl. **83**, fig. **971.**

Phylum PYRROPHYTA

Class *DINOPHYCEAE*

VEGETATIVE cells uninucleate, motile by means of flagella or immobile, unicellular or forming palmelloid colonies or filaments. The protoplast may be naked but is usually surrounded by a definite wall of 1 or 2 layers of which the outer is cellulose. A pectic sheath usually surrounds the walls of immobile genera and rarely certain of the motile species. Almost all of the motile genera have walls consisting of a characteristic number and arrangement of articulated plates separated by narrow inconspicuous sutures or wide, striated, intercalary bands.

Motile genera as well as zoospores of immobile genera always have a transverse furrow partially or completely encircling the cell. Motile cells are biflagellate, both flagella laterally inserted, one being ribbon-like and lying within the transverse furrow and the other thread-like and trailing backward. Yellow-brown or chocolate-brown chromatophores are usually present and may be discoid, bacilliform, stellate, or band-shaped. The pigments are chlorophyll *a* and *c*, beta-carotene and 4 xanthophylls. Pyrenoids with starch sheaths may be present either within or external to the chromatophores.

Nutrition is holophytic, holozoic, or saprophytic. Accumulated food of freshwater species usually is starch and that of marine species is oil. An eyespot is often present in the vegetative cells of motile genera and the zoospores of immobile genera. A few genera have a complex neuromotor apparatus, and the motile genera usually have a pair of non-contractile vacuoles.

Reproduction of motile genera occurs asexually by vegetative cell division and formation of aplanospores and that of immobile genera by means of zoospores and aplanospores. Sexual reproduction is definitely known for only two genera.

Most Dinophyceae are marine and those occurring in freshwater habitats are usually not abundant except in small bodies of water.

KEY TO THE GENERA OF DINOPHYCEAE

1. Plates delicate and indistinct.......................... Glenodinium (p. 307)
1. Plates distinct... 2
   2. With short antapical horns or none................... Peridinium (p. 310)
   2. With 1–3 short antapical horns and 1 usually long apical
      horn... Ceratium (p. 314)

Order PERIDINIALES

Vegetative cells uninucleate, solitary, free-swimming, rarely forming colonies, variously shaped, often somewhat flattened dorsiventrally; cell-wall (theca) divided near the center into an apical epitheca and an antapical hypotheca by a usually complete and slightly spiral transverse furrow (girdle) that is usually divided into 3–6 obscure girdle plates; plates of a definite number, largely cellulose, sometimes with a peripheral layer of pectic material, usually covered with small spines or a reticulum of small ridges; epitheca consists of an upper series of apical plates, a lower series of precingular plates adjoining the girdle, and in some genera an incomplete band of anterior intercalary plates between the apicals and precingulars; hypotheca consists of a series of postcingular plates adjoining the girdle, 1 or 2 antapical plates below them, and sometimes a single posterior intercalary plate between the antapicals and postcingulars; some genera with a ventral plate intercalated in the girdle region; plates separated by sutures or intercalary bands of variable width that are often striate; a longitudinal furrow (sulcus) extends from the girdle into the hypotheca and sometimes projects a slight distance into the epitheca; flagella emerge through a small pore near the ventral plate, one passing transversely through the girdle and the other trailing posteriorly; eyespot present in some; chromatophores usually numerous, yellow-brown or brown; with or without pyrenoids. Reproduction by division of motile or immobile cells; aplanospores; conjugation in 2 genera (*Ceratium* and *Glenodinium*).

Family **Glenodiniaceae**

Cells solitary, usually spherical to ovoid, sometimes flattened dorsiventrally, rarely the ventral surface concave; plates thin, smooth or delicately areolate, difficult to distinguish; sutures delicate; epitheca with 2–9 apical, 0–4 anterior intercalary, and 6–12 precingular plates; hypotheca with 5–12 postcingular, 0–2 posterior intercalary, and 1–2 antapical plates; prominent eyespot in some species; division of motile or immobile cells; aplanospores; isogamy.

Glenodinium Stein 1883

With characteristics of the family Glenodiniaceae; slightly spiral girdle extending entirely around the cell; chromatophores rarely green; aplanospores thick-walled, spherical or angular; isogamous gametes.

KEY TO THE SPECIES

1. Cells ovoid or pyriform in dorsal and ventral view............................ 2
1. Cells nearly spherical in dorsal and ventral view............................. 3
  2. Cells much flattened dorsiventrally; hypotheca without
     spines.. 1. G. gymnodinium

2. Cells slightly flattened dorsiventrally; hypotheca bearing
   spines... 2. G. quadridens
3. Ventral surface slightly concave....................... 3. G. cinctum
3. Ventral surface not concave........................... 4. G. palustre

1. *Glenodinium gymnodinium* Penard. Cells ovoid, greatly flattened
dorsiventrally, ventral surface concave, 35 × 40 μ; girdle slightly spiral;
longitudinal furrow extending from the girdle to the antapical end; the
epitheca with 7 precingular, 1 rhomboidal, 2 ventral apical, 1 large median
apical, and 1 small, rectangular, dorsal apical plate; the hypotheca with 6
postcingular and 2 antapical plates; plates sometimes thick and areolate;
chromatophores yellowish-brown or greenish. Pl. **86**, figs. **1000–1002.**

2. *Glenodinium quadridens* (Stein) Schiller. Cells ovoid to pyriform,
hypotheca shorter than the epitheca, slightly flattened dorsiventrally, 20–
33 × 24–39 μ; girdle spiral, posterior to center of cell; longitudinal furrow
short and wide, extending only a short distance into the epitheca; epitheca
conical, ending in a blunt point, number of plates variable, commonly with
4 central apicals, 1 dorsal apical, 1 rhomboidal, and 7 precingulars; the
hypotheca with 5 postcingular and 2 antapical plates; plates smooth, with
pores, or finely areolate; intercalary bands with or without striations;
hypotheca bearing a variable number of spines, usually 1 on each of the
2 antapical and the 2 lateral postcingular plates; eyespot evident in longitudinal furrow; chromatophores yellow-brown to dark brown. Pl. **86**, figs.
995–997.

3. *Glenodinium cinctum* (Mueller) Ehrenberg. Cells almost spherical,
slightly flattened dorsiventrally, ventral surface concave, 43–45 μ in diameter; girdle slightly spiral; the epitheca with 7 precingular, 1 rhomboidal, 2 ventral apical, 1 median apical, 2 lateral apical and 2 dorsal apical
plates; the hypotheca with 6 postcingular and 2 antapical plates; plates
generally smooth; eyespot horseshoe-shaped, under the longitudinal furrow; chromatophores yellowish-brown. Pl. **86**, fig. **999.**

4. *Glenodinium palustre* (Lemmermann) Schiller. Cells almost spherical,
hypotheca and epitheca about equal in size, 25–31 × 27–34 μ; girdle horizontal; longitudinal furrow broad, extending slightly anteriorly into the

FIGS. 972–975.—*Peridinium inconspicu-um* Lemmermann; fig. 972, apical; fig. 973, dorsal; fig. 974, ventral; fig. 975, antapical.

FIGS. 976–979.—*Peridinium umbonatum* Stein; fig. 976, apical; fig. 977, ventral; fig. 978, dorsal; fig. 979, antapical.

FIGS. 980–983.—*Peridinium cinctum* (Mueller) Ehrenberg; fig. 980, dorsal; fig.

981, ventral; fig. 982, apical; fig. 983, antapical.

FIGS. 984–987.—*Peridinium pusillum* (Penard) Lemmermann; fig. 984, ventral; fig. 985, dorsal; fig. 986, apical; fig. 987, antapical.

(Figs. 972–983, Thompson; figs. 984–987, Eddy. All ×*1000*.)

PLATE 84

(Figs. 972 to 987)

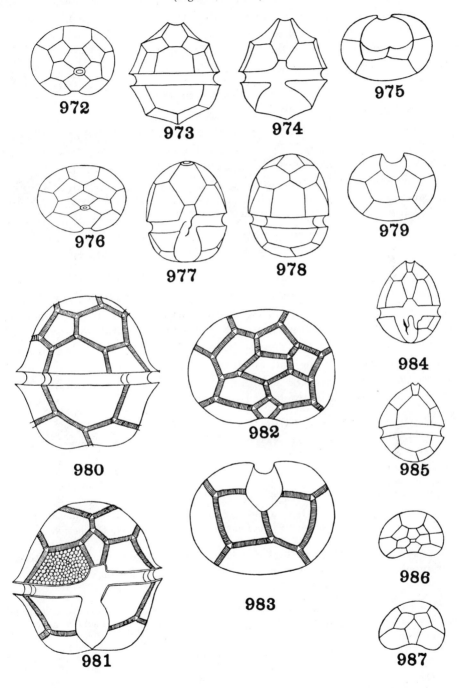

972

973

974

975

976

977

978

979

980

981

982

983

984

985

986

987

epitheca and posteriorly ⅔ the length of the hypotheca; plates smooth and without pores; lacking intercalary striations; the epitheca with 5 precingular, 1 rhomboidal, 2 ventral apical, and 1 dorsal apical plate; the hypotheca has 5 postcingular, 1 accessory, and 1 antapical plate; chromatophores many, small, parietal. Pl. **86**, fig. **998.**

Family **Peridiniaceae**

Cells spherical, ovoid, ellipsoid, or more or less angular, often strongly asymmetric, somewhat flattened dorsiventrally, frequently appearing concave in polar view, rarely with lateral fin or "comb"; epitheca usually larger than hypotheca; apical end rounded, or narrowed and elevated, antapical end rounded, with or without small spines; girdle slightly spiral, descending to right or left, slightly posterior to center of cell, usually with projecting rims; longitudinal furrow may extend slightly into epitheca; plates smooth, areolate, or with striations of small teeth; intercalary bands often striate; chromatophores numerous; with or without eyespot.

Peridinium Ehrenberg 1832

Cells usually spherical, ovoid, or angular in front view, with or without short apical and antapical horns; epitheca with 4 apical, 2–3 anterior intercalary, and 7 precingular plates; hypotheca with 5 postcingular and 2 antapical plates; 1 of the apicals (rhomboidal plate) extends along the ventral surface from the end of the longitudinal furrow to the apex or nearly so; eyespot present in some species; division of immobile cells; aplanospores spherical, thick- or thin-walled.

KEY TO THE SPECIES

1. Mature cells with a lateral fin on each side . . . . 1. P. bipes
1. Mature cells without lateral fins 2
  2. Apical end acute . . . . 2. P. inconspicuum
  2. Apical end conical . . . . 3. P. pusillum
  2. Apical end neither acute nor conical 3
3. Epitheca distinctly larger than hypotheca . . . . 4. P. umbonatum
3. Epitheca and hypotheca usually equal in size . . . . 5. P. cinctum

1. *Peridinium bipes* Stein. Cells spherical to ovoid, slightly flattened dorsiventrally, epitheca larger than hypotheca, anterior end somewhat

Figs. 988–991.—*Peridinium bipes* Stein; fig. 988, ventral; fig. 989, dorsal; fig. 990, antapical; fig. 991, apical.

Figs. 992, 993.—*Ceratium hirundinella* (Mueller) Schrank; fig. 992, ventral; fig. 993, dorsal.

Fig. 994.—*Ceratium cornutum* (Ehrenberg) Claparede and Lachmann, ventral view.

(Figs. 988–991, 994, Eddy; figs. 992, 993, Thompson. Figs. 988–991 ×*1000;* figs. 992–994 ×*500.*)

PLATE 85

(Figs. 988 to 994)

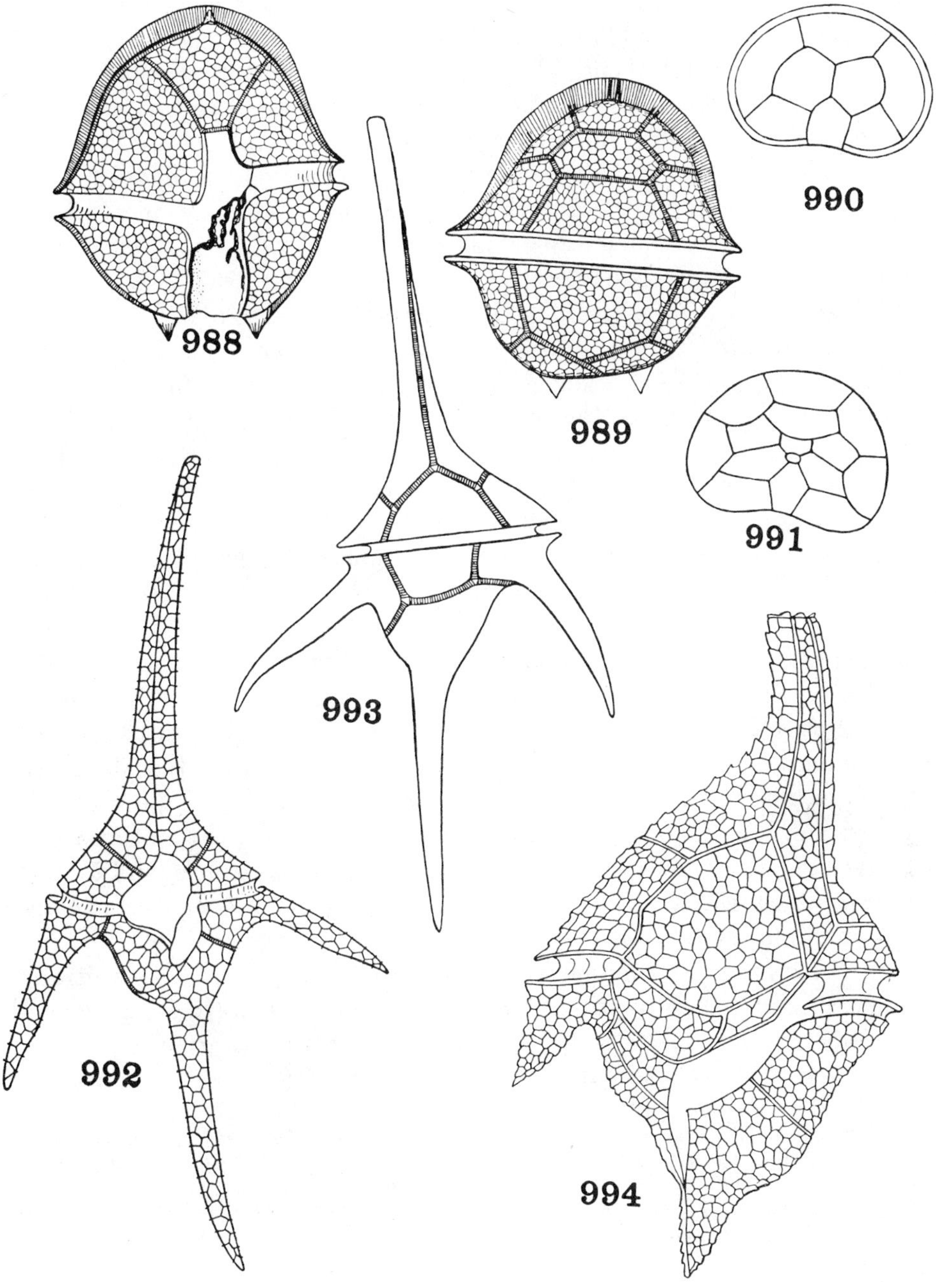

988

989

990

991

992

993

994

produced and bearing 2 spines at the apex, posterior end broadly rounded, 38–55 × 40–80 μ; girdle slightly spiral and posterior to center of cell; longitudinal furrow extending a little way anteriorly into epitheca and posteriorly to antapical end; plates granulate, areolate or reticulate, somewhat concave; intercalary bands with striations; mature cells with a lateral fin or "comb" on each side from apical to antapical end; the epitheca with 7 precingular, 1 rhomboidal, 2 ventral apical, 3 median apical and 1 dorsal apical plate; the hypotheca with 5 postcingular and 2 antapical plates; 2 spine-like processes on antapical plates, 1 on each side of the longitudinal furrow; chromatophores yellow to brown. Pl. **85,** figs. **988–991.**

2. *Peridinium inconspicuum* Lemmermann. Cells ovoid, somewhat flattened dorsiventrally, apical end acute, antapical end rounded, 12–25 × 15–30 μ; girdle median, wide, straight; longitudinal furrow extending a short distance into the epitheca, widened posteriorly in hypotheca; plates delicately areolate; intercalary spaces between antapical plates bearing small scattered spines; the epitheca with 7 precingular, 1 rhomboidal, 2 ventral apical, 1 median apical, and 2 dorsal apical plates; the hypotheca with 5 postcingular and 2 antapical plates; eyespot lacking; chromatophores numerous, parietal, brown. Pl. **84,** figs. **972–975.**

3. *Peridinium pusillum* (Penard) Lemmermann. Cells ovoid, somewhat flattened dorsiventrally, epitheca larger than hypotheca, apical end conical, antapical end rounded, 13–20 × 18–25 μ; girdle straight, posterior to center of cell; longitudinal furrow wide, extending slightly into epitheca and almost to posterior margin of hypotheca; plates smooth or delicately areolate; intercalary spaces narrow; hypotheca with small spines on the margins of intercalary spaces and longitudinal furrow; the epitheca with 7 precingular, 1 rhomboidal, 2 ventral apical, 1 median apical, and 2 dorsal apical plates; the hypotheca with 5 postcingular and 2 antapical plates; chromatophores yellowish-green to brown. Pl. **84,** figs. **984–987.**

4. *Peridinium umbonatum* Stein. Cells ovoid, flattened dorsiventrally, epitheca larger than hypotheca, apical end helmet-shaped, antapical end broadly rounded, 15–32 × 18–40 μ; girdle slightly spiral, usually posterior to center of the cell; longitudinal furrow extending a short distance into

FIGS. 995–997.—*Glenodinium quadridens* (Stein) Schiller; fig. 995, dorsal; fig. 996, apical and antapical; fig. 997, ventral.

FIG. 998.—*Glenodinium palustre* (Lemmermann) Schiller, ventral, dorsal, apical and antapical views.

FIG. 999.—*Glenodinium cinctum* (Mueller) Ehrenberg, ventral, dorsal, apical, and antapical views.

FIGS. 1000–1002.—*Glenodinium gymnodinium* Penard; fig. 1000, ventral view; fig. 1001, ventral view with uncinate process, and apical view; fig. 1002, dorsal view.

(Figs. 995–997, Thompson; figs. 998–1002, Eddy. All ×*1000*.)

PLATE 86

(Figs. 995 to 1002)

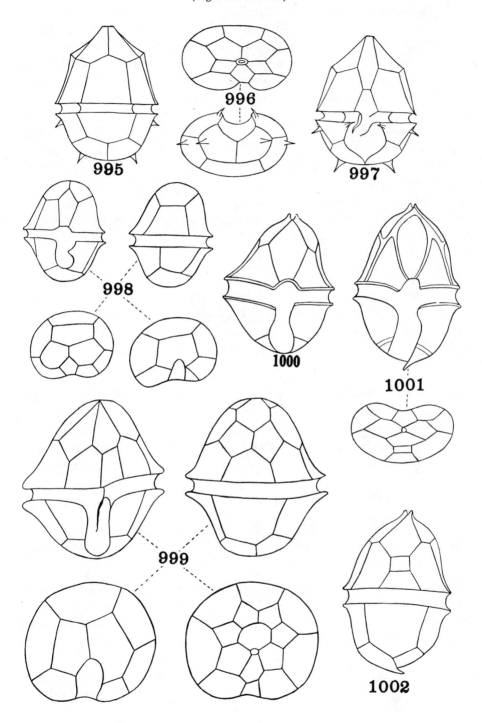

epitheca, much widened in the hypotheca and reaching to antapical end; plates thick and smooth or with scattered, coarse punctae connected by longitudinal lines of very delicate punctae; the epitheca with 7 precingular, 1 rhomboidal, 2 ventral apical, 1 median apical, and 2 dorsal apical plates; the hypotheca with 5 postcingular and 2 antapical plates; eyespot lacking; chromatophores numerous, parietal, red-brown or brown. Pl. 84, figs. **976–979.**

5. *Peridinium cinctum* (Mueller) Ehrenberg. Cells ovoid to spherical, slightly flattened dorsiventrally, epitheca sometimes larger than hypotheca, 35–73 × 40–75 μ; girdle median or slightly posterior to center of cell, slightly spiral; longitudinal furrow extending into the epitheca to the rhomboidal cell and to the posterior margin of the hypotheca; plates thick and areolate; intercalary bands heavily striate; epitheca with 7 precingular, 1 rhomboidal, 2 ventral apical, 2 median apical, and 2 dorsal apical plates; hypotheca with 5 precingular and 2 antapical plates; eyespot lacking; chromatophores numerous, parietal, dark brown. Pl. **84,** figs. **980–983.**

Family **Ceratiaceae**

Epitheca prolonged into a single long apical horn with or without a pore; hypotheca bearing 1–3 stout horns that are always shorter than the apical horn; otherwise similar to Peridiniaceae.

Ceratium Schrank 1793

Cells usually solitary, some species forming temporary colonies, angular, strongly asymmetric, frequently markedly flattened; with 1 usually long apical horn and 1–3 short antapical horns, plates heavy, conspicuously areolate; sutures narrow; epitheca with 3–5 (usually 4) apical and 5 precingular plates; hypotheca with 5 postcingular and 2 antapical plates; girdle interrupted on ventral surface by a large unsculptured, hyaline plate; division of motile cells; aplanospores thick-walled, angular; conjugation.

KEY TO THE SPECIES

1. Apical horn short, open at the end.............................. 1. C. cornutum
1. Apical horn long, closed at the end.......................... 2. C. hirundinella

1. *Ceratium cornutum* (Ehrenberg) Claparede and Lachmann. Cells stout, 75–80 μ wide; apical horn short, curved forward and to the right, the end truncate and open; antapical horn short, straight, the end pointed and closed. Pl. **85,** fig. **994.**

2. *Ceratium hirundinella* (Mueller) Schrank. Cells slender, extremely variable, 28–75 × 95–400 μ; apical horn long, slender, straight, the apex truncate and the end closed; 2–3 antapical horns, stouter and more pointed than the apical horn. Pl. **85,** figs. **992, 993.**

Phylum EUGLENOPHYTA

Class *EUGLENOPHYCEAE*

CELLS solitary, motile or rarely epiphytic, or forming immobile dendroid colonies, uninucleate, with 1–3 flagella or rarely none. The protoplast may be naked or enclosed either within a wall or a lorica. The lorica consists of a transparent, colorless gelatinous material that becomes opaque and colored yellow or brown with age due to impregnation with iron salts. The protoplast is colorless or pigmented and the outer portion is differentiated as a flexible or rigid periplast that is frequently ridged or striate. Chromatophores are dark green, usually several in a cell, and are discoid, band-shaped, or stellate. The pigments are chlorophylls *a* and *b*, beta-carotene and a xanthophyll. Pyrenoids when present may be within or outside the chromatophores. Nutrition is holophytic, saprophytic, or holozoic, and accumulated food is usually paramylum which occurs as characteristic spherical, discoid, rod-like, or granular bodies. Fats in the form of oil droplets are sometimes present. The nucleus is prominent and usually centrally located.

The anterior end is provided with a flask-shaped reservoir consisting of a narrow canal and an enlarged basal portion that is adjoined by 1 or more contractile vacuoles. In certain genera there may be a rod-organ parallel to the reservoir. The flagella are inserted at the base of the reservoir and project through the canal. There may be a single forward projecting flagellum with a basal bifurcation, or 2 flagella without a bifurcation and both projecting forward, or 1 forward and the other trailing. An eyespot is present in most of the pigmented species and in some of the colorless ones.

Asexual reproduction by division of motile or immobile cells, at times resulting in temporary palmelloid colonies; thin- or thick-walled cysts; fusion of autogamous gametes reported.

Most members of the Euglenophyceae occur in freshwater, frequently in large numbers, particularly in pools rich in organic materials.

KEY TO THE GENERA OF EUGLENOPHYCEAE

1. Forming dendroid immobile colonies. . . . . Colacium (p. 327)
1. Solitary, free-swimming. 2
  2. Cells metabolic. . . . . Euglena (p. 316)
  2. Cells rigid. 3

3. Protoplast enclosed in a lorica...................... Trachelomonas (p. 324)
3. Protoplast naked... 4
   4. Cells flattened................................. Phacus (p. 322)
   4. Cells not flattened... 5
5. Cells broadly ellipsoid to ovoid..................... Lepocinclis (p. 322)
5. Cells not broadly ellipsoid or ovoid.................. Euglena (p. 316)

Order EUGLENALES

Vegetative cells always solitary and motile. Otherwise the characteristics of the Class Euglenophyceae.

Family **Euglenaceae**

Cell variously shaped, usually round or sometimes flattened in cross-section; motile by means of flagella or amoeboid movement; uniflagellate or rarely the flagellum lacking; periplast smooth or ornamented, soft and strongly metabolic, or rigid and slightly or not at all metabolic; protoplasts mostly naked, certain genera with protoplast enclosed within a lorica; usually with chromatophores and an eyespot; division of cells that are generally immobile sometimes resulting in temporary palmelloid colonies; cysts; reports of sexual reproduction very rare.

Euglena Ehrenberg 1838

Cell elongate, oblong, lanceolate or spindle-shaped, ridged or spirally twisted, sometimes attenuate at posterior end, solitary, motile by means of a single flagellum, usually metabolic; flagellum of varied length, bifurcate at lower end and with a granular swelling at point of branching, each branch terminating in a blepharoplast; periplast more or less plastic and usually marked by striations; chromatophores numerous, discoid to band-shaped, with or without pyrenoids; usually with an eyespot at the anterior end; with a flask-shaped reservoir opening externally at anterior end of cell through the narrowed reservoir canal; 1 or more contractile vacuoles adjacent and opening into reservoir; formation of paramylum bodies of variable number and shape, attached to chromatophores or free in cytoplasm; nucleus usually relatively large and centrally located; development of hematochrome granules free in cytoplasm of some species, sometimes in sufficient quantity to obscure chromatophores.

Reproduction asexually by longitudinal division of motile cells or in temporary thick- or thin-walled cysts, the daughter cells at times forming temporary palmelloid colonies; union of amoeboid isogamous gametes reported for 1 species.

KEY TO THE SPECIES

1. Hematochrome granules free in cytoplasm; red pigment often
    obscuring green of chromatophores...................... 1. E. sanguinea
1. Hematochrome granules usually not present............................. 2
    2. Cell spirally twisted; sometimes with definite ridges or grooves............ 3
    2. Cell neither spirally twisted nor with definite ridges or grooves............ 5
3. Periplast longitudinally striate... 4
3. Periplast not longitudinally striate...................... 2. E. torta
    4. Cell with a single groove............................. 3. E. oxyuris
    4. Cell with 3 longitudinal ridges....................... 4. E. tripteris
    4. Cell lacking ridges or grooves....................... 5. E. spiroides
5. Periplast longitudinally striate... 6
5. Periplast not longitudinally striate...................... 6. E. elongata
    6. Striations composed of prominent raised processes....... 7. E. spirogyra
    6. Striations not composed of prominent raised processes................... 7
7. Cell 25 μ or more in width........................... 8. E. oblonga
7. Cell less than 25 μ in width...................................... 8
    8. Posterior end sharp-pointed......................... 9. E. acutissima
    8. Posterior end not sharp-pointed....................................... 9
9. Posterior end both narrowed and truncate................ 10. E. acus
9. Posterior end not both narrowed and truncate........................... 10
    10. Cell elongate-cylindric or flattened.................................... 11
    10. Cell usually fusiform or cylindrically fusiform...................... 12
11. Chromatophores discoid.............................. 11. E. deses
11. Chromatophores elongate rods.......................... 12. E. geniculata
    12. Cell widest below the middle........................ 13. E. viridis
    12. Cell widest at the middle............................. 14. E. gracilis

1. *Euglena sanguinea* Ehrenberg. Cell elongate-cylindric to fusiform, 24–44 × 55–170 μ, anterior end usually rounded and narrowed, posterior end broadly rounded or extended into a short narrow tip, metabolic; periplast with spiral striations; flagellum 1.5–2.0 times body length; reservoir approximately 10 μ in diameter, the canal almost straight, approximately 15 μ long; eyespot lateral to reservoir at base of canal, about 10 μ long; chromatophores numerous, usually spindle-shaped, parallel with striations, with pyrenoids, green color often obscured by hematochrome granules; nucleus spherical, about 20 μ in diameter, posterior to mid-body region; paramylum bodies numerous, rounded rectangularly, free in cytoplasm, or concave, discoid and attached to chromatophores; hematochrome granules diffuse in sunlight, centrally located in shade and darkness; union of gametes reported; division in thick- or thin-walled cysts. Pl. 87, fig. 1013.

2. *Euglena torta* Stokes. Cell elongate-fusiform, 60–63 μ long, spirally

twisted, not metabolic (?); periplast smooth; flagellum about equal to body length; paramylum bodies 2, long and rod-shaped, 1 anterior and 1 posterior to the nucleus; longitudinal division. Pl. **87**, fig. **1004**.

3. *Euglena oxyuris* Schmarda. Cell greatly elongated, cylindric or slightly flattened, usually twisted, spiral groove extending entire body length, $19-45 \times 140-490 \mu$, anterior end rounded and with slight indentation at opening of canal, posterior end with elongated colorless tip, usually with slight metabolic movement; periplast with prominent striations composed of short appressed processes; flagellum 0.3–0.5 body length; reservoir 10–15 μ in diameter, the canal curved, 6–20 μ long; eyespot lateral to body of reservoir, 8–14 μ long; chromatophores numerous, discoid, without pyrenoids; nucleus 31–48 μ in diameter, centrally located; paramylum bodies 2 annular elongate rings, 20–40 μ long, 1 anterior and 1 posterior to nucleus, and numerous small annular bodies scattered through cytoplasm; hyaline granules and reddish-brown hematochrome granules in cytoplasm; longitudinal division; encystment not known. Pl. **87**, fig. **1010**.

4. *Euglena tripteris* (Dujardin) Klebs. Cell elongate, 3-ridged, spirally twisted, $8-16 \times 70-120 \mu$, anterior end slightly truncate, posterior end extended into a long colorless, curved tip; only slightly metabolic; periplast with longitudinal striations; reservoir pyriform with a short canal; flagellum 0.7 body length; eyespot prominent lateral to anterior portion of reservoir; chromatophores discoid, numerous; nucleus central; paramylum bodies rod-shaped, 15–20 μ long, 1 anterior and 1 posterior to nucleus, also numerous small scattered granules; longitudinal division without thickened membrane. Pl. **87**, fig. **1014**.

5. *Euglena spiroides* Lemmermann. Cell elongated, band-shaped, spirally twisted, $12-16 \times 60-170 \mu$, anterior end rounded, posterior end extend-

Fig. 1003.—*Euglena acus* Ehrenberg.

Fig. 1004.—*Euglena torta* Stokes.

Fig. 1005.—*Euglena acutissima* Lemmermann.

Fig. 1006.—*Euglena elongata* Schewiakoff.

Fig. 1007.—*Euglena deses* Ehrenberg.

Fig. 1008.—*Euglena oblonga* Schmitz.

Fig. 1009.—*Euglena viridis* Ehrenberg.

Fig. 1010.—*Euglena oxyuris* Schmarda.

Fig. 1011.—*Euglena spirogyra* Ehrenberg.

Fig. 1012.—*Euglena gracilis* Klebs.

Fig. 1013.—*Euglena sanguinea* Ehrenberg.

Fig. 1014.—*Euglena tripteris* (Dujardin) Klebs.

Fig. 1015.—*Euglena geniculata* Dujardin.

Fig. 1016.—*Euglena spiroides* Lemmermann.

Fig. 1017.—*Colacium calvum* Stein.

Fig. 1018.—*Colacium vesiculosum* Ehrenberg.

(Figs. 1003, 1005, 1015, 1017, 1018, Walton; figs. 1004, 1006–1014, 1016, Johnson. Figs. 1003, 1004, 1006–1018, $\times 500$; fig. 1005 $\times 1000$.)

PLATE 87
(Figs. 1003 to 1018)

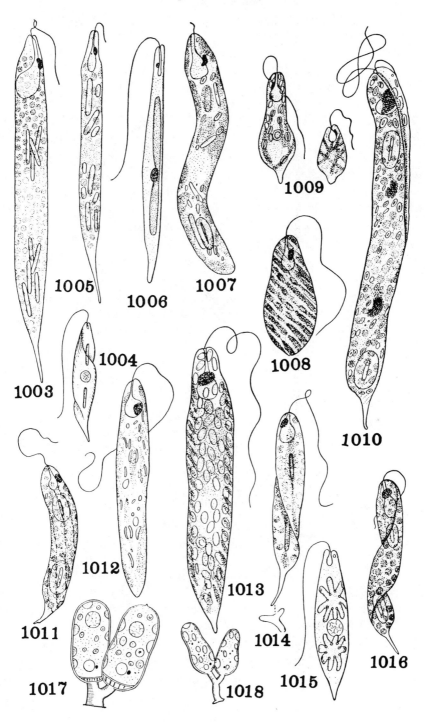

1005

1006

1007

1009

1010

1008

1003

1004

1011

1012

1013

1014

1015

1016

1017

1018

ed into a colorless tip at a pronounced angle to body, metabolic; periplast longitudinally striate; flagellum 0.2–0.3 body length; reservoir spherical, 7–9 μ in diameter, canal narrow, 8–11 μ long; eyespot about 5 μ in diameter, lateral to posterior end of canal; chromatophores numerous, discoid, 3–4 μ in diameter; nucleus 10–12 μ long, centrally located; paramylum bodies slightly elongate-annular, 1 anterior and 1 posterior to nucleus; thin-walled cysts. Pl. **87,** fig. **1016.**

6. *Euglena elongata* Schewiakoff. Cell much elongate, fusiform to spindle-shaped, 5–7 $\times$ 60–70 μ, anterior end truncate, posterior end pointed and usually hyaline, feebly metabolic; periplast smooth; flagellum 0.5–0.6 body length; reservoir 3 μ in diameter, the canal 8 μ long and narrow; eyespot evident, lateral to posterior end of canal; chromatophore single, flattened fusiform, without pyrenoids, approximately 40 μ long; nucleus approximately 10 μ long, slightly posterior to mid-body region; paramylum bodies unknown. Pl. **87,** fig. **1006.**

7. *Euglena spirogyra* Ehrenberg. Cell cylindric or flattened, 6–35 $\times$ 80–150 μ, anterior end rounded and slightly narrowed, posterior end produced into an acute and frequently curved tip, metabolic; periplast yellowish-brown, spirally striate with pyramidal to conical and frequently truncate processes, prominent striations often alternating with less prominent ones; flagellum 0.2 body length or shorter; reservoir 7–12 μ in diameter, the canal about 10 μ long; eyespot prominent, 4–8 μ long, lateral to posterior end of canal; chromatophores numerous, discoid, 3–5 μ in diameter, without pyrenoids; nucleus 15–20 μ long, centrally located; paramylum bodies large, elongate-annular, 1 anterior and 1 posterior to nucleus, sometimes with small annular rectangular bodies; longitudinal division, cysts without a gelatinous envelope. Pl. **87,** fig. **1011.**

8. *Euglena oblonga* Schmitz. Cell oval to short-cylindric, 25–40 $\times$ 50–70 μ, anterior end usually rounded, posterior end rounded or with a short tip, metabolic; periplast with spiral striations; flagellum of body length or longer; reservoir 7–9 μ in diameter, the canal slightly curved, 7–8 μ long; eyespot 4–6 μ in diameter, lateral to posterior end of canal; chromatophores numerous, fusiform to band-shaped in side view, usually parallel to striations, with pyrenoids; nucleus spherical, approximately 10 μ in diameter, centrally located; paramylum as 2 annular discoid bodies attached to each chromatophore or ovoid bodies free in cytoplasm; thin-walled cysts. Pl. **87,** fig. **1008.**

9. *Euglena acutissima* Lemmermann. Cell elongate-cylindric, 7–11 $\times$ 120–150 μ, anterior end narrowed and truncate, posterior end extended into a colorless sharp-pointed tip, slightly metabolic; periplast longitudi-

nally striate; flagellum 16–20 μ long; reservoir about 6 μ in diameter, the canal narrowly elongate, 12–16 μ long; eyespot prominent, lateral to posterior end of canal; chromatophores numerous, 4 μ in diameter, without pyrenoids; nucleus 10 μ long, centrally located; paramylum bodies 2 or more, usually rod-shaped, 15–20 μ long, located anterior and posterior to nucleus. Pl. **87,** fig. **1005.**

10. *Euglena acus* Ehrenberg. Cell cylindric to spindle-shaped, 7–18 $\times$ 52–200 μ, anterior end narrowed and truncate, posterior end narrowed into colorless truncate tip, weakly metabolic; periplast with delicate spiral striations; flagellum 0.2–0.3 body length; reservoir 6–16 μ in diameter, the canal 10–20 μ long; chromatophores numerous, discoid, 3 μ in diameter; without pyrenoids; eyespot usually evident, hyaline or with hematochrome granules at margin, lateral to posterior end of canal, 5–7 μ in diameter; nucleus 10–20 μ long, centrally located; paramylum bodies numerous, rod-shaped, 12–20 μ long. Pl. **87,** fig. **1003.**

11. *Euglena deses* Ehrenberg. Cell elongately cylindric or slightly flattened, 11–24 $\times$ 70–200 μ, anterior end round or slightly truncate, posterior end blunt and colored, metabolic movement sluggish; periplast with delicate spiral striations; flagellum short; reservoir canal slightly curved, 8–14 μ long; eyespot evident, crescent-shaped, 4–7 μ long, hematochrome granules 0.5 μ in diameter; chromatophores numerous, discoid, approximately 15 μ long, with pyrenoids; nucleus nearly spherical, 12–15 μ in diameter, position variable, usually central; paramylum bodies rod-shaped or elongate-annular, scattered; longitudinal division with or without encystment. Pl. **87,** fig. **1007.**

12. *Euglena geniculata* Dujardin. Cell elongate-cylindric to spindle-shaped, 12–22 $\times$ 70–85 μ, extended posteriorly to colorless tip; actively metabolic; periplast with delicate spiral striations; flagellum about equal to body length; eyespot prominent; chromatophores elongate rods in 2 or 3 star-shaped masses, 1 of which is posterior to the nucleus; nucleus central; paramylum bodies present; longitudinal division; encystment with thin membrane. Pl. **87,** fig. **1015.**

13. *Euglena viridis* Ehrenberg. Cell usually fusiform, variable, widest below mid-body region, 14–20 $\times$ 40–65 μ, anterior end rounded or bilabiate, posterior end usually extended into colorless tip of variable length, metabolic, locomotion rapid; periplast spirally striate; flagellum equal to body length or somewhat shorter; reservoir elongated, 4–5 μ in diameter, the canal 5–7 μ long; eyespot 4–5 μ in diameter, lateral to posterior end of canal; chromatophores 6 to numerous, variously arranged, spindle-shaped, 13–18 μ long; nucleus spherical, 10–15 μ in diameter, usually in posterior

third of cell, rarely centrally located; paramylum 2 annular discoid bodies attached to each chromatophore, sometimes ovoid and rectangular bodies free in cytoplasm; small spherical granules scattered in cytoplasm; longitudinal division or division in thick- or thin-walled cysts. Pl. **87**, fig. **1009**.

14. *Euglena gracilis* Klebs. Cell cylindrically fusiform, 6–22 × 35–55 μ, anterior end rounded, posterior end usually with a blunt tip or expanded due to metabolic movement, strongly metabolic, very active, periplast with delicate spiral striations; flagellum about equal to body length; reservoir 5–6 μ in diameter, the canal 5 μ long; eyespot prominent, cup-shaped, lateral to body of reservoir; chromatophores numerous, lenticular-fusiform, 12–20 μ long, with pyrenoids; nucleus spherical, 8–10 μ in diameter, centrally located; paramylum bodies usually 2, annular, discoid, attached on either side of chromatophore, 3 μ in diameter, occasionally free in cytoplasm; division in thin gelatinous membrane; encystment with thin or thick gelatinous membrane. Pl. **87**, fig. **1012**.

Lepocinclis Perty 1849

Cells solitary, radially symmetrical, not metabolic, broadly ellipsoid to ovoid, circular in polar view, the posterior pole sometimes more or less pointed, motile by means of a single flagellum; periplast rigid, usually spirally striate; chromatophores numerous, parietal, discoid; flagellum bifurcate at lower end, with a granular swelling at the point of branching; reservoir with canal similar to *Euglena;* paramylum bodies 2, annular, large, lateral in position; occasionally with 1 eyespot; division in a resting stage.

1. *Lepocinclis ovum* (Ehrenberg) Lemmermann. Cells ovoid, 15–18 × 30–38 μ, posterior end abruptly attenuated into a spine-like projection 6–7 μ in length; periplast spirally striate; flagellum twice body length. Pl. **88**, fig. **1025**.

Phacus Dujardin 1841

Cells solitary, usually flattened, the flat faces oval or elliptic in outline, sometimes twisted along the longitudinal axis, motile by means of a single flagellum; periplast rigid, not metabolic, smooth, longitudinally òr spirally striate, or covered with wart-like processes; posterior end sometimes bearing a straight, twisted, or uncinate spine of variable length; bifurcate flagellum, reservoir with canal similar to *Euglena;* chromatophores numerous, discoid, pointed; eyespot may be present at anterior end; some species with a longitudinal keel, longitudinal furrow, or with lateral edges each spread into 2 halves separated by a deep furrow; paramylum bodies discoid, disc-shaped with raised margins or ring-shaped, variable in number; longitudinal division of immobile cells; cysts; autogamy reported.

KEY TO THE SPECIES

1. Posterior spine long.. 2
1. Posterior spine short... 4
   2. Cell pyriform; periplast spirally ridged.................. 1. P. pyrum
   2. Cell broadly ovoid; periplast longitudinally striate......................... 3
3. Flat or slightly twisted along longitudinal axis.............. 2. P. longicauda
3. Spirally twisted along longitudinal axis..................... 3. P. torta
   4. Posterior spine straight or slightly oblique............... 4. P. acuminata
   4. Posterior spine uncinate.. 5
5. Dorsal keel extending full length of cell.................... 5. P. triqueter
5. Dorsal keel extending posteriorly to middle of cell........... 6. P. pleuronectes

1. *Phacus pyrum* (Ehrenberg) Stein. Cell pyriform, circular in end view, 13–19 × 30–55 μ; anterior portion slightly flattened laterally; posterior end bearing a long straight spine; periplast spirally ridged; flagellum approximately body length; paramylum bodies 2 and large or several, small and discoid; eyespot not very prominent. Pl. **88,** fig. **1021.**

2. *Phacus longicauda* (Ehrenberg) Dujardin. Cell ovoid, flat or slightly twisted along longitudinal axis, 45–70 × 85–170 μ; posterior end bearing spine up to 70 μ long; periplast longitudinally striate; flagellum approximately body length; 1 large paramylum body sometimes accompanied by several smaller ones; chromatophores discoid. Pl. **88,** fig. **1022.**

3. *Phacus torta* Lemmermann. (*P. longicauda* var. *torta* Lemmermann.) Cell spirally twisted along longitudinal axis, 40–44 × 80–100 μ; posterior end bearing a spine about equaling body length; periplast longitudinally striate; flagellum equaling cell length excluding spine; paramylum body 1, large, discoid with thick edge; chromatophores discoid. Pl. **88,** fig. **1023.**

4. *Phacus acuminata* Stokes. Cell oval in outline or appearing triangular in some cells having straight lateral margins, very thin, greatest width below the middle, 20–30 × 25–40 μ; periplast longitudinally striate; flagellum approximately body length; usually 1 large paramylum body, sometimes a second smaller one near the base of spine; shallow dorsal furrow extending 0.5–0.7 of body length. Pl. **88,** fig. **1024.**

5. *Phacus triqueter* (Ehrenberg) Dujardin. Cell ovoid, decidedly concavo-convex, 33–35 × 49–55 μ; posterior spine short and uncinate; periplast longitudinally striate; flagellum body length; dorsal keel prominent, extending full length of body; paramylum bodies 1 to 2, annular. Pl. **88,** fig. **1020.**

6. *Phacus pleuronectes* (Mueller) Dujardin. Cell broadly ovoid, slightly twisted, 29–70 × 40–100 μ; posterior spine short and uncinate; periplast longitudinally striate; flagellum approximately body length; dorsal keel extending from anterior end to middle of cell; paramylum body usually single, large, discoid. Pl. **88,** fig. **1019.**

Trachelomonas Ehrenberg 1833

Cell solitary, motile, usually with a single flagellum, the protoplast highly metabolic and loosely encased in a rigid lorica; reservoir at the anterior pole; flagellum bifurcate at the base, with a granular swelling, emerging through a wide circular aperture; usually with an eyespot at anterior pole; lorica spherical or ellipsoid, sometimes campanulate or fusiform, pore at anterior end with or without a collar, the surface smooth or variously ornamented, usually brown because of heavy impregnation with iron salts; chromatophores 2–15, or rarely absent, discoid, parietal, with or without pyrenoids; paramylum bodies small, present or absent.

Reproduction by division usually within lorica of immobile cells; division of protoplast outside lorica forming palmelloid colonies; cysts.

KEY TO THE SPECIES

1. Lorica with a posterior terminal process or spike.......................... 2
1. Lorica not with a posterior terminal process or spike........................ 5
   2. Lorica triangular or trapezoidal...................... 1. T. acuminata
   2. Lorica fusiform...................................... 2. T. magdaleniana
   2. Lorica cylindric..................................... 3. T. urceolata
   2. Lorica spherical or transversely ovoid................ 3
   2. Lorica longitudinally ovoid.......................... 4
3. Lorica smooth.. 4. T. ensifera
3. Lorica finely granulate............................... 5. T. schauinslandii
   4. Lorica irregularly corrugate........................ 6. T. tambowika
   4. Lorica not corrugate................................ 7. T. caudata

FIG. 1019.—*Phacus pleuronectes* (Mueller) Dujardin.

FIG. 1020.—*Phacus triqueter* (Ehrenberg) Dujardin.

FIG. 1021.—*Phacus pyrum* (Ehrenberg) Stein.

FIG. 1022.—*Phacus longicauda* (Ehrenberg) Dujardin.

FIG. 1023.—*Phacus torta* Lemmermann.

FIG. 1024.—*Phacus acuminata* Stokes.

FIG. 1025.—*Lepocinclis ovum* (Ehrenberg) Lemmermann.

FIG. 1026.—*Trachelomonas volvocina* Ehrenberg.

FIG. 1027.—*Trachelomonas hispida* (Perty) Stein.

FIG. 1028.—*Trachelomonas magdaleniana* Deflandre.

FIG. 1029.—*Trachelomonas tambowika* Swirenko.

FIG. 1030.—*Trachelomonas ensifera* Daday.

FIG. 1031.—*Trachelomonas similis* Stokes.

FIG. 1032.—*Trachelomonas urceolata* Stokes.

FIG. 1033.—*Trachelomonas acuminata* (Schmarda) Stein.

FIG. 1034.—*Trachelomonas schauinslandii* Lemmermann.

FIG. 1035.—*Trachelomonas armata* (Ehrenberg) Stein.

FIG. 1036.—*Trachelomonas caudata* (Ehrenberg) Stein.

(Figs. 1019, 1021–1024, Allerge and Jahn; figs. 1020, 1025–1027, 1030–1036, Walton; figs. 1028, 1029, Deflandre. Figs. 1019, 1020, 1022, 1023, 1027–1030, 1032, 1033 ×500; figs. 1021, 1024–1026, 1031, 1034 ×1000.)

PLATE 88

(Figs. 1019 to 1036)

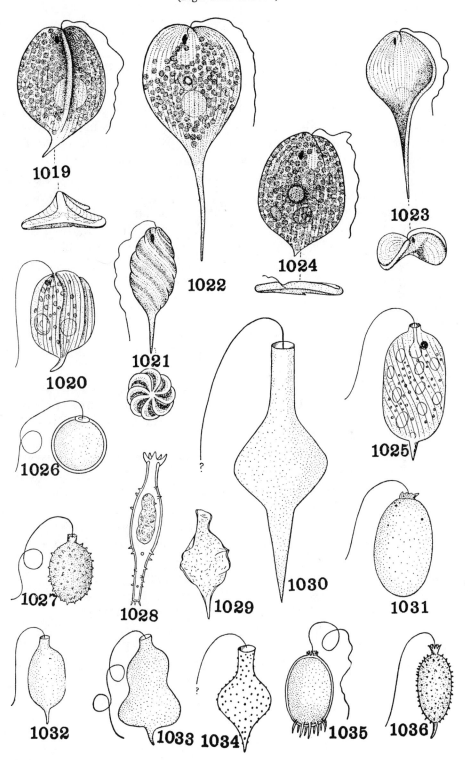

1019

1020

1021

1022

1023

1024

1025

1026

1027

1028

1029

1030

1031

1032

1033

1034

1035

1036

5. Lorica spherical.................................... 8. T. volvocina
5. Lorica ovoid... 6
   6. Lorica irregularly punctate........................... 9. T. similis
   6. Lorica provided with spines...................................... 7
7. Spines short, thickly covering lorica..................... 10. T. hispida
7. Spines long, in a circular posterior row................. 11. T. armata

1. *Trachelomonas acuminata* (Schmarda) Stein. Lorica triangular or trapezoidal, smooth, 50–59 μ in length; anterior end distinctly narrowed; posterior end with a prominent straight or slightly curved spike; collar obliquely truncate; flagellum twice cell length. Pl. **88**, fig. **1033**.

2. *Trachelomonas magdaleniana* Deflandre. Lorica narrowly fusiform, 15–17 × 80–82 μ, sides slightly curved, gradually attenuated anteriorly to a long neck-like process and posteriorly to a similar tail-like process; scattered stout spines on the posterior process and toward the base of the anterior process; collar straight, sides slightly convergent, the border thickened and bearing 4 or 5 thick, curved, divergent spines; tail straight, hollow, sides slightly convergent, the end truncate and having 3 or 4 small spines. Pl. **88**, fig. **1028**.

3. *Trachelomonas urceolata* Stokes. Lorica cylindric, smooth, 40–45 μ in length; anterior end narrowed abruptly into a short truncate neck-like process; posterior end with a prominent spike; flagellum about equal to cell length. Pl. **88**, fig. **1032**.

4. *Trachelomonas ensifera* Daday. Lorica smooth, spherical or transversely ovoid, 40–44 × 120–130 μ; anterior end narrowed into a long neck-like process; posterior end attenuated to a heavy terminal spike 42–70 μ in length. Pl. **88**, fig. **1030**.

5. *Trachelomonas schauinslandii* Lemmermann. Lorica transversely ovoid, covered with fine granulations, 14–16 × 27–28 μ; anterior end narrowed into a long neck-like process; posterior end narrowed into a terminal spike. Pl. **88**, fig. **1034**.

6. *Trachelomonas tambowika* Swirenko. Lorica ellipsoid to ovoid, irregularly corrugate, 27–30 × 50–55 μ; anterior end narrowed into a short, straight, denticulate neck-like process; posterior end narrowed into a long, straight or slightly curved, terminal spike. Pl. **88**, fig. **1029**.

7. *Trachelomonas caudata* (Ehrenberg) Stein. Lorica ovoid, narrowed slightly posteriorly, thickly covered with spines, 19–21 × 29–53 μ; posterior end with a straight or slightly curved spike; collar widened at mouth, bearing teeth; flagellum about equal to cell length. Pl. **88**, fig. **1036**.

8. *Trachelomonas volvocina* Ehrenberg. Lorica spherical, smooth, 7–21 μ in diameter; pore rarely with a low collar, usually slightly thickened at margin; flagellum 2 to 3 times cell length. Pl. **88**, fig. **1026**.

9. *Trachelomonas similis* Stokes. Lorica ovoid, broadly rounded at both ends, irregularly punctate, 12–14 × 26–30 μ; collar slightly curved and bearing irregular teeth. Pl. **88**, fig. **1031**.

10. *Trachelomonas hispida* (Perty) Stein. Lorica ovoid, thickly covered with short spines, 15–26 × 20–42 μ; collar short or absent; flagellum up to twice cell length. Pl. **88**, fig. **1027**.

11. *Trachelomonas armata* (Ehrenberg) Stein. Lorica broadly ovoid, 29–64 μ in length; posterior end bearing a circular row of relatively long spines, without a terminal spike; thickened around pore or with a low denticulate or crenulate collar; flagellum twice cell length. Pl. **88**, fig. **1035**.

Order COLACIALES

Vegetative cells uninucleate, united in amorphous or dendroid palmelloid colonies; protoplast enclosed within a permanent wall; flagella absent in protoplasts of colonies; temporary, naked, motile protoplasts with a single flagellum occasional; reproduction by division; sexual stages unknown.

Family **Colaciaceae**

With characteristics of the Order.

Colacium Ehrenberg 1833

Cells ovoid, fusiform, or cylindric, surrounded by a gelatinous wall, forming dendroid colonies in which the anterior ends are attached to a dichotomously branched system of gelatinous stalks; epizoophytic or epiphytic; free-swimming for brief period during developmental stages; reservoir and eyespot at anterior end; chromatophores numerous, discoid, with or without pyrenoids; reproduction by division of uni- or multinucleate amoeboid stages; motile cells may develop at any time, rarely undergo division, and after brief swarming period become attached and secrete a gelatinous sheath.

KEY TO THE SPECIES

1. Cells cylindric.. 1. C. calvum
1. Cells ovoid to fusiform.. 2. C. vesiculosum

1. *Colacium calvum* Stein. Cells cylindric, 19–20 × 42–48 μ; base cuplike, longitudinally striate; stalk short and thick; flagellum equaling body length. Pl. **87**, fig. **1017**.

2. *Colacium vesiculosum* Ehrenberg. Cells ovoid to fusiform, 9–17 × 19–29 μ, attenuated more posteriorly when extended, pyriform and widest anteriorly when contracted; basal stalk short; flagellum slightly exceeding body length; colonies made up of 2–8 individuals; motile cells resembling *Euglena*. Pl. **87**, fig. **1018**.

Phylum MYXOPHYTA

Class *MYXOPHYCEAE*

VEGETATIVE cells of the Myxophyceae or blue-green algae may be unicellular or form multicellular colonies of regular or irregular form, expanded sheets, and branched or unbranched filaments. Flagella are never present on either the vegetative or reproductive cells. The cellwall consists of 2 layers, an inner layer of cellulose and an outer layer of gelatinous pectic compounds. The gelatinous sheath of certain filamentous genera may enclose 1 or more trichomes. The sheaths may be colorless, transparent, and so thin they are observed with difficulty, or they may be thick, frequently stratified, firm, colored and readily evident. The protoplast consists of an inner colorless portion, the central body, and an outer pigmented portion, the chromoplasm, which is a fine reticulum with many inclusions and may in some species contain gas vacuoles (pseudovacuoles). There is never a definite nucleus although the central body is sometimes interpreted as being nuclear in nature. According to some investigators nuclear material is scattered at discrete points throughout the protoplast.

Chromatophores are never present and the pigments are diffusely distributed throughout the chromoplasm. The pigments are chlorophyll *a*, 2 carotenes, 2 xanthophylls, and the phycobilins: c-phycocyanin (blue) and c-phycoerythrin (red). The colors exhibited vary from bright green, blue-green, brown, black, and olive to various shades of red, violet, and purple. Accumulated foods include glycogen or glycogen-like compounds, oil droplets, and protein granules, but starch is never present.

Motility is characteristic of many filamentous genera. Movement consists of forward and backward gliding, or may be of an oscillating or waving type. The motion is ascribed to peristaltic contractions or to rapid swelling of secreted gelatinous material.

With the exception of most species of the Order Chamaesiphonales, a majority of species of Myxophyceae are freshwater organisms. They are very widespread in all types of aquatic environments and are frequently abundant on a large variety of moist subaerial and terrestrial substrates.

KEY TO THE GENERA OF MYXOPHYCEAE*

1. Plant colonial, not filamentous, rarely solitary.............................. 2
1. Plant filamentous.. 9
    2. Cells generally spherical, except in division............................ 3
    2. Cells generally ovoid or cylindric, except in division..................... 7
3. Colonies flat plates; cells in rows in 2 directions.... Merismopedia (p. 334)
3. Colonies not as above.. 4
    4. Colonies many-celled.. 5
    4. Colonies few-celled or of few-celled groups............................ 6
5. Colonies microscopic, not attached............... Microcystis (p. 334)
5. Colonies macroscopic, attached.................. Aphanocapsa (p. 331)
    6. Gelatinous envelope hyaline.................. Chroococcus (p. 331)
    6. Gelatinous envelope colored, with age.......... Pleurocapsa (p. 336)
    6. Gelatinous envelope not evident.............. Synechocystis (p. 336)
7. Cells dividing longitudinally....................................... 8
7. Cells dividing transversely...................... Anacystis (p. 330)
    8. Gelatinous matrix with radiating strands........ Gomphosphaeria (p. 332)
    8. Gelatinous matrix without such strands........ Coelosphaerium (p. 332)
9. Trichomes conspicuously attenuated................................. 10
9. Trichomes not attenuated, or only apically so......................... 13
    10. Trichomes without sheaths................... Raphidiopsis (p. 378)
    10. Trichomes with sheaths, sometimes not evident....................... 11
11. Heterocysts absent (see also Calothrix)............ Amphithrix (p. 372)
11. Heterocysts present or usually present.............................. 12
    12. Filaments forming spherical masses............ Gloeotrichia (p. 376)
    12. Filaments in indefinite masses, or solitary...... Calothrix (p. 374)
13. Heterocysts absent..................................... 14
13. Heterocysts present..................................... 20
    14. Trichomes without evident sheaths................................. 15
    14. Trichomes with evident sheaths................................... 16
15. Plant a regular spiral........................... Spirulina (p. 354)
15. Plant irregularly spiral, or straight................ Oscillatoria (p. 340)
    16. Trichomes generally single within sheaths........................... 17
    16. Trichomes few (5 or less) within sheaths....... Schizothrix (p. 353)
    16. Trichomes numerous within sheaths.......... Microcoleus (p. 352)
17. Sheaths not confluent with one another.............................. 18
17. Sheaths laterally confluent....................................... 19
    18. Sheaths hyaline or yellow-brown.............. Lyngbya (p. 338)
    18. Sheaths red, purple-red, orange-red............ Porphyrosiphon (p. 340)
19. Plant mass with vertical tufts.................... Symploca (p. 356)
19. Plant mass without vertical tufts................. Phormidium (p. 347)
    20. Trichomes with true branches..................................... 21
    20. Trichomes with false branches.................................... 22
    20. Trichomes without branches...................................... 24

* Dr. Francis Drouet of the Chicago Natural History Museum has in preparation a critical analysis of the Myxophyceae, indicating considerable change in the nomenclature of the genera and species of the group. Until that work is completed, it seems best to adhere to the generally accepted taxonomic epithets.

21. Branches similar to main filament.................... Stigonema (p. 370)
21. Branches sharply distinct from main filament....... Fischerella (p. 372)
    22. Heterocysts absent.......................... Plectonema (p. 366)
    22. Heterocysts present... 23
23. False branches usually occurring singly........... Tolypothrix (p. 370)
23. False branches usually in pairs................. Scytonema (p. 368)
    24. Heterocysts always terminal................ Cylindrospermum (p. 360)
    24. Heterocysts intercalary.. 25
25. Cells not as long as broad...................... Nodularia (p. 362)
25. Cells longer than broad, or spherical...................................... 26
    26. Trichomes parallel in the colony.............. Aphanizomenon (p. 358)
    26. Trichomes twisted or contorted in the colony............................. 27
27. Trichomes in a firm colonial envelope............ Nostoc (p. 364)
27. Trichomes not in a firm colonial envelope......... Anabaena (p. 356)

Order Chroococcales

Plants unicellular or more often colonial, not filamentous; endospores not or very rarely formed; fragmentation and cell division.

Family **Chroococcaceae**

With characteristics of the Order.

Anacystis Meneghini 1837

Cells ovoid, ovoid-cylindric, oblong-cylindric or elongate, almost spherical in division; colonies many-celled, attaining macroscopic size; gelatinous matrix homogeneous to conspicuously lamellose, hyaline, becoming yellow to brownish with age.

Cell division and fragmentation.

KEY TO THE SPECIES

1. Largest cells at least 3 times as long as broad, often curved. 1. A. peniocystis
1. Largest cells not more than twice as long as broad, not curved................ 2
    2. Maximal cell width 5 μ (mostly 3-4 μ)................ 2. A. marginata
    2. Maximal cell width 9 μ (mostly 4-6 μ)................................... 3
3. Colony of indefinite shape or a stratum.................. 3. A. rupestris
3. Colony a floating sphere............................. 3a. A. rupestris var.
                                                               prasina

    1. *Anacystis peniocystis* (Kuetzing) Drouet and Daily. Cells (without sheaths) up to 3 μ broad and 12 μ long, often curved, cylindric to elongate, homogeneous, blue-green or violet; cell aggregates forming layers or indefinitely shaped floating masses, blue-green, violet or gray, soft; gelatinous matrix homogeneous or somewhat lamellose. Pl. **89**, fig. **1037.**

    2. *Anacystis marginata* Meneghini. Cells (without sheaths) up to 5 (usually 2-4) μ broad and 9 μ long, ovoid or short-cylindric, homogeneous, blue-green; cell aggregates forming layers or indefinite masses; gelatinous

matrix homogeneous or more or less lamellose about the cells. Pl. **89,** fig. **1038.**

3. *Anacystis rupestris* (Lyngbye) Drouet and Daily. Cells (without sheaths) up to 9 (usually 4–6) μ broad and 12 μ long, ovoid or ovoid-cylindric, homogeneous or granular, blue-green; cell aggregates forming layers or floating masses of indefinite shape, blue-green; gelatinous matrix homogeneous or often with conspicuous hyaline sheaths becoming brownish or yellowish with age. Pl. **89,** fig. **1039.**

a. Var. *prasina* (A. Braun) Drouet and Daily. Cell aggregates forming spherical or ovoid masses, firm, up to 10 cm. in diameter; otherwise like the type. Pl. **89,** figs. **1040, 1041.**

Aphanocapsa Naegeli 1848

Cells spherical, appearing ellipsoid and nearly hemispherical in division; colonies many-celled, attached to substrates, usually macroscopic at maturity; gelatinous matrix homogeneous.

Cell division and fragmentation.

KEY TO THE SPECIES

1. Cells mostly 4–5 μ broad.................................... 1. A. grevillei
1. Cells mostly 2–3 μ broad.................................... 2. A. richteriana

1. *Aphanocapsa grevillei* (Berkeley) Rabenhorst. Cells (without sheaths) 4–5 μ in diameter, spherical, scattered or closely aggregated, bright blue-green, homogeneous or slightly granular; gelatinous matrix hyaline, homogeneous; often forming indefinite blue-green layers on submerged substrates. Pl. **90,** fig. **1047.**

2. *Aphanocapsa richteriana* Hieronymus. Cells (without sheaths) 2–3 μ in diameter, spherical, scattered or closely aggregated, blue-green or yellow-green, homogeneous or slightly granular; gelatinous matrix hyaline, homogeneous, forming indefinite blue-green strata on submerged substrates. (Reported from Pope County by Phinney, 1946.) Pl. **90,** fig. **1046.**

Chroococcus Naegeli 1848

Cells spherical, hemispherical or angular, forming microscopic, variously shaped, rarely spherical colonies with 2–64 or more cells; gelatinous matrix hyaline, homogeneous or lamellose.

Cell division and fragmentation.

KEY TO THE SPECIES

1. Thickness of sheath at least equal to cell diameter; planktonic... 1. C. limneticus
1. Thickness of sheath usually much less than cell diameter; aquatic or subaerial.... 2
   2. Cells 3–11 μ broad...................................... 2. C. rufescens
   2. Cells (6–) 12–40 μ broad................................. 3. C. turgidus

1. *Chroococcus limneticus* Lemmermann. Cells (without sheaths) 5–7 μ broad, homogeneous or granular, blue-green; sheath broad, homogeneous; colonies up to 16-celled, strictly planktonic. Pl. **91**, fig. **1050**.

2. *Chroococcus rufescens* (Kuetzing) Naegeli. Cells (without sheaths) 3–11 μ broad, homogeneous to coarsely granular, blue-green to yellowish or brownish; sheath homogeneous or lamellose, sometimes scarcely evident; colonies up to 64-celled. Pl. **91**, fig. **1049**.

3. *Chroococcus turgidus* (Kuetzing) Naegeli. Cells (without sheaths) 6–40 μ broad, blue-green, violet, yellow, brown or reddish brown; sheaths conspicuously lamellose to homogeneous; colonies few-celled to many-celled. Pl. **91**, fig. **1048**.

Coelosphaerium Naegeli 1848

Cells ovoid to obcylindric, the long axes radially disposed in a single (rarely double) peripheral layer in the colony; colony microscopic, aquatic, many-celled, spherical, ovoid, or in division variously tuberculose and constricted; gelatinous matrix hyaline and homogeneous.

Longitudinal cell division, fragmentation.

KEY TO THE SPECIES

1. With pseudovacuoles; forming extensive water-blooms......... 1. C. kuetzingianum
1. Not as above... 2. C. collinsii

1. *Coelosphaerium kuetzingianum* Naegeli. Cells up to 5 μ broad and 10 μ long, ovoid-cylindric, coarsely granular with pseudovacuoles, black in transmitted light (becoming blue-green or yellowish green in liquid preservative and in masses where pseudovacuoles have been lost); colonies planktonic, developing in extensive masses of water-blooms; gelatinous matrix diffluent to conspicuous. Pl. **90**, fig. **1045**.

2. *Coelosphaerium collinsii* Drouet and Daily. Cells 2–4 $\times$ 3–6 μ, ovoid to obcylindric, blue-green or yellowish green, without pseudovacuoles; gelatinous matrix diffluent; seldom planktonic, never forming extensive water-blooms. Pl. **90**, fig. **1044**.

Gomphosphaeria Kuetzing 1836

Cells pyriform, obovoid or obcylindric and in division heart-shaped or obcuniform in lateral view, peripherally distributed in a single layer with

Fig. 1037.—*Anacystis peniocystis* (Kuetzing) Drouet and Daily.

Fig. 1038.—*Anacystis marginata* Meneghini.

Fig. 1039.—*Anacystis rupestris* (Lyngbye) Drouet and Daily.

Figs. 1040, 1041.—*Anacystis rupestris* var. *prasina* (A. Braun) Drouet and Daily.

(Fig. 1037, Daily; figs. 1038, 1039, Geitler; fig. 1041, G. M. Smith. All $\times 1000$.)

PLATE 89

(Figs. 1037 to 1041)

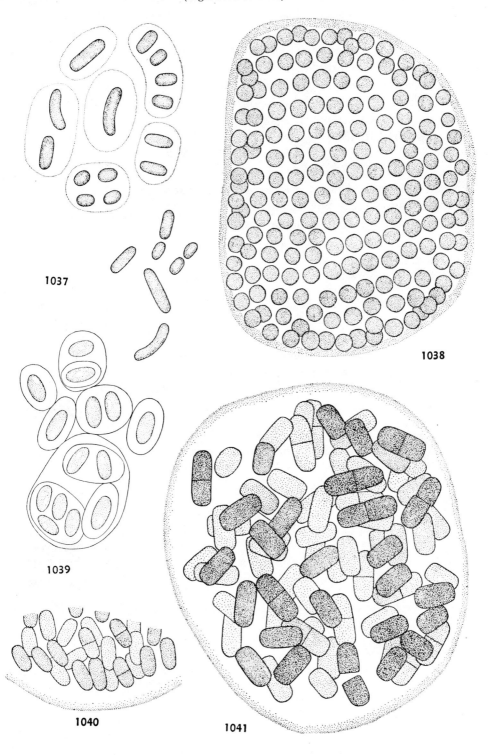

1037

1038

1039

1040

1041

long axes radiate, enveloped by distinct individual sheaths, each bearing a gelatinous projection at base and joined to others toward center of colony; plant aggregate microscopic, many-celled, spherical or ovoid, variously tuberculose and constricted during division; gelatinous matrix hyaline.
Longitudinal cell division.

1. *Gomphosphaeria aponina* Kuetzing. Cells 3–6 × 8–15 μ, blue-green, yellowish or brownish, homogeneous or granular; colonies blue-green, yellowish or brownish; gelatinous matrix evident or diffluent externally. Pl. **90**, figs. **1042, 1043**.

Merismopedia Meyen 1839

Cells spherical, in division hemispherical, forming a flat plate, composed of 1 layer of many cells arranged in 2 rows parallel in 2 directions; gelatinous matrix homogeneous, hyaline.
Cell division in 2 directions; fragmentation.

KEY TO THE SPECIES

1. Colonies of 4–32 cells...1. M. glauca
1. Colonies of many cells (up to 5 cm. broad).....................2. M. convoluta

1. *Merismopedia glauca* (Ehrenberg) Kuetzing. Cells up to 4 μ broad, blue-green, homogeneous, forming rectangular colonies composed of 4, 16, or 32 cells, blue-green. Pl. **91**, fig. **1052**.
2. *Merismopedia convoluta* Brébisson. Cells 3–6 μ broad, blue-green; colonies blue-green, laminate, circular, rectangular or polygonal in outline, smooth, undulate, or variously lacerate at the edges, flat or irregularly convolute, up to 5 cm. broad, very thin. Pl. **91**, fig. **1051**.

Microcystis Kuetzing 1833

Cells spherical or almost hemispherical in division, densely aggregated within a hyaline unstratified gelatinous matrix; colonies microscopic, many-celled, planktonic, variable in shape.
Cell division and fragmentation.

KEY TO THE SPECIES

1. Cells 0.5–2.0 μ in diameter..................................1. M. incerta
1. Cells 3–10 μ in diameter....................................2. M. aeruginosa

FIGS. 1042, 1043.—*Gomphosphaeria aponina* Kuetzing.

FIG. 1044.—*Coelosphaerium collinsii* Drouet and Daily.

FIG. 1045.—*Coelosphaerium kuetzingianum* Naegeli.

FIG. 1046.—*Aphanocapsa richteriana* Hieronymus, part of colony.

FIG. 1047.—*Aphanocapsa grevillei* (Berkeley) Rabenhorst.

(Figs. 1042, 1043, 1045, 1047, G. M. Smith; fig. 1044, Daily. All ×1000.)

PLATE 90
(Figs. 1042 to 1047)

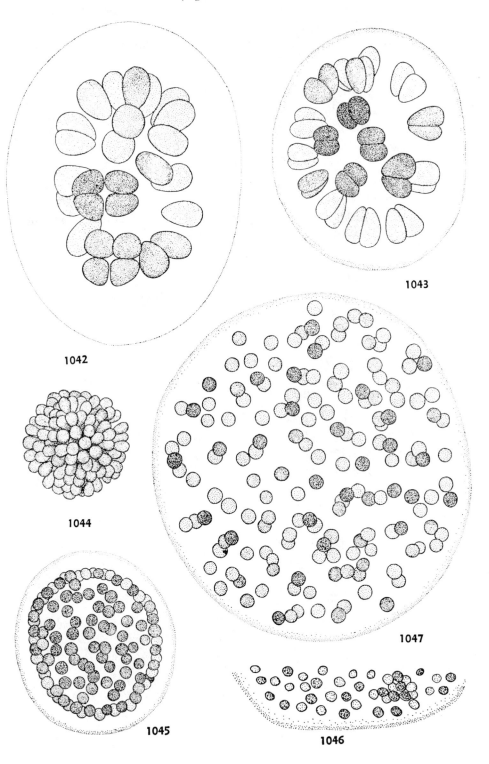

1043

1042

1044

1045

1046

1047

1. *Microcystis incerta* Lemmermann. Cells up to 2 μ broad, pale blue-green, with small and inconspicuous pseudovacuoles; colonies spherical, ovoid or irregularly lobed; gelatinous matrix diffluent at the margin; forming extensive water-blooms. Pl. **91**, fig. **1055**.

2. *Microcystis aeruginosa* Kuetzing. Cells up to 10 μ broad, blackish in transmitted light, with large and conspicuous pseudovacuoles; colonies variable in shape: spherical, ovoid, cylindric, irregularly lobed, clathrate or twisted; gelatinous matrix evident or inconspicuous externally. Pl. **91**, figs. **1053, 1054**.

Synechocystis Sauvageau 1892

Cells spherical, solitary or united into small colonies, generally without visible gelatinous matrix; cell division.

1. *Synechocystis aquatilis* Sauvageau. Cells 4–6 μ in diameter, pale blue-green, solitary or in groups of 2. Pl. **91**, fig. **1056**.

Order CHAMAESIPHONALES

Cells solitary, or densely aggregated into strata, essentially of branched filaments, sometimes more than one-cell thick; always epiphytic or attached to substrates; formation of endospores.

Family **Pleurocapsaceae**

Cell division resulting in a multicellular plant, cells usually densely aggregated into strata one-cell thick or consisting of basal and erect portions; endospores formed from entire contents of any cell or certain cells.

Pleurocapsa Thuret 1885

Cells spherical or nearly hemispherical in division; plant mass a stratum attaining macroscopic size, composed of small groups of cells arranged more or less in vertical rows; gelatinous matrix initially hyaline, becoming yellow or brown with age.

FIG. 1048.—*Chroococcus turgidus* (Kuetzing) Naegeli.

FIG. 1049.—*Chroococcus rufescens* (Kuetzing) Naegeli.

FIG. 1050.—*Chroococcus limneticus* Lemmermann.

FIG. 1051.—*Merismopedia convoluta* Brébisson.

FIG. 1052.—*Merismopedia glauca* (Ehrenberg) Kuetzing.

FIGS. 1053, 1054.—*Microcystis aerugi-* nosa Kuetzing; fig. 1054, part of an irregular colony.

FIG. 1055.—*Microcystis incerta* Lemmermann.

FIG. 1056.—*Synechocystis aquatilis* Sauvageau.

FIGS. 1057, 1058.—*Pleurocapsa varia* (A. Braun) Drouet and Daily.

(Figs. 1048, 1049, 1053–1056, G. M. Smith; figs. 1050, 1052, 1057, Daily; fig. 1051, Tiffany. Figs. 1048–1053, 1055, 1057 ×1000; fig. 1054 ×200; fig. 1056 ×2000.)

PLATE 91

(Figs. 1048 to 1058)

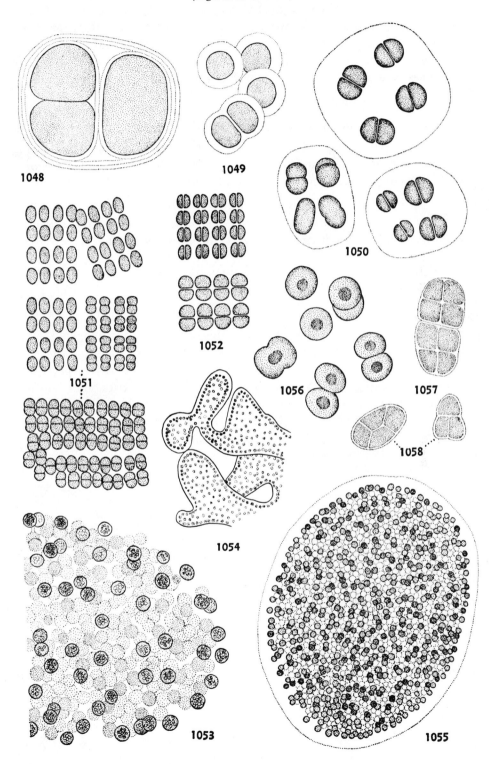

1048

1049

1050

1051

1052

1054

1056

1057

1058

1053

1055

1. *Pleurocapsa varia* (A. Braun) Drouet and Daily. Cells up to 7 μ broad, blue-green, yellowish or brownish, homogeneous to granular; plant aggregates blue-green or brownish; gelatinous matrix hyaline, becoming brownish, often lamellose; small, isolated groups of cells, separated from the mass, resembling *Gloeocapsa* or *Chroococcus*. Pl. **91**, figs. **1057, 1058.**

Order OSCILLATORIALES

Plants multicellular and filamentous; trichomes branched or unbranched, with or without visible sheath (if sheath is present, containing 1 or more trichomes), uniseriate or multiseriate; formation of hormogonia and frequently of heterocysts and/or akinetes.

Suborder OSCILLATORINEAE

Trichomes unbranched, uniseriate, essentially of the same diameter from base to apex; neither heterocysts nor akinetes formed.

Family **Oscillatoriaceae**

With characters of the suborder *Oscillatorineae*.

Lyngbya C. A. Agardh 1824

Filaments unbranched, cylindric, straight, curved or twisted, solitary or densely intertwined into floccose masses, or epiphytic; sheaths firm, generally hyaline but sometimes brownish or yellowish with age, often lamellose, usually extending beyond the trichomes; trichomes solitary (sometimes appearing otherwise when hormogonia form within tenacious sheaths), obtuse or sometimes apically attenuate, sometimes constricted at cross-walls; cell contents homogeneous, granulose, variously colored.

Fragmentation by formation of hormogonia.

KEY TO THE SPECIES

1. Trichomes with constrictions at cross-walls............. 1. L. putealis
1. Trichomes without such constrictions................................... 2
   2. Trichomes 2–3 × 1.0–3.5 μ........................ 2. L. diguetii
   2. Trichomes 2.8–3.2 × 2.0–6.5 μ.................... 3. L. versicolor
   2. Trichomes 4–7 μ broad.. 3
   2. Trichomes 8–24 μ broad... 4
3. Sheath thin, not colored blue by chlorzinciodide........ 4. L. aerugineo-coerulea
3. Sheath thick, colored blue by chlorzinciodide........... 5. L. taylorii
   4. Filaments always solitary....................... 6. L. birgei
   4. Filaments rarely solitary, often forming floccose masses 7. L. aestuarii

1. *Lyngbya putealis* Montagne. Cells 7.5–13.0 × 3–10 μ, generally granulose, blue-green; trichomes constricted at the cross-walls, terminal cell rounded; sheath thin, colorless, becoming blue with chlorzinciodide; fila-

ments forming elongate, penicillate, tufted masses, dark blue-green, flexuous or straight, up to 10 cm. in length. Pl. **92**, fig. **1063**.

2. *Lyngbya diguetii* Gomont. Cells 2–3 × 1.0–3.5 μ; trichomes not constricted at cross-walls, terminal cell rounded, without calyptra; sheath thin, colorless, becoming blue with chlorzinciodide; filaments slender, basally twisted and entangled, elongate, flexible, straight terminally, forming tufted, bright blue-green masses. Pl. **92**, fig. **1070**.

3. *Lyngbya versicolor* (Wartmann) Gomont. Cells 2.8–3.2 × 2.0–6.5 μ, not granulose; trichomes not constricted at cross-walls; terminal cell rounded, without calyptra; sheath colorless or yellowish, up to 2 μ thick, becoming blue with chlorzinciodide; filaments closely entangled, elongate, forming somewhat soft masses, reddish yellow on the outside, olive-green within, at first attached, later free. Pl. **92**, figs. **1061, 1062**.

4. *Lyngbya aerugineo-coerulea* (Kuetzing) Gomont. Cells 4–6 × 2–3 μ, generally granulose, pale blue-green; trichomes not constricted at cross-walls, sometimes apically capitate, terminal cell rounded with somewhat thickened outer membrane; sheath thin, colorless, firm, not lamellose, not becoming blue with chlorzinciodide; filaments flexuous, forming dark blue-green masses. Pl. **92**, figs. **1059, 1060**.

5. *Lyngbya taylorii* Drouet and Strickland. Cells 4–7 × 2–7 μ, granulate; trichomes blue-green, not apically attenuated, not constricted at cross-walls, except slightly near apex; sheath thick, obscurely lamellose, colorless, becoming blue with chlorzinciodide; filaments elongate, parallel, flexuous, forming extensive blue-green, penicillate and radiate tufts; generally attached, sometimes floating. Pl. **92**, figs. **1068, 1069**.

6. *Lyngbya birgei* G. M. Smith. Cells 18–23 × 2.5–5 μ, disciform, gray to olive-green, rarely homogeneous, usually with numerous pseudovacuoles; trichomes neither apically attenuated nor constricted at cross-walls; sheath hyaline, firm, sometimes thick, rarely lamellose; filaments free-floating, solitary, straight or slightly flexed, never forming floccose masses. Pl. **92**, figs. **1066, 1067**.

7. *Lyngbya aestuarii* (Mertens) Liebmann. Cells 8–24 × 2.7–5.6 μ, finely granulose, generally with pseudovacuoles; sheath at first thin and hyaline, later thick, yellowish brown, lamellose, with layers of different colors, not becoming blue with chlorzinciodide; trichomes blue-green or olive-green, not constricted at cross-wall, apically tapering and slightly capitate, rarely conically acute, terminal cell with slightly thickened outer membrane; filaments free-floating or more often forming brownish to dark blue-green layers of floccose masses, straight or twisted, sometimes encrusted with lime. Pl. **92**, figs. **1064, 1065**.

Porphyrosiphon Kuetzing 1850

Filaments unbranched (sometimes slightly branched); trichomes ordinarily single, sometimes 2, in a red, purplish red, orange-red or brownish red sheath; apical cell not capitate; otherwise similar to *Lyngbya*.

Fragmentation by formation of hormogonia.

1. *Porphyrosiphon notarisii* (Meneghini) Kuetzing. Cells 8–19 × 4–12 μ, protoplasm granulate; trichomes constricted at cross-walls or not, blue-green, with tapering obtuse apical cell; sheath at first thin, later thick and lamellose, orange- to purple-red, often colorless at the apex; filaments curved or tangled, forming deep purple, elongate, tomentose masses. (Reported from Pope County by Phinney, 1946.) Pl. 94, figs. **1093, 1094.**

Oscillatoria Vaucher 1803

Trichomes unbranched, cylindric, without evident sheaths or amorphous jelly, solitary or in floccose masses, straight or variously curved and contorted, sometimes apically narrowed, terminal cell rounded or calyptrate; cell contents homogeneous or granular, color variable; plants often exhibiting oscillating or gliding movements; end cells often obscure in fragmented material.

Fragmentation by formation of hormogonia.

KEY TO THE SPECIES

1. Cell length often less than 0.3 cell diameter.................................. 2
1. Cell length usually more than 0.3 cell diameter........................... 6
  2. Trichomes constricted at cross-walls.................................. 3
  2. Trichomes not constricted at cross-walls............................. 4
3. Diameter of cells 9–11 μ................................... 1. O. ornata
3. Diameter of cells 10–20 μ................................. 2. O. sancta
  4. Apical cell with thickened outer membrane............. 3. O. limosa
  4. Apical cell without such thickening.................................... 5
5. Cell diameter 10–17 μ.................................... 4. O. curviceps
5. Cell diameter 16–60 μ.................................... 5. O. princeps
  6. Cell diameter usually more than 10 μ................. 6. O. chalybea
  6. Cell diameter usually less than 10 μ.................................. 7

FIGS. 1059, 1060.—*Lyngbya aerugineo-coerulea* (Kuetzing) Gomont.

FIGS. 1061, 1062.—*Lyngbya versicolor* (Wartmann) Gomont.

FIG. 1063.—*Lyngbya putealis* Montagne.

FIGS. 1064, 1065.—*Lyngbya aestuarii* (Mertens) Liebmann.

FIGS. 1066, 1067.—*Lyngbya birgei* G. M. Smith.

FIGS. 1068, 1069.—*Lyngbya taylorii* Drouet and Strickland.

FIG. 1070.—*Lyngbya diguetii* Gomont.

(Figs. 1059–1065, Gomont; figs. 1066, 1067, G. M. Smith; fig. 1068, Strickland; fig. 1069, Fremy. All ×*1000*.)

PLATE 92

(Figs. 1059 to 1070)

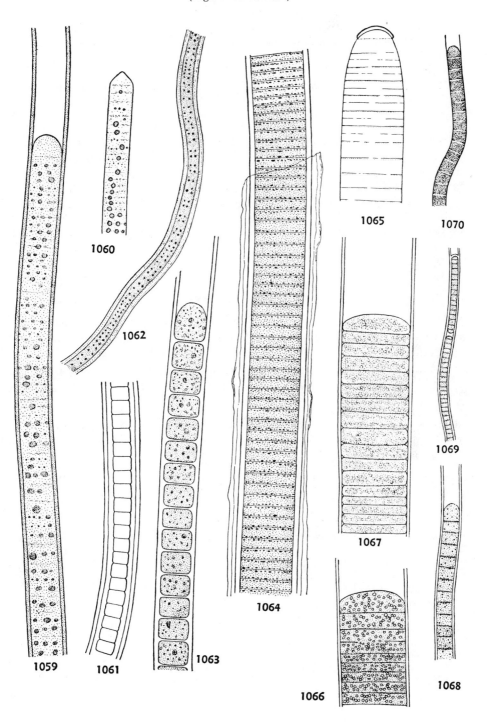

1060

1062

1065

1070

1069

1067

1059

1061

1063

1064

1066

1068

7. Trichomes usually yellowish green...................... 7. O. chlorina

7. Trichomes usually not yellowish green.. 8

  8. Trichomes evidently narrowed toward apex............................ 9

  8. Trichomes not evidently so narrowed................................ 15

9. Trichomes constricted at cross-walls.. 10

9. Trichomes not constricted at cross-walls................................. 11

  10. End cell capitate.................................. 8. O. amoena

  10. End cell conical.................................. 9. O. formosa

11. End cell capitate....................................... 12

11. End cell not capitate....................................... 13

  12. End cell almost globular..................... 10. O. splendida

  12. End cell not globular......................... 11. O. prolifica

13. Length of cells less than 5 μ........................ 14

13. Length of cells more than 5 μ...................... 12. O. acuminata

  14. Cell 3–4 μ in diameter; no pseudovacuoles............. 13. O. animalis

  14. Cell 4–6 μ in diameter, with pseudovacuoles........... 14. O. agardhii

15. Cell diameter 2.3–4.3 μ................................. 16

15. Cell diameter 4–10 μ............................... 15. O. tenuis

  16. Cell length usually more than 4 μ..................... 16. O. geminata

  16. Cell length usually less than 4 μ..................... 17. O. articulata

1. *Oscillatoria ornata* Kuetzing. Cells $9–11 \times 2–5$ μ, end cell rounded, not capitate and without calyptra; trichomes apically twisted, constricted at cross-walls, deeply blue-green, becoming very dark blue-green to blackish green in aggregates. Pl. **93**, fig. **1077**.

2. *Oscillatoria sancta* (Kuetzing) Gomont. Cells $10–20 \times 2.5–6.0$ μ, granulate at cross-wall, with half-rounded, slightly capitate end cell with thick outer membrane; trichomes straight or twisted, slightly constricted at cross-walls, slightly narrowed apically, deep blue-green to dirty olive-green; masses steel-blue, shiny, thin, slimy. Pl. **93**, fig. **1078**.

3. *Oscillatoria limosa* C. A. Agardh. Cells $11–22 \times 2–5$ μ, granulate at cross-walls; trichomes usually straight, dark blue-green to brown or olive-green, not constricted at cross-walls, with broadly rounded end cells, with

Fig. 1071.—*Oscillatoria chalybea* Mertens.

Fig. 1072.—*Oscillatoria acuminata* Gomont.

Fig. 1073.—*Oscillatoria amoena* (Kuetzing) Gomont.

Fig. 1074.—*Oscillatoria tenuis* C. A. Agardh.

Fig. 1075.—*Oscillatoria tenuis* var. *natans* Gomont.

Fig. 1076.—*Oscillatoria limosa* C. A. Agardh.

Fig. 1077.—*Oscillatoria ornata* Kuetzing.

Fig. 1078.—*Oscillatoria sancta* (Kuetzing) Gomont.

Fig. 1079.—*Oscillatoria animalis* C. A. Agardh.

Fig. 1080.—*Oscillatoria princeps* Vaucher.

(Figs. 1071–1073, 1075–1080, Gomont; fig. 1074, Fremy. Figs. 1071–1079 ×*1000*; fig. 1080 ×*500*.)

PLATE 93

(Figs. 1071 to 1080)

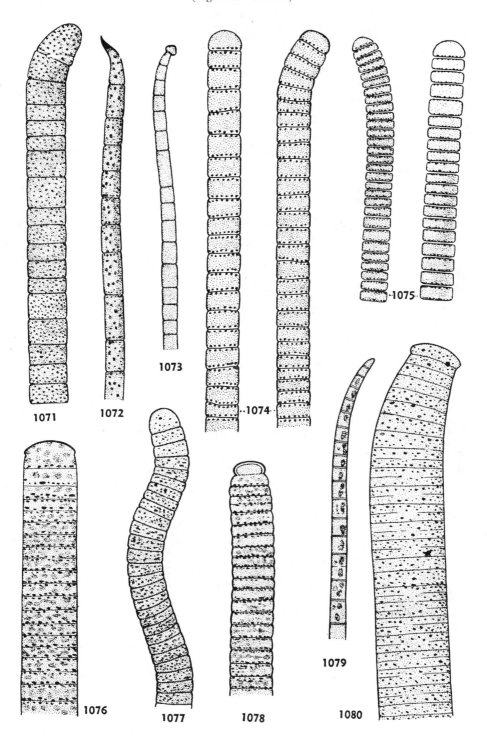

1071

1072

1073

1074

1075

1076

1077

1078

1079

1080

slightly thickened outer membrane, becoming blackish blue-green to brown in aggregates. Pl. **93,** fig. **1076.**

4. *Oscillatoria curviceps* C. A. Agardh. Cells 10–17 × 2–5 μ, often granulate at cross-walls; trichomes generally straight, terminally curved, hooked or somewhat spiral, end cell broadly rounded often with lightly thickened outer membrane, not capitate, not constricted at cross-walls, becoming bright or dark blue-green, often steel-blue (when dry) in aggregates. Pl. **94,** fig. **1081.**

5. *Oscillatoria princeps* Vaucher. Cells 16–60 × 3.5–7.0 μ, with granulose protoplasm, not granulate at cross-walls; trichomes blue-green to brownish, reddish or violet, not constricted at cross-walls, generally straight, terminally lightly and abruptly constricted and bent; end cells broadly rounded, lightly capitate, without calyptra; generally in masses, sometimes single; plant mass dark blue-green. Pl. **93,** fig. **1080.**

6. *Oscillatoria chalybea* Mertens. Cells 8–13 × 3.6–8.0 μ, cross-walls little or not at all granulate; trichomes straight or sometimes twisted, slightly constricted at cross-walls, gradually tapering for a long distance from the hooked or curved apex, terminal cell somewhat elongate and broadly rounded, blue-green to dark blue-green, becoming blackish green in masses. Pl. **93,** fig. **1071.**

7. *Oscillatoria chlorina* Kuetzing. Cells 3.5–4.0 (–6) × 3.7–8.0 μ, with scarcely granulose protoplasm; trichomes straight or bent, not apically tapering, not constricted at pellucid and ungranulated cross-walls, yellow-green, end cell rounded and without outer thickening, forming very thin, yellow-green masses. Pl. **94,** figs. **1088, 1089.**

8. *Oscillatoria amoena* (Kuetzing) Gomont. Cells 2.5–5.0 × 2.5–4.0 μ, granulate at cross-walls; trichomes straight, slightly constricted at cross-walls, gradually attenuated at the apex, with capitate, broadly rounded

FIG. 1081.—*Oscillatoria curviceps* C. A. Agardh.

FIG. 1082.—*Oscillatoria agardhii* Gomont.

FIG. 1083.—*Oscillatoria prolifica* (Greville) Gomont.

FIG. 1084.—*Oscillatoria formosa* Bory.

FIGS. 1085, 1086.—*Oscillatoria splendida* Greville.

FIG. 1087.—*Oscillatoria geminata* Meneghini.

FIGS. 1088, 1089.—*Oscillatoria chlorina* Kuetzing.

FIG. 1090.—*Oscillatoria grunowiana* Gomont var. *articulata* (Gardner) Drouet.

FIGS. 1091, 1092.—*Phormidium uncinatum* (Agardh) Gomont.

FIGS. 1093, 1094.—*Porphyrosiphon notarisii* (Meneghini) Kuetzing.

(Figs. 1081, 1083–1087, 1091, 1092, Gomont; fig. 1082, Geitler; figs. 1088–1090, Drouet; figs. 1093, 1094, Fremy. Fig. 1081–1092 ×*1000;* fig. 1090 ×*1300;* figs. 1093, 1094 ×*500.*)

PLATE 94

(Figs. 1081 to 1094)

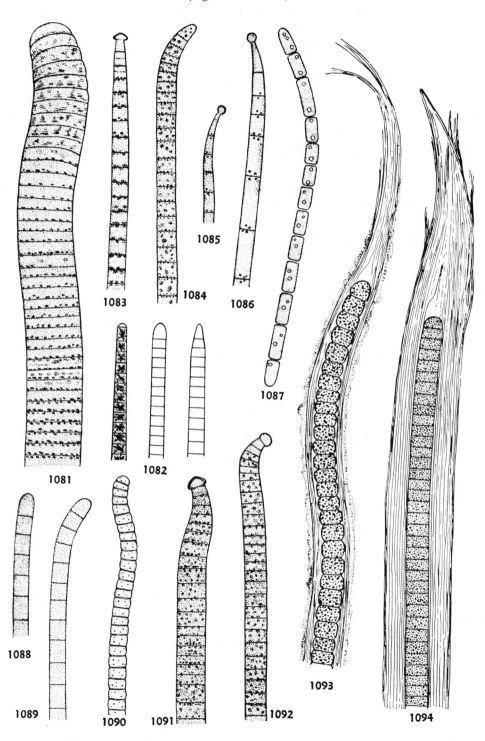

and outwardly thickened calyptrate end cell, scattered or forming blue-green masses. Pl. 93, fig. 1073.

9. *Oscillatoria formosa* Bory. Cells 4–6 × 2.5–5.7 μ, sometimes slightly granulate at cross-walls, bright blue-green; trichomes straight, slightly constricted at cross-walls, apically narrowed and bent, end cell bluntly rounded, neither capitate nor calyptrate, forming dark blue-green masses. Pl. 94, fig. 1084.

10. *Oscillatoria splendida* Greville. Cells 2–3 × 3–9 μ, homogeneous, blue-green; trichomes straight or bent, not constricted but somewhat granulate at cross-walls, gradually tapering at apex (often bent or twisted), end cell capitate, nearly round, forming dark blue-green thin masses, or scattered. Pl. 94, figs. 1085, 1086.

11. *Oscillatoria prolifica* (Greville) Gomont. Cells 2–5 × 4–6 μ, with pseudovacuoles, cross-wall often granulate; trichomes straight or bent, not constricted at cross-walls, gradually tapering at the apex, scattered or forming purple-red to violet irregular masses; end cell capitate, with calyptra. Pl. 94, fig. 1083.

12. *Oscillatoria acuminata* Gomont. Cells 3–5 × 5.5–8.0 μ, with granulate cross-walls; trichomes usually straight, not constricted at cross-walls or only very slightly so, with briefly tapering, very sharply pointed, hooked or twisted but not capitate apex, cross-walls often granulate; plant mass blue-green. Pl. 93, fig. 1072.

13. *Oscillatoria animalis* C. A. Agardh. Cells 3–4 × 1.5–5.0 μ, not granulate at cross-walls; trichomes straight, not constricted at cross-walls, tapering and somewhat bent at the apex, end cell acutely rounded, forming blue-green aggregates. Pl. 93, fig. 1079.

14. *Oscillatoria agardhii* Gomont. Cells 4–6 × 2.5–4.0 μ, coarsely granulate, with pseudovacuoles; trichomes straight or somewhat bent, not constricted at cross-walls, gradually tapering at the apex, free-floating or forming blue-green masses in water or on very moist soil; cross-walls granulate; end cell convex to broadly rounded, sometimes acute, often capitate, with convex calyptra. Pl. 94, fig. 1082.

15. *Oscillatoria tenuis* C. A. Agardh. Cells 4–10 × 2.5–5.0 μ, with coarsely granulose protoplasm, generally granulate at cross-walls; trichomes bright blue-green, straight, slightly constricted at cross-walls, gradually curved at the apex, end cell convex and with thick outer membrane, hemispherical, forming thin blue-green, slimy masses, attached or free-floating. Pl. 93, fig. 1074.

a. Var. *natans* Gomont. Trichomes 6–10 μ wide, cross-walls thick. Pl. 93, fig. 1075.

16. *Oscillatoria geminata* Meneghini. Cells 2.3–4.3 × 2.3–16.0 μ, terminal cell rounded and not capitate; trichomes apically bent or curved, evidently constricted at the thick, non-granulate cross-walls, dark blue-green; masses a dirty yellow-green. Pl. **94,** fig. **1087.**

17. *Oscillatoria grunowiana* Gomont var. *articulata* (Gardner) Drouet. Cells 2.8–3.2 μ, quadrate or 0.3–0.5 as long as broad; trichomes single or aggregated, straight or coiled, neither narrowed terminally nor constricted at cross-walls, the latter very thick in preserved materials, with rounded end cell having no thickened membrane. Pl. **94,** fig. **1090.**

Phormidium Kuetzing 1843

Trichomes unbranched, cylindric, enclosed by watery gelatinous sheaths, partially or wholly confluent, sometimes encrusted with calcium carbonate, not closed at the apices; plant mass aquatic, subaerial, composed of nearly parallel or densely interwoven trichomes, generally forming an extensive stratum, rarely solitary; apex various, sometimes capitate, often with calyptra.

Fragmentation by formation of hormogonia.

KEY TO THE SPECIES

1. Cell diameter 1–2 μ.. 2
1. Cell diameter 2–8 μ (see also No. 11)................................ 3
1. Cell diameter 9–12 μ... 8
   2. Cell length more than 2 μ.................... 1. P. tenue
   2. Cell length less than 2 μ..................... 2. P. foveolarum
3. End cell capitate.. 4
3. End cell rounded, not capitate....................................... 6
   4. Trichomes terminally straight.................... 3. P. favosum
   4. Trichomes terminally curved or bent.............................. 5
5. Cells 4–7 μ broad, generally terrestrial............... 4. P. autumnale
5. Cells 5.5–9.0 μ broad, generally aquatic............... 5. P. uncinatum
   6. Cell length less than 5 μ... 7
   6. Cell length more than 5 μ....................... 6. P. inundatum
7. Trichomes markedly constricted at septa.............. 7. P. minnesotense
7. Trichomes lightly constricted at septa................ 8. P. ambiguum
7. Trichomes not so constricted........................ 9. P. incrustatum var. cataractarum
   8. Cell length 2–4 μ................................ 10. P. subfuscum
   8. Cell length 4–8 μ................................ 11. P. retzii

1. *Phormidium tenue* (Meneghini) Gomont. Cells 1–2 × 2.5–5.0 μ, not granulate at cross-walls; trichomes straight or slightly curved, not at all or somewhat constricted, narrowed terminally, bright blue-green; sheaths thin, diffluent into a fibrous mucus, not blue with chlorzinciodide; end cell

acute-conical, without calyptra; plant mass expanded, bright blue-green, membranous. Pl. **95**, fig. **1098**.

2. *Phormidium foveolarum* (Montagne) Gomont. Cells about 1.5 μ broad and 0.8–2.0 μ long, not granulate at cross-walls; trichomes bent or twisted, constricted, not apically narrowed, end cells rounded without calyptra; sheaths soft, diffluent into an amorphous mucus, colorless, not blue with chlorzinciodide; plant mass thin, dark green. Pl. **95**, fig. **1095**.

3. *Phormidium favosum* (Bory) Gomont. Cells 4.5–9.0 $\times$ 3–7 μ, granulate at cross-walls; trichomes more or less bent, not constricted, apically narrowed and straight, with capitate end cell having a somewhat hemispherical calyptra; sheaths inconspicuous, not blue with chlorzinciodide; plant mass somewhat expanded, dark blue-green, becoming lead-colored when dry. Pl. **95**, figs. **1102, 1103**.

4. *Phormidium autumnale* (Agardh) Gomont. Cells 4–7 $\times$ 2–5 μ, often granulate at cross-walls; trichomes straight, parallel or variously intertwined, not constricted, briefly tapering, especially capitate, blue-green or dirty green, end cell calyptrate; sheaths distinct, mucous or forming an amorphous jelly, not blue with chlorzinciodide; plant mass expanded, fragile, dark blue-green or olive-green, often yellow or violet, subaerial or aerial. Pl. **96**, fig. **1108**.

5. *Phormidium uncinatum* (Agardh) Gomont. Cells 5.5–9.0 $\times$ 2–6 μ, often granulate at cross-walls; trichomes straight or slightly bent, not constricted, terminally narrowed, curved or short-spiraled, especially capitate, blue-green or dirty green; end cell with a rounded or conical calyptra; sheaths distinct or variously diffluent, not blue with chlorzinciodide; plant mass widely expanded, attached or floating, dark green to brownish black. Pl. **94**, figs. **1091, 1092**.

6. *Phormidium inundatum* Kuetzing. Cells 3–5 $\times$ 4–8 μ, granulate at cross-walls; trichomes generally straight, not constricted, apically straight, not capitate, blue-green; end cell broadly conical; sheaths thin

Fig. 1095.—*Phormidium foveolarum* (Montagne) Gomont.

Figs. 1096, 1097.—*Phormidium subfuscum* Kuetzing.

Fig. 1098.—*Phormidium tenue* (Meneghini) Gomont.

Fig. 1099.—*Phormidium minnesotense* (Tilden) Drouet.

Figs. 1100, 1101.—*Phormidium inundatum* Kuetzing.

Figs. 1102, 1103.—*Phormidium favosum* (Bory) Gomont.

Fig. 1104.—*Phormidium ambiguum* Gomont.

Figs. 1105–1107.—*Phormidium retzii* (Agardh) Gomont; fig. 1107, a habit sketch.

(Figs. 1095–1098, 1100–1104, Gomont; fig. 1099, Tilden; figs. 1105–1107, Fremy. Figs. 1095, 1098, 1100, 1101 $\times 1500$; figs. 1096, 1097, 1102–1106 $\times 1000$; fig. 1107 $\times 100$.)

PLATE 95

(Figs. 1095 to 1107)

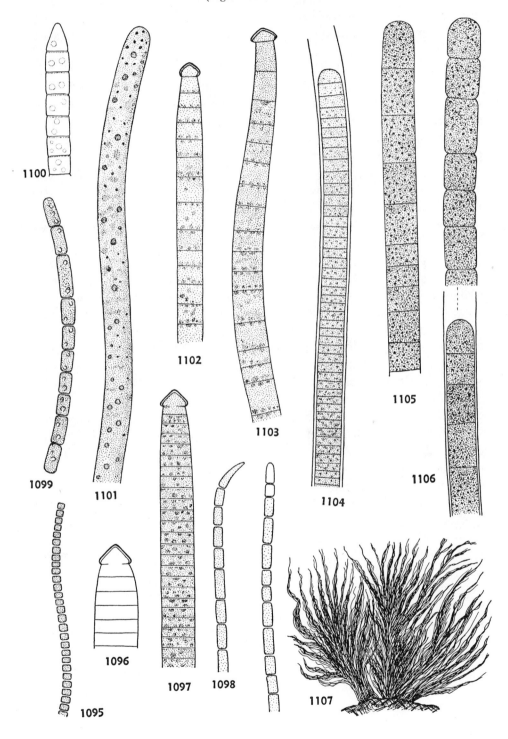

1100

1101

1102

1103

1104

1105

1106

1099

1095

1096

1097

1098

1107

and diffluent, blue with chlorzinciodide; plant mass membranous, blue-green to blackish or brownish green. Pl. **95**, figs. **1100, 1101.**

7. *Phormidium minnesotense* (Tilden) Drouet. Cells 2–4 × 2–6 μ, with pellucid cross-walls and homogeneous protoplasm; trichomes more or less curved, especially constricted at cross-walls, apically straight or slightly bent, neither tapering nor capitate, apical cell rounded, without calyptra; not turning blue with chlorzinciodide; sheaths thin, sometimes confluent; plant mass dark blue-green. Pl. **95**, fig. **1099.**

8. *Phormidium ambiguum* Gomont. Cells 4–6 (–7) × 1.5–2.7 μ, proto-plasm usually rather coarsely granulose, cross-walls rarely granulate; tri-chomes bright blue-green, slightly constricted at cross-walls, straight and not attenuate at apices, apical cell rotund with somewhat thickened outer wall; filaments elongate, flexuous, variously interwoven; sheaths firm or mucous and diffluent, sometimes thick and lamellose, blue with chlorzinc-iodide; stratum expanded, bright blue-green, yellow-green or blackish. Pl. **95**, fig. **1104.**

9. *Phormidium incrustatum* (Naegeli) Gomont var. *cataractarum* (Naege-li) Gomont. Cells 4–5 × 3–5 μ, cross-walls scarcely visible, sometimes granulate; trichomes not constricted at cross-walls, apically straight, briefly tapering, not capitate; end cell obtuse-conical, without calyptra; filaments erect-parallel; sheaths thin, mucous, agglutinated; plant mass hard, crustaceous, dark red or violet, often encrusted with lime. (Probably scarcely distinguishable from the species.) Pl. **96**, fig. **1109.**

10. *Phormidium subfuscum* Kuetzing. Cells 8.0–11.5 × 2–4 μ, often granulate at cross-walls; trichomes straight, more or less parallel, not con-stricted at cross-walls, sharply narrowed apically, capitate; dark blue-green or olive-green; sheaths confluent into a lamellose gelatinous mass, not blue with chlorzinciodide; end cells straight, sharply rounded, with calyptra; plant mass expanded, blackish green to dirty green, lamellose. Pl. **95**, figs. **1096, 1097.**

Fig. 1108.—*Phormidium autumnale* (Agardh) Gomont.

Fig. 1109.—*Phormidium incrustatum* (Naegeli) Gomont var. *cataractarum* (Nae-geli) Gomont.

Fig. 1110.—*Microcoleus acutissimus* Gardner.

Fig. 1111.—*Microcoleus rupicola* (Tilden) Drouet.

Fig. 1112.—*Microcoleus vaginatus* (Vau-cher) Gomont.

Figs. 1113, 1114.—*Microcoleus lacustris* (Rabenhorst) Farlow.

Figs. 1115–1117.—*Schizothrix pur-purascens* (Kuetzing) Gomont.

(Figs. 1108, 1112, 1114, 1117, Gomont; fig. 1110, Drouet; fig. 1111, Tilden; figs. 1113, 1115, 1116, Fremy. Figs. 1108–1113 ×*1000;* fig. 1114 ×*100;* figs. 1115–1117 ×*600.*)

PLATE 96
(Figs. 1108 to 1117)

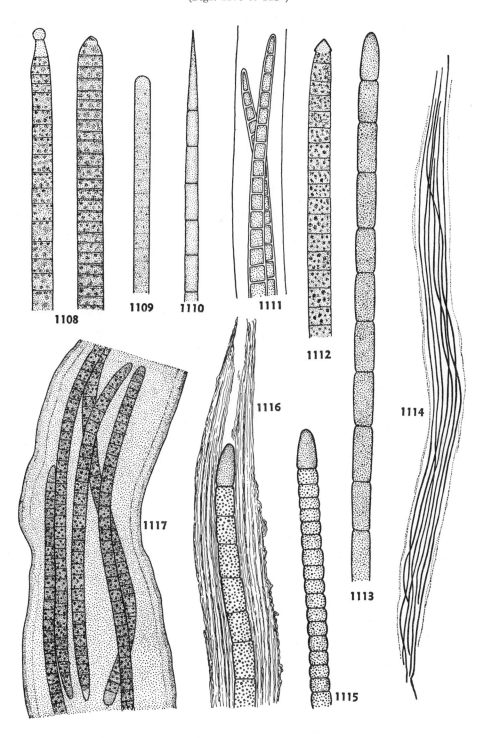

1108

1109

1110

1111

1112

1113

1114

1115

1116

1117

11. *Phormidium retzii* (Agardh) Gomont. Cells 5–12 × 4–8 μ, usually not granulate at the conspicuous cross-walls; trichomes blue-green, straight, fragile, not constricted at cross-walls, apical cell scarcely attenuate, truncate, blue-green; sheaths thin, more or less diffluent into an amorphous mucus, not blue with chlorzinciodide; plant mass bright blue-green, or blue-black, thick, compact or rarely penicillate. Pl. **95**, figs. **1105–1107**.

Microcoleus Desmazieres 1823

Trichomes numerous and closely aggregated within a wide, hyaline, cylindric, mucous and often entirely diffluent sheath; apices rounded, capitate, attenuate or calyptrate.

Fragmentation by formation of hormogonia.

KEY TO THE SPECIES

1. Trichomes 1.8–2.2 μ in diameter.........................1. M. acutissimus
1. Trichomes 3.5–6.0 μ in diameter..2
  2. End cell of trichome capitate.........................2. M. vaginatus
  2. End cell of trichome not capitate...3
3. Cells 5–8 μ long..3. M. rupicola
3. Cells 6–12 μ long.......................................4. M. lacustris

1. *Microcoleus acutissimus* Gardner. Cells 1.8–2.2 × 4–8 μ; trichomes mostly parallel, not constricted at cross-walls, apically constricted and attenuate, end cell sharply conical; sheath colorless, uneven, more or less gelatinous; filaments 20–35 × 400–550 μ, straight, containing 15–30 trichomes. Pl. **96**, fig. **1110**.

2. *Microcoleus vaginatus* (Vaucher) Gomont. Cells 3.5–7.0 × 3–7 μ, often granulate but not constricted at the cross-walls, blue-green or dirty green, end cell capitate and calyptrate; sheath colorless, uneven, often entirely diffluent; filaments creeping, sometimes entangled and twisted, forming black, shiny sheets. Pl. **96**, fig. **1112**.

3. *Microcoleus rupicola* (Tilden) Drouet. Cells 3–5 × 5–8 μ, apical cell truncate-conical; trichomes few to many in a sheath, not constricted at the scarcely visible cross-walls; sheaths thick, rough, usually colorless, not or scarcely lamellose; filaments 9–16 μ in diameter, forming loose blue-green to colorless masses on exposed and barren ground. Pl. **96**, fig. **1111**.

4. *Microcoleus lacustris* (Rabenhorst) Farlow. Cells 4–5 × 6–12 μ, with scattered, coarse granules, pale blue-green; trichomes especially constricted at cross-walls, somewhat parallel, with more or less obtusely conical apical cells; sheath thin, mucous and agglutinated, sometimes diffluent and absent at the apex; filaments forming a black or blue-green layer, twisted and entangled. Pl. **96**, figs. **1113, 1114**.

Schizothrix Kuetzing 1843

Trichomes 1–5, rarely more, loosely aggregated within the sheath, never capitate, unbranched; sheaths hyaline or colored, sometimes becoming blue with chlorzinciodide, definitely delimited, often lamellose, usually not mucous; plant mass aerial, subaerial or aquatic, compact and in some species impregnated with calcium carbonate or other foreign substances. Fragmentation by formation of hormogonia.

KEY TO THE SPECIES

1. Cells of trichomes 1.0–1.7 × 2–6 μ.......................... 1. S. calcicola
1. Cells of trichomes 4–6 × 3–7 μ............................. 2. S. stricklandii
1. Cells of trichomes 6–8 × 3–8 μ............................. 3. S. purpurascens
1. Cells of trichomes 8–10 × 2.5–5.0 μ....................... 4. S. rivularis

1. *Schizothrix calcicola* (Agardh) Gomont. Cells 1.0–1.7 × 2–6 μ, contents often granulose, pale blue-green; trichomes not constricted at cross-walls, 1 to 2 or more within a single sheath; filaments short, twisted and entangled, rarely with false branching; sheath firm, colorless, somewhat lamellose, rough and irregular, not coloring blue with chlorzinciodide; plant mass somewhat gelatinous, very hard when dry, papery-membranous, black or sometimes yellowish blue-green. Pl. 97, figs. 1118, 1119.

2. *Schizothrix stricklandii* Drouet. Cells 4–6 × 3–7 μ, usually more or less quadrate or shorter than the diameter, with granulose protoplasm; trichomes blue-green or olive-green, scarcely constricted at the cross-walls, not or slightly attenuate at the apices, apical cell shortly and truncately conical, with a thickened outer membrane; sheaths hyaline, thick, lamellose, rough; plant mass blue-green, olive-green or black, composed of entangled and twisted filaments in lower portions and contorted erect tufts in upper parts. Pl. 107, fig. 1180.

3. *Schizothrix purpurascens* (Kuetzing) Gomont. Cells 6–8 × 3–8 μ, protoplasm coarsely granulose; apical cell conical, often acutely so; trichomes pale blue-green, often more or less numerous within the sheath, generally constricted at cross-walls; sheaths brownish or purplish red, with acuminate hyaline apices, firm, very wide, lamellose, irregular, coloring blue with chlorzinciodide; plant mass indefinitely expanded, dark violet or brownish; filaments with false, divaricate branches, much contorted below and more or less agglutinated into tortuous fascicles above. Pl. 96, figs. 1115–1117. Pl. 97, figs. 1120, 1121.

4. *Schizothrix rivularis* (Wolle) Drouet. Cells 8–10 × 2.5–5.0 μ, cell contents dark steel-blue, or in portions yellow-green, cross-walls not granulate; trichomes not constricted at cross-walls; apical cell round or broadly rounded; sheaths thick, tenacious, more or less mucous; plant mass form-

ing dirty blue-green tufts that are twisted, creeping, rarely erect, densely crowded and entangled, filaments somewhat parallel.

Spirulina Turpin 1827

Trichomes more or less regularly and permanently spiraled throughout their entire lengths, conspicuously articulated, scarcely so, or not at all, without evident sheaths or amorphous jelly; plant mass mucous, rarely remaining intact when collected, submerged or aerial.

Transverse cell division.

KEY TO THE SPECIES

1. Trichomes constricted at cross-walls...................................... 2
1. Trichomes not constricted at cross-walls.............................. 3
   2. Diameter of trichomes 2.5–3.0 μ...................... 1. S. gomontiana
   2. Diameter of trichomes 5–8 μ.......................... 2. S. jenneri
   3. Turns of spirals not over 4 μ in diameter.................... 3. S. major
   3. Turns of spirals not less than 5 μ in diameter............... 4. S. nordstedtii

1. *Spirulina gomontiana* (Setchell) Geitler. Trichomes 2.5–3.0 μ in diameter, pale blue-green, not narrowed apically, regularly spiral, the turns about 6–8 μ in diameter and 16–35 μ apart, cross-walls often granulate, end cell broadly rounded; plant mass free-floating. Pl. **97**, fig. **1126**.

2. *Spirulina jenneri* (Stizenberger) Geitler. Trichomes 5–8 μ in diameter, sometimes finely granulate at cross-walls, end cell broadly rounded, blue-green, slightly constricted at septa or not at all, not narrowed apically, more or less regularly spiraled, turns 5–15 μ wide and 21–31 μ apart; plant mass bright blue-green. Pl. **97**, fig. **1123**.

3. *Spirulina major* Kuetzing. Trichomes pale blue-green, 1.2–1.7 μ in diameter, with regular spirals 2.5–4.0 μ wide and 2.7–6.0 μ apart. Pl. **97**, fig. **1124**.

4. *Spirulina nordstedtii* Gomont. Trichomes pale blue-green, about 2 μ in diameter, forming regular spirals 5 μ wide and about 5 μ apart; plant mass olive-green. Pl. **97**, fig. **1125**.

Figs. 1118, 1119.—*Schizothrix calcicola* (Agardh) Gomont.

Figs. 1120, 1121.—*Schizothrix purpurascens* (Kuetzing) Gomont.

Fig. 1122.—*Symploca muscorum* (Agardh) Gomont.

Fig. 1123.—*Spirulina jenneri* (Stizenberger) Geitler.

Fig. 1124.—*Spirulina major* Kuetzing.

Fig. 1125.—*Spirulina nordstedtii* Gomont.

Fig. 1126.—*Spirulina gomontiana* (Setchell) Geitler.

Fig. 1127.—*Anabaena flosaquae* (Lyngbye) Brébisson.

(Figs. 1118–1121, 1123, 1124, Gomont; figs. 1122, 1125, 1127, Fremy. Figs. 1118, 1122, 1127 ×600; figs. 1119–1121, 1123–1126 ×1000.)

PLATE 97

(Figs. 1118 to 1127)

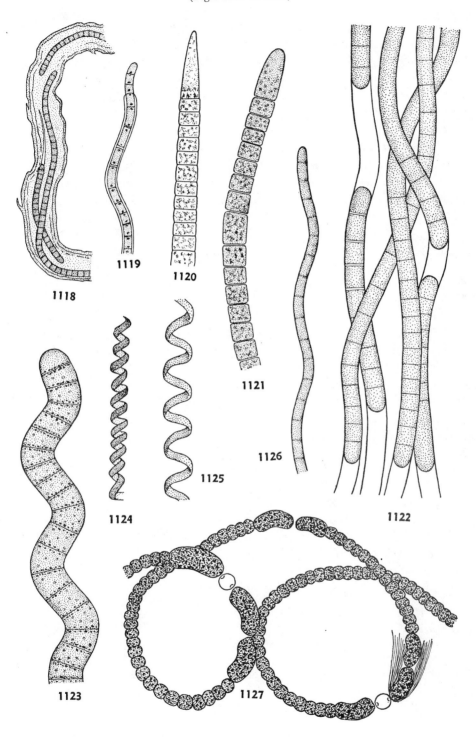

1118

1119

1120

1121

1122

1123

1124

1125

1126

1127

Symploca Kuetzing 1843

Trichomes solitary within distinct and never confluent sheaths (except in the bundles, where they may be mucous and confluent), not capitate, sometimes calyptrate, not with enlarged apical cell; filaments contorted, forming a compact stratum from which upright or horizontal bundles of filaments arise; plant mass aerial or subaerial; if submerged, erect tufts not evident.

Fragmentation by formation of hormogonia.

1. *Symploca muscorum* (C. A. Agardh) Gomont. Cells 5–8 × 5–11 μ, protoplasm coarsely granulose, cross-walls inconspicuous, not granulate; trichomes blue-green or olive-green, not constricted at cross-walls; apical cell rounded or obtusely conical, the outer membrane slightly thickened; sheaths firm or sometimes mucous, becoming blue with chlorzinciodide, up to 2 μ thick; filaments seldom branched, tortuous, much entangled in the basal stratum, less so in the tufts; plant mass blue-green, grayish, brown or blackish, sometimes fasciculate, forming cottony masses at times on damp ground. Pl. **97**, fig. **1122.**

Suborder NOSTOCHINEAE

Trichomes of uniform diameter or attenuated toward the apex or from the middle in both directions, uniseriate or multiseriate, branched or not, 1 to more than 1 trichome in a sheath; heterocysts and akinetes in most genera.

Family **Nostocaceae**

Trichomes unbranched, uniseriate, not apically attenuate, straight or twisted or spiral; heterocysts terminal or intercalary; akinetes.

Anabaena Bory 1822

Trichomes free-floating, solitary or aggregated into a thin mucous layer; trichomes cylindric or slightly attenuated at apices, straight, circinate, spiral or irregularly twisted, often destitute of a sheath; cells spherical to barrel-shaped, homogeneous or granulose, sometimes with pseudovacuoles, variously colored; heterocysts spherical, intercalary; akinetes variously shaped, solitary or in series, adjacent to heterocyst or not.

Multiplication by hormogonia and by akinetes.

KEY TO THE SPECIES

1. Diameter of cells over 8 μ.. 2
1. Diameter of cells less than 8 μ...................................... 4
   2. Akinetes 10–20 μ in diameter.................................. 3
   2. Akinetes 20–25 μ in diameter.................... 6a. A. spiroides var. crassa

3. Heterocysts 8–10 μ in diameter........................ 1. A. circinalis
3. Heterocysts 10–14 μ in diameter....................... 2. A. planctonica
   4. Length of akinetes 8–14 μ........................ 3. A. variabilis
   4. Length of akinetes 14–17 μ....................... 4. A. inaequalis
   4. Length of akinetes 16–50 μ.. 5
5. Heterocysts globose... 6
5. Heterocysts ellipsoid.. 7
5. Heterocysts ovoid..................................... 5. A. oscillarioides
   6. Cells 4–5 μ in diameter...................... 4. A. inaequalis
   6. Cells 6.5–8.0 μ in diameter...................... 6. A. spiroides
7. Akinetes 7–13 μ in diameter.. 8
7. Akinetes 13–20 μ in diameter....................... 9. A. unispora
   8. Akinetes up to 30 μ long........................... 7. A. catenula
   8. Akinetes up to 50 μ long........................... 8. A. flosaquae

1. *Anabaena circinalis* (Kuetzing) Rabenhorst. Cells 8–14 μ in diameter, spherical or oblate, usually with pseudovacuoles; heterocysts 8–10 μ in diameter, spherical or nearly so; akinetes 16–18 × 26–30 μ, cylindric or somewhat curved, usually remote from the heterocysts; trichomes free-floating, rarely solitary (curved or sigmoid), generally twisted into floccose aggregates. Pl. **98**, figs. **1129, 1130**.

2. *Anabaena planctonica* Brunnthaler. Cells 9–15 × 9–12 μ, rounded or broadly ellipsoid, usually with numerous pseudovacuoles; heterocysts spherical, 12–14 μ broad; akinetes 12–20 × 12–30 μ, solitary, remote from or adjacent to heterocysts, spherical to elongate; trichomes enclosed by a wide, hyaline, very gelatinous sheath; filaments free-floating, solitary, straight or slightly bent. Pl. **98**, fig. **1128**.

3. *Anabaena variabilis* Kuetzing. Cells 4–6 × 2.5–6 μ, barrel-shaped; heterocysts rounded or elongate, about 6 × 8 μ; akinetes 7–9 × 8–14 μ, barrel-shaped, remote from the heterocysts, generally in series, smooth and yellow-brown; trichomes variously bent, usually without sheaths, forming dark-green, gelatinous masses. Pl. **98**, fig. **1132**.

4. *Anabaena inaequalis* (Kuetzing) Bornet and Flahault. Cells broadly barrel-shaped, 4–5 μ in diameter; heterocysts rounded, 6 μ in diameter; akinetes single or in groups of 2–3, cylindric, 6–8 × 14–17 μ, smooth, yellow; trichomes straight, parallel, sheath absent, or distinct around akinetes, forming blue-green masses. Pl. **99**, fig. **1136**.

5. *Anabaena oscillarioides* Bory. Cells barrel-shaped, 4–6 μ broad, with rounded end cell; heterocysts 6–8 × 6–10 μ, rounded or ovoid; akinetes on both sides of the heterocysts, single or in groups of 2–3, ovoid to cylindric, smooth and yellow-brown, 8–10 × 20–40 μ; trichomes forming dark-green gelatinous masses. Pl. **99**, fig. **1137**.

6. *Anabaena spiroides* Klebahn. Cells 6.5–8.0 μ in diameter, nearly

rounded, with pseudovacuoles; heterocysts rounded, about 7 μ broad; akinetes at first rounded, later bent and angular; trichomes single, free-floating, spiraled, spirals 45–54 μ broad and 40–50 μ apart, with thick sheath. Pl. **98,** fig. **1133.**

a. Var. *crassa* Lemmermann. Cells 11–15 μ in diameter, spherical or oblate, usually with pseudovacuoles; heterocysts 10–17 μ in diameter, spherical, hyaline or pale yellow; akinetes 20–25 $\times$ 27–42 μ, broadly ovoid, solitary, remote from heterocysts; trichomes free-floating, solitary, forming rather regular spirals 50–60 μ broad and 45–55 μ between turns. Pl. **98,** figs. **1134, 1135.**

7. *Anabaena catenula* (Kuetzing) Bornet and Flahault. Cells 5–8 μ broad, barrel-shaped, homogeneous or granulose, without pseudovacuoles; heterocysts 6–9 $\times$ 9–13 μ, spherical to ellipsoid, akinetes 7–10 $\times$ 16–30 μ, cylindric, adjacent to heterocysts or remote, in series; trichomes blue-green, bent, with faint gelatinous envelopes. Pl. **98,** fig. **1131.**

8. *Anabaena flosaquae* (Lyngbye) Brébisson. Cells 4–8 μ in diameter, spherical or nearly so, generally with pseudovacuoles; heterocysts 6–9 μ in diameter, spherical; akinetes 7–13 $\times$ 20–50 μ, cylindric, often curved, solitary or in series, usually adjacent to heterocysts; trichomes free-floating, densely coiled or irregularly twisted into floccose aggregates. Pl. **97,** fig. **1127.**

9. *Anabaena unispora* Gardner. Cells 4–5 μ in diameter, cylindric, lightly constricted at cross-walls; heterocysts somewhat larger than the vegetative cells, cylindric; akinetes 13–20 $\times$ 20–34 μ, ellipsoid, brown, occurring singly on one side of the heterocysts; trichomes straight or curved, solitary among other algae or forming a slightly slimy, thin mass. (Reported from Pope County by Phinney, 1946.) Pl. **99,** fig. **1138.**

Aphanizomenon Morren 1838

Trichomes straight or somewhat curved, agglutinated laterally into free-floating, spindle-shaped bundles or small plates, usually without sheaths, sometimes constricted at the cross-walls and slightly attenuate;

FIG. 1128.—*Anabaena planctonica* Brunnthaler.

FIGS. 1129, 1130.—*Anabaena circinalis* (Kuetzing) Rabenhorst.

FIG. 1131.—*Anabaena catenula* (Kuetzing) Bornet and Flahault.

FIG. 1132.—*Anabaena variabilis* Kuetzing.

FIG. 1133.—*Anabaena spiroides* Klebahn.

FIGS. 1134, 1135.—*Anabaena spiroides* var. *crassa* Lemmermann.

(Figs. 1128–1130, 1134, 1135, G. M. Smith; figs. 1131–1133, Fremy. Figs. 1128, 1129, 1135 $\times$*1000;* figs. 1130–1134 $\times$*500.*)

PLATE 98

(Figs. 1128 to 1135)

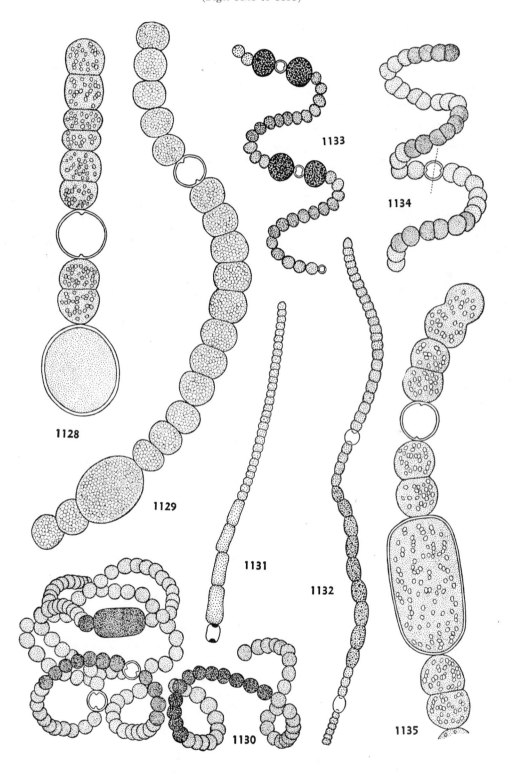

1128

1129

1130

1131

1132

1133

1134

1135

cells cylindric; heterocysts cylindric, intercalary; akinetes elongate, cylindric, solitary, remote from heterocysts or not.

Multiplication by formation of hormogonia and akinetes.

KEY TO THE SPECIES

1. Akinetes 6–8 × 35–80 μ, cylindric............................ 1. A. flosaquae
1. Akinetes 12–14 × 18–20 μ, ovoid........................... 2. A. ovalisporum

1. *Aphanizomenon flosaquae* (Linnaeus) Ralfs. Cells 4–6 × 5–15 μ; heterocysts 5–7 × 7–20 μ; akinetes 6–8 × 35–80 μ; with characters as in the genus. Pl. **99**, figs. **1143, 1144.**

2. *Aphanizomenon ovalisporum* Forti. Cells 3–5 μ in diameter and usually 1–3 times as long as broad, often much longer, blackish blue-green, with pseudovacuoles; trichomes single, straight or slightly curved, up to 1 mm. long, more or less apically narrowed, constricted at the cross-walls; heterocysts ellipsoid or rounded, 5–7 × 8–12 μ; akinetes ovoid, mostly free from the heterocysts, 12–14 × 18–20 μ, with yellow or brown membrane. Pl. **99**, fig. **1142.**

Cylindrospermum Kuetzing 1843

Trichomes straight and usually short, sometimes with *Oscillatoria*-like movement, usually aggregated into an indefinite mucous mass on soil, or free-floating; cells cylindric; heterocysts cylindric (or elongate) and terminal; akinetes contiguous to heterocyst, usually solitary and sometimes papillate.

Multiplication by formation of hormogonia and akinetes.

KEY TO THE SPECIES

1. Akinetes ovoid, 10–12 μ long............................. 1. C. muscicola
1. Akinetes ellipsoid, 20–38 μ long.. 2
    2. Wall of akinetes smooth.............................. 2. C. licheniforme
    2. Wall of akinetes ventricose or papillose when mature...... 3. C. majus

FIG. 1136.—*Anabaena inaequalis* (Kuetzing) Bornet and Flahault.

FIG. 1137.—*Anabaena oscillarioides* Bory.

FIG. 1138.—*Anabaena unispora* Gardner, part of filament with akinete and heterocyst.

FIG. 1139.—*Nodularia spumigena* Mertens.

FIGS. 1140, 1141.—*Nodularia harveyana* (Thwaites) Thuret var. *sphaerocarpa* (Bornet and Flahault) Elenkin.

FIG. 1142.—*Aphanizomenon ovalisporum* Forti.

FIGS. 1143, 1144.—*Aphanizomenon flosaquae* (Linnaeus) Ralfs.

(Figs. 1136, 1137, 1139–1141, Fremy; fig. 1138, Drouet; fig. 1142, Geitler; figs. 1143, 1144, G. M. Smith. Figs. 1136, 1137 ×*600;* fig. 1138 ×*2000;* figs. 1139–1141 ×*600;* figs. 1142, 1143 ×*1000;* fig. 1144 ×*400.)*

PLATE 99

(Figs. 1136 to 1144)

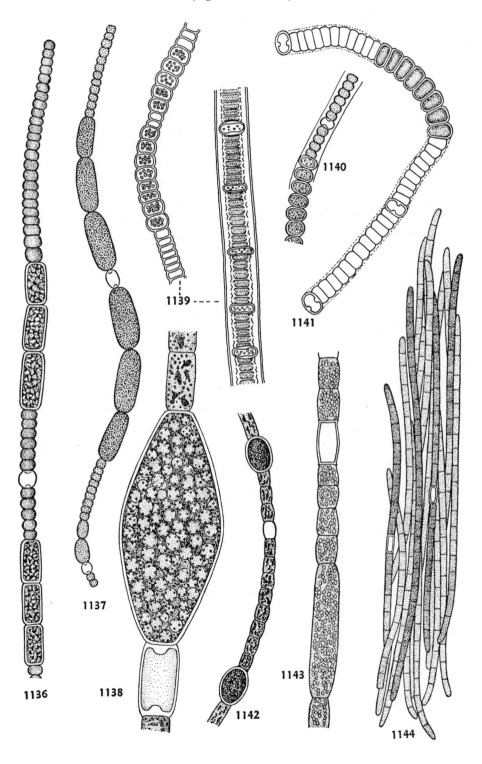

1136

1137

1138

1139

1140

1141

1142

1143

1144

1. *Cylindrospermum muscicola* Kuetzing. Cells 3.0–4.7 × 4–5 μ, constricted at cross-walls; heterocysts 4–5 × 5–7 μ; akinetes ovoid, 9–12 × 10–20 μ, with smooth, golden-brown walls; plant mass expanded, mucous, blackish green. Pl. **100**, fig. **1147**.

2. *Cylindrospermum licheniforme* (Bory) Kuetzing. Cells quadrate or cylindric, 2.5–4.2 × 4–5 μ, bright blue-green; heterocysts 5–6 × 7–12 μ; akinetes elongate or ellipsoid with somewhat flattened ends, 11–14 × 20–38 μ, with smooth and red-brown wall; plant mass mucous, more or less expanded, bright blue-green to blackish green. Pl. **100**, fig. **1146**.

3. *Cylindrospermum majus* Kuetzing. Cells 3–5 × 3–6 μ, cylindric or nearly quadrate, constricted at cross-walls, pale blue-green; heterocysts 5–6 μ broad and up to 10 μ long; akinetes single, ellipsoid, 10.0–15.4 × 20–38 μ, with brown papillose outer walls; plant mass mucous, generally widely expanded, blackish green. Pl. **100**, fig. **1145**.

Nodularia Mertens 1822

Filaments free-floating or forming a loose layer; trichomes more or less straight with short, depressed cells; sheaths hyaline, closely enveloping the trichome, sometimes becoming diffluent; heterocysts depressed; akinetes spherical or depressed, in series between heterocysts.

Multiplication by formation of hormogonia and by akinetes.

KEY TO THE SPECIES

1. Filaments 6–7 μ broad; akinetes 7–10 μ broad . . . . 1. N. harveyana var. sphaerocarpa

1. Filaments 8–12 μ broad; akinetes 11–12 μ broad . . . . 2. N. spumigena

1. *Nodularia harveyana* (Thwaites) Thuret var. *sphaerocarpa* (Bornet and Flahault) Elenkin. Cells 6–7 × 4 μ, depressed-spherical; heterocysts scarcely larger than vegetative cells; akinetes 7–10 μ in diameter, depressed-spherical, 2–12 in a series, brown; sheath thin, finally diffluent. Pl. **99**, figs. **1140, 1141**.

2. *Nodularia spumigena* Mertens. Cells 8–12 × 3–4 μ, disciform; heterocysts scarcely larger than vegetative cells; akinetes 12–15 × 6–10

Fig. 1145.—*Cylindrospermum majus* Kuetzing.

Fig. 1146.—*Cylindrospermum licheniforme* (Bory) Kuetzing.

Fig. 1147.—*Cylindrospermum muscicola* Kuetzing.

Fig. 1148.—*Nostoc ellipsosporum* Rabenhorst.

Fig. 1149.—*Nostoc muscorum* C. A. Agardh.

Fig. 1150.—*Nostoc spongiaeforme* C. A. Agardh.

(All figs., Fremy. Figs. 1145–1147 ×*500*; figs. 1148–1150 ×*700*.)

PLATE 100
(Figs. 1145 to 1150)

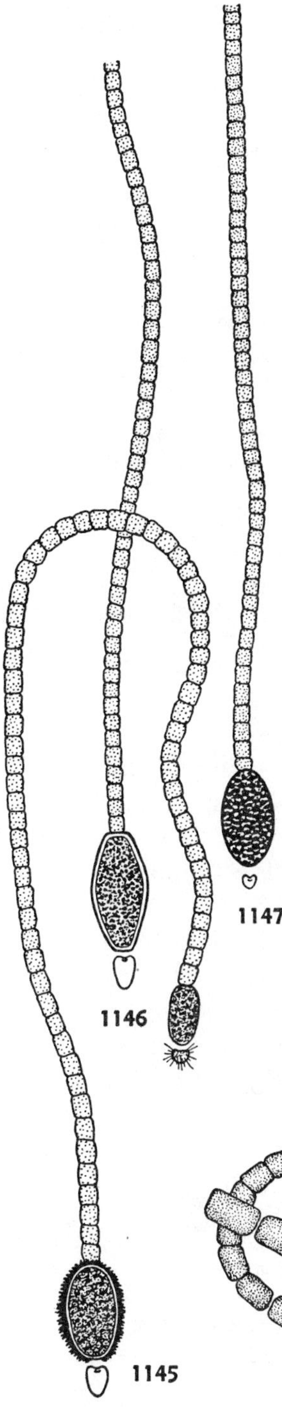

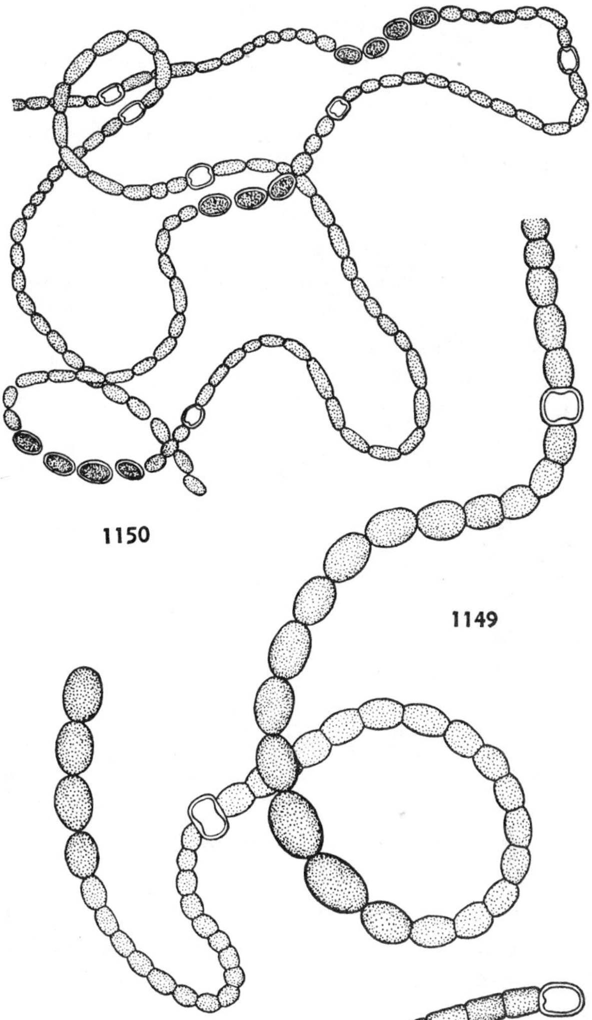

1150

1149

1147

1146

1145

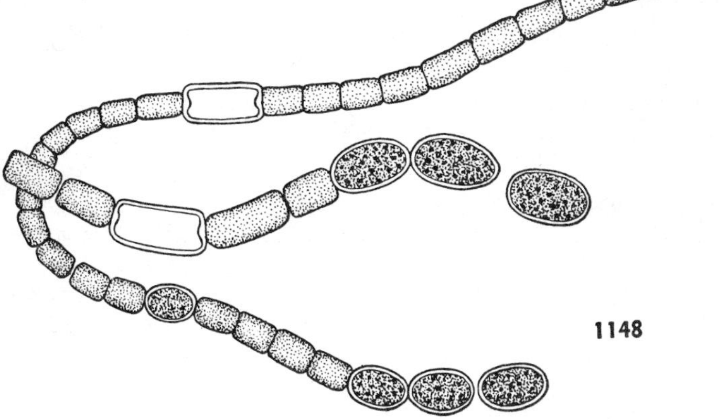

1148

μ, spherical, solitary, few or many in series, brown; filaments 8–18 μ in diameter, solitary, free-floating or mostly in a mucous mass, straight or curled. Pl. **99,** fig. **1139.**

Nostoc Vaucher 1803

Trichomes contorted, in a more or less firm gelatinous envelope, terrestrial or aquatic; colonial envelope free-floating or attached, globular to ovoid or frequently breaking open with age; otherwise similar to *Anabaena*.

Multiplication by hormogonia and by akinetes.

KEY TO THE SPECIES

1. Akinetes 7–12 μ long... 2
1. Akinetes 14–19 μ long.................................. 1. N. ellipsosporum
2. Cells 3–4 μ broad.. 3
2. Cells 4–6 μ broad.................................... 2. N. pruniforme
3. Generally terrestrial.................................... 3. N. muscorum
3. Generally aquatic... 4
4. Akinetes always colorless........................... 4. N. carneum
4. Akinetes yellowish or dark-colored....................................... 5
5. Plant mass with a firm outer layer; akinetes 5 × 7 μ....... 5. N. verrucosum
5. Plant mass soft and fragile; akinetes 6–7 × 10–12 μ........ 6. N. spongiaeforme

1. *Nostoc ellipsosporum* Rabenhorst. Cells cylindric, about 4 μ in diameter and 6–14 μ long, pale blue-green or olive-green; heterocysts more or less spherical or oblong, 6–7 × 6–14 μ; akinetes ellipsoid or oblong-cylindric, 6–8 × 14–19 μ, with smooth, transparent or yellowish walls; filaments flexuous, loosely entangled; plant mass gelatinous, expanded, irregularly margined, reddish or dark-colored. Pl. **100,** fig. **1148.**

2. *Nostoc pruniforme* (Linnaeus) C. A. Agardh. Cells compressed-spherical or a little longer than broad, 4–6 μ in diameter; heterocysts nearly rounded, 6–7 μ broad; akinetes spherical, about 10 μ in diameter; sheaths often distinct, colorless to yellowish; filaments loosely entangled; radiating from center of spherical colonies often reaching diameters of several centimeters, hollow at maturity, with tough outer layer, olive or dark blue-green, finally becoming brownish or blackish. Pl. **101,** figs. **1151–1153.**

3. *Nostoc muscorum* C. A. Agardh. Cells spherical, barrel-shaped or cylindric, about twice as long as broad, olive, 3–4 μ in diameter; heterocysts

---

Figs. 1151–1153.—*Nostoc pruniforme* (Linnaeus) C. A. Agardh; figs. 1151, 1153, sections of colonies.

Fig. 1154.—*Nostoc carneum* C. A. Agardh.

Fig. 1155.—*Nostoc verrucosum* Vaucher, section of colony.

(All figs., Fremy. Figs. 1151, 1153 ×*1;* fig. 1152 ×*550.*)

PLATE 101

(Figs. 1151 to 1155)

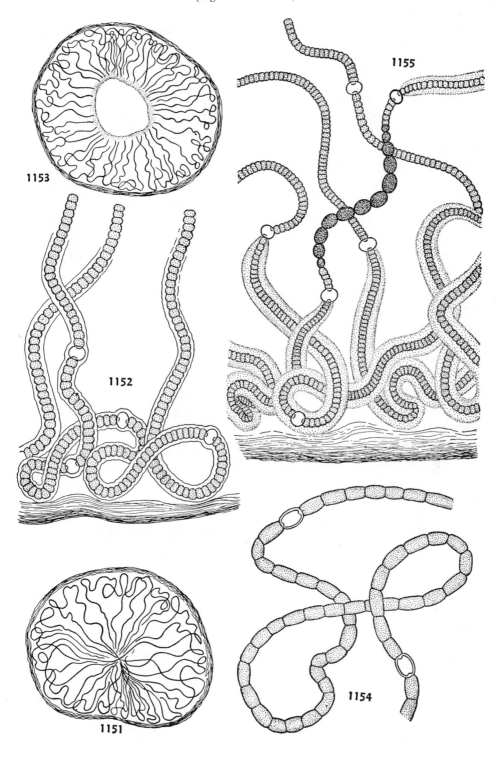

more or less globose, 6–7 μ in diameter; akinetes 4–8 × 8–12 μ, oblong, in series, with yellowish smooth wall; filaments flexuous, densely entangled; plant mass gelatinous-membranous, irregularly expanded, nodulate, attached, dull olive or dark-colored. Pl. **100**, fig. **1149**.

4. *Nostoc carneum* C. A. Agardh. Cells 3.5–4 μ in diameter, oblong-cylindric, about twice as long as wide; heterocysts oblong, about 6 μ in diameter; akinetes ovoid or ellipsoid, separated when mature, with smooth, thin outer wall, about 6 μ broad and 8–10 μ long; filaments loosely entangled, somewhat flexuous, with indistinct sheaths; colonies globose when young, later swollen, nodulose and hollow, finally irregularly expanded into a gelatinous mucus, flesh-colored, dark or pale blue-green. Pl. **101**, fig. **1154**.

5. *Nostoc verrucosum* Vaucher. Cells 3.0–3.5 μ in diameter, depressed-globose; heterocysts 6 μ broad, more or less globose; akinetes about 5 × 7 μ, ovoid, with smooth, yellowish wall; filaments flexuously twisted, densely entangled near the surface, with thick, often indistinct sheaths, colorless or yellowish brown; colonies often grouped into masses several centimeters in diameter, at first olive-black, solid, gelatinous, firm, spherical or irregularly so, later brownish green, hollow, vesicular, softer and torn. Pl. **101**, fig. **1155**.

6. *Nostoc spongiaeforme* C. A. Agardh. Cells variously shaped, from cylindric to depressed-spherical, about 4 × 7 μ, blue-green or violet; heterocysts, somewhat globose or oblong, 7–8 μ in diameter; akinetes 6–7 × 10–12 μ, oblong, separated, with smooth wall, dark-colored at maturity; filaments flexuous, loosely entangled, sheaths more or less distinct near the periphery of the colonies, yellowish or dark-colored; colonies gelatinous, at first globose, afterward expanded, swollen, nodulose, pale blue-green-violet or reddish. Pl. **100**, fig. **1150**.

Family Scytonemataceae

Trichomes generally of uniform diameter, sometimes apically attenuate, uniseriate; filaments with false branches, and sheaths with 1 or more trichomes; heterocysts and akinetes may be present.

Plectonema Thuret 1875

Trichomes composed of cylindric or discoid cells, generally constricted at the cross-walls, often bent, with false branching; sheaths firm, colorless or sometimes brownish yellow; akinetes and heterocysts not known to oc-

Fig. 1156.—*Plectonema tomasinianum* (Kuetzing) Bornet.

Fig. 1157.—*Plectonema nostocorum* Bornet.

Figs. 1158, 1159.—*Scytonema tolypothrichoides* Kuetzing; fig. 1159, habit.

(All figs., Fremy. Figs. 1156, 1158 ×*500*; fig. 1157 ×*1500*; fig. 1159 ×*1*.)

PLATE 102

(Figs. 1156 to 1159)

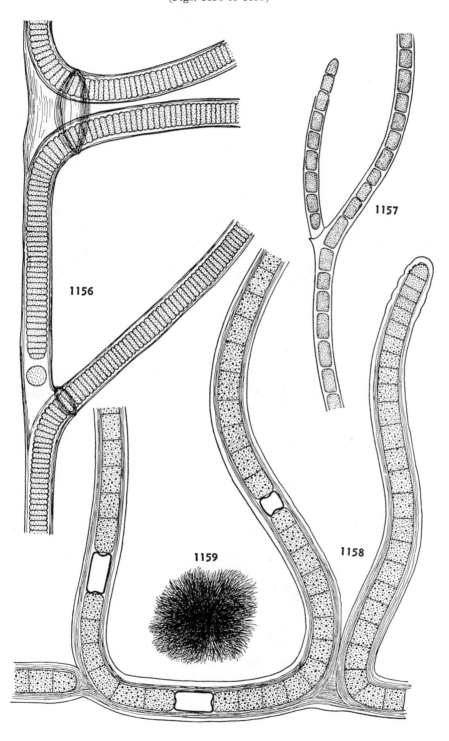

cur; filaments free-floating or forming felt-like masses which may be extensive in subaerial habitats.

Multiplication by formation of hormogonia.

KEY TO THE SPECIES

1. Cells 0.7–1.5 × 2–3 μ................................... 1. P. nostocorum
1. Cells 11–22 × 3–9 μ................................ 2. P. tomasinianum

1. *Plectonema nostocorum* Bornet. Cells 0.7–1.5 × 2–3 μ, cylindric, not granulose, pale yellow-green, end cell rounded; sheaths thin, colorless, not becoming blue with chlorzinciodide; false branches scarce, solitary or sometimes in pairs; filaments straight or bent; growing in sheaths of *Nostoc* or other algae, or free-floating. Pl. **102,** fig. **1157.**

2. *Plectonema tomasinianum* (Kuetzing) Bornet. Cells 11–22 × 3–9 μ (sometimes longer), blue-green, generally granulate at cross-walls, end cell rounded; sheaths thick, lamellose, at first colorless but later becoming yellow-brown, coloring blue with chlorzinciodide; dwarf branches usually in pairs, sometimes abundant, sometimes scarce; filaments flexuous, entangled; plant mass tufted, more or less expanded, brownish green or dull blue-green, tufts up to 2 cm. high. Pl. **102,** fig. **1156.**

Scytonema C. A. Agardh 1824

Trichomes straight, single within the sheath; false branches usually arising between 2 heterocysts, solitary or in pairs; sheaths firm, hyaline or yellowish to brownish, homogeneous or with parallel or oblique lamellae; akinetes not common, little larger than the vegetative cells, with smooth walls; subaerial or aquatic.

Multiplication by formation of hormogonia and sometimes by akinetes.

KEY TO THE SPECIES

1. Cells 6–14 μ.. 2
1. Cells 14–30 μ... 1. S. cincinnatum
  2. Sheaths homogeneous, or in parallel layers............ 2. S. ocellatum
  2. Sheaths lamellose, layers divergent.................. 3. S. tolypothrichoides

1. *Scytonema cincinnatum* (Kuetzing) Thuret. Cells 14–30 μ in diameter, about 0.3 as long as broad; filaments 16–36 μ in diameter and often 3 cm. or more long, curled, with false branching; sheaths firm, membranous, colorless or sometimes yellowish; heterocysts sometimes numerous, sometimes rare, depressed or quadrate; plant mass tufted, entangled, almost woolly, green but later becoming brown or olive. Pl. **103,** figs. **1160, 1161.**

Figs. 1160, 1161.—*Scytonema cincin-*   (All figs., Fremy. Figs. 1160, 1162 ×*500;*
natum (Kuetzing) Thuret; fig. 1161, habit.   fig. 1161 ×*1.*)
   Fig. 1162.—*Scytonema ocellatum* Lyngbye.

PLATE 103

(Figs. 1160 to 1162)

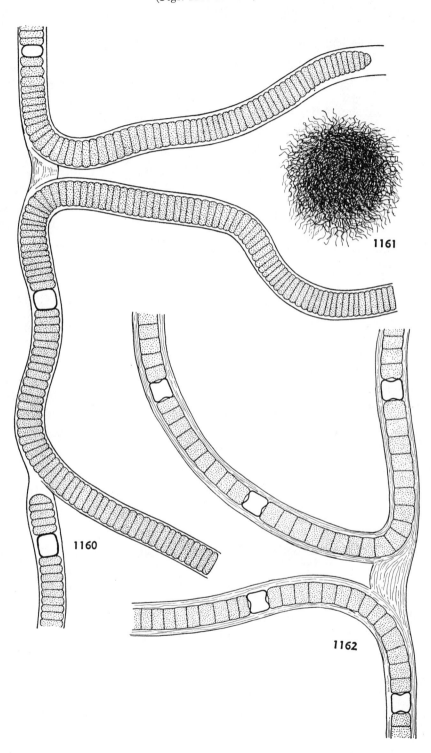

1161

1160

1162

2. *Scytonema ocellatum* Lyngbye. Cells 6–14 μ broad, olive-green, quadrate, or not as long as broad; heterocysts nearly quadrate, about the same diameter as the vegetative cells, yellowish; sheaths firm, lamellose, becoming brownish; filaments 10–18 μ in diameter, up to 3 mm. in length, entangled, with short false branches; plant mass cushion-shaped, black or gray, becoming bluish. Pl. 103, fig. 1162.

3. *Scytonema tolypothrichoides* Kuetzing. Cells 8–12 μ in diameter, somewhat quadrate or oblong, cross-walls often indistinct, protoplasm densely granulose, olive or yellowish; heterocysts about the same diameter as the vegetative cells, varying in length from 8–25 μ, rose-colored; sheaths at first colorless, becoming orange-brown, lamellose, outer layers often colorless; filaments 10–15 μ in diameter, 5–6 mm. in length, radiating from the center of the mass, with numerous false branches; plant mass tufted, floating, spherical, often a centimeter in diameter, brown or green. Pl. 102, figs. 1158, 1159.

Tolypothrix Kuetzing 1843

Filaments with false branches, single, usually arising in the immediate vicinity of the heterocysts, forming a floccose, floating mass or sessile; heterocysts single or 3–5-seriate; akinetes spherical, ovoid or ellipsoid, single or seriate.

Multiplication by formation of hormogonia and sometimes by akinetes.

1. *Tolypothrix tenuis* Kuetzing. Cells 5–10 μ in diameter, blue-green to olive-green; heterocysts 7–10 × 7–11 μ, 1 to 5 in a series, often colorless; filaments 6–12 μ in diameter, up to 2 cm. long, forming a tufted, floccose layer, sessile or later free-floating; sheaths colorless or yellowish. Pl. 105, fig. 1164.

Family **Stigonemataceae**

Trichomes uniseriate to multiseriate, with true branches; heterocysts terminal or intercalary; akinetes present in most genera, but not common.

Stigonema C. A. Agardh 1824

Trichomes branching, with main axis partially or wholly multiseriate, with branches unilateral in origin and not further branched or arising from all sides of the trichome and repeatedly branched; sheaths firm, smooth or rough, homogeneous or lamellate, colorless or yellowish brown, brown or black; heterocysts in main axes formed from marginal cells; hormogones formed usually in terminal parts of young branches; cells generally spheri-

FIG. 1163.—*Fischerella ambigua* (Naegeli) Gomont.   (Fig. 1163, Fremy. ×1000.)

PLATE 104

(Fig. 1163)

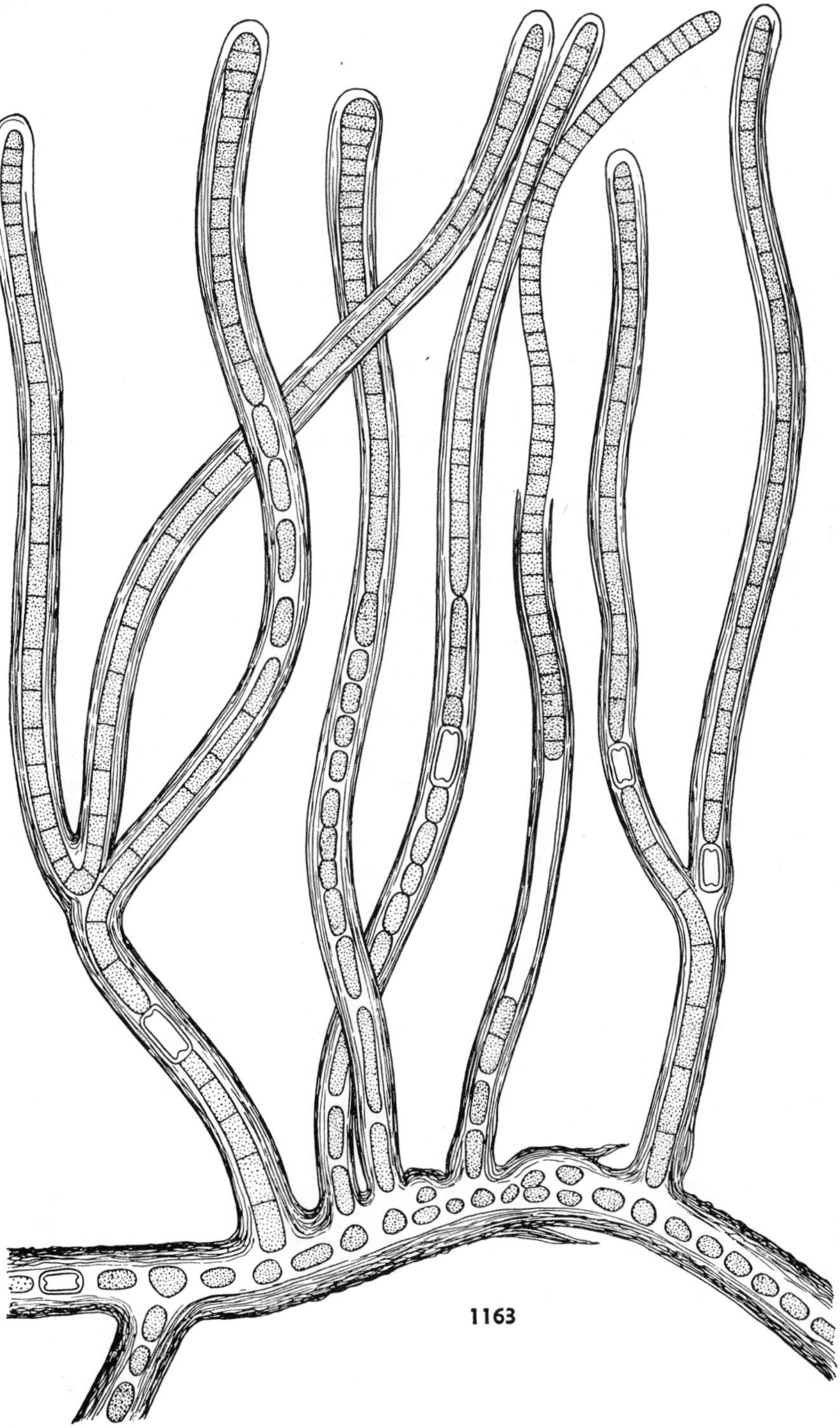

1163

cal or flattened by mutual compression, often separated and with individual sheaths in older filaments; plants terrestrial or aquatic, forming rigid or soft masses, often blackish brown.

Multiplication by formation of hormogonia.

1. *Stigonema minutum* (C. A. Agardh) Hassall. Trichomes 1–4-seriate within filaments 18–28 μ in diameter, about 1 mm. in length, decumbent at base, ascending, flexuous, richly branched; heterocysts numerous, lateral or intercalary, quadrate to oblong; sheaths yellowish or yellowish brown; hormogonia 12–15 $\times$ 25–35 μ; plant mass crustaceous or cushion-like, thin, fragile, blackish. Pl. **105**, fig. **1165**.

Fischerella (Bornet and Flahault) Gomont 1895

Primary trichome ordinarily branched, forming 1 to several rows of cells; branches unilateral, erect, elongate, sharply distinct from the main filament, usually a single row of cells; sheaths gelatinous, colorless to yellowish or brownish; heterocysts intercalary and lateral; long hormogonia formed at the extremities of the branches; plant mass forming a more or less expanded layer, terrestrial on wet ground, or aquatic.

Formation of hormogonia and akinetes.

1. *Fischerella ambigua* (Naegeli) Gomont. Primary trichomes generally 1-seriate, with cells subspherical to cylindric, 3–4 μ in diameter, in twisted, sometimes tangled filaments, 6–9 μ in diameter, sheath generally lamellose and yellow-brown; branches long, erect, fasciculate, cylindric, with cells rarely more than 2–3 μ in diameter; heterocysts elongate, 3–5 $\times$ 6–10 μ; hormogonia very long. (Reported from Pope County by Phinney, 1946.) Pl. **104**, fig. **1163**.

Family **Rivulariaceae**

Trichomes evidently attenuate toward apex or from the middle to both poles, uniseriate, often with false branching; heterocysts generally basal; akinetes present or not.

Amphithrix Kuetzing 1843; emend. Bornet and Flahault 1886

Plant mass made up of a nearly parenchymatous lower portion of densely interwoven trichomes and an upper portion of numerous, erect, parallel

Fig. 1164.—*Tolypothrix tenuis* Kuetzing.

Fig. 1165.—*Stigomena minutum* (Agardh) Hassall.

Figs. 1166–1170.—*Raphidiopsis curvata* Fritsch.

(Figs. 1164, 1165, Fremy; figs. 1166–1170, Geitler. Fig. 1164 $\times 500$; fig. 1165 $\times 300$; figs. 1166–1170 $\times 1000$.)

PLATE 105

(Figs. 1164 to 1170)

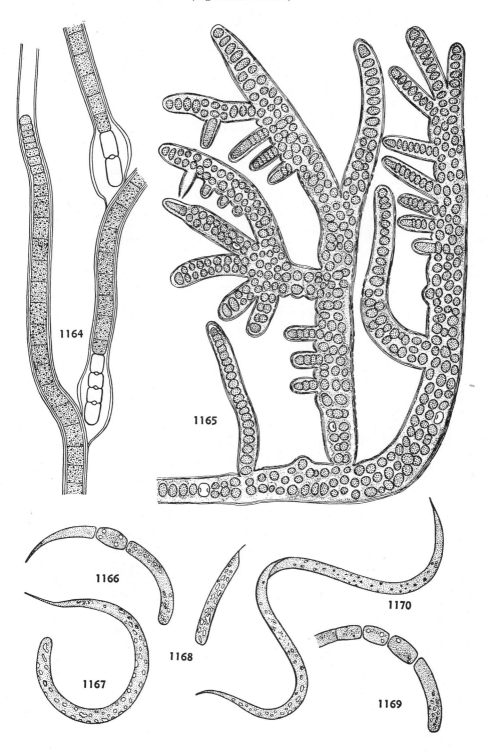

1164

1165

1166

1167

1168

1169

1170

trichomes attenuate outwardly to hair-like points, purple or violet; sheaths thin, continuous; heterocysts and akinetes not formed.

Multiplication by formation of hormogonia, formed singly or in series.

1. *Amphithrix janthina* (Montagne) Bornet and Flahault. Cells about 1–2 μ in diameter, about as long as broad, mutually compressed in lower portion of mass, with pale-green protoplasm; sheaths thin, uniform; filaments 1.5–2.2 μ in diameter, 0.3–0.5 mm. in length, erect, purple; hormogonia up to 20 μ long; plant mass crustaceous, thin, purple. Pl. **106**, fig. **1175**.

Calothrix C. A. Agardh 1824

Trichomes apically hair-like, tapering gradually or sometimes abruptly, sometimes with false branches; vegetative cells with granulose protoplasm, discoid at base of trichome, becoming cylindric toward the apex, with or without constrictions at the cross-walls; sheaths cylindric, uniform, homogeneous or lamellose, hyaline or colored; heterocysts usually basal, sometimes intercalary, absent in a few species; filaments single or united into strata which are cushion-like, brush-like, or stellate.

Akinetes known for a few species.

KEY TO THE SPECIES

1. Sheaths scarcely evident..................................... 1. C. kawrayskyi
1. Sheaths evident, usually thick.. 2
   2. Heterocysts globose or quadrate......................... 2. C. stagnalis
   2. Heterocysts hemispherical............................. 3. C. parietina

1. *Calothrix kawrayskyi* Schmidle. Cells about 4 μ in diameter, varying from quadrate to shorter or longer than the diameter, blue-green; trichomes terminating in long hairs; sheaths thin, closely appressed to trichomes, colorless, scarcely evident; heterocysts hemispherical or elongate, basal; hormogonia single; filaments straight, unbranched, 4–5 μ in diameter, sometimes reaching a height of nearly a millimeter.

2. *Calothrix stagnalis* Gomont. Cells 6–9 × 6–10 μ, nearly quadrate; trichomes much attenuate; heterocysts basal, mostly in 2's, rounded or al-

Figs. 1171, 1172.—*Gloeotrichia natans* (Hedwig) Rabenhorst; fig. 1172, section of colony.

Figs. 1173, 1174.—*Gloeotrichia pisum* (Agardh) Thuret; fig. 1174, section of colony.

Fig. 1175.—*Amphithrix janthina* (Montagne) Bornet and Flahault.

Fig. 1176.—*Calothrix stagnalis* Gomont.

(Figs. 1171–1175, Fremy; fig. 1176, Tilden. Fig. 1171 ×*200*; fig. 1172 ×*1*; fig. 1173 ×*500*; fig. 1174 ×*40*; fig. 1175 ×*1200*; fig. 1176 ×*500*.)

PLATE 106

(Figs. 1171 to 1176)

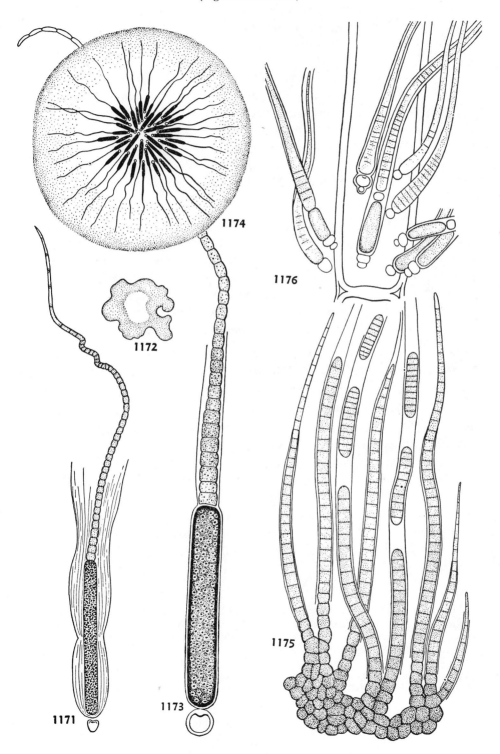

1174

1172

1176

1171

1173

1175

most quadrate; akinetes slightly conical, more or less cylindric, 10–11 ×
26–40 μ, single or in 2's, yellow, smooth; filaments up to 1 mm. long, forming stellate masses, decumbent and thickened at base. Pl. 106, fig. 1176.
Pl. 107, fig. 1177.

3. *Calothrix parietina* Thuret. Cells 5–10 × 8–28 μ, shorter than broad
at the base of the trichomes, blue-green; trichomes terminally hair-like;
heterocysts basal or intercalary, half-round, broader than the trichome;
sheath close, thick, lamellose, often shredded and brittle, yellow-brown;
filaments 10–12 μ in diameter and up to a millimeter in length, scattered
or aggregated into a crustose, thin, brown or black mass, erect or decumbent, flexuously contorted. Pl. 107, figs. 1178, 1179.

Gloeotrichia J. G. Agardh 1842

Filaments colonial, free-floating or sessile, spherical to irregular (especially when older), gelatinous to leathery; trichomes strongly attenuate
from base; sheath evident only near base of trichome, becoming confluent
toward apex; filaments radiating from center, falsely branched; heterocysts spherical to hemispherical, solitary, at the base of trichomes;
akinetes cylindric, solitary, adjacent to heterocysts.

Multiplication by formation of hormogonia and akinetes.

KEY TO THE SPECIES

1. Colonies rarely more than 2 mm. in diameter . . . . 1. G. pisum
1. Colonies up to 10 cm. in diameter . . . . 2. G. natans

1. *Gloeotrichia pisum* (C. A. Agardh) Thuret. Cells (at base of trichomes) 4–7 μ in diameter; somewhat quadrate; heterocysts 11–15 μ,
spherical; akinetes 9–15 × 60–400 μ, cylindric; colonies hard, spherical,
blackish green, free-floating or sessile. Pl. 106, figs. 1173, 1174.

2. *Gloeotrichia natans* (Hedwig) Rabenhorst. Cells (at base of trichomes)
7–9 μ in diameter; heterocysts 6–12 μ in diameter, spherical; akinetes 10–
18 × 40–250 μ; colonies hard, at first sessile, later free-floating, spherical
or nearly so, hollow, composed of loosely associated filaments; sheaths up
to 40 μ in diameter, often folded and wrinkled, colorless or brown. Pl. 106,
figs. 1171, 1172.

Fig. 1177.—*Calothrix stagnalis* Gomont.

Figs. 1178, 1179.—*Calothrix parietina*
Bornet and Flahault.

Fig. 1180.—*Schizothrix stricklandii*
Drouet.

Figs. 1181–1183.—*Batrachospermum
boryanum* Sirodot (fig. 1181, part of thallus;

fig. 1182, portion of branch of thallus;
fig. 1183, sexual filament from *Chantransia*
plant).

(Fig. 1177, Tilden; figs. 1178, 1179,
Fremy; figs. 1181–1183, Flint. Figs. 1177–
1181 ×500; fig. 1182 ×3; fig. 1183 ×100.)

PLATE 107
(Figs. 1177 to 1183)

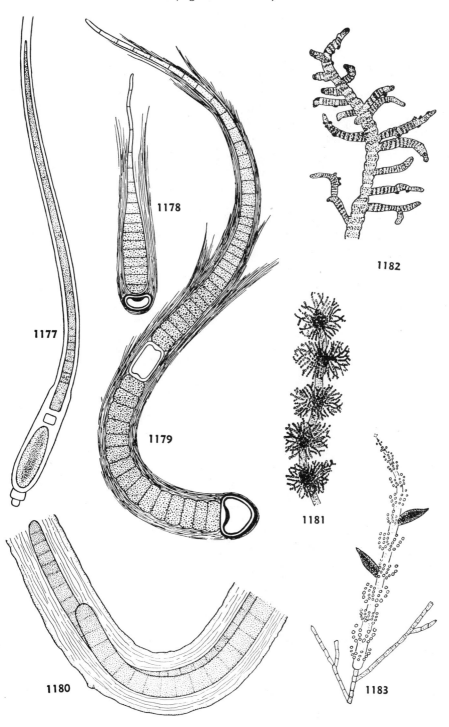

1178

1177

1179

1180

1181

1182

1183

Raphidiopsis Fritsch 1929

Trichomes short, more or less bent and curved, without sheath, narrowed and sharp-pointed at both ends, or rounded at one end and sharp-pointed at the other.

Multiplication by the formation of akinetes.

1. *Raphidiopsis curvata* Fritsch. Cells about 4.5 μ broad, 1.5–2.0 times as long as broad, often with pseudovacuoles; trichomes free-floating, single or oftener in bundles, S-shaped, circular, curved or straight, not constricted at the cross-walls; akinetes barrel-shaped, about 5 μ broad and 10.0–13.5 μ long, in the middle of the trichome. Pl. **105,** figs. **1166–1170.**

Phylum RHODOPHYTA

Class *RHODOPHYCEAE*

THE Rhodophyceae or red algae with but few exceptions are multicellular organisms ranging from simple or branched filaments to macroscopic thalli of considerable complexity. Vegetative cells usually have a peripheral distribution of cytoplasm and are generally uninucleate, although some species are multinucleate, or only so at times. Chromatophores may be single, stellate, and bear a pyrenoid without a starch sheath, or be discoid, more than 1 in a cell, and without pyrenoids. Pigments include chlorophylls *a* and *d*, alpha- and beta-carotene, the xanthophyll lutein, and the phycobilins: r-phycoerythrin (red) and r-phycocyanin (blue). Red pigment is often present in sufficient quantity to obscure other colors but various shades of green, olive, and brown are common. Accumulated foods include 2 carbohydrates: floridean starch and a soluble sugar, floridiside.

Asexual reproduction by nonflagellated spores of several types: neutral spores formed directly or indirectly from vegetative cells; monospores borne singly in sporangia upon the sexual generation; paraspores borne in sporangia upon diploid plants. Sexual reproduction by fusion of a nonflagellated male gamete, the spermatium, with a carpogonial nucleus.

The Rhodophyceae are largely marine, and the few freshwater forms are, with one exception, aquatics usually inhabiting cool, well-aerated, clear-water streams.

KEY TO THE GENERA OF RHODOPHYCEAE

1. Thallus monoaxial; branches in whorls................ Batrachospermum (p. 380)
1. Thallus multiaxial; branches not in whorls............ Thorea (p. 382)

Subclass FLORIDEAE

Thalli macroscopic, annual or perennial, filamentous, branched, monoaxial or multiaxial, and often embedded in a gelatinous matrix. Growth is entirely terminal and there are cytoplasmic connections between cells. The gametophytes are homothallic or heterothallic, and the carpogonia and spermatangia are usually borne terminally. At the time of fertilization a spermatium is freed from the enclosing spermatangium and migrates to the base of the carpogonium where it unites with the carpogonial nucleus.

379

The zygote, with or without a meiotic division, produces a cystocarp consisting of a mass of gonimoblast filaments bearing carposporangia and haploid or diploid carpospores. The diploid carpospores give rise to a free-living diploid tetrasporophyte which bears asexual tetraspores that develop into gametophytes. The haploid carpospores germinate directly into gametophytes. Tetrasporophytes may bear paraspores which upon germination produce tetrasporophytes.

Order NEMALIONALES

Thallus filamentous, branched, without true cortication, or nonfilamentous, cylindric, compressed, or foliaceous, the superficial cells sometimes forming a parenchymatous tissue; growth always apical and producing monoaxial thalli if there is 1, or multiaxial thalli if more than 1 apical cell; cells uninucleate, with evident cytoplasmic connections; chromatophores single and axial or more than 1 parietal and discoid; asexual reproduction usually by monospores, less frequently by 2 or 4 spores in a sporangium; sexual reproduction by spermatia and carpogonia, the zygote producing carpospores; tetraspores in some genera.

Family **Batrachospermaceae**

Thallus with a distinct monoaxial organization; lateral branches in whorls and smaller than the central axis; asexual reproduction by monospores usually borne on the *Chantransia* stage; sexual reproduction by spermatia and carpogonia borne only on adult plants; carpospores formed only on terminal cells of gonimoblasts.

Batrachospermum Roth 1797

Thallus macroscopic, 20 cm. or more in length, gelatinous, filiform, freely branched, the branches in dense globose whorls that appear bead-like to the naked eye; main axis a single row of large, broad cells bearing lateral branches just below the septa, and cortical threads which grow downward completely surrounding the central axis and often giving rise to secondary whorls of branches; lateral branches forked, about equal in length, of limited growth, often terminating in hairs; cells of branches small, ellipsoid or moniliform, with several parietal, discoid or elongate chromatophores

FIGS. 1184–1186.—*Thorea ramosissima* Bory (fig. 1184, habit sketch; fig. 1185, terminal portion of branch; fig. 1186, section of thallus showing intertwined filaments of the axial core and erect hair-like filaments with two monosporangia). (Figs. 1184, 1185, Wolle; fig. 1186, Hedgecock and Hunter. Figs. 1184, 1185 ×2; fig. 1186 ×450.)

PLATE 108

(Figs. 1184 to 1186)

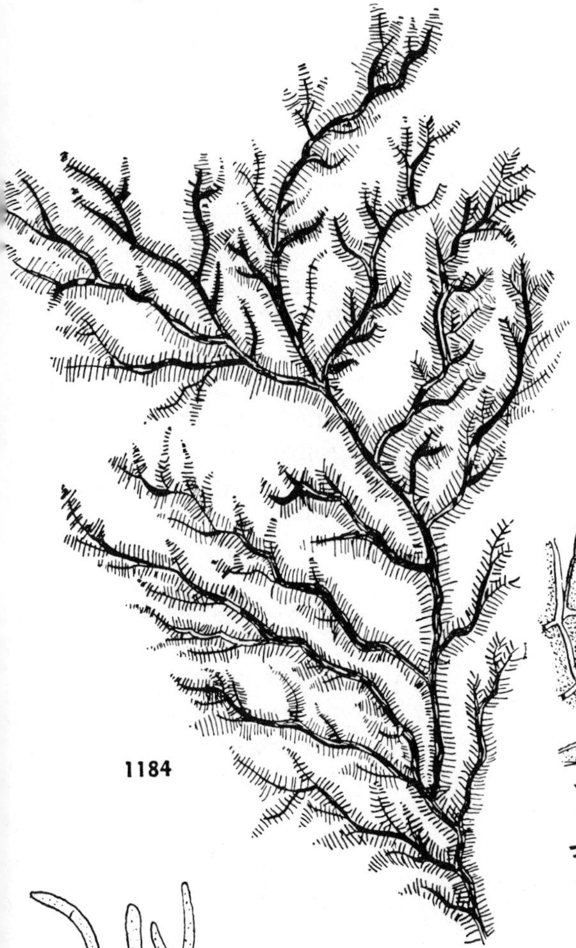

1184

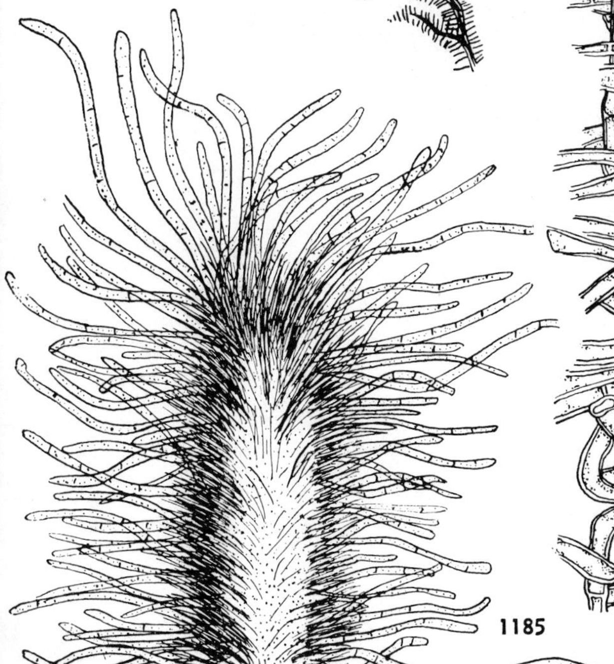

1185

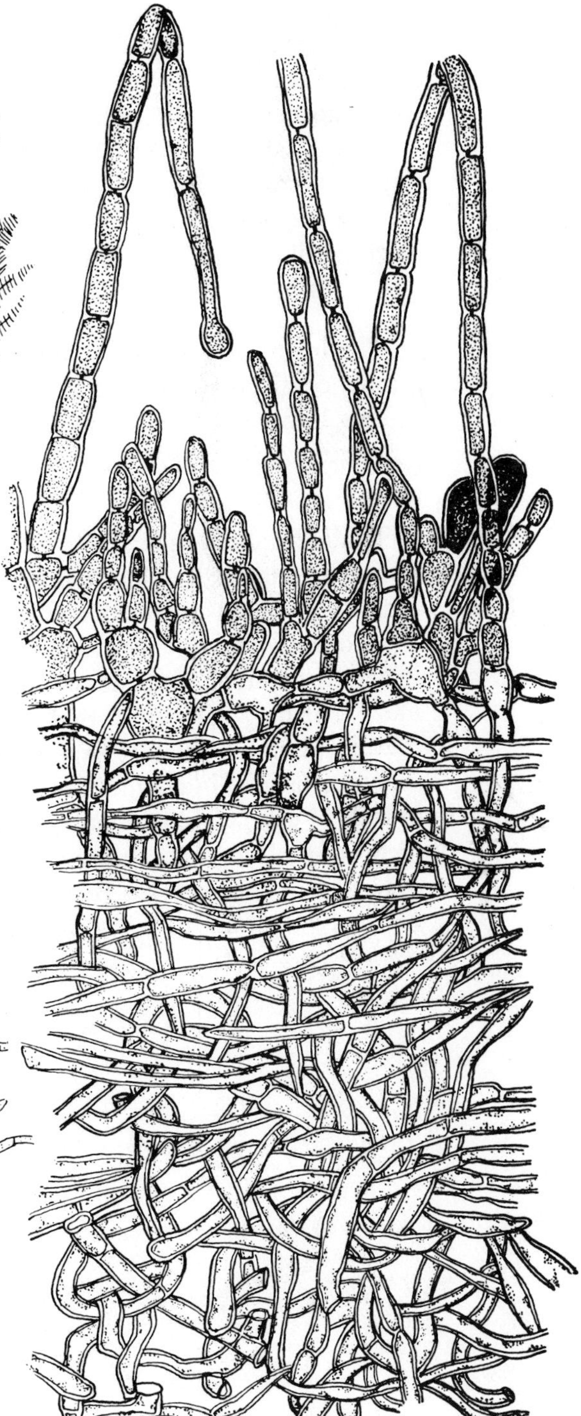

1186

with a single pyrenoid; pigmentation blue-green, olive or violet; monoecious or dioecious.

1. *Batrachospermum boryanum* Sirodot. Thallus up to 10 cm. in length, very gelatinous, usually much branched, the whorls close or remote from one another; secondary whorls few to more or less numerous; terminal hairs few, short, very little swollen at the base; cortical filaments numerous and loosely interwoven; dioecious; carpogonia usually on the primary lateral branches, sometimes on the secondary laterals, and rarely on the cortical filaments; trichogyne ellipsoid to ovoid. Pl. **107,** figs. **1181–1183.**

Family **Thoreaceae**

Thallus multiaxial in organization, gelatinous, much branched; lateral branches disposed along the entire axis; asexual reproduction by monospores borne by the *Chantransia* stage and by terminal cells of lateral branches of adult plants; sexual reproduction not known.

Thorea Bory 1808

Thallus macroscopic, freely branched, consisting of an axial core of irregularly interlaced hyaline filaments surrounded by a zone of similar but longitudinally disposed filaments; longitudinal filaments surrounded by a layer of spherical or irregularly shaped cells which give rise to short, densely arranged, erect filaments within the gelatinous envelope and to elongate hairs that may extend beyond the gelatinous envelope in a felt-like zone; mature plants consist of several shoots attached to a disc of interlaced, lime-encrusted filaments; chromatophores discoid or irregular, numerous in cells of erect filaments and outermost cells of the projecting hairs; pigmentation olive-green, brown, or black, purplish when dried.

1. *Thorea ramosissima* Bory. With characteristics of the genus; thallus 2–3 cm. wide and up to 1 m. in length. Pl. **108,** figs. **1184–1186.**

DOUBTFUL SPECIES

(The names below are in addition to the excluded species
listed by Britton in the *Catalog* in 1944.)

Amphiprora calumetica Thomas. Apparently undescribed, although listed
by Thomas and Chase (p. 328, 1887) and figured poorly by Wolle (pl.
48, figs. 22–24, 1890).

Coscinodiscus asteromphalus Ehrenberg. Probably an exclusively marine
species.

Gloeocystis confluens (Kuetzing) Richter. Reported by H. K. Phinney
(1946) for Pope County.

Surirella apiculata Wm. Smith. Although we have included this species in
our report (p. 294), the figure from Wolle (pl. 78, fig. 913) is inadequate.

Synedra hyalina Provazek. Neither the description nor the illustration as
given by Provazek (1900) is convincing.

GLOSSARY

Acicular, slenderly needle-shaped.

Acuminate, tapering gradually to the apex.

Akinete, a nonmotile spore, formed directly from a vegetative cell, whose wall is a greatly thickened parent-cell wall or not distinct from it.

Androsporangium, a cell in which an androspore forms.

Androspore, a motile spore which, after release from the androsporangium, gives rise to a dwarf male (nannandrium).

Anisogamy, sexuality characterized by union of two flagellated or non-flagellated gametes of unequal sizes.

Annular, in the form of a ring.

Antapical, opposite the apical end; the posterior end.

Antheridium, a cell containing one or more sperms.

Apical, at the top; the anterior end.

Apiculate, ending in a short, pointed tip.

Aplanospore, a nonmotile spore formed from all or a part of the protoplast of a vegetative cell and having a wall distinct from that of the parent-cell.

Arbuscular, branched in a tree-like manner.

Arcuate, moderately curved like a bow.

Areolate, marked out into a network of small spaces; coarsely reticulate.

Autogamy, the union of daughter nuclei or protoplasts without liberation from the cell.

Autospore, an aplanospore having the same shape as the vegetative cell from which it was formed.

Autotrophic, referring to an organism able to synthesize its own food from inorganic substances.

Auxospore, a spore formed by asexual metamorphosis of the protoplast of one cell or resulting from the sexual fusion

of two protoplasts or nuclei; occurring only in diatoms.

Axial, located along the axis or center line in a pole-to-pole direction.

Axial field, a longitudinal strip extending the length of the valve of pennate diatoms (Pennales), homogeneous in structure or perforated by a raphe.

Bacilliform, rod-shaped.

Bilabiate, two-lipped.

Binate, double; occurring in pairs.

Blepharoplast, a small granule at the base of a flagellum.

Bullate, bubble-like, as if blistered or puckered; swollen, spheroidal.

Calyptra, any hood- or cap-like covering, sometimes appearing on apical cells of filaments.

Campanulate, bell-shaped; cup-shaped with a broad base.

Capitate, having a head-like or knob-like apex.

Capitellate, having a small head-like or knob-like end.

Cardioid, heart-shaped.

Carinal, on or having relation to a ridge or keel.

Carpogonium, the unicellular female sex organ of the Rhodophyceae.

Carposporangium, a structure in which a carpospore develops.

Carpospore, a naked haploid or diploid spore formed in a carposporangium directly or indirectly from a zygote of Rhodophyceae.

Chromoplasm, the peripheral pigmented portion of the protoplast of Myxophyceae.

Cingulum, an open hoop-like band or girdle connecting the two valves of diatom cells.

Circinate, rolled inward from the apex.

Citriform, lemon-shaped.

Clathrate, with openings like lattice work.

Clavate, club-shaped.

Coenobium, a colony with a definite number of cells arranged in a specific way.

Coenocyte, a multinucleate vegetative cell or non-septate thallus.

Colligate, bound together as by a collar-like septum, H-shaped in lateral view.

Comb, a crest or long narrow ridge.

Confluent, growing or running together; blended, merged into an apparently single structure.

Conjugation, union of isogamous or anisogamous gametes.

Coralloidal, having the form or appearance of coral.

Cordiform, heart-shaped.

Corrugate, wrinkled, furrowed, or in folds.

Cortication, an external covering or ensheathing layer of cells.

Costate, having one or more ribs or ridges.

Crenate, marginally cut into rounded scallops; wavy.

Crenulate, having the margin minutely crenate or scalloped.

Cruciform, cross-shaped; cruciate.

Cuneate, wedge-shaped.

Cuniform, wedge-shaped.

Cyst, a more or less rounded, non-motile, often dormant cell with a thick or thin, gelatinous or rigid wall which is distinct from that of the vegetative cell; characteristic of certain amoeboid and flagellate organisms, such as Euglenophyceae, Dinophyceae, Chrysophyceae, etc.; not distinguishable from an aplanospore.

Cystocarp, the fruiting body of Rhodophyceae composed of a mass of carposporangia and sterile cells; an asexual spore-producing generation parasitic upon the thallus bearing the sex organs—a carposporophyte.

Decussate, marked with intersecting lines or rows; divided crosswise.

Dendroid, resembling a tree in appearance.

Dentate, having teeth.

Denticulate, finely dentate or toothed.

Diffluent, dissolving; deliquescent.

Dioecious, having male and female gametes borne on separate plants.

Disciform, flat and circular; disc-like.

Discoid, resembling a disc.

Divaricate, divergent at a wide angle; spreading.

Echinate, having small spines or prickles.

Emarginate, having a shallow notch at the apex.

Endospores, in the Myxophyceae spores formed by repeated division of the protoplast within a cell-wall or successively cut off at the distal end of the protoplast; in centric diatoms a thick-walled asexually formed spore (statospore).

Endozoophytic, growing within the cells or among cells of animal tissues.

Epigynous, situated above the oogonium.

Epiphytic, pertaining to a plant growing on another plant but not parasitic.

Epitheca, the "longer half," or epivalve, of a diatom cell; the portion of the wall of a Dinoflagellate anterior to the transverse furrow.

Epivalve; *see* Epitheca.

Epizoophytic, a plant growing upon a living animal but not parasitic.

Exospore, the outer layer of a spore-wall.

Exserted, extending beyond surrounding parts.

Eyespot, a small pigmented photo-sensitive body in certain flagellated algal cells.

Fascicle, a bundle or cluster.

Fasciculate, in close bundles or clusters.

Fertilization, union of male and female gametes.

Filiform, thread-like.

Floccose, having the appearance of matted woolly hairs.

Frustule, the silicified wall of the diatom cell; sometimes applied to the entire diatom cell.

Furcate, forked.

Fusiform, spindle-shaped; swollen in the middle and narrowing toward each end.

Gametangium, a cell or a group of cells containing gametes.

Gamete, a sex cell.

Geniculate, bent abruptly like a knee.

Genuflexion, a bending or kneeing.

Gibbous, protuberant or swollen on one side.

Girdle, a transverse groove, as in Dinophyceae; a ring or band connecting the two valves, as in Bacillariophyceae.

Glomerate, closely or compactly clustered.

Gonimoblast, in the Rhodophyceae, referring to filaments arising from a carpogonium or auxiliary cells and giving rise to carposporangia and carpospores.

Granulate, covered with minute grains or granules.

Granulose, composed of or appearing as if covered by minute grains or granules.

Gynandrosporous, having androspores produced on the same filament as the oogonium in the Oedogoniaceae.

Heterocyst, a metamorphosed vegetative cell, with a viscous protoplast, a newly secreted inner wall with one or more polar pores, and often a change in size and appearance; probably an abortive spore or sporangium (Myxophyceae); sometimes forming endospores or a filament.

Heterogamy, sexual union between gametes of different sizes.

Heterothallic, referring to a species in which gametes unite only if arising from different plants.

Heterotrophic, referring to an organism dependent upon an external source of food.

Holophytic, referring to an organism able to synthesize its food from inorganic substances.

Holozoic, referring to an organism dependent upon ingestion of an external food supply.

Homothallic, referring to a species in which gametes unite only if arising within the same plant.

Hormogonium, a short section of a trichome delimited in the filaments of certain Myxophyceae, and producing new plants vegetatively.

Horn, a stout spine-like or blunt process.

Hyaline, colorless and transparent or translucent.

Hypnospore, an aplanospore with greatly thickened cell-wall.

Hypogynous, situated below the oogonium.

Hypotheca, the "shorter half," or hypovalve, of a diatom cell; the portion of the wall of a Dinoflagellate posterior to the transverse furrow.

Hypovalve; *see* Hypotheca.

Idioandrosporous, having androspores produced on filaments not bearing oogonia, as in certain species of the Oedogoniaceae.

Incised, cut deeply into sharp lobes.

Inferior, lower or below in position.

Inframedian, slightly below median in position.

Isogamy, sexuality characterized by union of two flagellated or non-flagellated gametes of equal size.

Isopolar, equal poles or apices.

Isthmus, the usually constricted connection between the two semicells of desmids.

Keel, a projecting ridge usually dorsal in position.

Laciniate, cut into narrow segments or lobes.

Lamellose, composed of or arranged in layers.

Laminate, consisting of or shaped like plates.

Lanceolate, lance-shaped.

Lateral conjugation, conjugation between adjoining cells of same filament.

Lenticular, having the shape of a double-convex lens.

Lobule, a subdivision of a lobe.

Lorica, a firm envelope that is free from the protoplast and provided with an anterior opening.

Lotic, referring to waters in which the entire body moves continuously in a definite direction.

Lunate, crescent-shaped.

Macrandrous, referring to dioecious species having male gametes borne on filaments equal in size, or nearly so, to those bearing female gametes, as in *Oedogonium.*

Mammillate, having small nipple-like protuberances.

Metabolic, changeable in form.

Microaplanospore, a small asexually formed spore, probably uninucleate, in *Vaucheria.*

Moniliform, cylindrical with constrictions at intervals like a string of beads; chain-like.

Monoaxial, referring to a thallus having a single axial filament.

Monoecious, referring to a species bearing male and female gametes on the same plant.

Monospore, aplanospore formed singly within a sporangium, usually terminal on short lateral branches, as in Rhodophyceae and Phaeophyceae.

Monostromatic, having cells arranged in a single layer.

Mucronate, with a short, small, abrupt tip.

Multiaxial, referring to a thallus having a core of axial filaments.

Nannandrous, referring to a species having the male gametes borne on a nannandrium or dwarf male epiphytic upon the oogonial filament (Oedogoniales).

Naviculoid, boat-shaped.

Nodulose, provided with little knots or knobs.

Ocellus, a small unsculptured, rounded, or lenticular thickening in the valve wall of certain diatoms.

Oogamy, sexuality characterized by union of a small motile male gamete (sperm) with a large nonmotile female gamete (egg).

Oogonium, a cell containing one or more eggs.

Oospore, a zygote resulting from the union of a sperm and an egg.

Operculate, having a lid.

Operculum, a lid.

Palmella-stage, a growth phase of certain algae in which amorphous colonies of cells are embedded in a gelatinous matrix resembling species of *Palmella.*

Palmelloid, resembling *Palmella.*

Papilla, a small nipple-like protuberance.

Papillate, furnished with papillae.

Papillose, furnished with papillae.

Paraspore, an aplanospore formed within a sporangium of the tetrasporophyte generation of certain Rhodophyceae.

Parenchymatous, soft, tissue-like.

Parietal, borne on or pertaining to a wall.

Parthenospore, a zygote-like spore developed parthenogenetically from a gamete.

Patent, referring to the position of the oogonium in *Bulbochaete* when one of the double divisions of a vegetative cell in oogonium-formation is oblique, giving rise to a five-sided suffultory cell.

Pedicel, a stalk.

Pellucid, clear, transparent.

Penicillate, like a brush; tufted.

Perforate, pierced with holes or pores.

Periplast, more or less differentiated, peripheral portion of the cytoplasm.

Piliferous, bearing hairs.

Piliform, hair-like.

Placoderm, referring to a cell-wall composed of two or more pieces, as in the desmids.

Planktonic, free-floating.

Plicate, folded into plaits, like a fan.

Postcingular, referring to position of plates adjacent to the girdle (cingulum) in the hypotheca of Peridiniales.

Precingular, referring to position of plates adjacent to the girdle (cingulum) in the epitheca of Peridiniales.

Process, a projection or emergence.

Produced, extended or prolonged; elongated.

Pseudocilia, long, immobile, cytoplasmic processes resembling flagella.

Pseudoraphe, the axial field of the valves of pennate diatoms lacking a longitudinal cleft or raphe.

Pseudovacuoles, small cavities filled with gas (or perhaps viscous fluids) in the protoplast of certain species of Myxophyceae.

Pulvinate, cushion-shaped.

Puncta, a minute spot, point, or depression.

Punctate, having punctae; dotted.

Pyrenoid, a proteinaceous core usually enveloped by starch plates or aggregates.

Pyriform, pear-shaped.

Quadrifid, deeply divided into four parts.

Raphe, the longitudinal cleft in the axial field of certain pennate diatoms.

Receptacle, the firm envelope (lorica) of certain Chrysophyceae.

Reniform, kidney-shaped.

Repand, having a more or less wavy or sinuate margin.

Replicate, annular ingrowth of the transverse walls, as in certain *Spirogyra* species.

Reticulate, arranged as a network; having a surface marked out in a reticulum.

Reticulum, a network.

Retuse, with a shallow notch at a rounded apex.

Rimiform, rim-like; with a border or margin.

Rostrate, with a beak.

Saccate, sac-shaped.

Saccoderm, referring to a wall of one piece, as in certain desmids.

Saprophytic, pertaining to a plant deriving a food supply from dead organic material.

Scalariform, resembling a ladder, like the appearance of conjugation tubes formed between two filaments of certain Zygnemataceae.

Scrobiculate, having numerous small shallow depressions or pits.

Semicell, half of the vegetative cell of species of desmids.

Semireplicate, referring to an infolding of half of the transverse wall of certain Zygnemataceae.

Septum, a partition; a cross-wall.

Serrate, marginally sharp-toothed.

Serrulate, finely serrate.

Sessile, without a stalk.

Seta, a slender, more or less rigid bristle, or hair.

Setiferous, producing or bearing setae.

Setiform, shaped like a seta.

Sigmoid, curved in two directions like the letter S.

Sinuate, with strongly wavy margins.

Sinus, the space or recess between two lobes.

Siphonaceous, tubular; non-septate, or with septa only partially formed, and multinucleate.

Spermatangium, the male sex organ of the Rhodophyceae.

Spermatium, non-flagellated male gamete of the Rhodophyceae.

Spinescent, spiny; having spines.

Statospore, asexually formed spore with thick silicified walls of two overlapping halves (endospore).

Stauros, a thickened and transversely expanded central nodule interrupting the raphe of certain diatoms.

Stellate, star-shaped.

Stipe, a stalk-like support.

Stipitate, having a stipe.

Striate, marked with fine lines or ridges.

Subcapitate, slightly capitate.

Subepigynous, situated slightly but not immediately above the oogonium.

Subhypogynous, situated slightly but not immediately below the oogonium.

Suffultory, referring to the vegetative cell below the oogonium of Oedogoniaceae.

Sulcus, a groove or furrow.

Superior, high in position, as the above-median position of an operculum or a pore in the oogonium of certain Oedogoniales.

Supramedian, above median in position.

Supreme, the highest position, as that of the operculum of certain Oedogoniales.

Suture, the seam or ridge formed by two apposed margins, as the plates of Dino-flagellate thecae, or the two parts of a spore in some Zygnemataceae.

Tabular, shaped like a table; having a flat surface.

Tetraspore, haploid spore usually borne in fours in sporangia of diploid plants of Rhodophyceae and giving rise to gametophytes.

Tetrasporophyte, asexual diploid plants bearing tetraspores (Rhodophyceae).

Thallus, the plant body of an alga.

Theca, a wall, capsule or case.

Tomentose, closely hairy; woolly.

Trichogyne, the prolonged neck-like portion of the carpogonium of Rhodophyceae.

Trichome, a uniseriate row of cells in a filamentous colony of Myxophyceae; a filament exclusive of the gelatinous sheath.

Truncate, terminating abruptly by a nearly straight edge or surface.

Tubercule, a small wart-like projection.

Umbellate, arranged in branches arising from one point.

Uncinate, hooked at the tip.

Undulate, with a wavy surface or margin.

Utricle, a small bladder-like body; a little bag.

Valves, the more or less flattened silicified, longitudinally joined portions of a diatom cell.

Ventricose, swelling unequally or inflated on one side; bellied.

Verrucose, covered with wart-like elevations.

Vesicular, bladder-like.

Zoospore, a flagellate, asexually formed spore.

Zygote, a cell resulting from the union of two gametes or gametic nuclei.

BIBLIOGRAPHY

The references listed below are mainly those consulted in the preparation of this volume. Some literature referring to Illinois algae and not available in 1944 is included. For the bulk of the references giving information on the algae of the State, the reader should consult the Bibliography in Britton's *A Catalog of Illinois Algae* (1944).

AHLSTROM, E. H. 1937. Studies on variability in the genus *Dinobryon*. Tr. Am. Micr. Soc., 56:139–59.

ALLÉGRE, C. F., and JAHN, T. L. 1943. A survey of the genus *Phacus* Dujardin. Tr. Am. Micr. Soc., 62:233–44.

BORGE, O., and PASCHER, A. 1913. Zygnemales. In PASCHER, A., Die Süsswasserflora Deutschlands, Österreichs und der Schweiz, 9:1–51.

BORZI, A. 1883. Studi algologici, Fasc. 1. Palermo.

BOYER, C. S. 1916. The Diatomaceae of Philadelphia and vicinity. Philadelphia.

———. 1922. In Contrib. Biol. & Micr. Soc. Acad. Nat. Sc., No. 1. Philadelphia.

———. 1927. Synopsis of the North American Diatomaceae, Part I. Proc. Acad. Nat. Sc., Philadelphia, suppl., 78:1–228. Part II, *ibid.*, 79:229–583.

BRITTON, M. E. 1943. New species of Chlorophyceae. Am. J. Bot., 30:799–800.

———. 1944. A catalog of Illinois algae. Evanston, Ill.: Northwestern University.

BROWN, H. J. 1929. The algal family Vaucheriaceae. Tr. Am. Micr. Soc., 48:86–117.

CHODAT, R. 1894. Matériaux pour servir à l'histoire des Protococcoidées. Bull. Herb. Boiss., 2:585–616.

———. 1926. *Scenedesmus:* Étude de génétique, de systématique expérimentale et d'hydrobiologie. Rev. d'hydrol., 3:71–268.

CIENKOWSKI, L. 1865. Ueber einige chlorophyllhaltige Gloeocapsaceen. Bot. Ztschr., 23:21–27.

COLLINS, F. S. 1907. Some new green algae. Rhodora, 9:197–202.

———. 1909. The green algae of North America. Tufts College Studies, Sc. ser., 2:79–480.

———. 1918. Notes from the Woods Hole Laboratory—1917. Rhodora, 20:141–43.

COUCH, JOHN N. 1932. Gametogenesis in *Vaucheria*. Bot. Gaz., 94:272–96.

CURTIS, O. F., and CLARK, D. G. 1950. An introduction to plant physiology. New York.

CZURDA, V. 1932. Zygnemales. In PASCHER, A., Die Süsswasserflora Mitteleuropas, 9:1–232.

DAILY, W. A. 1942. The Chroococcaceae of Ohio, Kentucky, and Indiana. Am. Mid. Nat., 27:636–61.

DEFLANDRE, M. G. 1926. Monographie du genre *Trachelomonas* Ehr. Rev. gén. de bot., 38:358–80 ff.

———. 1927. *Ibid.*, 39:26–51, 73–96.

DeTONI, J. 1889. Sylloge algarum. I. Chlorophyceae. Padua.

———. 1891–94. Sylloge algarum. II (1–3). Bacillarieae. Padua.

———. 1907. Sylloge algarum. V. Myxophyceae. Padua.

DIPPEL, LEOPOLD. 1904. Diatomeen der Rhein-Mainebene. Brunswick, Germany.

DROUET, F. 1937. Some Myxophyceae from the Canal Zone. Bull. Torr. Bot. Club, 64: 599–604.

———. 1937. The Brazilian Myxophyceae. I. Am. J. Bot., 24:598–608.

———. 1938. The Brazilian Myxophyceae. II. Ibid., 25:657–66.

———. 1938. The Oscillatoriaceae of southern Massachusetts. Rhodora, 40:221–41.

DROUET, F., and DAILY, W. A. 1939. The planktonic freshwater species of Microcystis. Field Mus. Nat. Hist., Bot. ser., 20:67–83.

EDDY, S. 1930. The freshwater armored or thecate Dinoflagellates. Tr. Am. Micr. Soc., 49:277–321.

FLINT, L. H. 1948. Studies of freshwater red algae. Am. J. Bot., 35:428–33.

FRÉMY, P. 1930. Contribution à la flore algologique de l'Algérie et de la Tunisie. Bull. Soc. hist. nat. de l'Afrique du Nord, 21:74–75.

———. 1930. Les Myxophycées de l'Afrique Équatoriale Française. Edition of Arch. de bot. Caen.

———. 1930. Les Stigonémacées de la France. Rev. algolog., 5:147–213.

———. 1934. Les Cyanophycées des côtes d'Europe. Mém. Soc. nat., Sc. nat. et math., 41:1–236. Cherbourg.

FRITSCH, F. E. 1903. Observations on the young plants of Stigeoclonium Kuetz. Beih. Bot. Centralbl., 13:368–87.

———. 1935. The structure and reproduction of the algae, Vol. 1. New York and Cambridge.

———. 1945. The structure and reproduction of the algae, Vol. 2. Cambridge.

GEITLER, L., and PASCHER, A. 1925. Cyanophyceae, Cyanochloridineae, Chlorobacteriaceae. In PASCHER, A., Die Süsswasserflora Deutschlands, Österreichs und der Schweiz, 12:1–481.

———. 1932. Cyanophyceae. In RABENHORST's Kryptogamen-Flora von Deutschland, Österreich und der Schweiz, 14:1–1196.

GOETZ, H. 1897. Zur Systematik der Gattung Vaucheria D. C. speciell der Arten der Umgebung Basels. Flora, 83:88–134.

GOMONT, M. 1892. Monographie des Oscillariées. I. Ann. d. sc. nat., 15:263–368.

———. 1892. Monographie des Oscillariées. II. Ibid., 16:91–264.

GREGORY, WILLIAM. 1856. Notice of some new species of British freshwater Diatomaceae. Quart. J. Micr. Sc., 4:1–14.

HAMILTON, J. M. 1948. Sexual reproduction in the genus Basicladia. Tr. Am. Micr. Soc., 67:201–5.

HAZEN, T. E. 1902. The Ulotrichaceae and Chaetophoraceae of the United States. Mem. Torr. Bot. Club, 11:135–250.

HEDGECOCK, G. G., and HUNTER, A. 1899. Notes on Thorea. Bot. Gaz., 28:425–29.

HEERING, W. 1914. Ulotrichales, Microsporales, Oedogoniales. In PASCHER, A., Die Süsswasserflora Deutschlands, Österreichs und der Schweiz, 6:1–250.

———. 1921. Siphonocladiales, Siphonales. Ibid., 7:1–103.

HIRN, K. E. 1900. Monographie und Iconographie der Oedogoniaceen. Acta Soc. sc. Fenn., 27:1–394.

———. 1906. Studien über Oedogoniaceen. Ibid., 34:1–63.

HOFFMAN, W. E., and TILDEN, J. E. 1930. Basicladia, a new genus of Cladophoraceae. Bot. Gaz., 89:374–83.

HUSTEDT, FR. 1909. Süsswasser-Diatomeen Deutschlands. Stuttgart.

———. 1930. Bacillariophyta (Diatomeae). In PASCHER, A., Die Süsswasserflora Mittel-europas, 10:1–466.

———. 1930. Die Kieselalgen. In RABENHORST's Kryptogamen-Flora von Deutschland, Österreich und der Schweiz, 7(1):1–920.

———. 1931–37. Die Kieselalgen. *Ibid.*, 7(2):1–736.

IRÉNÉE-MARIE, FRÈRE. 1939. Flora desmidiale de la région de Montréal. Laprairie.

IYENGAR, M. O. P., and RAMANATHAN, K. R. 1940. On sexual reproduction in a *Dictyosphaerium*. J. Indian Bot. Soc., 18:195–200.

IYENGAR, M. O. P., and SUBRAHMANYAN, R. 1944. On reduction division and auxospore-formation in *Cyclotella meneghiniana* Kuetz. J. Indian Bot. Soc., 23:125–52.

JAO, CHIN-CHIH. 1934. *Oedogonium* in the vicinity of Woods Hole, Massachusetts. Rhodora, 36:197–214.

———. 1935. Studies on the freshwater algae of China. I. Zygnemataceae from Szechwan. Sinensia, 6:551–645.

JOHNSON, L. N. 1894. Some new and rare desmids of the United States. Bull. Torr. Bot. Club, 21:285–91.

———. 1895. Some new and rare desmids of the United States. II. *Ibid.*, 22:289–98.

JOHNSON, L. P. 1944. Euglenae of Iowa. Tr. Am. Micr. Soc., 63:97–135.

KLEBS, G. 1881. Beiträge zur Kenntnis niederer Algenformen. Bot. Ztschr., 39:249 ff.

KORSHIKOV, A. A. 1937. On the sexual reproduction·(oogamy) in the Micractineae. Proc. Kharkov A. Gorsky State Univ., 10:109–26.

KRIEGER, W. 1937. Conjugatae: Die Desmidiaceen. In RABENHORST's Kryptogamen-Flora von Deutschland, Österreich und der Schweiz, 13(1):1–712.

———. 1939. *Ibid.*, 13(2):1–117.

KUETZING, F. T. 1853. Tabulae phycologicae, Vol. 3.

LEMMERMANN, E.; BRUNNTHALER, J.; and PASCHER, A. 1915. Tetrasporales, Protococcales. In PASCHER, A., Die Süsswasserflora Deutschlands, Österreichs und der Schweiz, 5:1–250.

MEISTER, FR. 1912. Der Kieselalgen der Schweiz. In Beiträge zur Kryptogamenflora der Schweiz, Vol. 4, No. 1. Bern.

MILLS, F. W. 1933–34. An index to the genera and species of the Diatomaceae and their synonyms. London.

NORDSTEDT, O. 1878. De algis aquae dulcis et de Characeis ex insulis Sandvicensibus a Sv. Berggren 1875 reportatis. Minneskr. k. fysiog. sällsk. Lund, 7:1–24.

PASCHER, A. 1927. Volvocales, Phytomonadineae. In PASCHER, A., Die Süsswasserflora Deutschlands, Österreichs und der Schweiz, 4:1–506.

PASCHER, A., and LEMMERMANN, E. 1913. Chrysomonadinae, Cryptomonadinae, Eugleninae, Chloromonadinae. In PASCHER, A., Die Süsswasserflora Deutschlands, Österreichs und der Schweiz, 2:1–192.

PASCHER, A.; SCHILLER, J.; and MIGULA, W. 1925. Heterokontae, Phaeophyta, Rhodophyta, Charophyta. In PASCHER, A., Die Süsswasserflora Deutschlands, Österreichs und der Schweiz, 11:1–250.

PASCHER, A., and VISCHER, W. 1939. Heterokonten. In RABENHORST's Kryptogamen-Flora von Deutschland, Österreich und der Schweiz, 11:1–1092.

PETIT, PAUL. 1880. Spirogyra des environs de Paris. Paris.

PHINNEY, GRACE S. 1948. A taxonomic study of the genus *Microspora* Thuret. Summ. Doct. Diss. 1947, Northwestern Univ., 15:235–37.

PHINNEY, H. K. 1946. The freshwater Cladophoraceae. Summ. Doct. Diss. 1945, Northwestern Univ., 13:90–94.

———. 1946. Some algae from Pope County, Illinois. Am. Mid. Nat., 35:792–94.

PRESCOTT, G. W. 1927. The motile algae of Iowa. Univ. Iowa Studies, 12:1–40.

———. 1931. Iowa algae. *Ibid.*, 13:1–235.

———. 1951. Algae of the western Great Lakes area. Cranbrook Inst. Sc. Bull. 31: 1–946.

PRINGSHEIM, N. 1857. Beiträge zur Morphologie und Systematik des Algen. Jahrb. f. wissensch. Bot., 1:1–81.

PROVAZEK, S. 1900. *Synedra hyalina,* eine apochlorotische Bacillarie. Österreich. bot. Ztschr., 50:69–73.

RABENHORST, L. 1864–68. Florae Europaeae algarum aquae dulcis et submarinae. Leipzig.

SCHILLER, J. 1933. Dinoflagellatae (Peridineae). In RABENHORST's Kryptogamen-Flora von Deutschland, Österreich und der Schweiz, 10(1):1–617.

———. 1937. Dinoflagellatae (Peridineae). *Ibid.*, 10(2):1–589.

SCHILLING, A. C. 1913. Dinoflagellatae (Peridineae). In PASCHER, A., Die Süsswasserflora Deutschlands, Österreichs und der Schweiz, 3:1–66.

SCHMIDLE, W. 1901. Einige Algen, welche Prof. Dr. Volkens auf den Carolinen gesammelt hat. Hedwigia, 40:343–49.

SCHMIDT, ADOLPH. (Continued by SCHMIDT, M.; FRICKE, F.; MÜLLER, O.; HEIDEN, H.; and HUSTEDT, FR.) 1874–1928. Atlas der Diatomeen-Kunde. Leipzig.

SILFVENIUS, A. J. 1903. Zur Kenntnis der Verbreitung finnischer Chlorophyceen und Cyanophyceen. Meddel. Soc. pro fauna et flora fenn., 29:10–22.

SKVORTZOW, B. V. 1937. Diatoms of Lake Michigan. I. Am. Mid. Nat., 18:652–58.

SMITH, G. M. 1916. A monograph of the algal genus *Scenedesmus* based upon pure culture studies. Tr. Wisconsin Acad. Sc., 18:422–530.

———. 1920. Phytoplankton of the inland lakes of Wisconsin. I. Bull. Wisconsin Geol. & Nat. Hist. Surv., 57:1–243.

———. 1924. Phytoplankton of the inland lakes of Wisconsin. II. *Ibid.*, 57:1–227.

———. 1938. Cryptogamic botany, Vol. 1. New York.

———. 1944. A comparative study of the species of *Volvox.* Tr. Am. Micr. Soc., 63:265–310.

———. 1950. The freshwater algae of the United States. 2d ed. New York.

——— (ed.). 1951. Manual of phycology. Waltham, Mass.

SMITH, H. L. 1878. Description of new species of diatoms. Am. Quart. Micr. J., 1:12–18.

SMITH, WILLIAM. 1853. A synopsis of the British Diatomaceae, Vol. 1. London.

———. 1856. *Ibid.*, Vol. 2.

SPOEHR, H. A.; STRAIN, H. H.; and MANNING, W. M. 1943. Pigments of algae. Carnegie Inst. Washington Yearbook, 42:79–83.

STEIN, F. RITTER VON. 1878. Der Organismus der Infusionsthiere, Part III. Leipzig.

STRICKLAND, J. C. 1940. The Oscillatoriaceae of Virginia. Am. J. Bot., 27:629–33.

TAFT, C. E. 1931. Desmids of Oklahoma. Univ. Oklahoma Surv., 3:274–322.

———. 1934. Desmids of Oklahoma. II. Tr. Am. Micr. Soc., 53:95–101.

———. 1935. The Oedogoniaceae of Oklahoma, including new species and varieties. Bull. Torr. Bot. Club, 62:281–90.

———. 1937. Desmids of Oklahoma. III. Tr. Am. Micr. Soc., 56:397–404.

———. 1945. The desmids of the west end of Lake Erie. Ohio J. Sc., 45:180–205.

TAYLOR, W. R. (1933) 1934. The freshwater algae of Newfoundland. I. Papers Michigan Acad. Sc., Arts & Letters, **19**:217–78.

———. (1934) 1935. The freshwater algae of Newfoundland. II. *Ibid.*, **20**:185–230.

THOMAS, H. D., and CHASE, H. H. 1887. Diatomaceae of Lake Michigan during the last sixteen years from the water supply of Chicago. Notarisia, **2**:328–30.

THOMPSON, R. H. 1947. Freshwater Dinoflagellates of Maryland. Pub. Chesapeake Biol. Lab., No. 67, pp. 1–28.

TIFFANY, L. H. 1927. New species and varieties of Chlorophyceae. Bot. Gaz., **83**:202–6.

———. 1930. The Oedogoniaceae, a monograph. Columbus, Ohio.

———. 1934. The plankton algae of the west end of Lake Erie. F. T. Stone Lab., Ohio State Univ. Contrib., **6**:1–112.

———. 1937. The filamentous algae of the west end of Lake Erie. Am. Mid. Nat., **18**: 911–51.

———. 1937. The Oedogoniales. North American Flora, **11**:1–102.

———. 1949. The status of a Saaremaan *Oedogonium*. Chicago Acad. Sc., Nat. Hist. Miscell., No. 51, pp. 1–3.

TILDEN, J. E. 1910. Minnesota algae. I. Ser. 8. Minneapolis.

TRANSEAU, E. N. 1914. New species of green algae. Am. J. Bot., **1**:289–301.

———. 1925. The genus *Debarya*. Ohio J. Sc., **25**:193–201.

———. 1926. The genus *Mougeotia*. *Ibid.*, **26**:311–38.

———. 1933. The genus *Zygogonium*. *Ibid.*, **33**:156–62.

———. 1934. Notes on Zygnemataceae. *Ibid.*, **34**: 420.

———. 1938. Notes on Zygnemataceae. Am. J. Bot., **25**:524–28.

———. 1951. The Zygnemataceae. Columbus: Ohio State University Press.

TRANSEAU, E. N.; TIFFANY, L. H.; TAFT, C. E.; and LI, L. C. 1934. New species of Zygnemataceae. Tr. Am. Micr. Soc., **53**:208–30.

VAN HEURCK, H. F. 1880–85. Synopsis der Diatomées de Belgique. Antwerp.

WALTON, L. B. 1915. A review of the described species of the order Euglenoidina Bloch. Ohio Biol. Surv., **19**:343–459.

WEST, W., and WEST, G. S. 1896. On some North American Desmidieae. Tr. Linnean Soc. London, 2d ser., **5**:229–74.

———. 1904–12. A monograph of the British Desmidiaceae, Vols. 1–4. London.

WEST, W.; WEST, G. S.; and CARTER, N. 1923. A monograph of the British Desmidiaceae, Vol. 5. London.

WITTROCK, V. B. 1870. Dispositio Oedogoniacearum Suecicarum. Oefv. sv. vet.-akad. förh., **27**:119–44.

WOLLE, F. A. 1887. Freshwater algae of the United States. Bethlehem, Pa.

———. 1890. Diatomaceae of North America. Bethlehem, Pa.

———. 1892. Desmids of the United States and list of American Pediastrums. Bethlehem, Pa.

INDEX

Numbers in roman refer to pages where descriptions or discussions occur; those in boldface indicate the pages on which illustrations occur. The numbers in italics following "f." refer to the figures on the plates of illustrations. Names in italics are algae incompletely known, or synonyms.

Achnanthaceae, 240

Achnanthes, 241
  exilis, 242, **239**, f. *723*
  lanceolata, 241, **239**, f. *724*
    v. rostrata, 241, **239**, f. *725*
  microcephala, 242, **239**, f. *726*
  minutissima, 242, **239**, f. *727*

Achnanthineae, 240

Actinastrum, 120
  hantzschii, 120, **103**, f. *327*
    v. fluviatile, 120, **103**, f. *328*

Actinocyclus, 224
  niagarae, 226, **219**, f. *666*

Algae, 1, 2, 3

Amphipleura, 244
  pellucida, 244, **243**, f. *749*

Amphiprora, 245
  calumetica, 383
  ornata, 245, **243**, f. *750*

Amphithrix, 372
  janthina, 374, **375**, f. *1175*

Amphora, 274
  normani, 274, **273**, f. *854*
  ovalis, 274, **273**, f. *855*

Anabaena, 356
  catenula, 358, **359**, f. *1131*
  circinalis, 357, **359**, f. *1129, 1130*
  flosaquae, 358, **355**, f. *1127*
  inaequalis, 357, **361**, f. *1136*
  oscillarioides, 357, **361**, f. *1137*
  planctonica, 357, **359**, f. *1128*
  spiroides, 357, **359**, f. *1133*
    v. crassa, 358, **359**, f. *1134, 1135*
  unispora, 358, **361**, f. *1138*
  variabilis, 357, **359**, f. *1132*

Anacystis, 330
  marginata, 330, **333**, f. *1038*
  peniocystis, 330, **333**, f. *1037*
  rupestris, 331, **333**, f. *1039*
    v. prasina, 331, **333**, f. *1040, 1041*

Ankistrodesmus, 113
  falcatus, 114, **99**, f. *307*
  longissimus, 114

Anomoeoneis, 245
  exilis, 246, **243**, f. *739*
  follis, 246, **243**, f. *740*
  serians, 246, **243**, f. *738*

Aphanizomenon, 358
  flosaquae, 360, **361**, f. *1143, 1144*
  ovalisporum, 360, **361**, f. *1142*

Aphanocapsa, 331
  grevillei, 331, **335**, f. *1047*
  richteriana, 331, **335**, f. *1046*

Aphanochaete, 40
  repens, 40, **31**, f. *57*

Apiocystis, 22
  brauniana, 24, **25**, f. *34*

Arthrodesmus, 196
  convergens, 196, **165**, f. *536*

Asterionella, 231
  formosa, 231, **235**, f. *709*
  gracillima, 231, **233**, f. *707, 708*

Bacillariophyceae, 3, 6, 214

Basicladia, 46
  chelonum, 48, **47**, f. *89*

Batrachospermaceae, 380

Batrachospermum, 380
  boryanum, 382, **377**, f. *1181-83*

Binuclearia, 28
  tatrana, 28, **27**, f. *46*

Botrydiaceae, 210

Botrydium, 211
  granulatum, 211, **209**, f. *645*
  walrothii, 211, **209**, f. *646*

Botryococcaceae, 207

Botryococcus, 207
  braunii, 207, **209**, f. *642, 643*
  sudeticus, 207, **209**, f. *644*

Bulbochaete, 49
  brebissonii, 52, **51**, f. *94*
  crassiuscula, 52, **51**, f. *99, 100*
  crenulata, 50, **51**, f. *98*
  furberae, 52, **55**, f. *111*
  gigantea, 52, **51**, f. *97*
  hiloensis, 56, **53**, f. *108*
  insignis, 57, **53**, f. *109*
  intermedia, 54, **51**, f. *96*
  minor, 56, **53**, f. *107*
  mirabilis, 50, **51**, f. *95*
  nana, 50, **55**, f. *112*
  nordstedtii, 50, **55**, f. *114*
  pygmaea, 57, **53**, f. *106*
  rectangularis, 56, **53**, f. *105*

Bulbochaete—*continued*
  repanda, 54, **53**, f. *101*
  reticulata, 57, **53**, f. *110*
  subintermedia, 54, **55**, f. *113*
  varians, 56, **53**, f. *102*
    v. hawaiensis, 56, **53**, f. *104*
    v. subsimplex, 56, **53**, f. *103*

Caloneis, 246
  alpestris, 248, **243**, f. *741*
  bacillaris, 248, **243**, f. *742*
  bacillum, 248, **243**, f. *748*
  fasciata, 248
  silicula, 248, **243**, f. *743*
    v. alpina, 248, **243**, f. *747*
    v. *genuina*, 248
    v. gibberula, 248, **243**, f. *746*
    v. inflata, 249, **243**, f. *744*
    v. undulata, 249, **243**, f. *745*
  trinodis, 248, **293**, f. *919*

Calothrix, 374
  kawraiskyi, 374
  parietina, 376, **377**, f. *1178, 1179*
  stagnalis, 374, **375**, f. *1176; 377*, f. *1177*

Campylodiscus, 289
  noricus, 289, **295**, f. *934*

Carteria, 14
  multifilis, 14, **15**, f. *3*

Centrales, 217

Ceratiaceae, 314

Ceratium, 314
  cornutum, 314, **311**, f. *994*
  hirundinella, 314, **311**, f. *992, 993*

Chaetophora, 32
  attenuata, 32, **33**, f. *64*
  elegans, 32, **31**, f. *62*
  incrassata, 32, **31**, f. *61*
  pisiformis, 32, **33**, f. *63*

Chaetophoraceae, 30

Chaetosphaeridium, 44
  globosum, 44, **31**, f. *60*
  pringsheimii, 44, **31**, f. *59*

Chamaesiphonales, 336

Characiaceae, 108

Characium, 108
  ambiguum, 108, **95**, f. *286*
  naegelii, 108, **95**, f. *284*
  pringsheimii, 108, **95**, f. *285*

Charophyceae, 3, 6

Chlamydomonadaceae, 13

Chlamydomonas, 13
  globosa, 13, **15**, f. *4*

Chloraster, 13
  gyrans, 13, **15**, f. *7-9*

Chlorella, 114
  conductrix, 114, **95**, f. *282*
  parasitica, 114, **95**, f. *281*
  vulgaris, 114, **95**, f. *280*

Chlorochytrium, 106
  knyanum, 106
  lemnae, 106, **95**, f. *288*

Chlorococcaceae, 102

Chlorococcales, 102

Chlorococcum, 102
  humicola, 102, **95**, f. *277, 278*

Chlorophyceae, 3, 6, 7

Chlorophyta, 3, 7

Chlorotheciaceae, 207

Chlorotylium, 40
  mammiforme, 40, **43**, f. *84*

Chroococcaceae, 330

Chroococcales, 330

Chroococcus, 331
  limneticus, 332, **337**, f. *1050*
  rufescens, 332, **337**, f. *1049*
  turgidus, 332, **337**, f. *1048*

Chrysomonadales, 297

Chrysophyceae, 3, 6, 296

Chrysophyta, 3, 206

Chrysosphaerella, 297
  longispina, 298, **299**, f. *941, 942*

Cladophora, 45
  canalicularis, 45
  crispata, 45, **47**, f. *92*
  racta, 45
    f. *flotowiana*, 45
  glomerata, 45, **47**, f. *93*
    v. *callicoma*, 45
  kuetzingianum, 45

Cladophoraceae, 45

Cladophorales, 44

Closteriopsis, 114
  longissima, 114, **99**, f. *306*

Closterium, 167
  acerosum, 169, **171**, f. *550*
    v. elongatum, 169, **171**, f. *551*
  acutum, 173, **171**, f. *555*
  braunii, 176, **165**, f. *541*
  dianae, 169, **171**, f. *548*
  didymotocum, 169, **171**, f. *560*
  ehrenbergii, 172, **171**, f. *558*
  gracile, 174, **171**, f. *556*
    v. elongatum, 176, **171**, f. *557*
  intermedium, 172, **171**, f. *559*
  juncidum v. brevior, 172, **171**, f. *562*
  lanceolatum, 173, **171**, f. *552*
  leibleinii, 172, **171**, f. *547*
  littorale, 173, **165**, f. *544*
  lunula, 169, **171**, f. *561*
  moniliferum, 172, **171**, f. *549*
  parvulum, 173, **165**, f. *543*
  pritchardianum, 170, **171**, f. *554*
  strigosum, 174, **165**, f. *545*
  striolatum, 170, **165**, f. *546*
  turgidum, 170, **171**, f. *553*
  venus, 173, **165**, f. *542*

Cocconeis, 240
  flexella, 240, **239**, f. *737*
  pediculus, 241, **239**, f. *733*
  placentula, 241, **239**, f. *734, 735*
    v. lineata, 241, **239**, f. *736*

Coelastraceae, 112

Coelastrum, 113
  cambricum, 113, **99**, f. *310*
  microporum, 113, **99**, f. *312*
  reticulatum, 113, **99**, f. *311*
  sphaericum, 113, **99**, f. *313*

Coelosphaerium, 332
  collinsii, 332, **335**, f. *1044*
  kuetzingianum, 332, **335**, f. *1045*

Colaciaceae, 327

Colaciales, 327

Colacium, 327
  calvum, 327, **319**, f. *1017*
  vesiculosum, 327, **319**, f. *1018*

Coleochaetaceae, 42

Coleochaete, 42
  irregularis, 44, **39**, f. *76*
  nitellarum, 42, **39**, f. *77, 78*
  orbicularis, 44, **39**, f. *75*
  scutata, 44, **39**, f. *74*
  soluta, 44, **39**, f. *73*

Coscinodiscaceae, 217

Coscinodiscineae, 217

Coscinodiscus asteromphalus, 383

Cosmarium, 182
  biretum v. trigibberum, 188, **175**, f. *563*
  botrytis, 191, **175**, f. *568*
  broomei, 192, **175**, f. *575*
  circulare, 186, **179**, f. *614, 615*
  constrictum, 185, **177**, f. *594*
  crenatum, 192, **175**, f. *574*
  cucumis, 185, **175**, f. *569*
  curtum, 184, **175**, f. *576*
  dentatum, 187, **175**, f. *571*
  depressum, 184, **175**, f. *564*
  formosulum, 189, **177**, f. *589*
    v. nathorstii, 190, **177**, f. *590*
  granatum, 186, **175**, f. *565*
  holmiense, 186, **175**, f. *566*
    v. integrum, 186, **175**, f. *567*
  meneghinii, 186, **177**, f. *597*
  moniliforme, 184, **175**, f. *577*
  nitidulum, 185, **175**, f. *572*
  pachydermum v. aethiopicum, 185, **175**, f. *581*
  pericymatium, 185, **175**, f. *573*
  polygonum, 187, **177**, f. *591*
  porrectum, 192, **175**, f. *587*
  protractum, 190, **175**, f. *570*
  punctulatum, 188, **177**, f. *592*
  quadrum, 193, **175**, f. *580*
  quinarium, 190, **177**, f. *595*
  rectangulare, 187, **175**, f. *583*
  reniforme, 188, **175**, f. *586*
  sexangulare, 187, **175**, f. *578*
    f. minima, 187, **175**, f. *579*
  speciosum, 191, **175**, f. *584*
  subcostatum, 189, **175**, f. *585*
  subcrenatum, 189, **177**, f. *596*
  subimpressulum, 186, **177**, f. *588*
  supraspeciosum, 188, **177**, f. *598*
  triplicatum, 192, **175**, f. *582*
  turpinii, 191, **177**, f. *593*

Cosmocladium, 193
  saxonicum, 193, **179**, f. *619*

Crucigenia, 120
  irregularis, 121, **103**, f. *334*
  lauterbornei, 121, **103**, f. *332*
  rectangularis, 121, **103**, f. *333*
  tetrapedia, 121, **103**, f. *331*

Cryptophyceae, 4

Cyanophyta, 5

Cyclotella, 217
  antiqua, 220, **219**, f. *651*
  bodanica, 220, **219**, f. *653*
    v. michiganensis, 220, **219**, f. *654*
    v. stellata, 220, **219**, f. *655*
  comta, 220, **219**, f. *652*
    v. glabriuscula, 220, **219**, f. *659*
  glomerata, 220, **219**, f. *656*
  kuetzingiana, 218, **219**, f. *657*
  melosiroides, 220, **219**, f. *658*
  meneghiniana, 218, **219**, f. *660*
  michiganiana, 220, **219**, f. *663–65*
  ocellata, 220, **219**, f. *662*
  operculata, 220, **219**, f. *661*

Cylindrocapsa, 30
  geminella, 30, **27**, f. *55*
    v. minor, 30, **27**, f. *56*

Cylindrocapsaceae, 30

Cylindrospermum, 360
  licheniforme, 362, **363**, f. *1146*
  majus, 362, **363**, f. *1145*
  muscicola, 362, **363**, f. *1147*

Cymatopleura, 289
  elliptica, 290, **287**, f. *909*
    v. hibernica, 290, **291**, f. *911*
    f. spiralis, 290, **287**, f. *910*
  solea, 290, **287**, f. *905*
    v. apiculata, 290, **287**, f. *908*
    v. subconstricta, 290, **287**, f. *906*
    v. vulgaris, 290, **287**, f. *907*

Cymbella, 275
  aequalis, 276, **277**, f. *866*
  affinis, 279, **273**, f. *856*
  amphicephala, 278, **277**, f. *870*
  aspera, 279, **273**, f. *858*
  cistula, 278, **277**, f. *861*
  cuspidata, 278, **277**, f. *863*
  cymbiformis, 278, **277**, f. *873*
  ehrenbergii, 276, **277**, f. *875*
  gracilis, 279, **277**, f. *865*
  lacustris, 276, **277**, f. *867*
  laevis, 280, **277**, f. *869*
  lanceolata, 280, **277**, f. *872*
  leptoceros, 278, **277**, f. *868*
  naviculiformis, 278, **277**, f. *864*
  parva, 279, **277**, f. *874*
  prostrata, 279, **277**, f. *859*
  triangulum, 280, **273**, f. *857*
  tumida, 278, **277**, f. *860*
  turgida, 279, **277**, f. *862*
  ventricosa, 279, **277**, f. *871*

Cymbellaceae, 274

Dactylococcus, 114
  infusionum, 114, 99, f. 303
Denticula, 288
  tenuis, 288, 283, f. 888
Desmidiaceae, 167
Desmidium, 204
  aptogonum, 205, 203, f. 627
  grevillei, 204, 203, f. 629
  swartzii, 205, 203, f. 628
Desmokontae, 4
Diatoma, 230
  anceps, 230, 229, f. 683
  elongatum v. tenuis, 230, 229, f. 688
  hiemale, 230, 229, f. 684
    v. mesodon, 230, 229, f. 685
  vulgare, 230, 229, f. 686, 687
Diatomaceae, 228
Diatoms; see Bacillariophyceae
Dichotomosiphon, 124
  tuberosus, 124, 111, f. 375-77
Dichotomosiphonaceae, 124
Dictyosphaerium, 114
  ehrenbergianum, 115, 99, f. 304
  pulchellum, 115, 99, f. 305
Dimorphococcus, 115
  lunatus, 115, 99, f. 314
Dinobryon, 302
  bavaricum, 304, 303, f. 961-64
  cylindricum, 302, 301, f. 955, 956
  divergens, 304, 301, f. 943-46
  pediforme, 304, 301, f. 947-50
  sertularia, 304, 301, f. 951-54
    v. protuberans, 304, 303, f. 957-60
  sociale, 304, 303, f. 965-68
    v. americanum, 304, 303, f. 969, 970
Dinoflagellates, 4
Dinophyceae, 4, 6, 306
Diploneis, 249
  elliptica, 249, 243, f. 752
  puella, 249, 243, f. 751
Draparnaldia, 36
  acuta, 36, 41, f. 81
  glomerata, 38, 41, f. 80
  plumosa, 36, 41, f. 82
  ravenelii, 36, 41, f. 79

Endosphaeraceae, 106
Epithemia, 280
  argus, 281, 283, f. 878
    v. alpestris, 281, 283, f. 879
  muelleri, 281, 283, f. 880
  ocellata, 281, 283, f. 883
  sorex, 281, 283, f. 881
  turgida, 281, 283, f. 876
    v. westermanii, 281, 283, f. 877
  zebra, 281, 283, f. 882
Euastrum, 180
  johnsonii, 181, 179, f. 618
  oblongum, 181, 179, f. 617
  pulchellum, 181, 179, f. 616

Eudorina, 17
  elegans, 17, 19, f. 14
Euglena, 316
  acus, 321, 319, f. 1003
  acutissima, 320, 319, f. 1005
  deses, 321, 319, f. 1007
  elongata, 320, 319, f. 1006
  geniculata, 321, 319, f. 1015
  gracilis, 322, 319, f. 1012
  oblonga, 320, 319, f. 1008
  oxyuris, 318, 319, f. 1010
  sanguinea, 317, 319, f. 1013
  spirogyra, 320, 319, f. 1011
  spiroides, 318, 319, f. 1016
  torta, 317, 319, f. 1004
  tripteris, 318, 319, f. 1014
  viridis, 321, 319, f. 1009
Euglenaceae, 316
Euglenales, 316
Euglenophyceae, 4, 6, 315
Euglenophyta, 4, 315
Eunotia, 237
  flexuosa, 238, 239 f. 728
  formica, 238, 239, f. 731
  lunaris, 238, 239, f. 730
  monodon v. major, 240, 239, f. 732
  pectinalis v. minor, 240, 239, f. 729
Eunotiaceae, 237
Eupodiscaceae, 224

Fischerella, 372
  ambigua, 372, 371, f. 1163
Florideae, 379
Fragilaria, 231
  capucina, 234, 233, f. 698
    v. mesolepta, 234, 233, f. 699
  constricta, 232, 233, f. 695
  construens, 232, 233, f. 696
    v. venter, 234, 233, f. 697
  crotonensis, 232, 233, f. 703
    v. prolongata, 232, 233, f. 704
  harrisonii, 232, 233, f. 705
    v. rhomboides, 232, 233, f. 706
  pinnata, 234, 233, f. 700
    v. lancettula, 234, 233, f. 701
  virescens, 234, 233, f. 702
Fragilariaceae, 231
Fragilarineae, 227
Frustulia, 244
  rhomboides, 245, 247, f. 754
  viridula, 245, 247, f. 755
  vulgaris, 245, 247, f. 756
Fungi, 3

Genicularia, 164
  spirotaenia, 164, 165, f. 532
Glenodiniaceae, 307
Glenodinium, 307
  cinctum, 308, 313, f. 999
  gymnodinium, 308, 313, f. 1000-1002
  palustre, 308, 313, f. 998
  quadridens, 308, 313, f. 995-97

Gloeocystis, 20
  ampla, 21, 23, f. *23*
  confluens, 383
  gigas, 21, 23, f. *24*
  planctonica, 21, 23, f. *25*
Gloeotaenium, 115
  loitlesbergerianum, 115, **101**, f. *317*
Gloeotrichia, 376
  natans, 376, **375**, f. *1171, 1172*
  pisum, 376, **375**, f. *1173, 1174*
Golenkinia, 104
  radiata, 104, **95**, f. *279*
Gomphoneis, 274
  herculeana, 274, **273**, f. *852*
    v. robusta, 274, **273**, f. *853*
Gomphonema, 270
  acuminatum, 272, **267**, f. *830*
    v. coronatum, 272, **267**, f. *833*
    v. elongatum, 272, **267**, f. *834*
    v. laticeps, 272, **267**, f. *832*
    v. trigonocephalum, 272, **267**, f. *831*
    v. turris, 272, **267**, f. *835*
  angustatum, 271, **267**, f. *842*
    v. obtusatum, 271, **267**, f. *843*
  constrictum, 271, **267**, f. *839*
    v. capitatum, 271, **267**, f. *840*
    f. turgidum, 271, **267**, f. *841*
  geminatum, 270, **273**, f. *850*
  gracile v. dichotoma, 271, **267**, f. *848*
  intricatum, 271, **267**, f. *836*
    v. vibrio, 271, **267**, f. *837*
  montanum v. subclavatum, 272, **273**, f. *851*
  olivaceum, 270, **267**, f. *844, 845*
    v. calcarea, 271, **267**, f. *846*
  parvulum, 272, **267**, f. *838*
  semiapterum, 271, **267**, f. *849*
  sphaerophorum, 272, **267**, f. *847*
Gomphonemataceae, 269
Gomphosphaeria, 332
  aponina, 334, **335**, f. *1042, 1043*
Gonatozygon, 166
  brebissonii, 166, **165**, f. *535*
Gonium, 16
  formosum, 16, **15**, f. *11*
  pectorale, 16, **15**, f. *12*
  sociale, 16, **15**, f. *10*
Gyrosigma, 268
  acuminatum, 268, **247**, f. *759*
  attenuatum, 268, **247**, f. *758*
  eximium, 269, **247**, f. *760*
  kuetzingii, 269, **247**, f. *761*
  scalproides, 269, **247**, f. *762*
  spencerii, 269, **247**, f. *763*
  wormleyi, 268, **247**, f. *757*

Haematococcaceae, 20
Haematococcus, 20
  lacustris, 20, **19**, f. *22*
Hantzschia, 288
  amphioxys, 289, **283**, f. *886*
    f. capitata, 289, **283**, f. *887*
    v. vivax, 289, **285**, f. *889*

Heterococcales, 206
Heterosiphonales, 210
Heterotrichales, 210
Hormidium, 26
  flaccidum, 28, 27, f. *43*
  klebsii, 28, 25, f. *39–41*
  subtile, 28, 27, f. *44*
Hyalotheca, 202
  dissiliens, 204, **203**, f. *631*
  mucosa, 204, **203**, f. *630*
Hydrodictyaceae, 109
Hydrodictyon, 109
  reticulatum, 110, **95**, f. *289*

Kentrosphaera, 108
  facciolae, 108, **95**, f. *287*
Kirchneriella, 115
  lunaris, 116, **99**, f. *308*
  obesa v. major, 116, **99**, f. *309*

Lepocinclis, 322
  ovum, 322, **325**, f. *1025*
Lyngbya, 338
  aerugineo-caerulea, 339, **341**, f. *1059, 1060*
  aestuarii, 339, **341**, f. *1064, 1065*
  birgei, 339, **341**, f. *1066, 1067*
  diguetii, 339, **341**, f. *1070*
  putealis, 338, **341**, f. *1063*
  taylorii, 339, **341**, f. *1068, 1069*
  versicolor, 339, **341**, f. *1061, 1062*

Mallomonadaceae, 297
Mallomonas, 298
  acaroides, 298, **299**, f. *937*
  caudata, 298, **299**, f. *935*
  producta, 298, **299**, f. *936*
Mastogloia, 249
  smithii, 250, **253**, f. *792*
    v. amphicephala, 250, **253**, f. *793*
    v. lacustris, 250, **253**, f. *794*
Melosira, 221
  crenulata, 222, **223**, f. *670*
  distans, 221, **223**, f. *671*
  granulata, 221, **223**, f. *667*
  italica, 221, **223**, f. *668*
    f. *crenulata*, 222
    v. tenuissima, 221, **223**, f. *669*
  juergensii, 221, **223**, f. *672*
  varians, 221, **223**, f. *673*
Meridion, 228
  circulare, 228, **229**, f. *689, 690*
    v. constricta, 228, **229**, f. *691*
Meridionaceae, 228
Merismopedia, 334
  convoluta, 334, **337**, f. *1051*
  glauca, 334, **337**, f. *1052*
Mesotaeniaceae, 164
Micractiniaceae, 104
Micractinium, 104
  pusillum, 106, **103**, f. *329*
  quadrisetum, 106, **103**, f. *330*

Micrasterias, 194
  americana, 194, **165,** f. *537*
  apiculata, 195, **179,** f. *620*
  rotata, 196, **165,** f. *538*
  truncata, 195, **165,** f. *539*
Microcoleus, 352
  acutissimus, 352, **351,** f. *1110*
  lacustris, 352, **351,** f. *1113, 1114*
  rupicola, 352, **351,** f. *1111*
  vaginatus, 352, **351,** f. *1112*
Microcystis, 334
  aeruginosa, 336, **337,** f. *1053, 1054*
  incerta, 336, **337,** f. *1055*
Microspora, 29
  floccosa, 29, **27,** f. *54*
  pachyderma, 29, **27,** f. *47*
  quadrata, 29, **27,** f. *52*
  stagnorum, 29, **27,** f. *50, 51*
  tumidula, 29, **27,** f. *53*
  willeana, 29, **27,** f. *48, 49*
Microsporaceae, 28
Microthamnion, 38
  kuetzingianum, 38, **43,** f. *83*
  strictissimum, 38, **43,** f. *85*
Mougeotia, 126
  boodlei, 128, **129,** f. *403, 404*
  calcarea, 130, **127,** f. *397–402*
  elegantula, 128, **129,** f. *405–8*
  floridana, 134
  genuflexa, 132, **129,** f. *413;* **131,** f. *417, 418*
  gracillima, 130, **129,** f. *415, 416*
  nummuloides, 130, **127,** f. *388*
  parvula, 132, **131,** f. *425*
  quadrangulata, 130, **129,** f. *411, 412*
  reinschii, 130, **131,** f. *421*
  robusta, 132, **127,** f. *394–96*
  scalaris, 132, **131,** f. *419, 420*
  sphaerocarpa, 132, **127,** f. *389–93*
  transeaui, 132, **131,** f. *422–24*
  tumidula, 128, **129,** f. *414*
  viridis, 128, **129,** f. *409, 410*
Myxophyceae, 5, 6, 328
Myoxphyta, 5, 328

Navicula, 250
  anglica, 256, **251,** f. *764*
  bacillum, 254, **251,** f. *765*
  confervacea, 254, **251,** f. *766*
  cryptocephala, 255, **251,** f. *767*
  cuspidata, 254, **253,** f. *789*
    v. ambigua, 254, **253,** f. *790*
  dicephala, 256, **251,** f. *768*
    v. elginensis, 256, **251,** f. *769*
  exigua, 256, **251,** f. *770*
  gastrum, 256, **251,** f. *786*
  gracilis, 255, **251,** f. *772*
  mutica, 254, **251,** f. *773*
  oblonga, 255, **251,** f. *787*
    v. subcapitata, 255, **251,** f. *788*
  platystoma, 256, **251,** f. *774*
  protracta, 254, **251,** f. *775*
  pupula, 254, **251,** f. *776*
  radiosa, 255, **251,** f. *780*

  v. tenella, 255, **251,** f. *781*
  reinhardtii, 256, **251,** f. *771*
  rhyncocephala, 255, **251,** f. *782*
  salinarum, 255, **251,** f. *783*
    v. intermedia, 255, **251,** f. *784*
  scutelloides, 254, **251,** f. *778*
  seminulum, 255, **251,** f. *777*
  tuscula, 255, **251,** f. *779*
  viridula, 255, **251,** f. *785*
Naviculaceae, 244
Naviculineae, 244
Neidium, 262
  amphigomphus, 263, **261,** f. *818*
  amphirhyncus, 263, **261,** f. *814*
  dubium, 263, **261,** f. *815*
  hitchcockii, 263, **265,** f. *819*
  iridis, 263, **261,** f. *816*
    v. firma, 263, **261,** f. *817*
  productum, 263, **265,** f. *820*
Nemalionales, 380
Nephrocytium, 116
  agardhianum, 116, **101,** f. *315*
  lunatum, 116, **101,** f. *316*
Netrium, 166
  digitus, 166, **165,** f. *534*
Nitzschia, 282
  acicularis, 286, **287,** f. *904*
  clausii, 286, **285,** f. *893*
  closterium, 286, **285,** f. *894*
  commutata, 286, **287,** f. *903*
  denticula, 286, **287,** f. *902*
  dissipata, 288, **285,** f. *898*
  hungarica, 286, **285,** f. *899*
  linearis, 288, **285,** f. *891*
    v. tenuis, 288, **285,** f. *892*
  palea, 288, **285,** f. *900*
    v. tenuirostris, 288, **285,** f. *901*
  sigmoidea, 286, **285,** f. *895*
  sinuata, 286, **285,** f. *896*
    v. tabellaria, 286, **285,** f. *897*
  vermicularis, 286, **285,** f. *890*
Nitzschiaceae, 282
Nodularia, 362
  harveyana v. sphaerocarpa, 362, **361,** f. *1140, 1141*
  spumigena, 362, **361,** f. *1139*
Nostoc, 364
  carneum, 366, **365,** f. *1154*
  ellipsosporum, 364, **363,** f. *1148*
  muscorum, 364, **363,** f. *1149*
  pruniforme, 364, **365,** f. *1151–53*
  spongiaeforme, 366, **363,** f. *1150*
  verrucosum, 366, **365,** f. *1155*
Nostocaceae, 356
Nostochineae, 356

Ochromonadaceae, 300
Oedogoniaceae, 49
Oedogoniales, 48
Oedogonium, 57
  acmandrium, 77, **75,** f. *201*

acrosporum, 96, **93,** f. *270*
americanum, 76, **73,** f. *186, 187*
amplum, 72, **71,** f. *175, 176*
angustum, 70, **71,** f. *173, 174*
aster, 86, **87,** f. *257*
bohemicum, 84, **75,** f. *204*
borisianum, 90, **83,** f. *246*
boscii, 74, **73,** f. *183*
braunii, 88, **87,** f. *264*
capillare, 66, **67,** f. *139, 140*
capilliforme, 68, **69,** f. *153, 154*
capitellatum, 77, **79,** f. *213, 214*
cardiacum, 65, **63,** f. *131*
    v. carbonicum, 65, **63,** f. *132*
concatenatum, 88, **83,** f. *239*
    v. superornatum, 89, **83,** f. *240*
crassiusculum, 90, **83,** f. *244*
    v. cataractum, 90, **83,** f. *245*
crenulatocostatum, 74, **69,** f. *158, 159*
    v. cylindricum, 74, **69,** f. *160*
crispum, 80, **79,** f. *205, 206*
    v. gracilescens, 82, **79,** f. *207*
croasdaleae, 92, **93,** f. *272–75*
cryptoporum, 62, **63,** f. *122*
curvum, 62, **55,** f. *120*
cyathigerum, 89, **85,** f. *251, 252*
decipiens, 91, **81,** f. *233*
    v. africanum, 91, **81,** f. *236*
    v. dissimile, 92, **81,** f. *234, 235*
diversum, 68, **69,** f. *151, 152*
echinospermum, 88, **87,** f. *255*
epiphyticum, 80, **75,** f. *191, 192*
flavescens, 88, **87,** f. *256*
fragile, 66, **67,** f. *145*
    v. abyssinicum, 66, **67,** f. *141*
franklinianum, 64, **55,** f. *119*
globosum, 65, **63,** f. *134*
gracilius, 68, **67,** f. *148*
gracillimum, 82, **79,** f. *217*
grande, 70, **71,** f. *169–71*
    v. aequatoriale, 70, **71,** f. *172*
howardii, 77, **75,** f. *193–95*
hystricinum, 86, **87,** f. *258*
idioandrosporum, 90, **87,** f. *265, 266*
illinoisense, 86, **83,** f. *241–43*
intermedium, 65, **63,** f. *133*
irregulare, 90, **87,** f. *263*
kirchneri, 82, **79,** f. *212*
laeve, 64, **63,** f. *130*
landsboroughi, 98, **85,** f. *247, 248*
lemmermannii, 65, **63,** f. *138*
longiarticulatum, 74, **73,** f. *181, 182*
longicolle, 91, **81,** f. *224, 225*
macrandrium, 94, **81,** f. *226*
    v. aemulans, 94, **81,** f. *228*
    v. propinquum, 96, **81,** f. *227*
macrospermum, 91, **81,** f. *237, 238*
magnusii, 61, **55,** f. *116*
majus, 70, **71,** f. *167, 168*
mitratum, 78, **79,** f. *208, 209*
monile, 92, **81,** f. *222, 223*
multisporum, 90, **87,** f. *261, 262*
oblongellum, 82, **79,** f. *220*
oblongum, 84, **79,** f. *218*
    v. majus, 84, **79,** f. *219*

oboviforme, 70, **71,** f. *165, 166*
obsoletum, 64, **63,** f. *121*
obtruncatum, 96, **81,** f. *230*
occidentale, 74, **69,** f. *155–57*
ouchitanum, 84, **79,** f. *216*
paludosum, 72, **69,** f. *163*
    v. parvisporum, 72, **69,** f. *164*
paucocostatum, 76, **73,** f. *177, 178*
paulense, 72, **69,** f. *161, 162*
perfectum, 89, **85,** f. *253, 254*
pisanum, 80, **75,** f. *196, 197*
plagiostomum, 70, **67,** f. *142, 143*
plusiosporum, 64, **55,** f. *117, 118*
pratense, 77, **75,** f. *198, 199*
praticolum, 96, **93,** f. *267, 268*
pringsheimii, 78, **75,** f. *188*
    v. nordstedtii, 80, **75,** f. *189, 190*
pseudoboscii, 65, **67,** f. *150*
punctatostriatum, 78, **79,** f. *221*
punctatum, 76, **73,** f. *179, 180*
pungens, 86, **87,** f. *259, 260*
pusillum, 77, **79,** f. *210*
reinschii, 100, **67,** f. *149*
rivulare, 68, **67,** f. *147*
rothii, 91, **79,** f. *215*
rufescens, 64, **63,** f. *124–26*
    v. exiguum, 64, **63,** f. *127*
    v. lundellii, 64, **63,** f. *128, 129*
rugulosum, 94, **81,** f. *231*
    v. minutum, 94, **81,** f. *232*
simplex, 82, **79,** f. *211*
sociale, 65, **63,** f. *136, 137*
stictospermum, 76, **75,** f. *202, 203*
subplenum, 92, **93,** f. *269*
suecicum, 61, **55,** f. *115*
taphrosporum, 76, **73,** f. *184, 185*
tentoriale, 98, **93,** f. *271*
undulatum, 84, **81,** f. *229*
upsaliense, 66, **67,** f. *144*
varians, 62, **63,** f. *135*
vaucherii, 66, **67,** f. *146*
vulgare, 62, **63,** f. *123*
welwitschii, 78, **75,** f. *200*
wolleanum, 89, **85,** f. *249, 250*

Onychonema, 200
    filiforme, 201, **203,** f. *621–23*
    laeve v. latum, 201, **203,** f. *624*

Oocystaceae, 113

Oocystis, 116
    borgei, 117, **101,** f. *322*
    crassa, 117, **101,** f. *323*
    elliptica, 117, **101,** f. *318*
    gigas, 117, **101,** f. *321*
    naegelii, 117, **101,** f. *320*
    solitaria, 116, **101,** f. *319*
        f. major, 117

Ophiocytium, 207
    arbusculum, 208, **203,** f. *635*
    capitatum, 208, **203,** f. *634*
    cochleare, 208, **203,** f. *633*
    gracilipes, 208, **203,** f. *638, 639*
    majus, 208, **203,** f. *636, 637*
    parvulum, 208, **203,** f. *632*

Oscillatoria, 340
  acuminata, 346, **343,** f. *1072*
  agardhii, 346, **345,** f. *1082*
  amoena, 344, **343,** f. *1073*
  animalis, 346, **343,** f. *1079*
  chalybea, 344, **343,** f. *1071*
  chlorina, 344, **345,** f. *1088, 1089*
  curviceps, 344, **345,** f. *1081*
  formosa, 346, **345,** f. *1084*
  geminata, 347, **345,** f. *1087*
  grunowiana v. articulata, 347, **345,** f. *1090*
  limosa, 342, **343,** f. *1076*
  ornata, 342, **343,** f. *1077*
  princeps, 344, **343,** f. *1080*
  prolifica, 346, **345,** f. *1083*
  sancta, 342, **343,** f. *1078*
  splendida, 346, **345,** f. *1085, 1086*
  tenuis, 346, **343,** f. *1074*
    v. natans, 346, **343,** f. *1075*
Oscillatoriaceae, 338
Oscillatoriales, 338
Oscillatorineae, 338

Palmella, 21
  miniata, 21, **23,** f. *28, 29*
Palmellaceae, 20
Pandorina, 16
  morum, 16, **15,** f. *13*
Pediastrum, 110
  angulosum, 112, **97,** f. *299*
  boryanum, 112, **97,** f. *295, 296*
    v. longicorne, 112, **97,** f. *297*
  duplex, 112, **97,** f. *300*
    v. clathratum, 112, **97,** f. *301*
    v. rotundatum, 112, **97,** f. *302*
  integrum, 112, **97,** f. *298*
  simplex, 110, **97,** f. *290, 291*
    v. duodenarium, 110, **97,** f. *292*
  tetras, 110, **97,** f. *293*
    v. tetraodon, 112, **97,** f. *294*
Penium, 176
  margaritaceum, 176, **165,** f. *540*
Pennales, 226
Peridiniaceae, 310
Peridiniales, 307
Peridinium, 310
  bipes, 310, **311,** f. *988–91*
  cinctum, 314, **309,** f. *980–83*
  inconspicuum, 312, **309,** f. *972–75*
  pusillum, 312, **309,** f. *984–87*
  umbonatum, 312, **309,** f. *976–79*
Phacotaceae, 14
Phacotus, 14
  lenticularis, 14, **15,** f. *1, 2*
Phacus, 322
  acuminata, 323, **325,** f. *1024*
  longicauda, 323, **325,** f. *1022*
  pleuronectes, 323, **325,** f. *1019*
  pyrum, 323, **325,** f. *1021*
  torta, 323, **325,** f. *1023*
  triqueter, 323, **325,** f. *1020*

Phaeophyta, 5
Phormidium, 347
  ambiguum, 350, **349,** f. *1104*
  autumnale, 348, **351,** f. *1108*
  favosum, 348, **349,** f. *1102, 1103*
  foveolarum, 348, **349,** f. *1095*
  incrustatum v. cataractarum, 350, **351,** f. *1109*
  inundatum, 348, **349,** f. *1100, 1101*
  minnesotense, 350, **349,** f. *1099*
  retzii, 352, **349,** f. *1105–7*
  subfuscum, 350, **349,** f. *1096, 1097*
  tenue, 347, **349,** f. *1098*
  uncinatum, 348, **345,** f. *1091, 1092*
Pinnularia, 256
  appendiculata, 258, **259,** f. *796*
  braunii, 258, **259,** f. *797*
  brebissonii, 260, **259,** f. *802*
  brevicosta v. leptostauron, 257, **259,** f. *805*
  cardinalis, 262, **259,** f. *808*
  divergens, 260, **259,** f. *804*
  gibba, 260, **259,** f. *801*
  globiceps, 258, **259,** f. *798*
  hemiptera, 258, **259,** f. *800*
  interrupta f. bicapitata, 258, **259,** f. *803*
  major, 260, **253,** f. *795*
    v. transversa, 262, **259,** f. *807*
  mesolepta, 258, **259,** f. *799*
  nobilis, 262, **259,** f. *806*
  parva, 257, **261,** f. *813*
  tabellaria, 260, **261,** f. *811*
  termes, 260, **261,** f. *812*
  viridis, 262, **261,** f. *809*
    v. elliptica, 262, **261,** f. *810*
Pithophora, 48
  kewensis, 48
  oedogonia, 48, **43,** f. *86*
  varia, 48, **43,** f. *87, 88*
Platydorina, 17
  caudata, 18, **19,** f. *15*
Plectonema, 366
  nostocorum, 368, **367,** f. *1157*
  tomasinianum, 368, **367,** f. *1156*
Pleodorina, 17
  californica, 17, **19,** f. *16*
  illinoisense, 17, **19,** f. *17*
Pleurocapsa, 336
  varia, 338, **337,** f. *1057, 1058*
Pleurocapsaceae, 336
Pleurosigma, 269
  angulatum, 269, **253,** f. *791*
Pleurotaenium, 178
  coronatum, 180, **179,** f. *606*
  ehrenbergii, 180, **179,** f. *607, 608*
  trabecula, 178, **179,** f. *609*
  truncatum, 180, **179,** f. *605*
Polyblepharidaceae, 13
Porphyrosiphon, 340
  notarisii, 340, **345,** f. *1093, 1094*
Protococcaceae, 40
Protococcus, 40
  viridis, 42, **31,** f. *58*

Protosiphon, 109
  botryoides, 109, **111**, f. *374*
Protosiphonaceae, 109
Pyrrophyta, 4, 306

Radiofilum, 26
  irregulare, 26, **25**, f. *42*
Raphidiopsis, 378
  curvata, 378, **373**, f. *1166–70*
Rhizochrysidaceae, 304
Rhizochrysidales, 304
Rhizochrysis, 305
  limnetica, 305, **303**, f. *971*
Rhizoclonium, 45
  fontanum, 46, **47**, f. *90*
  hieroglyphicum, 46, **47**, f. *91*
    v. macromeres, 46
Rhizosolenia, 226
  eriensis, 226, **223**, f. *674*
  longiseta, 226, **223**, f. *675*
Rhizosoleniaceae, 226
Rhizosolenineae, 226
Rhodophyceae, 5, 6, 379
Rhodophyta, 4, 5, 379
Rhoicosphenia, 242
  curvata, 244, **243**, f. *753*
Rhopalodia, 281
  gibba, 282, **283**, f. *884*
  ventricosa, 282, **283**, f. *885*
Rivulariaceae, 372
Roya, 166
  obtusa, 167, **165**, f. *533*

Scenedesmaceae, 120
Scenedesmus, 121
  abundans, 123, **107**, f. *365*
    v. longicauda, 123, **107**, f. *366*
  acuminatus, 123, **107**, f. *368*
  acutiformis, 123, **107**, f. *356*
  arcuatus, 123, **107**, f. *360*
    v. platydisca, 123, **107**, f. *361*
  armatus, 122, **107**, f. *353*
  bijuga, 123, **107**, f. *371*
    v. alternans, 123, **107**, f. *372*
  brasiliensis, 123, **107**, f. *363*
  carinatus,' 122, **107**, f. *362*
  denticulatus, 123, **107**, f. *367*
  dimorphus, 123, **107**, f. *370*
  longus, 123, **107**, f. *364*
    v. minutus, 123, **107**, f. *373*
  obliquus, 123, **107**, f. *369*
  opoliensis, 122, **107**, f. *355*
  protuberans, 122, **107**, f. *354*
  quadricauda, 122, **107**, f. *357*
    v. quadrispina, 122, **107**, f. *358*
    v. westii, 122, **107**, f. *359*
Schizomeridaceae, 100
Schizomeris, 100
  leibleinii, 102, **95**, f. *276*
Schizothrix, 353
  calcicola, 353, **355**, f. *1118, 1119*

purpurascens, 353, **351**, f. *1115–17;* **355**, f. *1120, 1121*
  rivularis, 353
  stricklandii, 353, **377**, f. *1180*
Schroederia, 109, 117
  setigera, 109, **101**, f. *324*
Scytonema, 368
  cincinnatum, 368, **369**, f. *1160, 1161*
  ocellatum, 370, **369**, f. *1162*
  tolypothrichoides, 370, **367**, f. *1158, 1159*
Scytonemataceae, 366
Selenastrum, 117
  bibraianum, 117, **101**, f. *325*
    v. gracile, 117, **101**, f. *326*
Siphonales, 3, 124
Sirogonium, 162
  illinoisense, 164, **163**, f. *529, 530*
  sticticum, 162, **163**, f. *531*
Sorastrum, 112
  spinulosum, 112, **95**, f. *283*
Sphaerella lacustris, 20
Sphaerocystis, 21
  schroeteri, 21, **23**, f. *26, 27*
Spirogyra, 140
  areolata, 161, **163**, f. *528*
  borgeana, 146, **145**, f. *467*
  catenaeformis, 147, **145**, f. *469*
  circumlineata, 147, **145**, f. *470*
  cleveana, 160, **163**, f. *524*
  communis, 146, **143**, f. *455*
  condensata, 146, **145**, f. *458*
  corrugata, 156, **155**, f. *500*
  crassa, 153, **151**, f. *486*
  crassoidea, 150, **151**, f. *485*
  daedalea, 148, **149**, f. *471*
  daedaleoides, 148, **149**, f. *473, 474*
  decimina, 153, **151**, f. *489*
  denticulata, 160, **157**, f. *516*
  diluta, 154, **151**, f. *491, 492*
  discreta, 160, **157**, f. *509*
  distenta, 152
  dubia, 153, **149**, f. *472*
  ellipsospora, 152, **151**, f. *484*
  fluviatilis, 154, **151**, f. *493*
  formosa, 153, **151**, f. *495*
  gracilis, 146, **143**, f. *453*
  grevilleana, 161, **163**, f. *526, 527*
  groenlandica, 160, **157**, f. *510, 511*
  hassallii, 161, **159**, f. *523*
  hydrodictya, 156, **155**, f. *501*
  inconstans, 162, **157**, f. *507, 508*
  inflata, 158, **159**, f. *518*
  insignis, 161, **163**, f. *525*
  irregularis, 152, **151**, f. *490*
  juergensii, 146, **145**, f. *463*
  jugalis, 153, **151**, f. *494*
  lagerheimii, 150, **145**, f. *459*
  latviensis, 158
  longata, 148, **145**, f. *460*
  majuscula, 150, **149**, f. *475*
  maxima, 153, **149**, f. *478, 479*
  micropunctata, 156, **155**, f. *497*

Spirogyra—*continued*
 mirabilis, 148, **145**, f. *462*
 narcissiana, 144, **143**, f. *451, 452*
 neglecta, 152, **149**, f. *476, 477*
 nitida, 152, **151**, f. *487, 488*
 novae-angliae, 154, **155**, f. *503*
 occidentalis, 153, **155**, f. *499*
 parvula, 147, **145**, f. *461*
 petitiana, 158
 porticalis, 147, **145**, f. *468*
 pratensis, 144, **143**, f. *457*
 propria, 153
 protecta, 160, **157**, f. *506*
 punctiformis, 154, **155**, f. *496*
 quadrata, 160, **157**, f. *514, 515*
 rectangularis, 161, **159**, f. *521, 522*
 reflexa, 154, **155**, f. *504, 505*
 reticulata, 161, **159**, f. *520*
 rugosa, 160
 rugulosa, 156, **155**, f. *498*
 scrobiculata, 150, **149**, f. *481, 482*
 setiformis, 152, **149**, f. *480*
 silvicola, 146, **143**, f. *456*
 singularis, 146, **143**, f. *454*
 spreeiana, 158, **157**, f. *513*
 submaxima, 150, **149**, f. *483*
 tenuissima, 158, **159**, f. *519*
 teodoresci, 147
 tetrapla, 162, **159**, f. *517*
 triplicata, 152
 varians, 147, **145**, f. *464*
 velata, 148, **145**, f. *465, 466*
 wabashensis, 156, **155**, f. *502*
 weberi, 158, **157**, f. *512*
Spirulina, 354
 gomontiana, 354, **355**, f. *1126*
 jenneri, 354, **355**, f. *1123*
 major, 354, **355**, f. *1124*
 nordstedtii, 354, **355**, f. *1125*
Spondylosium, 201
 planum, 201, **203**, f. *625*
 pygmaeum, 202, **203**, f. *626*
Staurastrum, 197
 alternans, 198, **177**, f. *601*
 crenatum, 198, **179**, f. *612*
 cuspidatum, 197, **179**, f. *610*
 dilatatum, 198, **177**, f. *602*
 gracile, 199, **179**, f. *613*
 hexacerum, 199, **179**, f. *611*
 margaritaceum, 200, **177**, f. *599*
 oxyacanthum, 199, **177**, f. *604*
 polymorphum, 200, **177**, f. *600*
 punctulatum, 198, **177**, f. *603*
Stauroneis, 264
 acuta, 264, **267**, f. *829*
 anceps, 266, **265**, f. *822*
  v. birostris, 268, **265**, f. *823*
  v. linearis, 268, **265**, f. *824*
 gracilis, 264, **265**, f. *828*
 phoenicentron, 266, **265**, f. *825*
  v. amphilepta, 266, **265**, f. *826*
 phyllodes, 266, **265**, f. *821*
 producta, 266, **265**, f. *827*
Stephanodiscus, 222
 astraea, 222, **225**, f. *676*

 v. intermedia, 224, **225**, f. *677*
 v. minutula, 224, **225**, f. *678*
 hantzschii, 222, **225**, f. *679*
 niagarae, 224, **225**, f. *680*
 v. magnifica, 224, **225**, f. *681, 682*
Stichococcus, 26
 bacillaris, 26, **27**, f. *45*
 flaccidus, 28
 subtilis, 28
Stigeoclonium, 32
 glomeratum, 36, **37**, f. *69*
 longipilum, 36, **35**, f. *65*
 lubricum, 34, **35**, f. *66*
  v. varians, 34, **35**, f. *67*
 nanum, 34, **39**, f. *71*
 stagnatile, 34, **39**, f. *72*
 subsecundum, 36, **35**, f. *68*
 tenue, 34, **39**, f. *70*
Stigonema, 370
 minutum, 372, **373**, f. *1165*
Stigonemataceae, 370
Surirella, 290
 angusta, 294, **293**, f. *928*
 apiculata, 294, 383, **291**, f. *913*
 biseriata, 294, **291**, f. *916, 917*
  v. bifrons, 294, **291**, f. *918*
 didyma, 292, **293**, f. *929*
 elegans, 296, **291**, f. *914*
  v. norvegica, 296, **291**, f. *915*
 guatemalensis, 294, **295**, f. *933*
 linearis, 294, **293**, f. *920*
  v. constricta, 294, **293**, f. *921*
 minuta, 296, **291**, f. *912*
 oregonica, 294, **293**, f. *927*
 ovalis, 296, **293**, f. *922*
  v. pinnata, 296, **293**, f. *923*
 ovata, 296, **293**, f. *926*
 patella, 294, **293**, f. *925*
 robusta, 296, **295**, f. *931*
 saxonica, 294, **295**, f. *932*
 spiralis, 292, **295**, f. *930*
 splendida, 294, **293**, f. *924*
Surirellaceae, 289
Surirellineae, 282
Symploca, 356
 muscorum, 356, **355**, f. *1122*
Syncrypta, 300
 volvox, 300, **299**, f. *938*
Syncryptaceae, 300
Synechocystis, 336
 aquatilis, 336, **337**, f. *1056*
Synedra, 234
 acus, 237, **235**, f. *720*
  v. radians, 237, **235**, f. *721*
 capitata, 236, **235**, f. *722*
 dorsiventralis, 236, **235**, f. *712*
 hyalina, 383
 parasitica, 236, **235**, f. *710*
 pulchella, 236, **235**, f. *718*
 rumpens, 237, **235**, f. *711*
 tenera, 236, **235**, f. *719*
 ulna, 237, **235**, f. *713*
  v. aequalis, 237, **235**, f. *714*
  v. biceps, 237, **235**, f. *717*

v. danica, 237, **235,** f. *715*
v. spathulifera, **237, 235,** f. *716*
Synura, 300
uvella, 300, **299,** f. *939, 940*
Synuraceae, 300

Tabellaria, 227
fenestrata, 227, **229,** f. *692, 693*
flocculosa, 227, **229,** f. *694*
Tabellariaceae, 227
Tetraedron, 117
bifurcatum, 119, **105,** f. *346*
gigas, 119, **105,** f. *343*
gracile, 118, **105,** f. *339*
limneticum, 119, **105,** f. *347*
lobulatum, 119, **105,** f. *344*
minimum, 118, **105,** f. *335*
f. tetralobulatum, 118, **105,** f. *336*
muticum, 118, **105,** f. *337*
f. punctulatum, 118, **105,** f. *338*
quadratum, 119, **105,** f. *348*
f. minus-acutum, 119, **105,** f. *349*
regulare, 119, **105,** f. *345*
trigonum, 118, **105,** f. *340*
f. majus, 118
v. minus, 118, **105,** f. *342*
v. tetragonum, 118, **105,** f. *341*
Tetraspora, 22
cylindrica, 22, **25,** f. *32*
gelatinosa, 22, **25,** f. *33*
lubrica, 22, **23,** f. *30, 31*
Tetrasporaceae, 21
Tetrasporales, 20
Thallophyta, **2,** 3
Thorea, 382
ramosissima, 382, **381,** f. *1184–86*
Thoreaceae, 382
Tolypothrix, 370
tenuis, 370, **373,** f. *1164*
Trachelomonas, 324
acuminata, 326, **325,** f. *1033*
armata, 327, **325,** f. *1035*
caudata, 326, **325,** f. *1036*
ensifera, 326, **325,** f. *1030*
hispida, 327, **325,** f. *1027*
magdaleniana, 326, **325,** f. *1028*
schauinslandii, 326, **325,** f. *1034*
similis, 327, **325,** f. *1031*
tambowika, 326, **325,** f. *1029*
urceolata, 326, **325,** f. *1032*
volvocina, 326, **325,** f. *1026*
Treubaria, 119
crassispina, 119, **105,** f. *350*
Tribonema, 210
bombycinum, 210, **209,** f. *648*
v. tenue, 210, **209,** f. *649*
minus, 210, **209,** f. *650*
utriculosum, 210, **209,** f. *647*
Tribonemataceae, 210
Trochiscia, 119
arguta, 120, **105,** f. *352*
reticularis, 120, **105,** f. *351*

Ulothrix, 24
tenerrima, 26, **25,** f. *38*
variabilis, 26, **25,** f. *37*
zonata, 26, **25,** f. *35, 36*
Ulotrichaceae, 24
Ulotrichales, 24
Ulvales, 100

Vaucheria, 211
aversa, 212, **125,** f. *381*
gardneri, 213, **125,** f. *384*
geminata, 212, **125,** f. *385*
hamata, 213, **125,** f. *380*
longipes, 213, **125,** f. *386*
ornithocephala, 212, **111,** f. *379*
polysperma, 212, **125,** f. *382*
repens, 212, **125,** f. *383*
sessilis, 213, **111,** f. *378*
terrestris, 213, **125,** f. *387*
Vaucheriaceae, 211
Volvocaceae, 16
Volvocales, 13
Volvox, 18
aureus, 18, **19,** f. *21*
globator, 18, **19,** f. *18, 19*
spermatosphaera, 18, **19,** f. *20*

Wislouchiella, 14
planctonica, 16, **15,** f. *5, 6*

Xanthophyceae, 3, 6, 206

Zygnema, 136
adpectinatum, 137, **135,** f. *444*
azureum, 139, **131,** f. *432*
catenatum, 139
chalybeospermum, 138, **133,** f. *442*
collinsianum, 139, **131,** f. *428, 429*
conspicuum, 137, **133,** f. *433*
cruciatum, 138, **133,** f. *439*
cylindricum, 137, **131,** f. *427*
decussatum, 137, **135,** f. *445*
excrassum, 138, **133,** f. *435*
insigne, 138, **131,** f. *430*
leiospermum, 138, **133,** f. *443*
neocruciatum, 139, **133,** f. *440*
neopectinatum, 138, **133,** f. *434*
pectinatum, 138, **135,** f. *446*
stellinum, 139, **133,** f. *437*
sterile, 137, **131,** f. *426*
subcruciatum, 138, **133,** f. *438*
subtile, 139, **133,** f. *436*
tenue, 139, **131,** f. *431*
vaucherii, 139, **133,** f. *441*
Zygnemataceae, 126
Zygnematales, 3, 124
Zygnemopsis, 134
decussata, 134, **135,** f. *450*
Zygogonium, 134
ericetorum, 136, **135,** f. *447–49*